Prentice Hall

Setting the Standard for Excellence in California

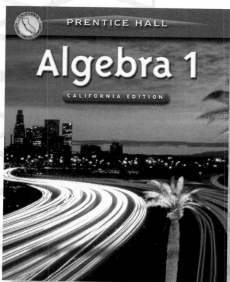

Prentice Hall *Pre-Algebra* and *Algebra*—developed exclusively for California educators and students.

Comprehensive coverage of all California Mathematics Standards.

Prentice Hall *Pre-Algebra* covers all content mandated by the California Standards, with an emphasis on working with numbers and equations and understanding the underlying mathematics principles.

Prentice Hall *Algebra 1* covers all content mandated by the California Standards, with an emphasis on writing, solving, and graphing linear and quadratic equations. Mathematical reasoning is interwoven throughout.

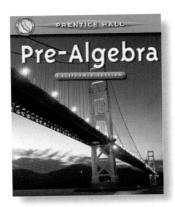

Table of Contents

Table of Contents

Comprehensive correlation chart and content background ensure coverage and understanding of California Standards.

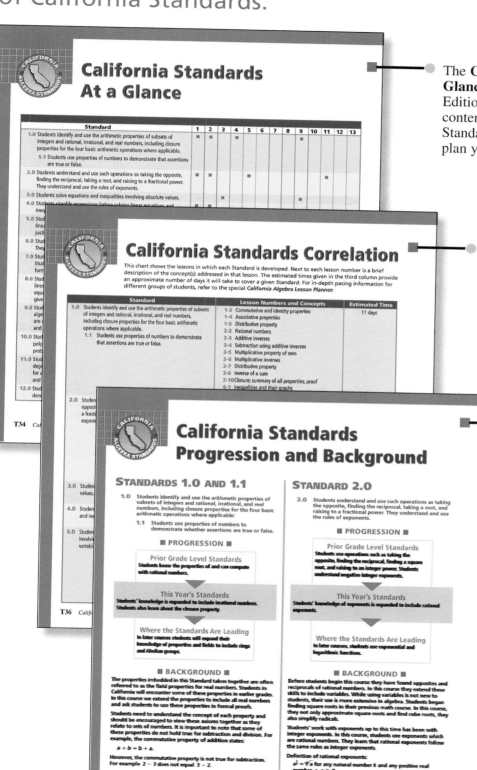

The **California Standards At a Glance** chart, in the Teacher's Edition, provides an overview of content coverage as it relates to the Standards—assisting you as you plan your instruction.

A detailed **California Standards Correlation** is provided to assure coverage of each Standard. This correlation lets you know exactly which portion of the Standard is covered by a particular lesson, and when the coverage of that Standard is completed.

California Standards Progression and Background is provided for each Standard to give you the information you need to effectively teach that Standard. Included are a discussion of Standards covered in previous grades, the key concepts at this level, and the connection to subsequent study of math. Key mathematical background is included to provide ongoing professional development.

Content

Direct instructional approach with clearly stated goals assures competency for all.

The **California Mathematics Standards** appear at the beginning of each lesson so that students know the exact concepts or skills for which they will be held accountable.

Abundant worked-out **Examples** followed by **Try This** exercises build procedural competency and prepare students for success on homework assignments.

CA 2.0: Understand and use the rules of exponents.

5-1 Exponents

What You'll Learn

1 To multiply numbers in exponential form

2 To divide numbers in exponential form

... And Why

To simplify expressions containing exponents

Recall that an exponent tells how many times we use a base as a factor. For example, $a^3 = a \cdot a \cdot a$. An expression written with exponents is written using **exponential notation.**

PART 1 Multiplying Using Exponents

Objective: Multiply numbers in exponential form.

We can use the meaning of an exponent to develop a rule for multiplying powers with like bases.

$8^3 \cdot 8^2$ means $(8 \cdot 8 \cdot 8)(8 \cdot 8) = 8^5$
$5^2 \cdot 5^4$ means $(5 \cdot 5)(5 \cdot 5 \cdot 5 \cdot 5) = 5^6$
$a^5 \cdot a$ means $(a \cdot a \cdot a \cdot a \cdot a)(a) = a^6$

Notice we could add the exponents to find the exponent of the product.

$8^3 \cdot 8^2 = 8^{3+2} = 8^5$
$5^2 \cdot 5^4 = 5^{2+4} = 5^6$
$a^5 \cdot a = a^{5+1} = a^6 \qquad a = a^1$

Multiplying Powers with Like Bases

For any rational number a, and for all whole numbers m and n,
$a^m \cdot a^n = a^{m+n}$

EXAMPLES Simplify. Express using exponents.

1 $8^4 \cdot 8^3 = 8^{4+3}$ $(8 \cdot 8 \cdot 8 \cdot 8)(8 \cdot 8 \cdot 8) = 8^7$
$= 8^7$

2 $y \cdot y^2 \cdot y^5 = y^{1+2+5}$ $(y)(y \cdot y)(y \cdot y \cdot y \cdot y \cdot y) = y^8$
$= y^8$

3 $(a^3b^2)(a^3b^5) = (a^3a^3)(b^2b^5)$
$= a^{3+3}b^{2+5}$
$= a^6b^7$

Try This Simplify. Express using exponents.

a. $5^2 \cdot 5^4$ **b.** $a^5 \cdot a^3$ **c.** $y^3 \cdot y^2 \cdot y^5$ **d.** $(mn^2)(m^4n^6)$

PART 2 Dividing Using Exponents

Objective: Divide numbers in exponential form.

The following suggests a rule for simplifying expressions in the form $\frac{a^m}{a^n}$.

$$\frac{3^5}{3^2} = \frac{3 \cdot 3 \cdot 3 \cdot 3 \cdot 3}{3 \cdot 3} = 3 \cdot 3 \cdot 3 = 3^3$$

Notice that we can subtract the exponents to find the exponent of the quotient.

Dividing Powers with Like Bases

For any rational number a except 0, and for all whole numbers m and n,
$$\frac{a^m}{a^n} = a^{m-n}$$

EXAMPLES Simplify. Express using exponents.

4 $\frac{4^5}{4^2} = 4^{5-2} = 4^3$ $\frac{4 \cdot 4 \cdot 4 \cdot 4 \cdot 4}{4 \cdot 4} = 4^3$

5 $\frac{x^6}{x^2} = x^{6-2} = x^4$ $\frac{x \cdot x \cdot x \cdot x \cdot x \cdot x}{x \cdot x} = x^4$

6 $\frac{p^5 \cdot q^7}{p^2 \cdot q^5} = p^{5-2}q^{7-5}$ *Think* $\frac{p^5}{p^2} \cdot \frac{q^7}{q^5}$.
$= p^3q^2$

Try This Simplify. Express using exponents.

e. $\frac{7^6}{7^2}$ **f.** $\frac{a^7}{a^2}$ **g.** $\frac{m^4}{m^5}$ **h.** $\frac{x^4y^3}{x^2y^2}$

You can use the meaning of an exponent to simplify $\frac{5^2}{5^5}$.

$$\frac{5^2}{5^5} = \frac{5 \cdot 5}{5 \cdot 5 \cdot 5 \cdot 5 \cdot 5} = \frac{1}{5^3}$$

You can also use the rule above to simplify the expression $\frac{5^2}{5^5}$.

$$\frac{5^2}{5^5} = 5^{2-5} = 5^{-3}$$

This suggests that $5^{-3} = \frac{1}{5^3}$.

Highlighted mathematical **Vocabulary,** along with easy-to-read direct instruction, gives students (and parents) the information they need to acquire the skill or concept.

Lessons are divided into **parts**, according to lesson objective, to make it easy to vary the pacing of instruction.

Internet
Extra Help
On the Web
Look for worked-out
examples at the Prentice
Hall Web site.
www.phschool.com

A
Simplify. Express using exponents.

1. $2^4 \cdot 2^3$ 2. $3^5 \cdot 3^2$ 3. $8^5 \cdot 8^9$ 4. $n^3 \cdot n^{20}$
5. $x^4 \cdot x^3$ 6. $y^7 \cdot y^9$ 7. $n^3 \cdot n$ 8. $z^7 \cdot z^7$
9. $x^3 \cdot x^1$ 10. $a^6 \cdot a^8$ 11. $m^7 \cdot m^0$ 12. $p \cdot p \cdot p$
13. $x^4 \cdot x^2 \cdot x$ 14. $y^2 \cdot y^4 \cdot y^3$ 15. $a^3 \cdot a^4 \cdot a \cdot a$ 16. $b \cdot b^5 \cdot b^2 \cdot b^2$
17. $(a^3b^6)(a^5b)$ 18. $(x^2y)(x^5y^2)$ 19. $(p^2q^3r^2)(pqr^3)$
20. $(x^7y^4z^4)(x^2y^5z^8)$ 21. $(5s^2t^3)(5s^2t)$ 22. $(2xy^2)(2x^2y^2)$

23. $\frac{7^5}{7^2}$ 24. $\frac{4^7}{4^3}$ 25. $\frac{8^{12}}{8^6}$ 26. $\frac{9^{15}}{9^2}$
27. $\frac{6^4}{6^4}$ 28. $\frac{2^7}{2^7}$ 29. $\frac{y^9}{y^5}$ 30. $\frac{x^{12}}{x^{11}}$
31. $\frac{g^5}{g^5}$ 32. $\frac{h^4}{h}$ 33. $\frac{m^8}{m^8}$ 34. $\frac{x^7}{x^5}$
35. $\frac{a^3b^4}{ab}$ 36. $\frac{x^8y}{x^7y}$ 37. $\frac{4^3x^3}{4^2x}$ 38. $\frac{6^4a^5b}{6^2a^2b}$

Express using positive exponents.

39. 3^{-2} 40. 6^{-3} 41. x^{-4} 42. n^{-6}
43. $3a^{-1}$ 44. $(3x)^{-1}$ 45. $(2y)^{-1}$ 46. $4x^{-3}$
47. $5c^{-4}$ 48. $8m^{-1}$ 49. $(3a)^{-1}$ 50. cd^{-2}

Mental Math Simplify. Express without using exponents.

51. 4^{-2} 52. 8^{-1} 53. 5^{-3} 54. 1^{-4}
55. 5^0 56. 2^{-4} 57. 10^0 58. x^0

B
Simplify.

59. $(-2)^4(-2)^2$ 60. $(-5)^2(-5)$ 61. $\frac{(-3)^6}{(-3)^4}$ 62. $\frac{(-10)^7}{(-10)^6}$

63. $\frac{4^3}{4^5}$ 64. $\frac{3^4}{3^6}$ 65. $\frac{(-2)^2}{(-2)^5}$ 66. $\frac{(-5)^3}{(-5)^4}$

Simplify. Express using (a) negative exponents; (b) positive exponents.

67. $\frac{x^3}{x^7}$ 68. $\frac{y}{y^4}$ 69. $\frac{a^2}{a^6}$ 70. $\frac{m^5}{m^{10}}$

Evaluate each expression.

71. $x^5 \cdot x^3$ for $x = 2$ 72. $10^m \cdot 10^n$ for $m = 2$ and $n = 4$
73. $a^3 \cdot a^2 \cdot a$ for $a = -2$ 74. $2^a \cdot 2^b \cdot 2^c$ for $a = 3, b = 2, c = 2$

75. *Multi-Step Problem* Use the figures at the left.
  a. What fraction of each figure is shaded?
  b. Rewrite each fraction in part (a) as a power of 2.
  c. *Mathematical Reasoning* What pattern occurs in your answers to part (b)?
  d. If the pattern were to continue to Figure 10, what portion of the square would be shaded?

Error Analysis Find and correct each error in Exercises 76 and 77.
76. $(3x^2)(2x^5) = 6x^{2 \cdot 5} = 6x^{10}$ 77. $x^5 \cdot x \cdot x^2 = x^{5+2} = x^7$

78. **TEST PREP** If $5^{x+1} = 125$, what is the value of x?
A. 2 B. 3 C. 4 D. 5

Simplify.
79. $\frac{4^2 \cdot 4^5}{4^3}$ 80. $\frac{2^5 \cdot 3^4}{2^2 \cdot 3^2}$ 81. $\frac{a^2 \cdot b^3}{a^2 \cdot b^5}$ 82. $\frac{m^5 \cdot n^6}{m^2 \cdot m^2}$

83. $4^{-1} \cdot 4^5$ 84. $\frac{(-3)}{(-3)^{-4}}$ 85. $\frac{x^6 \cdot x^{-2}}{x^2}$ 86. $\frac{a^{-2} \cdot b^{-3}}{a^4 \cdot b^{-1}}$

87. *Critical Thinking* Is $(a + b)^m = a^m + b^m$ true for all numbers? If yes, justify your answer. If no, give a counterexample.

Challenge

Write each of the following as a power of 2.
88. 16 89. 4^3 90. 8^2 91. $4^3 \cdot 8 \cdot 16$
92. Write $2^8 \cdot 16^3 \cdot 64$ as a power of 4.
93. Write $9 \cdot 27 \cdot 3 \cdot 81$ as a power of 3.

Simplify.
94. $\frac{\left(\frac{1}{c}\right)^4}{\left(\frac{1}{c}\right)^5}$ 95. $\frac{\left(\frac{a}{b}\right)^3}{\left(\frac{a}{b}\right)^6}$

Mixed Review

Simplify. 96. $3[8 - 2(t + 3)]$ 97. $(5m + 6n) - (6m + 9n)$
98. $6a - 9a(4a + 3)$ 99. $7a(a + 2) + 3a^2 + 2a^2$ *2-8*

Write as an algebraic expression.
  100. the difference of w and 4
101. 8 less than the product of a and c 102. twice the sum of m and n *1-6*

Solve. 103. $m - 422 = -53$ 104. $21t = -693$
105. $6(m + 3) = 10m - 2$ 106. $\frac{3}{4}c + 4 = \frac{1}{4}c - 2$ *3-1, 3-2, 3-5*
107. Frank needs a new shirt and sweater and wants to spend at most $45. If he finds a shirt for $18, how much can he spend on a sweater? *4-5*

Abundant **Practice** and
daily **Mixed Review** assure
that all students will acquire
the skills and conceptual
understanding they need
to be successful.

Instructional Approach

T5

Innovative transition components guarantee skills mastery and grade-level success for all students.

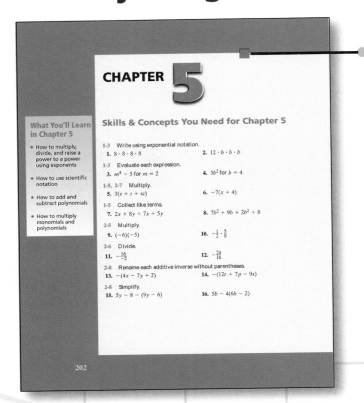

CHAPTER 5

What You'll Learn in Chapter 5

- How to multiply, divide, and raise a power to a power using exponents
- How to use scientific notation
- How to add and subtract polynomials
- How to multiply monomials and polynomials

Skills & Concepts You Need for Chapter 5

1-3 Write using exponential notation.
1. $8 \cdot 8 \cdot 8 \cdot 8$ 2. $12 \cdot b \cdot b \cdot b$

1-3 Evaluate each expression.
3. $m^4 - 5$ for $m = 2$ 4. $3b^2$ for $b = 4$

1-5, 2-7 Multiply.
5. $3(s + t + w)$ 6. $-7(x + 4)$

1-5 Collect like terms.
7. $2x + 8y + 7x + 5y$ 8. $7b^2 + 9b + 2b^2 + 8$

2-5 Multiply.
9. $(-6)(-5)$ 10. $-\frac{1}{2} \cdot \frac{5}{8}$

2-6 Divide.
11. $-\frac{16}{-2}$ 12. $-\frac{74}{16}$

2-8 Rename each additive inverse without parentheses.
13. $-(4x - 7y + 2)$ 14. $-(12r + 7p - 9s)$

2-8 Simplify.
15. $5y - 8 - (9y - 6)$ 16. $5b - 4(6b - 2)$

202

The **Skills and Concepts You Need** page at the beginning of each chapter provides a diagnostic check of the skills students need to successfully learn the concepts in the chapter.

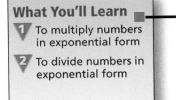

What You'll Learn

1 To multiply numbers in exponential form

2 To divide numbers in exponential form

. . . And Why

To simplify expressions containing exponents

Lessons are divided into **Parts** to allow you to easily adjust the pace at which content is covered.

The California Student Performance Pack provides even more transition support—
- Success-Building Puzzle and Problem Masters
- Help at Home Masters
- Practice Workbook
- Student Tutorial CD-ROM

California Skills Intervention Kit— a remedy for gaps in basic skills.

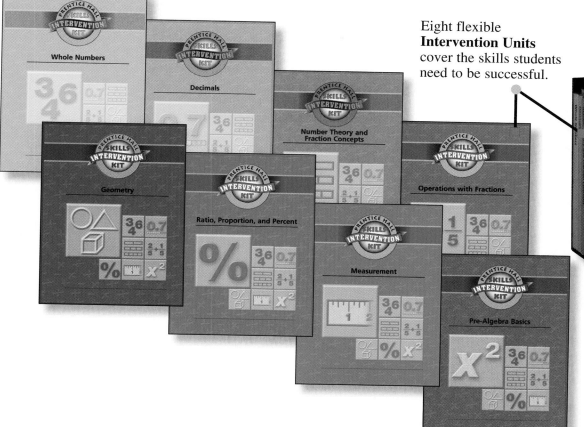

Whole Numbers

Decimals

Number Theory and Fraction Concepts

Geometry

Ratio, Proportion, and Percent

Operations with Fractions

Measurement

Pre-Algebra Basics

For Grades 6–9 Mathematics

Great for use in —
- After-school programs
- Summer school
- Fundamentals of math classes
- Your daily math classes

Eight flexible **Intervention Units** cover the skills students need to be successful.

Skills

Targeted Intervention Lessons foster independent learning.

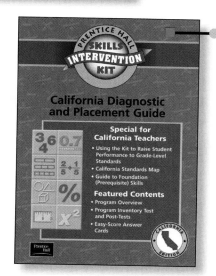

California Diagnostic and Placement Guide

Special for California Teachers
- Using the Kit to Raise Student Performance to Grade-Level Standards
- California Standards Map
- Guide to Foundation (Prerequisite) Skills

Featured Contents
- Program Overview
- Program Inventory Test and Post-Tests
- Easy-Score Answer Cards

Prentice Hall

California Diagnostic and Placement Guide allows teachers to diagnose gaps in understanding and prescribe an individualized course of study.

Available separately—
Package of 8 Instructional Videotapes
Features master teacher demonstrating key concepts. Includes handy User's Guide.

Test prep and assessment options integrated throughout let students monitor their own progress and prepare for testing success.

The **Practice Multiple Choice** feature, **Test Prep** questions, and **Standardized Test Prep** pages in the Student Edition teach test-taking skills and prepare students for high-stakes tests.

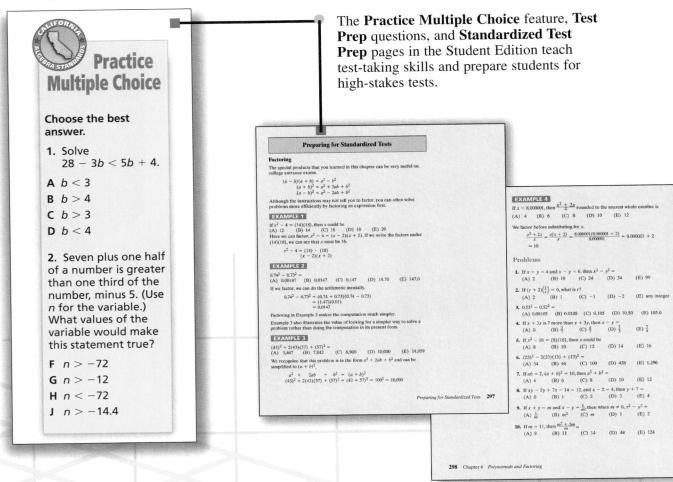

Practice Multiple Choice

CALIFORNIA ALGEBRA STANDARDS

Choose the best answer.

1. Solve
$28 - 3b < 5b + 4$.

A $b < 3$

B $b > 4$

C $b > 3$

D $b < 4$

2. Seven plus one half of a number is greater than one third of the number, minus 5. (Use n for the variable.) What values of the variable would make this statement true?

F $n > -72$

G $n > -12$

H $n < -72$

J $n > -14.4$

Preparing for Standardized Tests

Factoring

The special products that you learned in this chapter can be very useful on college entrance exams.

$(a - b)(a + b) = a^2 - b^2$
$(a + b)^2 = a^2 + 2ab + b^2$
$(a - b)^2 = a^2 - 2ab + b^2$

Although the instructions may not tell you to factor, you can often solve problems more efficiently by factoring an expression first.

EXAMPLE 1

If $x^2 - 4 = (14)(18)$, then x could be
(A) 12 (B) 14 (C) 16 (D) 18 (E) 20
Here we can factor, $x^2 - 4 = (x - 2)(x + 2)$. If we write the factors under $(14)(18)$, we can see that x must be 16.

$x^2 - 4 = (14) \cdot (18)$
$(x - 2)(x + 2)$

EXAMPLE 2

$0.74^2 - 0.73^2 =$
(A) 0.00147 (B) 0.0147 (C) 0.147 (D) 14.70 (E) 147.0
If we factor, we can do the arithmetic mentally.
$0.74^2 - 0.73^2 = (0.74 + 0.73)(0.74 - 0.73)$
$= (1.47)(0.01)$
$= 0.0147$
Factoring in Example 2 makes the computation much simpler.
Example 3 also illustrates the value of looking for a simpler way to solve a problem rather than doing the computation in its present form.

EXAMPLE 3

$(43)^2 + 2(43)(57) + (57)^2 =$
(A) 3,467 (B) 7,842 (C) 8,900 (D) 10,000 (E) 14,959
We recognize that this problem is in the form $a^2 + 2ab + b^2$ and can be simplified to $(a + b)^2$.
$a^2 + 2ab + b^2 = (a + b)^2$
$(43)^2 + 2(43)(57) + (57)^2 = (43 + 57)^2 = 100^2 = 10,000$

Preparing for Standardized Tests **297**

EXAMPLE 4

If $x = 8.000001$, then $\frac{x^2 + 2x}{x}$ rounded to the nearest whole number is
(A) 4 (B) 6 (C) 8 (D) 10 (E) 12

We factor before substituting for x.
$\frac{x^2 + 2x}{x} = \frac{x(x + 2)}{x} = \frac{8.000001(8.000001 + 2)}{8.000001} = 8.000001 + 2$
≈ 10

Problems

1. If $x + y = 4$ and $x - y = 6$, then $x^2 - y^2 =$
(A) 2 (B) 10 (C) 24 (D) 34 (E) 99

2. If $(r + 2)\left(\frac{1}{r}\right) = 0$, what is r?
(A) 2 (B) 1 (C) -1 (D) -2 (E) any integer

3. $0.53^2 - 0.52^2 =$
(A) 0.00105 (B) 0.0105 (C) 0.105 (D) 10.50 (E) 105.0

4. If $x + 3x$ is 7 more than $y + 3y$, then $x - y =$
(A) 0 (B) $\frac{3}{2}$ (C) $\frac{5}{2}$ (D) $\frac{7}{3}$ (E) $\frac{7}{4}$

5. If $x^2 - 16 = (8)(16)$, then x could be
(A) 8 (B) 10 (C) 12 (D) 14 (E) 16

6. $(23)^2 - 2(23)(13) + (13)^2 =$
(A) 34 (B) 46 (C) 100 (D) 438 (E) 1,296

7. If $ab = 2$, $(a + b)^2 = 10$, then $a^2 + b^2 =$
(A) 4 (B) 6 (C) 8 (D) 10 (E) 12

8. If $xy - 2y + 7x - 14 = 12$, and $x - 2 = 4$, then $y + 7 =$
(A) 0 (B) 1 (C) 2 (D) 3 (E) 4

9. If $x + y = m$ and $x - y = \frac{1}{m}$, then when $m \neq 0$, $x^2 - y^2 =$
(A) $\frac{1}{m}$ (B) m^2 (C) m (D) 1 (E) 2

10. If $m = 11$, then $\frac{m^2 + 3m}{m} =$
(A) 9 (B) 11 (C) 14 (D) 44 (E) 124

298 Chapter 6 *Polynomials and Factoring*

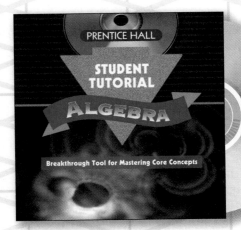

PRENTICE HALL
STUDENT TUTORIAL
ALGEBRA
Breakthrough Tool for Mastering Core Concepts

The **Student Tutorial CD-ROM** provides easy-to-use self-assessment directly linked to text lessons.

The **Companion Web Site** provides self-tests in standardized test format to encourage self-directed monitoring of progress. See **www.phschool.com**

California Assessment Success Kit—all the tools you need for entry-level assessment, progress monitoring, and summative evaluation.

This innovative kit contains:

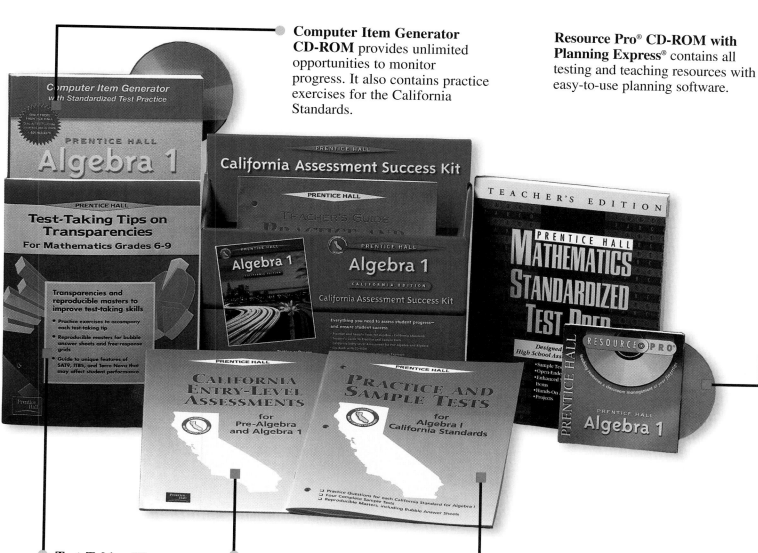

Computer Item Generator CD-ROM provides unlimited opportunities to monitor progress. It also contains practice exercises for the California Standards.

Resource Pro® CD-ROM with Planning Express® contains all testing and teaching resources with easy-to-use planning software.

Test-Taking Tips on Transparencies provide ongoing opportunities to teach test-taking skills.

California Entry-Level Assessments for Pre-Algebra and Algebra 1 help you assess readiness for the course and make appropriate placement decisions.

Practice and Sample Tests for California Standards prepare students for testing success.

Comprehensive lesson planning support helps you effectively cover the Standards.

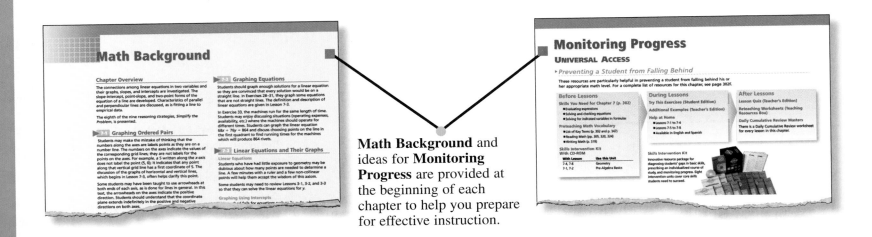

Math Background and ideas for **Monitoring Progress** are provided at the beginning of each chapter to help you prepare for effective instruction.

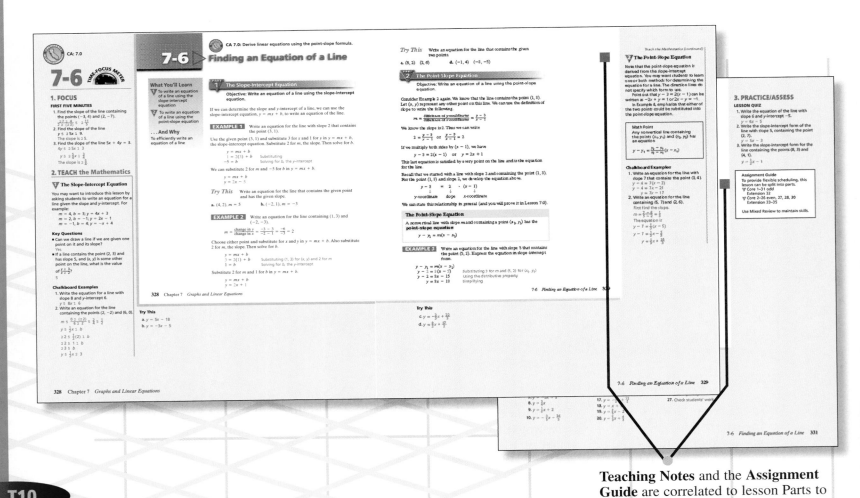

Teaching Notes and the **Assignment Guide** are correlated to lesson Parts to provide flexible pacing.

Teacher's Edition Handbook provides unmatched support for meeting the Standards.

See pages T34–T63.

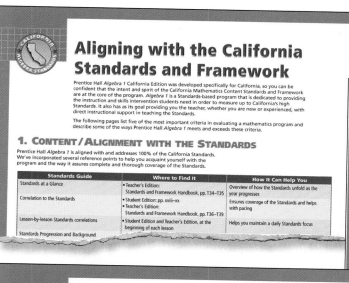

Aligning with the California Standards and Framework

Prentice Hall *Algebra 1 California Edition* was developed specifically for California, so you can be confident that the intent and spirit of the California Mathematics Content Standards and Framework are at the core of the program. *Algebra 1* is a Standards-based program that is dedicated to providing the instruction and skills intervention students need in order to measure up to California's high Standards. It also has as its goal providing you the teacher, whether you are new or experienced, with direct instructional support in teaching the Standards.

The following pages list five of the most important criteria in evaluating a mathematics program and describe some of the ways Prentice Hall *Algebra 1* meets and exceeds these criteria.

1. CONTENT/ALIGNMENT WITH THE STANDARDS

Prentice Hall *Algebra 1* is aligned with and addresses 100% of the California Standards. We've incorporated several reference points to help you acquaint yourself with the program and the way it assures complete and thorough coverage of the Standards.

Standards Guide	Where to Find It	How It Can Help You
Standards at a Glance	• Teacher's Edition: Standards and Framework Handbook, pp. T34–T35	Overview of how the Standards unfold as the year progresses
Correlation to the Standards	• Student Edition: pp. xviii–xx • Teacher's Edition: Standards and Framework Handbook, pp. T36–T39	Ensures coverage of the Standards and helps with pacing
Lesson-by-lesson Standards correlations	• Student Edition and Teacher's Edition, at the beginning of each lesson	Helps you maintain a daily Standards focus
Standards Progression and Background		

2. PROGRAM ORGANIZATION

The Student Book

Content Sequence The student book is organized with the goal of addressing all of the California Mathematics Content Standards, building concept upon concept, skill upon skill in an order that is pedagogically sound. The Table of Contents shows the smooth flow of the book, with prerequisite skills and ideas presented before the more complex topics that depend upon them. Review topics are kept to a minimum.

Lesson Organization Lessons are organized using a direct-instruction approach so students know exactly what they will learn and how. The added benefit of this structure is that parents, adult tutors, or older siblings can help students in the learning process. From start to end, all lessons do the following:

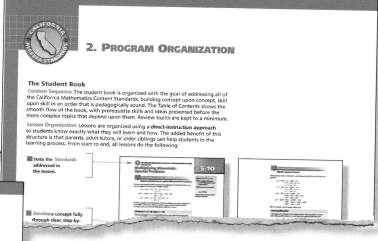

- State the Standards addressed in the lesson.
- Develop a concept fully through clear, step-by-

3. ASSESSMENT

Mastering Grade-Level Standards

The California Mathematics Content Framework outlines three broad categories of assessment.

"The purposes of assessment that are the most crucial to achieving the Standards are as follows: entry-level assessment, progress monitoring, and summative evaluation."

- **Entry-Level Assessment**
The *Entry-Level Assessments* book provides you with an assessment and diagnostic system to guide you in assessing each student's achievement level at the beginning of the school year. It will help you in determining whether a student should work with the grade-level materials, with the materials for the previous grade level, at a more advanced grade level, or should start at a point later in the course. It will also help you identify whether a student might need the transitional materials found in the Prentice Hall *Skills Intervention Kit*. For more information on the *Skills Intervention Kit*, see page T61.

- **Progress Monitoring**
It is through continual monitoring of students' work that you will be able to adjust instruction so students can progress. Below are some of the program's curriculum-embedded assessment opportunities. There is also an extensive Web-based assessment support system that ties...

4. UNIVERSAL ACCESS

The California Framework states:

"The ultimate goal of mathematics instruction is to ensure universal access to high-quality curriculum and instruction so that all students can meet or exceed the content Standards."

All learners are different. Some will be ready to soar, while others will need to slow down or even back up. The program contains a number of tools to help you tailor instruction to the needs of all students.

Assessing Readiness Prior to Each Chapter

Instructional variation begins in the student book with its system for checking understanding and skill level. The *Skills and Concepts You Need* page is designed as a review of the prerequisite skills needed before each chapter. Some students may have difficulty, signaling a need for more in-depth review and reteaching. The Teacher's Edition refers you to several tools in the program, such as earlier lessons or the *Skills Intervention Kit* (discussed on the following page), depending upon the amount of remediation needed.

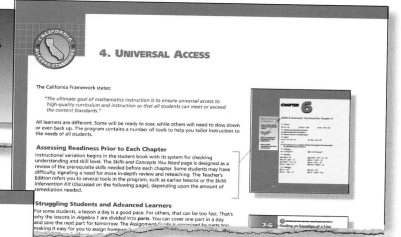

Struggling Students and Advanced Learners

For some students, a lesson a day is a good pace. For others, that can be too fast. That's why the lessons in *Algebra 1* are divided into parts. You can cover one part in a day and save the next part for tomorrow. The Assignment Guide is organized by parts too, making it easy for you to assign homework.

5. INSTRUCTIONAL SUPPORT

As a teacher, you are a caretaker in the learning process of young minds. You seek to keep up with your profession on an ongoing basis. But sometimes it is difficult to find the time to treat yourself, and to refresh your base in mathematics content. We have done several things to help you.

Standards at a Glance—Seeing the Big Picture

In order to be able to guide students through this course, it is helpful to have a big-picture vision of where you are going. The Standards at a Glance chart on pages T34–T35 will help you see not only which standards are the focal point of each chapter, but also how the Standards unfold as the year progresses.

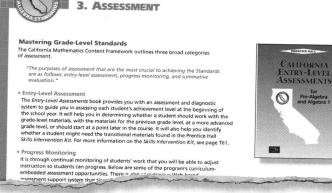

The **California Standards and Framework Handbook** in the Teacher's Edition gives you background on key elements of the Standards and Framework and provides specific suggestions on using program features and components to successfully implement the Standards.

Lesson Planning Support

A vast array of teaching support components addresses all learning and teaching needs.

Easy-to-manage California Teaching Resources

Practice, Reteaching, Enrichment, and **Problem Solving Practice**—blackline masters to meet all student needs.

First Five Minutes Transparency Masters—an excellent springboard into each lesson.

Teacher's Forms and Letters provide handy materials for teaching and communicating with parents.

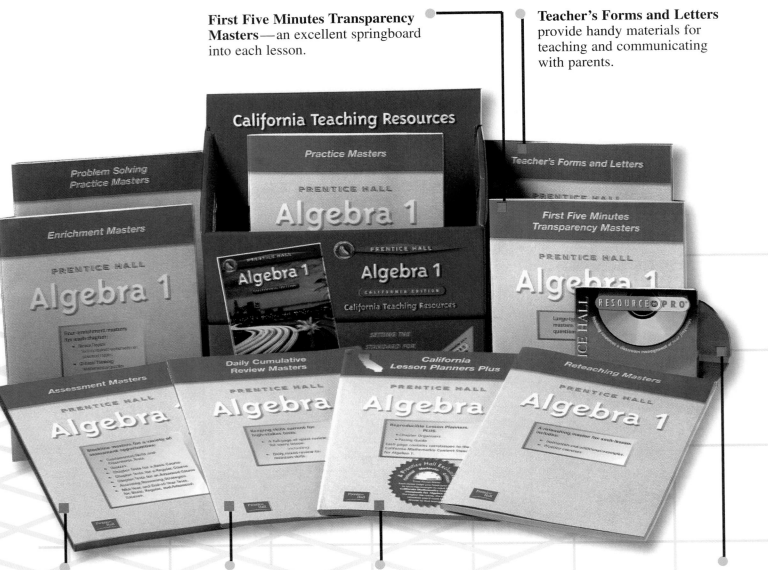

Assessment Masters—chapter tests, cumulative assessment, and end-of-course exam.

Daily Cumulative Review Masters—provide extended opportunities for concept review and mastery.

California Lesson Planners Plus—daily lesson plans correlated to California Mathematics Content Standards.

Resource Pro® with Planning Express® CD-ROM—contains electronic versions of all teaching resources along with easy-to-use lesson planning software and the Computer Item Generator.

Comprehensive Transparency Support

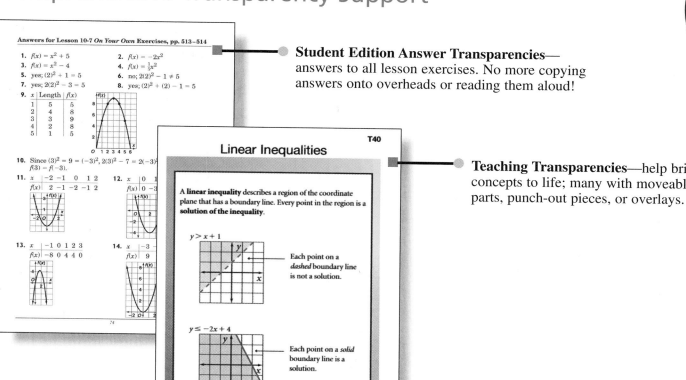

Student Edition Answer Transparencies—answers to all lesson exercises. No more copying answers onto overheads or reading them aloud!

Teaching Transparencies—help bring concepts to life; many with moveable parts, punch-out pieces, or overlays.

Professional Development Opportunities

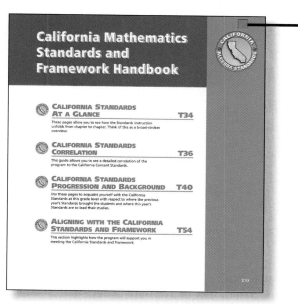

California Standards and Framework Handbook, right in the Teacher's Edition, provides a wealth of background and support to help you implement the Framework and successfully teach the Standards.

Algebra Instructional Videos, designed for classroom use, provide step-by-step instruction of Algebra skills.

www.phschool.com

Prentice Hall Web Site provides on-line support materials, teaching notes, teaching links, and professional development resources. See **www.phschool.com.** Also see the Prentice Hall California Web Site for even more professional development resources.

Assessment and Test Prep

Prentice Hall Pre-Algebra Program Resources

California Student Edition
(0-13-044263-1)

California Teacher's Edition
(0-13-044265-8)

California Student Performance Pack

- Practice Workbook
- Help at Home Blackline Masters
- Success-Building Puzzle and Problem Masters
- Student Tutorial CD-ROM

California Teaching Resources

- Practice, Reteaching, Enrichment, and Problem Solving Masters
- Daily Cumulative Review Blackline Masters
- First Five Minutes Transparency Masters
- Assessment Masters
- California Lesson Planners Plus
- Teacher's Forms and Letters
- Resource Pro® CD-ROM with Planning Express®

Solution Key

Teaching Transparencies

Student Edition Answers on Transparencies

California Assessment Success Kit

- Practice and Sample Tests for California Algebra Standards
- Teacher's Guide to Practice and Sample Tests
- California Entry-Level Assessments for Pre-Algebra and Algebra
- Computer Item Generator with Standardized Test Practice CD-ROM
- Resource Pro® with Planning Express® CD-ROM
- Test-Taking Tips on Transparencies
- Mathematics Standardized Test Prep, Teacher's Edition

Video Field Trips: Algebra Applications

Algebra Instructional Videos

PLUS! Prentice Hall California Skills Intervention Kit

- 8 Student Intervention Units (also available as workbooks)
- 8 Intervention Teacher's Guides
- California Diagnostic and Placement Guide
- 30 Student Progress Folders
- Student Tutorial CD-ROM

Prentice Hall . . . Setting the Standard for Excellence in California.

PRENTICE HALL

Algebra 1

CALIFORNIA EDITION

Stanley A. Smith

Randall I. Charles

John A. Dossey

Marvin L. Bittinger

Prentice
Hall

Needham, Massachusetts
Upper Saddle River, New Jersey
Glenview, Illinois

REVIEWERS

Donald R. Price
Alvarado Intermediate School
Rowland Heights, California

Joyce F. Henderson
Robert A. Millikan High School
Long Beach, California

CONTENT CONSULTANTS

Elizabeth Cunningham
Mathematics
Prentice Hall National Consultant
Mansfield, Texas

Shawyn Jackson
Mathematics
Prentice Hall National Consultant
Bayshore, New York

Bridget Hadley
Mathematics
Director, Prentice Hall National Consultants
Hopkinton, Massachusetts

Sandra Mosteller
Mathematics
Prentice Hall National Consultant
Anderson, South Carolina

Loretta Rector
Mathematics
Prentice Hall National Consultant
Foresthill, California

ISBN 0-13-044265-8
7 8 9 10   04 03

AUTHORS

Stanley A. Smith served as Coordinator, Office of Mathematics (K–12), for Baltimore County Public Schools, Maryland. He has taught junior high school mathematics and science, and senior high school mathematics. He earned his M.A. degree in Mathematics Education at the University of Maryland. Mr. Smith was named Outstanding Mathematics Educator by the Maryland Council of Teachers of Mathematics in 1987. He is co-author of many high school mathematics textbooks.

Randall I. Charles is Professor of Mathematics Emeritus at San Jose State University, where he also directed the Center for Mathematics and Computer Science Education. He has taught at all levels and has been an elementary and secondary school mathematics supervisor. Dr. Charles holds a Ph.D. in Mathematics Education from Indiana University. He is co-author of several mathematics textbooks.

John A. Dossey is Distinguished University Professor of Mathematics Emeritus at Illinois State University. He has taught at every level from grade 7 through graduate school and has served as K–12 supervisor of mathematics. He received his Ph.D. in Mathematics Education from the University of Illinois. From 1986–1988, Dr. Dossey served as President of the National Council of Teachers of Mathematics, and from 1996–1998 as chair of the Conference Board of Mathematical Sciences. In 1996 he was awarded a Lifetime Achievement Award from the National Council of Teachers of Mathematics. He is co-author of several mathematics textbooks.

Marvin L. Bittinger is Professor of Mathematics Education at Indiana University-Purdue University at Indianapolis. He is a member of the National Council of Teachers of Mathematics and the Mathematical Association of America. He earned his Ph.D. at Purdue University in Mathematics Education. Dr. Bittinger is the co-author of many mathematics textbooks, from basic mathematics through calculus.

CALIFORNIA TEACHER'S EDITION
CONTENTS

Table of Contents

iv   Contents

The "To the Student" pages help students make the best use of the features of the textbook to facilitate their learning.

The Mixed Practice provides two pages of exercises for each chapter, and the Teacher's Edition contains a correlation of

the exercises to the lessons. The Milestones in Mathematics contains an overview of developments in mathematics

beginning with 30,000 B.C. The Glossary provides a definition and page reference for each vocabulary term.

California Standards covered in this chapter

Algebra I

1.0	2.0
4.0	10.0
24.0	25.2

REVIEW

ASSESSMENT

Students begin the year by learning about expressions and simplifying them using number properties (Algebra Standards 1.0 and 4.0). They review the use of exponents (Standard 2.0) and begin to use logical arguments and justify steps in solving equations (Standards 24.0 and 25.2).

CHAPTER 2

Integers and Rational Numbers

California Standards covered in this chapter

Algebra I

1.0	1.1
2.0	4.0
10.0	25.0
25.1	25.2

REVIEW

ASSESSMENT

*S*tudents learn to use rational numbers and their operations, including taking the absolute value, taking the opposite, and simplifying expressions (Algebra Standards 2.0 and 4.0). They continue to study basic operations and their properties, including the closure properties of rational numbers and various subsets (Standard 1.0). They use the properties that are taken as axioms to prove other properties (Standards 1.1, 25.0, 25.1, and 25.2).

CHAPTER 3

Equations

California Standards covered in this chapter

Algebra I

3.0	5.0
24.0	25.0
25.2	25.3

REVIEW

Mixed Review in every Lesson

ASSESSMENT

Try This exercises after every Example

Practice Multiple Choice — 128, 144, 150, 164

The emphasis of this chapter is on Algebra Standard 5.0. Students learn to use the addition and multiplication properties of equality to solve linear equations, justifying each step of the solution (Standards 25.0 and 25.2). They solve multi-step word problems by translating them into linear equations. They solve absolute value equations (Standard 3.0) and determine when absolute value statements are true (Standard 25.3).

CHAPTER 4 ▷ Inequalities

California Standards covered in this chapter

Algebra I

1.1	5.0
24.0	24.1
24.2	24.3

ASSESSMENT

The emphasis of this chapter is again on Algebra Standard 5.0. Students learn to use the addition and multiplication properties of inequality to solve linear inequalities, justifying each step of the solution. They solve multi-step word problems by translating them into linear inequalities. And they learn about deductive and inductive reasoning and how to use logical reasoning to solve problems (Algebra Standards 24.0, 24.1, 24.2, and 24.3).

CHAPTER 5

Exponents and Polynomials

California Standards covered in this chapter

Algebra I
2.0   10.0
24.0

REVIEW

ASSESSMENT

Contents

Students learn to use the rules of exponents where the exponents are integers (Algebra Standard 2.0). Then the emphasis of the chapter is on Algebra Standard 10.0; students learn to add, subtract, multiply, and divide monomials and also add, subtract, and multiply polynomials. Polynomials are also used in solving problems.

CHAPTER 6

Polynomials and Factoring

California Standards covered in this chapter

Algebra I
10.0   11.0
14.0

x   Contents

The emphasis of this chapter is on Algebra Standard 11.0. Students learn to find common factors and to factor differences of two squares, trinomial squares, and other trinomials. Then factoring and the principle of zero products are used to solve quadratic equations (Standard 14.0). Finally, polynomials are used to solve multi-step problems (Standard 10.0).

CHAPTER 7

Graphs and Linear Equations

California Standards covered in this chapter

Algebra I

6.0	7.0
8.0	24.0
24.1	25.0

REVIEW

ASSESSMENT

The emphasis of this chapter is on linear equations and their graphs (Algebra Standards 6.0, 7.0, and 8.0). Students learn to find x- and y-intercepts and determine whether a point lies on a line. They learn about slope, the slope-intercept and point-slope forms of an equation, and the slopes of parallel and perpendicular lines. Properties of the slope-intercept form are proved (Standard 25.0) and students learn more about reasoning (Standards 24.0, and 24.1).

CHAPTER 8

Systems of Equations

California Standards covered in this chapter

Algebra I

9.0   15.0

REVIEW

ASSESSMENT

The emphasis of this chapter is on Algebra Standard 9.0. Students solve systems of equations graphically and algebraically and use systems of equations to solve motion and other multi-step problems (Standard 15).

CHAPTER 9

Inequalities and Absolute Values

California Standards covered in this chapter

Algebra I

1.0	3.0
5.0	6.0
9.0	24.0

REVIEW

ASSESSMENT

Contents   **xiii**

𝒮tudents learn about unions and intersections of sets and use these ideas to graph the solutions of compound sentences. Then they solve equations and inequalities involving absolute value (Algebra Standard 3.0) and graph solutions of systems of inequalities (Standards 6.0 and 9.0).

California Standards covered in this chapter

Algebra I

10.0	12.0
13.0	15.0
24.0	25.0
25.1	

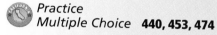
Students learn to simplify rational expressions (Algebra Standard 12.0). Then they multiply, divide, add, and subtract rational expressions and use rational equations to solve rate, work, and mixture problems (Standards 13.0 and 15.0).

They divide polynomials (Standard 10.0), prove theorems related to rational expressions (Standards 25.0 and 25.1), and employ logical arguments (Standard 24.0).

CHAPTER 11

Radical Expressions and Equations

California Standards covered in this chapter

Algebra I

2.0   25.1

REVIEW

ASSESSMENT

Contents   **xv**

The emphasis of this chapter is on Algebra Standard 2.0. Students learn about real numbers, including square roots and cube roots. They learn to simplify radical expressions and to multiply, divide, add, and subtract them. They learn to use fractional exponents and to simplify expressions containing fractional exponents. They also solve radical equations.

T30

CHAPTER 12

Relations and Functions

California Standards covered in this chapter

Algebra I

13.0	15.0
16.0	17.0
18.0	21.0
22.0	

Students learn about relations and functions and their graphs, and to add, subtract, multiply, and divide functions (Algebra Standards 13.0, 16.0, 17.0, and 18.0). They learn about quadratic functions (Standards 21.0 and 22.0) and variation, and use these ideas to solve problems (Algebra Standard 15.0).

Quadratic Equations

California Standards covered in this chapter

Algebra I

13.0	14.0
19.0	20.0
21.0	22.0
23.0	25.0

REVIEW

Mixed Review in every Lesson

ASSESSMENT

Try This exercises after every Example

Students learn to solve quadratic equations by graphing the related function, factoring, completing the square, and using the quadratic formula (Algebra Standards 14.0, 19.0, 20.0, 21.0), and they use quadratic equations to solve physical problems (Standard 23.0). Students also solve rational equations (Standard 13.0) and continue to provide justification of steps in their work (Standard 25.0).

California Mathematics Standards and Framework Handbook

California Standards At a Glance

Standard	1	2	3	4	5	6	7	8	9	10	11	12	13
1.0 Students identify and use the arithmetic properties of subsets of integers and rational, irrational, and real numbers, including closure properties for the four basic arithmetic operations where applicable.	■	■		■					■				
1.1 Students use properties of numbers to demonstrate that assertions are true or false.													
2.0 Students understand and use such operations as taking the opposite, finding the reciprocal, taking a root, and raising to a fractional power. They understand and use the rules of exponents.	■	■			■						■		
3.0 Students solve equations and inequalities involving absolute values.			■						■				
4.0 Students simplify expressions before solving linear equations and inequalities in one variable.	■	■											
5.0 Students solve multi-step problems, including word problems, involving linear equations and linear inequalities in one variable and provide justification for each step.			■	■									
6.0 Students graph a linear equation and compute the *x*- and *y*-intercepts. They are also able to sketch the region defined by a linear inequality.							■		■				
7.0 Students verify that a point lies on a line, given an equation of the line. Students are able to derive linear equations by using the point-slope formula.							■						
8.0 Students understand the concepts of parallel lines and perpendicular lines and how their slopes are related. Students are able to find the equation of a line perpendicular to a given line that passes through a given point.							■						
9.0 Students solve a system of two linear equations in two variables algebraically and are able to interpret the answer graphically. Students are able to solve a system of two linear inequalities in two variables and to sketch the solution set.								■	■				
10.0 Students add, subtract, multiply, and divide monomials and polynomials. Students solve multi-step problems, including word problems, by using these techniques.	■	■			■	■				■			
11.0 Students apply basic factoring techniques to second- and simple third-degree polynomials. These techniques include finding a common factor for all terms in a polynomial, recognizing the difference of two squares, and recognizing perfect squares of binomials.						■							
12.0 Students simplify fractions with polynomials in the numerator and denominator by factoring both and reducing them to lowest terms.										■			

Prentice Hall Algebra Chapters

Standard	1	2	3	4	5	6	7	8	9	10	11	12	13
13.0 Students add, subtract, multiply, and divide rational expressions and functions. Students solve both computationally and conceptually challenging problems by using these techniques.										■		■	■
14.0 Students solve a quadratic equation by factoring or completing the square.						■							■
15.0 Students apply algebraic techniques to solve rate problems, work problems, and percent mixture problems.								■		■		■	
16.0 Students understand the concepts of a relation and a function, determine whether a given relation defines a function, and give pertinent information about given relations and functions.												■	
17.0 Students determine the domain of independent variables and the range of dependent variables defined by a graph, a set of ordered pairs, or a symbolic expression.												■	
18.0 Students determine whether a relation defined by a graph, a set of ordered pairs, or a symbolic expression is a function, and justify the conclusion.												■	
19.0 Students know the quadratic formula and are familiar with its proof by completing the square.													■
20.0 Students use the quadratic formula to find the roots of a second-degree polynomial and to solve quadratic equations.													■
21.0 Students graph quadratic functions and know that their roots are the *x*-intercepts.												■	■
22.0 Students use the quadratic formula, factoring techniques, or both to determine whether the graph of a quadratic function will intersect the *x*-axis in zero, one, or two points.												■	■
23.0 Students apply quadratic equations to physical problems, such as the motion of an object under the force of gravity.													■
24.0 Students use and know simple aspects of a logical argument.	■		■	■	■		■		■	■			
24.1 Students explain the difference between inductive and deductive reasoning and identify and provide examples of each.													
24.2 Students identify the hypothesis and conclusion in logical deduction.													
24.3 Students use counterexamples to show that an assertion is false and recognize that a single counterexample is sufficient to refute an assertion.													
25.0 Students use properties of the number system to judge the validity of results, to justify each step of a procedure, and to prove or disprove statements.	■	■	■				■			■	■		■
25.1 Students use properties of numbers to construct simple, valid arguments (direct or indirect) for, or formulate counterexamples to, claimed assertions.													
25.2 Students judge the validity of an argument according to whether the properties of the real number system and order of operations have been applied correctly at each step.													
25.3 Given a specific algebraic statement involving linear, quadratic, or absolute value expressions, equations or inequalities, students determine whether the statement is true sometimes, always, or never.													

California Standards Correlation

This chart shows the lessons in which each Standard is developed. Next to each lesson number is a brief description of the concept(s) addressed in that lesson. The estimated times given in the third column provide an approximate number of days it will take to cover a given Standard. For in-depth pacing information for different groups of students, refer to the special *California Algebra Lesson Planner.*

Standard	Lesson Numbers and Concepts	Estimated Time
1.0 Students identify and use the arithmetic properties of subsets of integers and rational, irrational, and real numbers, including closure properties for the four basic arithmetic operations where applicable. **1.1** Students use properties of numbers to demonstrate that assertions are true or false.	1-2 Commutative and identity properties 1-4 Associative properties 1-5 Distributive property 2-2 Rational numbers 2-3 Additive inverses 2-4 Subtraction using additive inverses 2-5 Multiplicative property of zero 2-6 Multiplicative inverses 2-7 Distributive property 2-8 Inverse of a sum 2-10 Closure; summary of all properties; proof 4-1 Inequalities and their graphs 9-1 Sets, intersections, and unions	11 days
2.0 Students understand and use such operations as taking the opposite, finding the reciprocal, taking a root, and raising to a fractional power. They understand and use the rules of exponents.	1-3 Exponential notation 2-1 Opposites 2-6 Reciprocals 2-8 Inverse of a sum 5-1 Multiplying and dividing with exponents 5-2 Raising to powers with exponents 5-4 Scientific notation 11-1 Square roots 11-2 Radical expressions 11-3 Cube roots 11-4 Fractional powers 11-5 Operations with rational exponents	10 days
3.0 Students solve equations and inequalities involving absolute values.	3-8 Equations with absolute value 9-3 Equations with absolute value expressions 9-4 Inequalities with absolute value	5 days
4.0 Students simplify expressions before solving linear equations and inequalities in one variable.	1-5 Simplifying using the distributive property 2-7 Like terms 2-8 Inverse of a sum; multiple grouping symbols	5 days
5.0 Students solve multi-step problems, including word problems, involving linear equations and linear inequalities in one variable, and provide justification for each step.	3-3 Multi-step linear equations 3-4 Writing equations for word problems 3-5 Variables on both sides 3-6 Fractions and decimals in equations 3-7 Formulas 3-9 Problems about proportions 3-10 Problems about percent 3-11 Multi-step word problems 4-4 Multi-step linear inequalities 4-5 Problems involving inequalities	11 days

Standard		Lesson Numbers and Concepts		Estimated Time
6.0	Students graph a linear equation and compute the *x*- and *y*-intercepts. They are also able to sketch the region defined by a linear inequality.	7-2 7-3 7-5 9-5	Graphs of linear equations Computing and using *x*- and *y*-intercepts Graphs using slope-intercept form Graphs of linear inequalities in two variables	6 days
7.0	Students verify that a point lies on a line, given an equation of the line. Students are able to derive linear equations by using the point-slope formula.	7-2 7-4 7-6 7-7	Solutions of equations Slope Point-slope formula Fitting equations to data	6 days
8.0	Students understand the concepts of parallel lines and perpendicular lines and how their slopes are related. Students are able to find the equation of a line perpendicular to a given line that passes through a given point.	7-4 7-8	Slopes of horizontal and vertical lines Equation of a line parallel or perpendicular to a given line	5 days
9.0	Students solve a system of two linear equations in two variables algebraically and are able to interpret the answer graphically. Students are able to solve a system of two linear inequalities in two variables and to sketch the solution set.	8-1 8-2 8-3 8-4 9-6	Graphical solutions Substitution method Addition method and addition with multiplication Using systems to solve word problems Systems of linear inequalities	8 days
10.0	Students add, subtract, multiply, and divide monomials and polynomials. Students solve multi-step problems, including word problems, by using these techniques.	1-5 2-7 2-8 5-3 5-5 5-6 5-7 5-8 5-9 5-10 5-11 6-9 10-9	Adding monomials Adding and subtracting monomials Simplifying polynomials Multiplying and dividing monomials Collecting like terms Ordering polynomials Adding polynomials Subtracting polynomials Multiplying monomials and binomials Special products Multiplying polynomials Solving problems using polynomials Dividing polynomials	12 days
11.0	Students apply basic factoring techniques to second- and simple third-degree polynomials. These techniques include finding a common factor for all terms in a polynomial, recognizing the difference of two squares, and recognizing perfect squares of binomials.	6-1 6-2 6-3 6-4 6-5 6-6 6-7	Polynomials and common factors Difference of two squares Perfect square trinomials Trinomial factoring with a leading coefficient of 1 General trinomial factoring Factoring third-degree polynomials by grouping Summary of factoring techniques	11 days
12.0	Students simplify fractions with polynomials in the numerator and denominator by factoring both and reducing them to lowest terms.	10-1	Simplifying rational expressions by factoring and reducing	3 days

Standard	Lesson Numbers and Concepts	Estimated Time
13.0 Students add, subtract, multiply, and divide rational expressions and functions. Students solve both computationally and conceptually challenging problems by using these techniques.	**10-2** Multiplying rational expressions **10-3** Dividing rational expressions **10-4** Adding and subtracting rational expressions with like denominators **10-5** Adding and subtracting rational expressions with unlike denominators **10-6** Solving rational equations **10-10** Simplifying complex rational expressions **12-1** Operations with rational functions **13-5** Solving rational equations	10 days
14.0 Students solve a quadratic equation by factoring or completing the square.	**6-8** Factoring to solve quadratic equations **6-9** Problems using quadratic equations **13-1** Factoring to solve quadratic equations **13-3** Completing the square to solve quadratic equations **13-5** Rational equations that involve quadratic factoring **13-6** Radical equations that involve quadratic factoring **13-7** Problems using quadratic equations	9 days
15.0 Students apply algebraic techniques to solve rate problems, work problems, and percent mixture problems.	**8-5** Motion problems **10-7** Work problems **10-8** Percent mixture problems **12-5** Rate problems (direct variation) **12-6** Rate problems (inverse variation) **12-7** Rate problems (joint variation)	9 days
16.0 Students understand the concepts of a relation and a function, determine whether a given relation defines a function, and give pertinent information about given relations and functions.	**12-1** Relations and functions **12-2** Domain and range of functions involving absolute value, rational expressions, and radical expressions **12-3** Writing linear functions to solve problems	4 days
17.0 Students determine the domain of independent variables and the range of dependent variables defined by a graph, a set of ordered pairs, or a symbolic expression.	**12-1** Domain and range from ordered pairs **12-2** Domain and range from graphs and from symbolic expressions	3 days
18.0 Students determine whether a relation defined by a graph, a set of ordered pairs, or a symbolic expression is a function and justify the conclusion.	**12-1** Determining whether a relation expressed as a set of ordered pairs is a function, with justification **12-2** Determining whether a relation expressed graphically or symbolically is a function, with justification	3 days
19.0 Students know the quadratic formula and are familiar with its proof by completing the square.	**13-4** Quadratic formula; proof by completing the square	3 days

Standard	Lesson Numbers and Concepts	Estimated Time
20.0 Students use the quadratic formula to find the roots of a second-degree polynomial and to solve quadratic equations.	**13-4** Using the quadratic formula to solve equations; finding roots of a second-degree polynomial **13-5** Using the quadratic formula **13-7** Using the quadratic formula	5 days
21.0 Students graph quadratic functions and know that their roots are the *x*-intercepts.	**12-4** Graphing quadratic functions; *x*-intercepts and roots **13-1** Roots of quadratic functions and *x*-intercepts	4 days
22.0 Students use the quadratic formula or factoring techniques or both to determine whether the graph of a quadratic function will intersect the *x*-axis in zero, one, or two points.	**12-4** Factoring a quadratic function to find *x*-intercepts **13-4** Using the discriminant to determine the number of *x*-intercepts of a quadratic function	4 days
23.0 Students apply quadratic equations to physical problems, such as the motion of an object under the force of gravity.	**13-2** Applying quadratic equations to physical problems; motion under the force of gravity **13-7** Solving physical problems	4 days

24.0 Students use and know simple aspects of a logical argument.
  24.1 Students explain the difference between inductive and deductive reasoning and identify and provide examples of each.
  24.2 Students identify the hypothesis and conclusion in logical deduction.
  24.3 Students use counterexamples to show that an assertion is false and recognize that a single counterexample is sufficient to refute an assertion.
	4-5 Deductive reasoning; hypothesis and conclusion; inductive reasoning; counterexample
	4-6 Logical reasoning
	9-2 Truth tables
	1-8, 1-10, 3-12, 5-12, 7-10, 10-12 Reasoning strategies; writing a convincing argument
	In addition, there are numerous exercises throughout the text that ask students to provide counterexamples, write a convincing argument, or apply mathematical reasoning.
		9 days

25.0 Students use properties of the number system to judge the validity of results, to justify each step of a procedure, and to prove or disprove statements.
  25.1 Students use properties of numbers to construct simple valid arguments (direct or indirect) for, or formulate counterexamples to, claimed assertions.
  25.2 Students judge the validity of an argument according to whether the properties of the real number system and order of operations have been applied correctly at each step.
  25.3 Given a specific algebraic statement involving linear, quadratic, or absolute value expressions, equations or inequalities, students determine whether the statement is true sometimes, always, or never.
	1-7 True, false, and open equations
	2-10 Number properties and proofs
	3-3 Justifying each step in solving equations
	3-7 Justifying each step in transforming formulas
	3-8 Determining whether a statement is sometimes, always, or never true
	7-9 Proving theorems related to slope
	10-11 Proving theorems related to division and reciprocals
	11-1 Proof by contradiction
	13-6 Justifying each step in transforming formulas
	In addition, there are numerous exercises throughout the text that ask students to justify statements, justify steps, analyze errors, provide counterexamples, or judge statements to be sometimes, always, or never true.
		9 days

California Standards Progression and Background

STANDARDS 1.0 AND 1.1

1.0 Students identify and use the arithmetic properties of subsets of integers and rational, irrational, and real numbers, including closure properties for the four basic arithmetic operations where applicable:

1.1 Students use properties of numbers to demonstrate whether assertions are true or false.

■ PROGRESSION ■

Prior Grade Level Standards
Students know the properties of and can compute with rational numbers.

This Year's Standards
Students' knowledge is expanded to include irrational numbers. Students also learn about the closure property.

Where the Standards Are Leading
In later courses students will expand their knowledge of properties and fields to include rings and Abelian groups.

■ BACKGROUND ■

The properties imbedded in this Standard taken together are often referred to as the field properties for real numbers. Students in California will encounter some of these properties in earlier grades. In this course we extend the properties to include all real numbers and ask students to use these properties in formal proofs.

Students need to understand the concept of each property and should be encouraged to view these axioms together as they relate to sets of numbers. It is important to note that some of these properties do not hold true for subtraction and division. For example, the commutative property of addition states:

$a + b = b + a.$

However, the commutative property is not true for subtraction. For example $2 - 3$ does not equal $3 - 2$.

STANDARD 2.0

2.0 Students understand and use such operations as taking the opposite, finding the reciprocal, taking a root, and raising to a fractional power. They understand and use the rules of exponents.

■ PROGRESSION ■

Prior Grade Level Standards
Students use operations such as taking the opposite, finding the reciprocal, finding a square root, and raising to an integer power. Students understand negative integer exponents.

This Year's Standards
Students' knowledge of exponents is expanded to include rational exponents.

Where the Standards Are Leading
In later courses, students use exponential and logarithmic functions.

■ BACKGROUND ■

Before students begin this course they have found opposites and reciprocals of rational numbers. In this course they extend these skills to include variables. While using variables is not new to students, their use is more extensive in algebra. Students began finding square roots in their previous math course. In this course, they not only approximate square roots and find cube roots, they also simplify radicals.

Students' work with exponents up to this time has been with integer exponents. In this course, students use exponents which are rational numbers. They learn that rational exponents follow the same rules as integer exponents.

Definition of rational exponents:

$a^{\frac{1}{k}} = \sqrt[k]{a}$ for any natural number k and any positive real number a, $a > 0$.

$$25^{\frac{1}{2}} = \sqrt{25} = 5 \qquad 8^{\frac{1}{3}} = \sqrt[3]{8} = 2$$

Taking roots is the inverse of raising to powers.

STANDARD 3.0

3.0 Students solve equations and inequalities involving absolute values.

■ PROGRESSION ■

Prior Grade Level Standards
Students understand the meaning of absolute value. They interpret the absolute value as the distance of the number from zero on a number line and determine the absolute value of real numbers.

▼

This Year's Standards
Students extend the use of absolute value from finding distance on the number line to include solving equations and inequalities.

▼

Where the Standards Are Leading
In future math courses students will understand and use absolute value of complex numbers.

■ BACKGROUND ■

In their previous math course, students learned the definition of absolute value and solved simple equations involving absolute value. In this course, students learn that solving an equation involving absolute value means solving a disjunction.

Solving Equations with Absolute Value:
To solve an equation of the form $|A| = b$, where b is a positive number, solve the disjunction $A = b$ or $A = -b$.

Solve $|2x - 4| = 10$.

There are two numbers whose distance from 0 is 10, namely 10 and −10.

$$2x - 4 = 10 \quad \text{or} \quad 2x - 4 = -10$$
$$2x = 14 \quad \text{or} \quad 2x = -6$$
$$x = 7 \quad \text{or} \quad x = -3$$

The solution set is $\{7, -3\}$.

Solving Inequalities with Absolute Values:
To solve an inequality of the form $|A| < b$ where b is a positive number, solve the conjunction

$$-b < A < b$$

A similar rule holds for $|A| \leq b$.

To solve an inequality of the form $|A| > b$ where b is a positive number, solve the disjunction

$$A < b \text{ or } A > b.$$

A similar rule holds for $|A| \geq b$.

STANDARD 4.0

4.0 Students simplify expressions before solving linear equations and inequalities in one variable, such as $3(2x - 5) + 4(x - 2) = 12$.

■ PROGRESSION ■

Prior Grade Level Standards
Students simplify numerical expressions by applying properties of rational numbers (e.g., identity, inverse, distributive, associative, commutative).

▼

This Year's Standards
Students extend their knowledge of simplifying expressions to include multiple grouping symbols, the inverse of a sum property, rational expressions, and radical expressions.

▼

Where the Standards Are Leading
In advanced algebra, students will add, subtract, multiply, divide, reduce, and evaluate rational expressions with monomial and polynomial denominators and simplify complicated rational expressions, including those with negative exponents in the denominators.

■ BACKGROUND ■

Students have been simplifying expressions since fifth grade. In this course, students will be simplifying more complex expressions. Parentheses, brackets, and braces are grouping symbols that are used in algebra. When an expression contains more than one grouping symbol, the computations in the innermost grouping symbols are done first.

$$\text{Simplify: } \{9 - [7 - (13 + 4)]\} = \{9 - [7 - 17]\}$$
$$= \{9 - [-10]\}$$
$$= 19$$

To simplify rational expressions, factor the numerator and denominator. The common factors simplify to 1. The values of the variables are restricted to values that do not make the denominator 0.

$$\text{Simplify: } \frac{a^2 + 3a}{a^2 - 9} = \frac{a(a + 3)}{(a + 3)(a - 3)}$$
$$= \frac{a}{(a - 3)}$$

To simplify radical expressions, look for perfect square factors in the radicand.

$$\text{Simplify } \sqrt{75x^4} = \sqrt{25} \cdot \sqrt{3} \cdot \sqrt{(x^2)^2}$$
$$= 5x^2\sqrt{3}$$

STANDARD 5.0

5.0 Students solve multistep problems, including word problems, involving linear equations and linear inequalities in one variable and provide justification for each step.

■ PROGRESSION ■

Prior Grade Level Standards
Students solve multistep problems involving rate, average speed, distance, and time or a direct variation.

This Year's Standards
Students expand their ability to solve multistep problems to include applications besides speed, distance, and time involving linear equations and inequalities

Where the Standards Are Leading
In later math courses, students solve multistep problems involving nonlinear equations and inequalities.

■ BACKGROUND ■

Students need experience solving a variety of multistep problems, such as digit and coin problems, compound interest problems, mixture problems, motion problems, and sales tax problems.

Direct variation: An equation in the form $y = kx$, where k is a nonzero constant, expresses direct variation.

Inverse variation: An equation of the form $y = \frac{k}{x}$, where k is a nonzero constant, expresses inverse variation.

Joint variation: An equation of the form $z = kxy$, where k is a nonzero constant, expresses joint variation.
Joint variation has many real-world applications, such as finding the volume of a cone. The volume of the cone varies jointly as the height of the cone and the area of the base.

STANDARD 6.0

6.0 Students graph a linear equation and compute the x- and y-intercepts (e.g., graph $2x + 6y = 4$). They are also able to sketch the region defined by linear inequality (e.g., they sketch the region defined by $2x + 6y < 4$).

■ PROGRESSION ■

Prior Grade Level Standards
Students represent relationships graphically and interpret the meaning of a specific part of a graph in the situation represented by the graph and understand the slope for linear functions.

This Year's Standards
Students extend their understanding of linear equations to include the x- and y-intercepts and graph the region defined by a linear inequality.

Where the Standards Are Leading
Students use linear functions to solve application problems, such as in economics with budget and supply equations.

■ BACKGROUND ■

Some of the most basic skills that students need to learn in algebra involve linear equations.

You can graph a linear equation by finding any two points that belong to the graph. Often the easiest points to find are the points where the graph crosses the axes.

The graph at the right crosses the x-axis at $(-2, 0)$ and the y-axis at $(0, 3)$. We say that the x-intercept is -2 and that the y-intercept is 3.

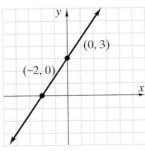

The x-intercept of a line is the x-coordinate of the point where the line intercepts the x-axis.

The y-intercept of a line is the y-coordinate of the point where the line intercepts the y-axis.

STANDARD 7.0

7.0 Students verify that a point lies on a line, given an equation of the line. Students are able to derive linear equations by using the point-slope formula.

■ PROGRESSION ■

Prior Grade Level Standards
Students have graphed linear functions noting that rise over run is called the slope of the graph.

This Year's Standards
Students' understanding of slope is widened. New this year is the idea that if we are given the equation of a line, we can verify a point lies on the line. We can also write the equation of a line when two points are given. Students will use these concepts to graph and derive linear equations.

Where the Standards Are Leading
Students will build on their knowledge of linear equations, later encountering quadratic functions where the slope is not constant.

■ BACKGROUND ■

By definition the slope of a line is equal to the change in the y-coordinates divided by the change in the x-coordinates:

$$\frac{\text{Change in } y\text{–coordinates}}{\text{Change in } x\text{–coordinates}}$$

This is commonly referred to as the "rise over run." Students might be able to relate this vocabulary to a staircase, with a rise (vertical part) and run (horizontal part). For a linear function it is important to note that although the individual values of the rise and run may vary, the ratio of the two, defined as the slope, does not change. In other words, a linear function represents a constant rate of change.

STANDARD 8.0

8.0 Students understand the concepts of parallel lines and perpendicular lines and how their slopes are related. Students are able to find the equation of a line perpendicular to a given line that passes through a given point.

■ PROGRESSION ■

Prior Grade Level Standards
Students graph linear functions, noting that the vertical change per unit of horizontal change is always the same and know that the ratio is called the slope of the graph.

This Year's Standards
Students extend their knowledge of slope to understanding the relationship between parallel and perpendicular lines and can find the equation of a line perpendicular to a given line that passes through a given point.

Where the Standards Are Leading
Students use their knowledge of slope when they learn the principles of trigonometry, such as the tangent of the angle that a line makes with the x-axis is equal to the slope of the line.

■ BACKGROUND ■

Parallel lines are lines in the same plane that never intersect. Nonvertical lines are parallel if they have the same slope and different y-intercepts

The graphs at the right are for the linear equations $y = 3x + 1$ and $y = 3x - 2$. The slope of each line is 3. The coordinates of the y-intercepts are 1 and -2. The lines are parallel.

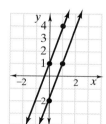

Two lines are perpendicular if the product of their slopes is -1.

The graphs at the right are for the linear equations $y = 3x + 1$ and $y = -\frac{1}{3}x - 2$. The slopes of the lines are 3 and $-\frac{1}{3}$. The product of the slopes is -1. The lines are perpendicular.

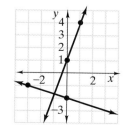

STANDARD 9.0

9.0 Students solve a system of two linear equations in two variables algebraically and are able to interpret the answer graphically. Students are able to solve a system of two linear inequalities in two variables and to sketch the solution sets.

■ PROGRESSION ■

Prior Grade Level Standards
Students write a system of equations that represents a verbal description.

This Year's Standards
Students extend their knowledge of systems of equations and inequalities to sketching the solution sets and interpreting the graphic answer.

Where the Standards Are Leading
Students will find the simultaneous solution set in applications and linear programming.

■ BACKGROUND ■

Two linear equations form a system of equations. Any ordered pair that is a solution of both of the equations in the system is a solution of the system. One way to solve a system of equations is by graphing the equations and finding the point or points of intersection of the graphs.

To solve the system of $y = x + 2$ and $y = -3x + 2$, graph each line on the same coordinate plane.

The lines intersect at the point $(0, 2)$.

Check $x = 0$ and $y = 2$ in both equations.

$y = x + 2 \qquad y = -3x + 2$

$2 = 0 + 2 \qquad 2 = -3(0) + 2$

$2 = 2 \qquad\qquad 2 = 2$

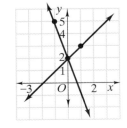

A system of equations can also be solved algebraically by using the substitution method or elimination method.

STANDARD 10.0

10.0 Students add, subtract, multiply, and divide monomials and polynomials. Students solve multistep problems, including word problems, by using these techniques.

■ PROGRESSION ■

Prior Grade Level Standards
Students multiply and divide monomials.

This Year's Standards
Students extend their knowledge of monomials to adding and subtracting. They also add, subtract, multiply, and divide polynomials and use these techniques to solve multistep problems.

Where the Standards Are Leading
Students learn the factor theorem, the remainder theorem, and synthetic division to find solutions to polynomial equations leading to the Fundamental Theorem of Algebra.

■ BACKGROUND ■

We add polynomials by adding like terms. We usually arrange the terms of the polynomials in descending order for a particular variable.

To subtract polynomials change subtraction to addition of the inverse and add like terms.

In this course, students learn the FOIL method to multiply two binomials.

$$(x + 3)(2x - 4) = 2x^2 - 4x + 6x - 12$$

Outside
First
Inside
Last

To divide a polynomial by a monomial, divide each term by the monomial.

To divide a polynomial by a polynomial, use long division.

STANDARD 11.0

11.0 Students apply basic factoring techniques to second- and simple third-degree polynomials. These techniques include finding a common factor for all terms in a polynomial, recognizing the difference of two squares, and recognizing perfect squares of binomials.

■ PROGRESSION ■

Prior Grade Level Standards
Students understand factoring whole numbers.

This Year's Standards
Students expand their knowledge of factoring whole numbers to factoring polynomials.

Where the Standards Are Leading
Students expand their knowledge of factoring polynomials to the difference of two cubes in advanced algebra and to simplifying complicated rational expressions.

■ BACKGROUND ■

Before this course, students have only factored whole numbers. In this course they will factor polynomials for the first time. The following techniques are covered in this course:

Find a common factor for all terms of a polynomial:

To factor $5ab^2 + 15b$:

$$5ab^2 + 15b = 5b(ab) + 5b(3)$$
$$= 5b(ab + 3)$$

Recognize the difference of two squares: For a binomial to be the difference of two squares, there must be two terms that are both squares and a minus sign between the terms.

$$(a + b)(a - b) = a^2 - b^2$$

Factor $25x^2 - 9$:

$$25x^2 - 9 = (5x)^2 - (3)^2$$
$$= (5x + 3)(5x - 3)$$

Recognize the perfect square of binomials: The square of a binomial is the square of the first term, plus or minus twice the product of the two terms, plus the square of the last term.

$$(a + b)^2 = a^2 + 2ab + b^2$$
$$(a - b)^2 = a^2 - 2ab + b^2$$

STANDARD 12.0

12.0 Students simplify fractions with polynomials in the numerator and denominator by factoring both and reducing them to lowest terms.

■ PROGRESSION ■

Prior Grade Level Standards
Students simplify expressions by applying the properties of rational numbers.

This Year's Standards
Students expand their knowledge of simplifying expressions using the properties of rational numbers to simplifying fractions with polynomials in the numerator and denominator.

Where the Standards Are Leading
In advanced algebra students simplify complicated rational expressions.

■ BACKGROUND ■

Fractions with polynomials in the numerator and denominator are called rational expressions. Rational expressions have the same properties as rational numbers. A rational expression is in simplest form when the numerator and denominator have no common factors other than 1 or -1. It is very important that students understand that only common factors of the numerator and denominator can be removed. It is a frequent mistake to try to remove from fractions algebraic expressions occurring not as factors of the numerator and denominator but as parts of sums. For example, a common mistake would be to try to reduce the fraction

$$\frac{x + 2}{y + 2} \text{ to } \frac{x}{y}$$

These fractions are not equivalent because 2 is an addend instead of a common factor. Only factors of both the numerator and denominator may be removed from a fraction.

To simplify rational expressions, factor the numerator and denominator. The common factors simplify to 1. Values of variables are restricted to values that do not make the denominator zero.

To simplify $\frac{a^2 - 9}{2a^2 + 3a - 9}$:

$$\frac{a^2 - 9}{2a^2 + 3a - 9} = \frac{(a + 3)(a - 3)}{(a + 3)(2a - 3)}$$
$$= \frac{(a + 3)}{(a + 3)} \cdot \frac{(a - 3)}{(2a - 3)}$$
$$= 1 \cdot \frac{a - 3}{2a - 3}$$
$$= \frac{a - 3}{2a - 3}$$

STANDARD 13.0

13.0 Students add, subtract, multiply, and divide rational expressions and functions. Students solve both computationally and conceptually challenging problems by using these techniques.

■ PROGRESSION ■

Prior Grade Level Standards
Students add, subtract, multiply, and divide rational numbers. They evaluate expressions and graph functions to solve problems.

▼

This Year's Standards
Students' knowledge of operations on rational numbers is expanded to adding, subtracting, multiplying, and dividing rational expressions and functions, and students use these techniques to solve problems.

▼

Where the Standards Are Leading
In calculus students will use theorems to evaluate the limits of sums, products, quotients, and composition of functions.

■ BACKGROUND ■

A rational expression is the quotient of two polynomials. A rational expression always indicates division. For example,

$\frac{x^2 + 3x - 10}{3x + 2}$ means $(x^2 + 3x - 10) \div (3x + 2)$

To add or subtract rational expressions with unlike denominators, use the patterns

$\frac{a}{b} + \frac{c}{d} = \frac{ad + bc}{bd}$ and $\frac{a}{b} - \frac{c}{d} = \frac{ad - bc}{bd}$

To multiply rational expressions, factor numerators and denominators to simplify by finding names for 1. Then multiply the remaining numerators and multiply denominators.

To divide rational expressions, multiply the first expression by the reciprocal of the divisor.

STANDARD 14.0

14.0 Students solve a quadratic equation by factoring or completing the square.

■ PROGRESSION ■

Prior Grade Level Standards
Students graph functions of the form $y = nx^2$.

▼

This Year's Standards
Students' knowledge of quadratic functions is expanded from graphing to solving quadratic equations by factoring or by completing the square.

▼

Where the Standards Are Leading
In advanced algebra students will solve quadratic equations in the complex number system.

■ BACKGROUND ■

A quadratic or second-degree equation is an equation that can be written in the form $ax^2 + bx + c = 0$, where a, b, and c are real numbers and $a \neq 0$. A quadratic equation involves a squared term, but no higher degree terms. The term ax^2 is called the quadratic term and cannot be missing from the equation. The term bx is called the linear term and may or may not be missing from the equation depending on whether or not $b = 0$. The term c is called the constant term and may or may not be missing from the equation depending on whether or not $c = 0$.

To solve the equation $10x^2 + 5x = 0$ by factoring:

$10x^2 + 5x = 0$

$5x(2x + 1) = 0$

$5x = 0$ or $2x + 1 = 0$

$x = 0 \qquad 2x = -1$

$x = -\frac{1}{2}$

The solutions are 0 and $-\frac{1}{2}$.

To solve the equation $x^2 - 4x - 5 = 0$ by completing the square:

$x^2 - 4x - 5 = 0$

$x^2 - 4x = 5$

$x^2 - 4x + 4 = 5 + 4$

$(x - 2)^2 = 9$

$x - 2 = \pm\sqrt{9}$

$x = 2 \pm 3$

$x = 5$ or $x = -1$

The solutions are 5 and -1.

STANDARD 15.0

15.0 Students apply algebraic techniques to solve rate problems, work problems, and percent mixture problems.

■ PROGRESSION ■

Prior Grade Level Standards
Students solve multistep problems involving rate.

▼

This Year's Standards
Students' ability to solve multistep problems is expanded to include work problems and percent mixture problems.

▼

Where the Standards Are Leading
In calculus students use differentiation to solve optimization problems.

■ BACKGROUND ■

Students have solved rate problems previous to this course. In this course, the problems are solved using rational equations.

Rate problems
An airplane goes 1275 miles in the same time a boat goes 25 miles. If the airplane goes 500 mi/h faster than the boat, what is the rate of each one?

Let $r =$ the rate of the boat.

Then $r + 500 =$ the rate of the airplane.

The time $(distance \div rate)$ for the airplane is $\frac{1275}{r + 500}$ and the time for the boat is $\frac{25}{r}$.

Because the times are equal, $\frac{1275}{r + 500} = \frac{25}{r}$.

$$\frac{1275}{r + 500} = \frac{25}{r}$$
$$1275r = 25(r + 500)$$
$$1275r = 25r + 12{,}500$$
$$1250r = 12{,}500$$
$$r = 10$$

The rate of the boat is 10 mi/h and the rate of airplane is 510 mi/h.

STANDARD 16.0

16.0 Students understand the concepts of a relation and a function, determine whether a given relation defines a function, and give pertinent information about given relations and functions.

■ PROGRESSION ■

Prior Grade Level Standards
Students graph functions.

▼

This Year's Standards
Students' understanding of functions expands to include relations and students determine whether a given relation defines a function.

▼

Where the Standards Are Leading
Functions, relations, and graphs are important not only in algebra but in every branch of mathematics as well as in all sciences.

■ BACKGROUND ■

A relation is a set of ordered pairs. The domain of a relation is the set of first coordinates. The range is the set of second coordinates. The members of the domain can be called inputs and the members of the range can be called outputs.

A function is a relation that assigns to each member of the domain exactly one member of the range. A function can be described by a set of ordered pairs in the form (x, y) with exactly one value for y for each value of x.

The equation $x + y^2 = 1$ does not define y as a function of x. If you let $x = 0$, then $y^2 = 1$ and $y = 1$ and -1. Since there is a value of x to which there corresponds more than one value of y, we see that y is not a function of x.

STANDARD 17.0

17.0 Students determine the domain of independent variables and the range of dependent variables defined by a graph, a set of ordered pairs, or a symbolic expression.

■ PROGRESSION ■

Prior Grade Level Standards

Students graph functions.

This Year's Standards

Students expand their knowledge of functions from graphing to include determining the domain of independent variables and the range of dependent variables

Where the Standards Are Leading

Students will use their knowledge of domain and range when they study continuity of a function in calculus.

■ BACKGROUND ■

A precise definition of domain and range is necessary for students to understand since they will continue to study functions in later mathematics courses.

To find the domain of a relation, go through the set of ordered pairs and pick out all the first coordinates; this set of numbers is the domain. If you pick out the set of all second coordinates, you have the range.

Symbolic Notation

Students are introduced to the notation $f(x)$. The symbol $f(x)$ is read "f of x" and it denotes the number assigned to x by the relation f. If x is the input, $f(x)$ is the output. The outputs of a function are also called function values. Remind students that $f(x)$ does not mean f times x.

STANDARD 18.0

18.0 Students determine whether a relation defined by a graph, a set of ordered pairs, or a symbolic expression is a function and justify the conclusion.

■ PROGRESSION ■

Prior Grade Level Standards

Students graph functions.

This Year's Standards

Students expand their knowledge of functions from graphing to determining when a relation is a function.

Where the Standards Are Leading

Students continue the study of functions in their future mathematics courses.

■ BACKGROUND ■

A function is a relation that assigns to each member of the domain exactly one member of the range. A function can be described by a set of ordered pairs in the form (x, y) with exactly one value for y for each value of x. Any vertical line will intersect the graph of a function in exactly one point. If a vertical line crosses a graph more than once, the graph is not a graph of a function.

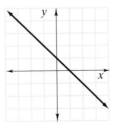

A function

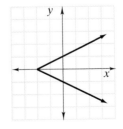

Not a function

STANDARD 19.0

19.0 Students know the quadratic formula and are familiar with its proof by completing the square.

■ PROGRESSION ■

Prior Grade Level Standards
Students graph functions of the form $y = nx^2$.

▼

This Year's Standards
Students extend their knowledge of graphing quadratic functions to using the quadratic formula.

▼

Where the Standards Are Leading
Students use this skill to solve quadratic equations and will find solutions which are complex numbers in advanced algebra.

■ BACKGROUND ■

The quadratic formula can be used to solve any quadratic equation, and this fact makes it important in the theory of quadratic equations.

The Quadratic Formula:

If $ax^2 + bx + c = 0$, $a \neq 0$, then $x = \dfrac{-b \pm \sqrt{b^2 - 4ac}}{2a}$ gives the solutions of the quadratic equation. The expression under the radical, $b^2 - 4ac$, is called the discriminant. When the discriminant is positive there are two real-number solutions to the quadratic equation. When the discriminant is 0, there is only one real-number solution, and when the discriminant is negative, there are no real-number solutions.

Students have used completing the square to solve quadratic equations. They use the same steps to prove the quadratic formula.

$$ax^2 + bx + c = 0, \ a \neq 0$$

$$x^2 + \frac{b}{a}x + \frac{c}{a} = 0$$

$$x^2 + \frac{b}{a}x = -\frac{c}{a}$$

Half of $\frac{b}{a}$ is $\frac{b}{2a}$. The square is $\frac{b^2}{4a^2}$.

$$x^2 + \frac{b}{a}x + \frac{b^2}{4a^2} = -\frac{c}{a} + \frac{b^2}{4a^2}$$

$$(x + \frac{b}{2a})^2 = \frac{b^2 - 4ac}{4a^2}$$

$$x + \frac{b}{2a} = \pm\sqrt{\frac{b^2 - 4ac}{4a^2}}$$

$$x = -\frac{b}{2a} \pm \frac{\sqrt{b^2 - 4ac}}{2a}$$

$$x = \frac{-b \pm \sqrt{b^2 - 4ac}}{2a}$$

STANDARD 20.0

20.0 Students use the quadratic formula to find the roots of a second-degree polynomial and to solve quadratic equations.

■ PROGRESSION ■

Prior Grade Level Standards
Students graph functions of the form $y = nx^2$.

▼

This Year's Standards
Students extend their knowledge of graphing quadratic functions to include using the quadratic formula to find the roots of second-degree polynomials and to solve quadratic equations.

▼

Where the Standards Are Leading
In later math courses students will solve quadratic equations in the complex number system.

■ BACKGROUND ■

The quadratic formula shows that we can find the solution to a quadratic equation by substituting the constants a, b, c into the formula. The quadratic formula can be used to solve quadratic equations or find the roots of second degree polynomials, but they must be in the form $ax^2 + bx + c = 0$.

The Quadratic Formula:

If $ax^2 + bx + c = 0$, $a \neq 0$, then $x = \dfrac{-b \pm \sqrt{b^2 - 4ac}}{2a}$

To find the roots of $x^2 + 2x = 4$:

$$x^2 + 2x = 4$$

$$x^2 + 2x - 4 = 0 \quad \text{Standard form}$$

$$a = 1, \ b = 2, \ c = -4$$

$$x = \frac{-2 \pm \sqrt{2^2 - 4\boxed{1(-4)}}}{2(1)} \quad \text{Substitute for } a, b, \text{ and } c.$$

$$= \frac{-2 \pm \sqrt{4 + 16}}{2}$$

$$= \frac{-2 \pm \sqrt{20}}{2} \quad \text{Simplifying the radical.}$$

$$= \frac{-2 \pm 2\sqrt{5}}{2}$$

$$= -1 \pm \sqrt{5}$$

$$= 1.2 \text{ or } -3.2 \text{ to the nearest tenth}$$

STANDARD 21.0

21.0 Students graph quadratic functions and know that their roots are the *x*-intercepts.

■ PROGRESSION ■

Prior Grade Level Standards
Students graph functions of the form $y = nx^2$.

▼

This Year's Standards
Students extend their knowledge of graphing quadratic functions to include understanding that the roots are the *x*-intercepts.

▼

Where the Standards Are Leading
In calculus students use differentiation to sketch graphs of functions. They can identify maxima, minima, inflection points, and intervals in which the function is increasing and decreasing.

■ BACKGROUND ■

A quadratic function is a function defined by an equation equivalent to one of the form $y = ax^2 + bx + c$, where *a*, *b*, and *c* are constants and $a \neq 0$.

In this definition, we have the variable *y* as a function of the variable *x*. So *x* is the independent variable and *y* is the dependent variable. We do not have to call the variables *x* and *y* but the independent variable must occur in the equation to the second power and no higher power.

The function $y = x^2 - 4$ is a quadratic function with $a = 1$, $b = 0$, and $c = -4$. The graph is an example of a parabola.

We can see that the graph intersects the *x*-axis at $(-2, 0)$ and $(2, 0)$. If we substitute these values in the function, we can verify whether these are the roots.

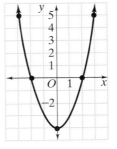

$$y = x^2 - 4 \qquad y = x^2 - 4$$
$$0 = (-2)^2 - 4 \qquad 0 = 2^2 - 4$$
$$0 = 4 - 4 \qquad 0 = 4 - 4$$
$$0 = 0 \qquad 0 = 0$$

STANDARD 22.0

22.0 Students use the quadratic formula or factoring techniques or both to determine whether the graph of a quadratic function will intersect the *x*-axis in zero, one, or two points.

■ PROGRESSION ■

Prior Grade Level Standards
Students graph functions of the form $y = nx^2$.

▼

This Year's Standards
Students expand their understanding of graphing quadratic functions to determine whether the graph of a quadratic function will intersect the *x*-axis in zero, one, or two points.

▼

Where the Standards Are Leading
In later math courses students will determine how the graph of a parabola changes as *a*, *b*, and *c* vary in the equation $y = a(x - b)^2 + c$.

■ BACKGROUND ■

The discriminant (*D*) of a quadratic equation is $b^2 - 4ac$.

If $D > 0$, then $\sqrt{D}$ is a real number and the equation has two solutions.

If $D = 0$, then $\sqrt{D} = 0$ and the equation has one solution.

If $D < 0$, then $\sqrt{D}$ is not a real number, the function has no real solutions, and the graph does not cross the *x*-axis.

$y = (x - 1)^2$	$y = x^2 - 2x + 2$	$y = -2x^2 - 4x + 1$
$y = x^2 - 2x + 1$	$D = b^2 - 4ac$	$D = b^2 - 4ac$
$D = b^2 - 4ac$	$D = (-2)^2 - 4 \cdot 1 \cdot 2$	$D = (-4)^2 - 4(-2)(1)$
$D = (-2)^2 - 4 \cdot 1 \cdot 1$	$D = 4 - 8$	$D = 16 + 8$
$D = 4 - 4$	$D = -4$	$D = 24$
$D = 0$		
One point	No intersections	Two points

STANDARD 23.0

23.0 Students apply quadratic equations to physical problems, such as the motion of an object under the force of gravity.

■ PROGRESSION ■

Prior Grade Level Standards
Students graph functions of the form $y = nx^2$.

▼

This Year's Standards
Students expand their knowledge of graphing quadratic equations to using them to solve application problems.

▼

Where the Standards Are Leading
In later math course students use the graphs of quadratic functions to determine the maxima, mimima, and zeros of the function.

■ BACKGROUND ■

Quadratic equations can be used to solve physical problems.

Suppose an object is dropped from some height. Let t denote the time that has elapsed since the object was dropped and let d denote the distance the object has fallen. Then t and d are variables and d depends on t. In this situation the distance the object has fallen gets larger as more time elapses until the object hits the ground. It is a basic law of physics, discovered by Galileo, that d depends only on t and does not on such variables as the mass of the object. We say that d is a function of t.

The equation is $d = \frac{1}{2}gt^2$, where g is a constant called the acceleration due to gravity. If t is measured in seconds and d is measured in feet, then the value of g is approximately 32 feet/sec^2.

The Leaning Tower of Pisa is about 190 feet high. How long will it take an object dropped from the top to reach the ground?

$$d = \tfrac{1}{2}gt^2$$
$$190 = \tfrac{1}{2}(32)t^2$$
$$190 = 16t^2$$
$$11.875 = t^2$$
$$3.4 \approx t$$

The time is about 3.4 seconds.

STANDARDS 24.0 AND 24.1

24.0 Students use and know simple aspects of a logical argument.

24.1 Students explain the difference between inductive and deductive reasoning and identify and provide examples of each.

■ PROGRESSION ■

Prior Grade Level Standards
Students make and test conjectures by using both inductive and deductive reasoning.

▼

This Year's Standards
Students extend their understanding of inductive and deductive reasoning to explaining the difference between them and by identifying and giving examples of each.

▼

Where the Standards Are Leading
Students will use inductive and deductive reasoning in writing proofs in geometry and mathematical analysis.

■ BACKGROUND ■

Inductive reasoning is making conclusions based on patterns you observe. A conclusion by inductive reasoning is a conjecture. An example that proves a statement false is a counterexample. You only need one counterexample to prove that a conjecture is incorrect.

For a pattern, a conjecture can be a rule that explains how to make and continue the pattern.

Write rule for the pattern:

Input	Output
1	2
3	10
4	17

The pattern is square the input and add 1.

Deductive reasoning is the process of reasoning logically from given facts to a conclusion. When you use properties, rules, and definitions to justify steps in a problem, you are using deductive reasoning.

Simplify $x - 3(x + y)$:

$x - 3(x + y) = x + \left[-3(x + y)\right]$	Add the inverse of $3(x + y)$.
$= x + \left[-3x + (-3)y\right]$	Use the distributive property.
$= x - 3x - 3y$	Subtraction rule.
$= -2x - 3y$	Combine like terms.

STANDARDS 24.2 AND 24.3

24.2 Students identify the hypothesis and conclusion in logical deduction.

24.3 Students use counterexamples to show that an assertion is false and recognize that a single counterexample is sufficient to refute an assertion.

■ PROGRESSION ■

Prior Grade Level Standards
Students make and test conjectures by using both inductive and deductive reasoning.

This Year's Standards
Students expand their knowledge of logical reasoning from making and testing conjectures to include identifying the hypothesis and conclusion.

Where the Standards Are Leading
Students will use hypothesis and conclusions to write proofs in geometry and mathematical analysis.

■ BACKGROUND ■

A common statement used in reasoning is a statement of the form: if A, then B. For example, if $x = 1$, then $x + 1 = 2$.

A statement of this form is called a **conditional statement**. If A, then B means that if statement A is true, then statement B is true. In the statement if A, then B, A is the **hypothesis** and B is the **conclusion**.

The **converse** of a conditional statement can be found by interchanging the hypothesis and the conclusion. The converse of a true conditional statement may or may not be true. To show that a converse is not true, you need to give a **counterexample**.

Conditional statement: If a figure is square, then it has 4 sides.

Converse: If a figure has 4 sides, it is a square.

Counterexample: A figure with 4 sides can be a rectangle.

STANDARDS 25.0 AND 25.1

25.0 Students use properties of the number system to judge the validity of results, to justify each step of a procedure, and to prove or disprove statements.

25.1 Students use properties of numbers to construct simple, valid arguments (direct and indirect) for, or formulate counterexamples to, claimed assertions.

■ PROGRESSION ■

Prior Grade Level Standards
Students simplify numerical expressions by applying properties of rational numbers and justify the process used.

This Year's Standards
Students' use of the numerical properties is expanded to constructing arguments for, or formulating counterexamples to, claimed assertions.

Where the Standards Are Leading
In geometry students will write geometric proofs, including proofs by contradiction.

■ BACKGROUND ■

The properties of numbers can be used to prove the following theorem:

For any rational number a, $a \cdot 0 = 0$.

1. $a \cdot 0 = a \cdot 0 + 0$	1. Additive identity
2. $\quad = a \cdot 0 + a + (-a)$	2. Additive inverse
3. $\quad = a \cdot 0 + a \cdot 1 + (-a)$	3. Multiplicative identity
4. $\quad = a(0 + 1) + (-a)$	4. Distributive property
5. $\quad = a \cdot 1 + (-a)$	5. Additive identity
6. $\quad = a + (-a)$	6. Multiplicative identity
7. $\quad = 0$	7. Additive inverse
8. $a \cdot 0 = 0$	8. Transitive property of equality

STANDARD 25.2

25.2 Students judge the validity of an argument according to whether the properties of the real number system and the order of operations have been applied correctly at each step.

■ PROGRESSION ■

Prior Grade Level Standards
Students simplify numerical expressions by applying properties of rational numbers and justify the process used and use the correct order of operations to evaluate algebraic expressions.

This Year's Standards
Students expand their use of the number properties from simplifying expressions to judging the validity of an argument according to whether the properties have been used properly and whether the order of operations have been applied correctly.

Where the Standards Are Leading
In later math courses students will write various proofs by using mathematical induction.

■ BACKGROUND ■

In this course, students are given different opportunities to judge the validity of an argument according to the use of the properties and the order of operations.

Students are asked to determine whether $\frac{a}{b} = \frac{a + c}{b + c}$ where $b \neq 0$ and $c \neq 0$ is true or false and if it is false, they give a counterexample.

Students look for errors in exercises like the following:

$4 - 3x = 5$

$\quad 4 = 3x + 5$

$\quad 9 = 3x$

$\quad x = 3$

Answer: $3x$ was added to both sides to get $4 = 3x + 5$. Then 5 was subtracted from the right side, but added to the left side. 5 should have been subtracted from both sides to get $-1 = 3x$. The correct answer is $x = -\frac{1}{3}$.

$ax - b = c$

$ax = b + c$

$x = \frac{(b + c)}{a}$

Answer: no error

STANDARD 25.3

25.3 Given a specific algebraic statement involving linear, quadratic, or absolute value expressions or equations or inequalities, students determine whether the statement is true sometimes, always, or never.

■ PROGRESSION ■

Prior Grade Level Standards
Students graph linear functions and functions of the form $y = nx^2$.

This Year's Standards
Students extend their knowledge of linear, quadratic, and absolute value expressions, equations, and inequalities to determine whether a statement about one them is sometimes, always, or never true.

Where the Standards Are Leading
Students extend their knowledge of linear, quadratic, and absolute value expressions and equations to integrals and derivatives in calculus.

■ BACKGROUND ■

A concept central to the theme of equations and inequalities is the solution set. The solution set of an equation or an inequality is the set of real numbers that satisfy the equation or inequality when substituted for the variable.

In this course students will use mathematical reasoning for problems such as the following:

Show that this statement is sometimes true. Then give a counterexample to show that the statement is not always true.

$$|x + y| = |x| + |y|$$

To show that this is sometimes true let $x = 3$ and $y = 5$, then

$|x + y| = |x| + |y|$

$|3 + 5| = |3| + |5|$

$\quad |8| = 3 + 5$

$\quad\quad 8 = 8 \text{ true}$

For a counterexample to show this is not always true, let $x = -3$ and $y = 5$.

$$|x + y| = |x| + |y|$$

$$|-3 + 5| = |-3| + |5|$$

$$|2| = 3 + 5$$

$$2 = 8 \text{ false}$$

Solving equations and inequalities is one of the basic topics of algebra.

Aligning with the California Standards and Framework

Prentice Hall *Algebra 1* California Edition was developed specifically for California, so you can be confident that the intent and spirit of the California Mathematics Content Standards and Framework are at the core of the program. *Algebra 1* is a Standards-based program that is dedicated to providing the instruction and skills intervention students need in order to measure up to California's high Standards. It also has as its goal providing you the teacher, whether you are new or experienced, with direct instructional support in teaching the Standards.

The following pages list five of the most important criteria in evaluating a mathematics program and describe some of the ways Prentice Hall *Algebra 1* meets and exceeds these criteria.

1. CONTENT/ALIGNMENT WITH THE STANDARDS

Prentice Hall *Algebra 1* is aligned with and addresses 100% of the California Standards. We've incorporated several reference points to help you acquaint yourself with the program and the way it assures complete and thorough coverage of the Standards.

Standards Guide	Where to Find It	How It Can Help You
Standards at a Glance	• Teacher's Edition: Standards and Framework Handbook, pp. T34–T35	Overview of how the Standards unfold as the year progresses
Correlation to the Standards	• Student Edition: pp. xviii–xx • Teacher's Edition: Standards and Framework Handbook, pp. T36–T39	Ensures coverage of the Standards and helps with pacing
Lesson-by-lesson Standards correlations	• Student Edition and Teacher's Edition, at the beginning of each lesson	Helps you maintain a daily Standards focus
Standards Progression and Background	• Teacher's Edition: Standards and Framework Handbook, pp. T40–T53	A guide to understanding this year's Standards, what was taught in previous years, and where the Standards are leading

We've listed the Standards at the beginning of each lesson in the Student Edition. That not only allows you to introduce the lesson by noting both the Standards and the lesson goals, but it also helps students know what Standards they are accountable for. And listing the Standards at the top of the student page has another advantage—it allows parents and guardians to be in touch with what is expected.

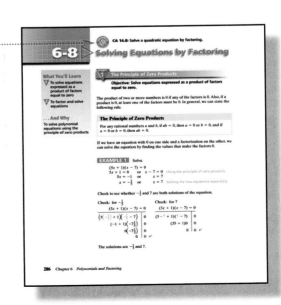

The Mathematical Reasoning Strand

"It should be noted that the strand of mathematical reasoning is different from the other four strands. This strand, which is inherently embedded in each of the other strands, is fundamental in developing the basic skills and conceptual understanding for a solid mathematical foundation."

—Mathematics Framework for California Public Schools

Because mathematical reasoning is so essential to the study of mathematics, it is at the core of all lessons and therefore is woven throughout this entire book.

Mathematical reasoning is involved in explaining the "why" of facts and procedures in solving problems, in understanding concepts and formulas, and in justifying steps and conclusions. Inductive reasoning and deductive reasoning begin informally in the elementary grades. They are at the heart of mathematics. In Prentice Hall *Algebra 1* students learn about axioms and theorems and write simple proofs, all with the goal of providing students with a foundation for constructing logical arguments.

As lessons unfold, regular opportunities are provided for the students to demonstrate mathematical reasoning. Look for questions such as the ones shown below. You will find many such rich reasoning tasks labeled Critical Thinking, Mathematical Reasoning, Error Analysis, or Writing a Convincing Argument. The index listings under *Mathematical Reasoning* give you a good idea of the kinds of opportunities woven throughout the book.

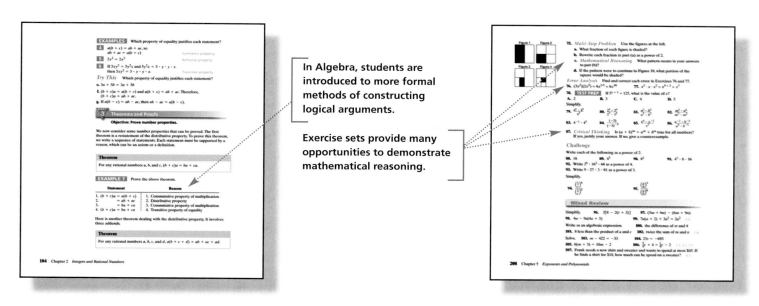

In Algebra, students are introduced to more formal methods of constructing logical arguments.

Exercise sets provide many opportunities to demonstrate mathematical reasoning.

Math Background

Most teachers, especially new ones, appreciate having extra math background material to turn to from time to time, to provide them with in-depth understanding of the mathematics they are teaching. For extra insights, look for the Math Background sections at the front of each chapter of the Teacher's Edition. You may not need these sections all of the time, but it's nice to know that the direct instructional support is there for you when you do.

2. PROGRAM ORGANIZATION

The Student Book

Content Sequence The student book is organized with the goal of addressing all of the California Mathematics Content Standards, building concept upon concept, skill upon skill in an order that is pedagogically sound. The Table of Contents shows the smooth flow of the book, with prerequisite skills and ideas presented before the more complex topics that depend upon them. Review topics are kept to a minimum.

Lesson Organization Lessons are organized using a **direct-instruction approach** so students know exactly what they will learn and how. The added benefit of this structure is that parents, adult tutors, or older siblings can help students in the learning process. From start to end, all lessons do the following:

1 State the Standards addressed in the lesson.

2 Develop a concept fully through clear, step-by-step Examples.

3 Check understanding along the way.

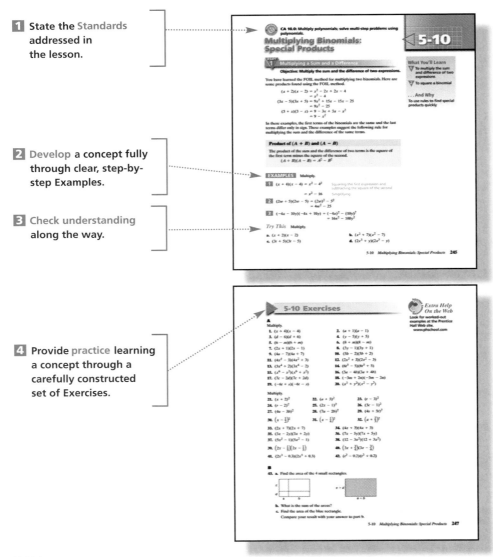

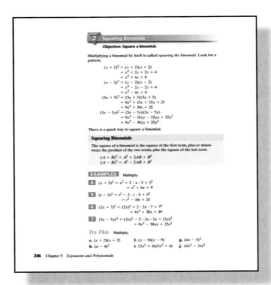

4 Provide practice learning a concept through a carefully constructed set of Exercises.

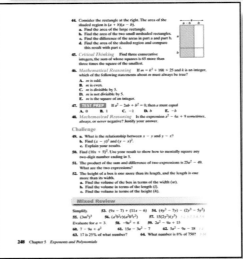

The Teacher's Edition

Consistent Organization You will appreciate the consistent organization of the Teacher's Edition, which allows you to find what you need quickly.

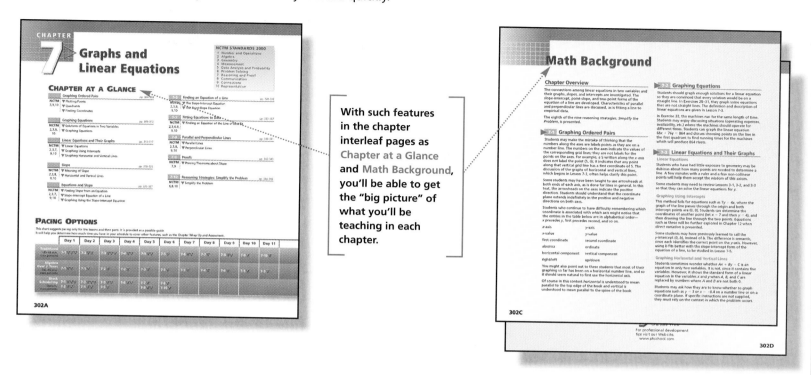

With such features in the chapter interleaf pages as Chapter at a Glance and Math Background, you'll be able to get the "big picture" of what you'll be teaching in each chapter.

Consistent Instruction Then, in the lessons themselves, you'll be able to focus on the 1-2-3 of teaching the lesson and its direct-instruction approach. In short, the Teacher's Edition is organized to provide you with all of the information you need, all in one place.

Teaching Ideas show how to teach the concept—what to say and what to do.

Extra Chalkboard Examples help you extend discussions when needed.

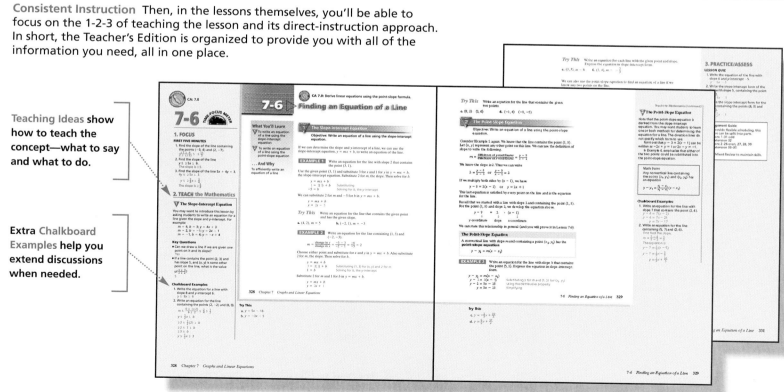

3. ASSESSMENT

Mastering Grade-Level Standards

The California Mathematics Content Framework outlines three broad categories of assessment.

> *"The purposes of assessment that are the most crucial to achieving the Standards are as follows: entry-level assessment, progress monitoring, and summative evaluation."*

- **Entry-Level Assessment**
  The *Entry-Level Assessments* book provides you with an assessment and diagnostic system to guide you in assessing each student's achievement level at the beginning of the school year. It will help you in determining whether a student should work with the grade-level materials, with the materials for the previous grade level, at a more advanced grade level, or should start at a point later in the course. It will also help you identify whether a student might need the transitional materials found in the Prentice Hall *Skills Intervention Kit*. For more information on the *Skills Intervention Kit*, see page T61.

- **Progress Monitoring**
  It is through continual monitoring of students' work that you will be able to adjust instruction so students can progress. Below are some of the program's curriculum-embedded assessment opportunities. There is also an extensive Web-based assessment support system that ties together teachers, students, and parents at **www.phschool.com**.

In the Student Book

On CD-ROM

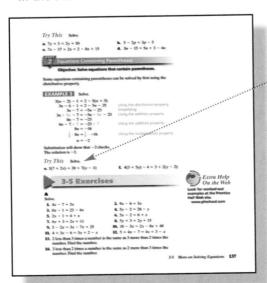

Try This exercises appear after the examples. Use them to check understanding.

The **Student Tutorial CD-ROM** is an excellent self-check tool, featuring how-to videos for even more clarity.

On the Web

Companion Web Site at **www.phschool.com** contains self-tests so that students can monitor progress.

• Summative Evaluations

Summative evaluations measure the progress students have made toward meeting the Standards. Prentice Hall *Algebra 1* has an array of summative evaluation tools, all of which are Standards-based. Use the materials in the student book for student "practice tests" and the ones in the Teaching Resources or on CD-ROM for secure tests.

Student Book	Teaching Resources	Technology
Chapter Wrap Up	Chapter Assessments (five forms per chapter)	Computer Item Generator CD-ROM
Chapter Assessment	Cumulative Assessments	
Cumulative Review	Daily Cumulative Review Masters	

Readiness for Algebra

The California Framework calls for the administration of an Algebra readiness test to find out if students are ready to move into a full course in Algebra. The Prentice Hall *Algebra Readiness Tests* assess all of the essential content spelled out in the Framework. The test booklet includes four parallel copies of these tests so that they can be administered at any time during the school year to inform students and parents of any potential difficulties. This way, a remediation plan can be put into place, if necessary, *prior to* placing the student in Algebra.

Standardized Test Prep

Preparation for the STAR exam is going to be very important to your students' success. The program includes a number of resources to provide ongoing preparation for the test.

In the Student Book

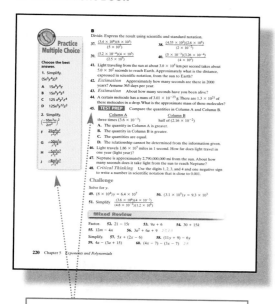

California Practice **questions appear periodically throughout the text. Plus,** Test Prep **exercises are woven into the daily lessons.**

In Accompanying Components

Practice and Sample Tests for Algebra California Standards **and** Test-Taking Tips on Transparencies **make certain that all students become familiar with the skills needed for the California timed tests.**

On CD-ROM

The Computer Item Generator **also has a special feature allowing you to generate unlimited** SAT 9 **and** Standard-by-Standard practice.

4. UNIVERSAL ACCESS

The California Framework states:

"The ultimate goal of mathematics instruction is to ensure universal access to high-quality curriculum and instruction so that all students can meet or exceed the content Standards."

All learners are different. Some will be ready to soar, while others will need to slow down or even back up. The program contains a number of tools to help you tailor instruction to the needs of all students.

Assessing Readiness Prior to Each Chapter

Instructional variation begins in the student book with its system for checking understanding and skill level. The *Skills and Concepts You Need* page is designed as a review of the prerequisite skills needed before each chapter. Some students may have difficulty, signaling a need for more in-depth review and reteaching. The Teacher's Edition refers you to several tools in the program, such as earlier lessons or the *Skills Intervention Kit* (discussed on the following page), depending upon the amount of remediation needed.

Struggling Students and Advanced Learners

For some students, a lesson a day is a good pace. For others, that can be too fast. That's why the lessons in *Algebra 1* are divided into **parts**. You can cover one part in a day and save the next part for tomorrow. The Assignment Guide is organized by parts too, making it easy for you to assign homework practice. A multi-level Pacing Options chart, included in the *California Lesson Planners Plus,* outlines a slower pace for struggling students and an accelerated pace for advanced learners. These pacing options ensure that all of your students will get complete coverage of the Standards, with appropriate depth of coverage.

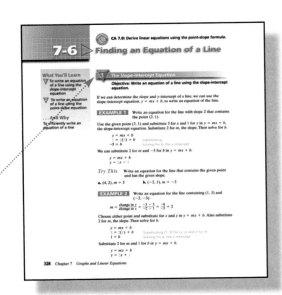

Assignment Guides are also organized by parts to make it easy to vary the pacing.

> **Assignment Guide**
> To provide flexible scheduling, this lesson can be split into parts.
> ▽ Core 1–31 odd
>   Extension 32
> ▽ Core 2–26 even, 27, 28, 30
>   Extension 33–35
>
> Use Mixed Review to maintain skills.

Lessons are divided into parts, according to lesson objectives.

English Language Learners

While the *Reading Math* and *Writing Math* notes in the student book are helpful for all learners, they are designed with English language learners in mind. In addition, look for the notes for preteaching the chapter vocabulary, found in the introductory material for each chapter in the Teacher's Edition.

Intervention for Students Making the Transition to the Standards

The Prentice Hall *California Skills Intervention Kit* is a system of diagnostic and prescriptive materials designed to help students transition into grade-level materials and get back on track in meeting grade-level Standards. It includes a master guide for you to identify all of the foundation skills necessary for success in meeting the grade-level Standards. Plus, it includes many different diagnostic instruments that can be used throughout the year to identify areas in need of intervention.

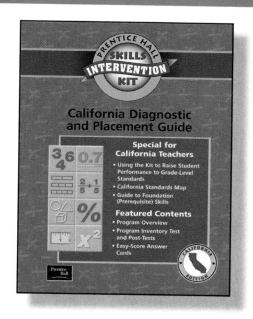

Here is how the system works. For more detail, examine the *California Diagnostic and Placement Guide* that accompanies the kit.

1 Diagnose Use the diagnostic pre-tests provided in the teacher's materials of the kit to pinpoint the skills for which a student needs remedial instruction.

2 Prescribe The eight Intervention Units are designed for students to use on their own. That's important if you have students working on many different levels. If computers are available, students can work on the Student Tutorial CD-ROM instead.

3 Monitor After students have completed their assigned work, use post-tests to measure their success. Students can record their own progress along the way using Student Progress Folders contained in the kit.

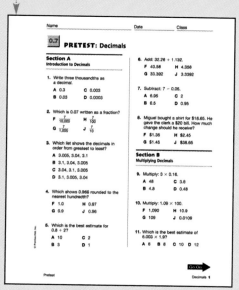

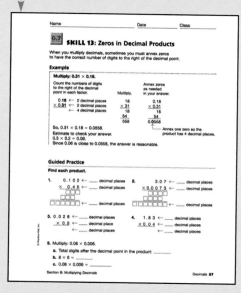

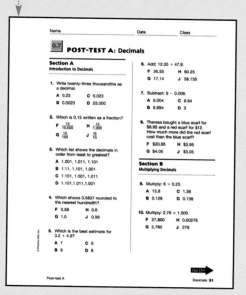

5. INSTRUCTIONAL SUPPORT

As a teacher, you are a caretaker in the learning process of young minds. You seek to keep up with your profession on an ongoing basis. But sometimes it is difficult to find the time to treat yourself, and to refresh your base in mathematics content. We have done several things to help you.

Standards at a Glance—Seeing the Big Picture

In order to be able to guide students through this course, it is helpful to have a big-picture vision of where you are going. The Standards at a Glance chart on pages T34–T35 will help you see not only which standards are the focal point of each chapter, but also how the Standards unfold as the year progresses.

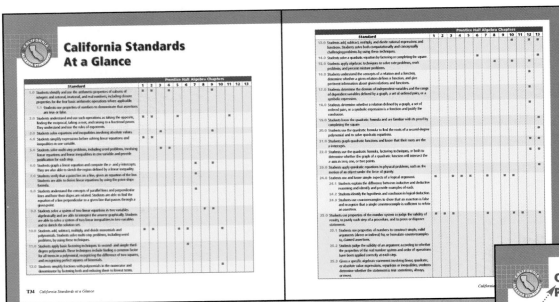

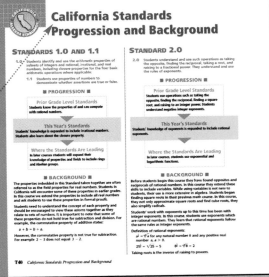

Standards Progression and Background

The California Content Standards flow smoothly from grade level to grade level. Seeing the big picture and understanding the goal of the Standards will help you as you guide your students through the year. On pages T40–T53 we have provided a special section discussing each of the *Algebra 1* Content Standards. It will provide you with insights into each Algebra Standard, what was taught in previous grades, and where the Standards are leading.

Background Notes for Lesson Instruction

In the Teacher's Edition you will find special *Math Background* sections. Although these sections are designed to give you more in-depth information than you would want to present to students, they can provide you with greater insights into teaching the mathematics.

Extra Teacher Helps

Additional Examples Do you need more examples to present a concept? For every worked-out example in the student book there is another one in the Teacher's Edition.

Resources in the Teacher's Edition Prentice Hall *Algebra 1* is a complete instructional system with extensive tools for you to use to tailor instruction to the needs of your students, to support mastery of the Standards, and to assess progress. For your convenience, all components are referenced in the Teacher's Edition at point-of-use.

Lesson Planning Two lesson planning devices are provided with the program: the *Resource Pro® CD-ROM* and the *California Lesson Planners Plus* booklet. Both are made specifically for California and correlate to the Content Standards. It's your choice which one you use to make your lesson plans.

Professional Development

"Anyone who stops learning is old, whether at twenty or eighty. Anyone who keeps learning stays young. The greatest thing in life is to keep your mind young."

—Henry Ford

Prentice Hall will meet with school districts to develop a customized and ongoing calendar of professional development events.

Inservice Users of Prentice Hall instructional materials will benefit from initial orientation sessions to aid them in understanding best instructional practices using the complete program.

Ongoing Workshops Prentice Hall California Mathematics staff development workshops are targeted to providing teachers with insights to connect pedagogy, learning, and assessment.

Summer Institutes Prentice Hall sponsors annual summer institutes in several sites in California. The goal for these institutes is to recharge and rejuvenate each participant.

On-line Staff Development Forums Visit the Prentice Hall Web site at **www.phschool.com** for discussions with other teachers, our authors, and other well-known educators. Look for opportunities to link to Web-based universities for credited professional development programs.

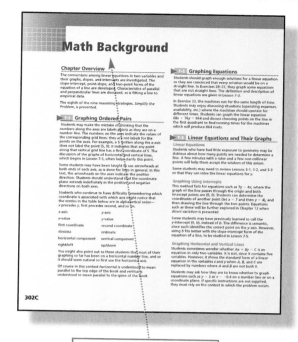

Math Background **pages prior to each chapter are especially helpful for new teachers.**

Correlation of Algebra 1 Lessons to the California Standards

STANDARD

1.0 Students identify and use the arithmetic properties of subsets of integers and rational, irrational, and real numbers, including closure properties for the four basic arithmetic operations where applicable.

   1.1 Students use properties of numbers to demonstrate that assertions are true or false.
   Lessons 1-2, 1-4, 1-5, 2-2, 2-3, 2-4, 2-5, 2-6, 2-7, 2-8, 2-10, 4-1, and 9-1

2.0 Students understand and use such operations as taking the opposite, finding the reciprocal, taking a root, and raising to a fractional power. They understand and use the rules of exponents.
Lessons 1-3, 2-1, 2-6, 2-8, 5-1, 5-2, 5-4, 11-1, 11-2, 11-3, 11-4, and 11-5

3.0 Students solve equations and inequalities involving absolute values.
Lessons 3-8, 9-3, and 9-4

4.0 Students simplify expressions before solving linear equations and inequalities in one variable.
Lessons 1-5, 2-7, and 2-8

5.0 Students solve multi-step problems, including word problems, involving linear equations and linear inequalities in one variable and provide justification for each step.
Lessons 3-3, 3-4, 3-5, 3-6, 3-7, 3-9, 3-10, 3-11, 4-4, and 4-5

6.0 Students graph a linear equation and compute the *x*- and *y*-intercepts. They are also able to sketch the region defined by a linear inequality.
Lessons 7-2, 7-3, 7-5, and 9-5

7.0 Students verify that a point lies on a line, given an equation of the line. Students are able to derive linear equations by using the point-slope formula.
Lessons 7-2, 7-4, 7-6, and 7-7

8.0 Students understand the concepts of parallel lines and perpendicular lines and how their slopes are related. Students are able to find the equation of a line perpendicular to a given line that passes through a given point.
Lessons 7-4 and 7-8

9.0 Students solve a system of two linear equations in two variables algebraically and are able to interpret the answer graphically. Students are able to solve a system of two linear inequalities in two variables and to sketch the solution set.
Lessons 8-1, 8-2, 8-3, 8-4, and 9-6

STANDARD

10.0 Students add, subtract, multiply, and divide monomials and polynomials. Students solve multi-step problems, including word problems, by using these techniques.
Lessons 1-5, 2-7, 2-8, 5-3, 5-5, 5-6, 5-7, 5-8, 5-9, 5-10, 5-11, 6-9, and 10-9

11.0 Students apply basic factoring techniques to second- and simple third-degree polynomials. These techniques include finding a common factor for all terms in a polynomial, recognizing the difference of two squares, and recognizing perfect squares of binomials.
Lessons 6-1, 6-2, 6-3, 6-4, 6-5, 6-6, and 6-7

12.0 Students simplify fractions with polynomials in the numerator and denominator by factoring both and reducing them to lowest terms.
Lesson 10-1

13.0 Students add, subtract, multiply, and divide rational expressions and functions. Students solve both computationally and conceptually challenging problems by using these techniques.
Lessons 10-2, 10-3, 10-4, 10-5, 10-6, 10-10, 12-1, and 13-5

14.0 Students solve a quadratic equation by factoring or completing the square.
Lessons 6-8, 6-9, 13-1, 13-3, 13-5, 13-6, and 13-7

15.0 Students apply algebraic techniques to solve rate problems, work problems, and percent mixture problems.
Lessons 8-5, 10-7, 10-8, 12-5, 12-6, and 12-7

16.0 Students understand the concepts of a relation and a function, determine whether a given relation defines a function, and give pertinent information about given relations and functions.
Lessons 12-1, 12-2, and 12-3

17.0 Students determine the domain of independent variables and the range of dependent variables defined by a graph, a set of ordered pairs, or a symbolic expression.
Lessons 12-1 and 12-2

18.0 Students determine whether a relation defined by a graph, a set of ordered pairs, or a symbolic expression is a function and justify the conclusion.
Lessons 12-1 and 12-2

19.0 Students know the quadratic formula and are familiar with its proof by completing the square.
Lesson 13-4

continued ➤

Note to Parents

California's world-class Mathematics Standards outline the knowledge that students will need to succeed in the 21st Century. This text was created to help students achieve these high standards—and to help you as you lend a hand.

STANDARD

20.0 Students use the quadratic formula to find the roots of a second-degree polynomial and to solve quadratic equations.
Lessons 13-4, 13-5, and 13-7

21.0 Students graph quadratic functions and know that their roots are the *x*-intercepts.
Lessons 12-4 and 13-1

22.0 Students use the quadratic formula, factoring techniques, or both to determine whether the graph of a quadratic function will intersect the *x*-axis in zero, one, or two points.
Lessons 12-4 and 13-4

23.0 Students apply quadratic equations to physical problems, such as the motion of an object under the force of gravity.
Lessons 13-2 and 13-7

24.0 Students use and know simple aspects of a logical argument.

    24.1 Students explain the difference between inductive and deductive reasoning and identify and provide examples of each.

    24.2 Students identify the hypothesis and conclusion in logical deduction.

    24.3 Students use counterexamples to show that an assertion is false and recognize that a single counterexample is sufficient to refute an assertion.

    Lessons 1-8, 1-10, 3-12, 4-5, 4-6, 5-12, 7-10, 9-2, and 10-12 *In addition, there are numerous exercises throughout the text that ask students to provide counterexamples, write a convincing argument, or apply mathematical reasoning.*

25.0 Students use properties of the number system to judge the validity of results, to justify each step of a procedure, and to prove or disprove statements.

    25.1 Students use properties of numbers to construct simple valid arguments (direct and indirect) for, or formulate counterexamples to, claimed assertions.

    25.2 Students judge the validity of an argument according to whether the properties of the real number system and order of operations have been applied correctly at each step.

    25.3 Given a specific algebraic statement involving linear, quadratic, or absolute value expressions, equations or inequalities, students determine whether the statement is true sometimes, always, or never.

    Lessons 1-7, 2-10, 3-3, 3-7, 3-8, 7-9, 10-11, 11-1, and 13-6 *In addition, there are numerous exercises throughout the text that ask students to justify statements, justify steps, analyze errors, provide counterexamples, or judge statements to be sometimes, always, or never true.*

The To the Student section of the Student Edition of Algebra 1 outlines the basic structure of a lesson as well as some important assessment features. Consider spending a few minutes with students reviewing these pages so that they are able to put the text to best use. Similarly, consider using these pages to review the features of the text with parents during a Back-to-School night or parent conference.

To the Student

Welcome to Prentice Hall *Algebra 1*. There are many features built into the daily lessons of this text that will help you learn the important concepts and skills you will need to be successful in this course. Listed below, and on the following pages, are some study tips which you will find useful as you complete each lesson.

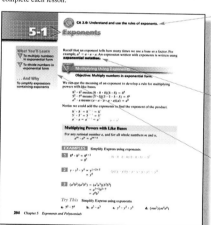

The **California Mathematics Standard** covered by the lesson—and for which you will be held accountable—is included at the beginning of each lesson. Be sure to read this Standard before you start the lesson and then again afterward, when it will have more meaning.

New mathematical **Vocabulary** is highlighted when it is introduced for the first time. You will need to learn this vocabulary to be successful in this course and in your later study of mathematics.

The **What You'll Learn** feature lists the specific skills you will learn in each Part of the lesson. Your teacher may cover all of the Parts of the lesson in one day or over a series of days. Be sure to read the objective as you begin each Part so you will be able to state mathematically what you are learning.

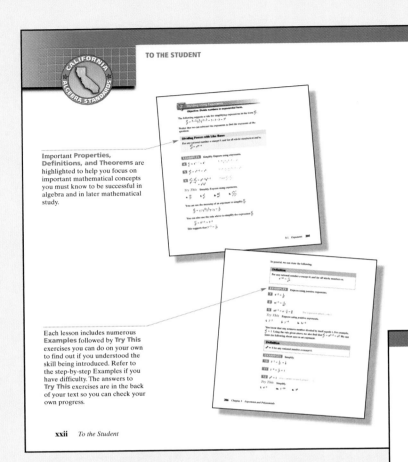

Important **Properties, Definitions, and Theorems** are highlighted to help you focus on important mathematical concepts you must know to be successful in algebra and in later mathematical study.

Each lesson includes numerous **Examples** followed by **Try This** exercises you can do on your own to find out if you understood the skill being introduced. Refer to the step-by-step Examples if you have difficulty. The answers to **Try This** exercises are in the back of your text so you can check your own progress.

xxii *To the Student*

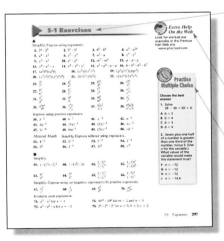

There are numerous **Exercises** in each lesson to give you the practice you need to learn. Your teacher may assign some of these exercises or all of them depending on the **Parts** of the lesson you are covering in a day. You should refer back to the **Examples** in the lesson if you need help completing these exercises.

You can get **Extra Help On the Web** in the form of additional worked-out examples to help you complete homework assignments.

Practice Multiple Choice exercises are included in the lesson to help you prepare for success on your state test. Your teacher may assign these exercises, or you can do them on your own.

To the Student **xxiii**

Error Analysis exercises give you
an opportunity to explain why an
answer is wrong and then to correct
it. This will increase your ability to
think mathematically.

Test Prep exercises give you
practice in completing multiple
choice test items. Problems like
these will be on state tests you will
have to take in the future.

Critical Thinking exercises give
you an opportunity to justify the
mathematical steps needed to
solve a problem. You should
practice explaining these steps
in written form.

Challenge exercises give you
an opportunity to apply your
skills to problems that stretch
your thinking.

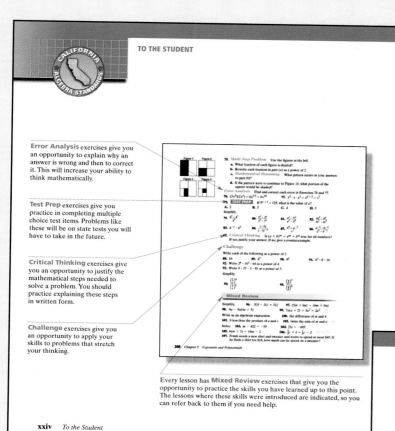

Every lesson has **Mixed Review** exercises that give you the
opportunity to practice the skills you have learned up to this point.
The lessons where these skills were introduced are indicated, so you
can refer back to them if you need help.

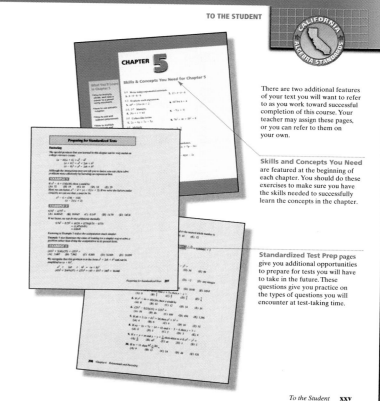

There are two additional features
of your text you will want to refer
to as you work toward successful
completion of this course. Your
teacher may assign these pages,
or you can refer to them on
your own.

Skills and Concepts You Need
are featured at the beginning of
each chapter. You should do these
exercises to make sure you have
the skills needed to successfully
learn the concepts in the chapter.

Standardized Test Prep pages
give you additional opportunities
to prepare for tests you will have
to take in the future. These
questions give you practice on
the types of questions you will
encounter at test-taking time.

CHAPTER 1 ▷ Introduction to Algebra

CHAPTER AT A GLANCE

PACING OPTIONS

This chart suggests pacing only for the lessons and their parts. It is provided as a possible guide.
It will help you determine how much time you have in your schedule to cover other features, such as the Chapter Wrap Up and Assessment.

	Day 1	Day 2	Day 3	Day 4	Day 5	Day 6	Day 7	Day 8	Day 9	Day 10	Day 11
Traditional (40–45 min. class periods)	1-1 ▼1▼2	1-2 ▼1▼2	1-2 ▼3 1-3 ▼1	1-3 ▼2 1-4 ▼1	1-4 ▼2▼3	1-5 ▼1▼2	1-5 ▼3	1-6 ▼	1-7 ▼1▼2▼3	1-8 ▼	1-9 ▼
Algebra 1 Over 2 Years (40–45 min. class periods)	1-1 ▼1	1-1 ▼2	1-2 ▼1	1-2 ▼2	1-2 ▼3	1-3 ▼1	1-3 ▼2	1-4 ▼1	1-4 ▼2	1-4 ▼3	1-5 ▼1
Block Scheduling (90 min. class periods)	1-1 ▼1▼2 1-2 ▼1▼2	1-2 ▼3 1-3 ▼1▼2 1-4 ▼1	1-4 ▼2▼3 1-5 ▼1▼2	1-5 ▼3 1-6 ▼	1-7 ▼1▼2▼3 1-8 ▼	1-9 ▼ 1-10 ▼					

SKILLS TRACE

SKILL	FOUNDATION	DEVELOPED IN LESSONS	REVIEWED/REINFORCED/EXTENDED
Evaluating algebraic expressions	previous course	**1-1**	1-3, 1-9, 5-6
Using the order of operations	previous course	**1-1**	Used throughout the text
Using exponential notation	previous course	**1-3**	5-1, 11-4, 11-5
Using commutative, associative and identity properties	previous course	**1-2, 1-4**	1-10, 2-10
Using the distributive property	previous course	**1-5**	2-7, 2-10
Writing algebraic expressions	previous course	**1-6**	2-9
Solving equations and using formulas	previous course	**1-7, 1-9**	3-1 through 3-7; used throughout the text
Using reasoning strategies	previous course	**1-8, 1-10**	3-12, 4-6, 5-12

CORRELATION TO STANDARDIZED TESTS

YOUR LOCAL TEST*

Lesson		CAT5	CTBS/5 TerraNova™	ITED	MAT7	SAT9		CA Algebra
1-1	Symbols and Expressions				■	■		1.0
1-2	The Commutative and Identity Properties	■			■			1.0
1-3	Exponential Notation	■						2.0
1-4	The Associative Properties							1.0
1-5	The Distributive Property of Multiplication Over Addition							1.0, 4.0, 10.0
1-6	Writing Expressions							5.0
1-7	Solving Equations: An Introduction	■	■					25.2
1-8	Reasoning Strategies: Draw a Diagram	■	■					24.0
1-9	Using Formulas			■	■	■		5.0
1-10	Reasoning Strategies: Try, Test, Revise	■						24.0

CAT5 California Achievement Test, 5th Edition
CTBS/5 Comprehensive Test of Basic Skills, 5th Edition
ITED Iowa Test of Educational Development
       Level 15, Complete Battery, Form M

MAT7 Metropolitan Achievement Test, 7th Edition
SAT 9 Stanford Achievement Test/Task 1

For other standardized test correlations, follow the link to your state at **www.phschool.com**.

*See pp. T34–T39 for the California Standards.

Day 12	Day 13	Day 14	Day 15	Day 16	Day 17	Day 18	Day 19	Day 20	Day 21	Day 22	Day 23	Day 24
10 ▽												
5 ▽	1-5 ▽	1-6 ▽	1-6 ▽	1-7 ▽	1-7 ▽	1-7 ▽	1-8 ▽	1-8 ▽	1-9 ▽	1-9 ▽	1-10 ▽	1-10 ▽

Math Background

Chapter Overview

The basic concepts and terminology of algebra and the fundamental concept of an algebraic expression are introduced and related to students' previous arithmetic experience. The use of grouping symbols and the conventions for the order of operations are reviewed and expanded to include expressions involving exponents. Algebraic expressions are transformed into equivalent expressions by using exponents and the commutative, associative, identity, and distributive properties. Again, these properties are explained using students' previous (informal) arithmetic experience. The use of the distributive property is emphasized, both to collect like terms and to factor.

Simple English phrases are translated into algebraic notation and solution sets of equations are determined by examining replacement sets. The Problem-Solving Guidelines are introduced and used to solve simple word problems, both mentally and by using the strategies *Draw a Diagram* and *Try, Test, Revise*. Formulas are evaluated, and the technique of dimensional analysis is discussed.

▶ 1-1 Symbols and Expressions

Algebraic Expressions

Students may later confuse *algebraic expressions* with *open sentences*. Point out to them that an algebraic expression will not contain an equal sign, an inequality sign, or any other "mathematical verb." $3t - 9$ is an algebraic expression, while $3t \geq 9$ is an open sentence that relates two algebraic expressions.

Some students may be familiar with the use of variables as parts of cell locators in computer spreadsheets or calculator lists (for example, C3 or L2). Some may already have used the word *variable* in work with patterns, in reference to an unknown in an open sentence (Lesson 1-7), or in discussing formulas (Lesson 1-9). Later, students will see other uses of variables.

The word *variable* has the same root as the word *vary*; a variable has something to do with change. However, until Lesson 1-7, students will substitute only one number for a variable. The value of the algebraic expression

$$3t - 9 \text{ for } t = 5$$

is

$$3(5) - 9 = 6;$$

t is replaced by 5, or 5 *is substituted for t in the expression.*

Order of Operations

The order of operations presented here is accepted worldwide in the mathematical community. Scientific and graphing calculators and computer spreadsheets follow the same rules.

Emphasize the importance of agreement on meaning; mathematicians do not like ambiguity.

▶ 1-2 The Commutative and Identity Properties

You might ask students to explain why the identity properties could have been stated with only one equation for each. (The commutative properties supply the other equations because $a + 0 = 0 + a$ and $1 \cdot a = a \cdot 1$.)

Students should know that not all operations have all these properties. They should check that 0 is the identity for subtraction ($a - 0 = a$), that 1 is the identity for division ($a \div 1 = a$), and then go on to discover that neither subtraction nor division has a commutative property. (See also Lesson 1-4, Exercises 55 and 56.)

Note the use of the multiplicative identity to introduce 1 as a factor in either the numerator or denominator in Examples 8, 9, 11, and 12. This is done because 1 is needed as either the numerator or denominator in the resultant simplified fraction. At first it is difficult for students to know when this is necessary, and some fall into the error of using a 0 "since everything else is 'used up'." Such students might be encouraged to introduce a 1 into every numerator and denominator, and then proceed, ending by re-applying the multiplicative identity property. For example,

$$\frac{3a}{6ac} = \frac{1 \cdot 3a}{1 \cdot 2 \cdot 3ac} = \frac{1}{1 \cdot 2c} \cdot \frac{3a}{3a} = \frac{1}{1 \cdot 2c} \cdot 1 = \frac{1}{2c}$$

▶ 1-3 Exponential Notation

Some students may have a faulty understanding of the connection between a *power* and *multiplication*. If students interpret 4^3 as $4 \cdot 3$, suggest that they read 4^3 as "4 to the third power" and always write out $4 \cdot 4 \cdot 4$. If they have somehow heard the incorrect phrase "4 multiplied by itself three times" and so write $4 \cdot 4 \cdot 4 \cdot 4$, suggest that they say "4 is used as a factor three times."

Emphasize that, according to the order of operations, after simplifying within grouping symbols, students should next simplify powers.

Students may be interested to learn that the use of *squared* for the exponent 2 arises from considering the basic problem: Find the area of a square of side s. The answer, of course, is s^2. Similarly, since the volume of a cube of edge p is p^3, *cubed* is used for the exponent 3.

1-4 The Associative Properties

To help students remember the difference between the commutative and associative properties, you might relate them to ordinary uses of the words *commute* and *associate*: *commute* has the sense of changing place, and *associate* has the sense of being with, or grouping.

Point out to students that they may have already used the associative and commutative properties in doing mental math. Faced with adding

$$4 + 5 + 13 + 2 + 7 + 10,$$

for example, some would probably add as

$$10 + (13 + 7) + 4 + 5 + 2.$$

If the exercise were $7 \cdot 6 \cdot 2 \cdot 5,$

students might think $(5 \cdot 2) \cdot 6 \cdot 7.$

1-5 The Distributive Property of Multiplication Over Addition

Here, only addition exercises are presented. The distributive property of multiplication over subtraction is deferred to Lesson 2-7.

When factoring, students don't have to use the greatest common factor. They can go step by step. For example,

$$6ab^2c^3 + 12abc + 18bc^6 = 2bc(3abc^2 + 6a + 9c^5)$$

is not a very efficient way to begin. But there is nothing incorrect, and the student who continues in this fashion will arrive at the correct answer.

1-6 Writing Expressions

Translating English statements into the language of algebra, and vice versa, is a vital skill. It is helpful for students to know that disagreements and misunderstandings can arise when the meaning of the language used is not clearly agreed on. For example, in this text the "difference of 5 and n" is agreed to mean $5 - n$. Students should be encouraged to always question anything they do not understand.

1-7 Solving Equations: An Introduction

True, False, and Open Equations

A variable "varies," or changes value, each time it is replaced by a different number from a given set. Each time a replacement value is chosen from the set, that value must be used in place of **each** occurrence of the variable.

Students who view arithmetic as "finding **the** true answer" are often troubled when algebra forces them to consider that there might be **several** true answers to an exercise, or even no answer at all.

Equations and Solutions

Equivalent equations are a natural extension of equivalent expressions. Remind students that an equation, unlike an expression, always has a mathematical verb, and that expressions do not have solutions. Substitution of numbers for variables gives an expression a value. Substitution in an equation gives a statement that may be true or false. If it is true, the number substituted is a solution of the equation.

1-8, 1-10 Reasoning Strategies

Draw a Diagram and *Try, Test, Revise* are the first two of nine reasoning strategies that students will be expected to use throughout the book. Some students may intuitively draw a diagram when solving a problem. Others may not naturally think of such a strategy. This is one reason why problem-solving strategies cannot be assumed; they are skills that should be taught. All students can be helped to draw clearly, by example and practice.

Similarly, some students may have been discouraged from trying to figure out possible answers. These students need to be shown that the "Test, Revise" part of the strategy, and practice in beginning with a reasonable possible answer, is a solid reasoning strategy.

All students should be exposed to as many strategies as possible and given practice in using them. Again, students from different backgrounds may know variations of these techniques. Sharing their insights with others will give students even stronger reasoning skills.

1-9 Using Formulas

Some students may have learned common formulas but with different variable names. Rectangles may have base and height, instead of length and width, for example; or distance might be represented by s instead of d. Students should be encouraged to discover that the name of a variable does not affect its use in a formula. The product of an average rate and length of time is the distance traveled no matter what letters are used to represent the variables.

Internet Activity On the Web

For professional development tips visit our Web site.
www.phschool.com

Monitoring Progress

UNIVERSAL ACCESS

▶ *Preventing a Student from Falling Behind*

These resources are particularly helpful in preventing a student from falling behind his or her appropriate math level. For a complete list of resources for this chapter, see page 2F.

Before Lessons

Skills You Need for Chapter 1 (p. 2)
- Adding and subtracting whole numbers, decimals, and fractions
- Multiplying and dividing whole numbers, decimals, and fractions

Preteaching Math Vocabulary
- List of Key Terms (p. 2 and p. 47)
- Reading Math (p. 20)
- Writing Math (p. 5)

Skills Intervention Kit With CD-ROM

With Lesson	Use this Unit
1-1	Whole Numbers
1-2, 1-3, 1-8	Number Theory and Fraction Concepts
1-9	Measurement
1-3, 1-4, 1-5, 1-6, 1-7	Pre-Algebra Basics

During Lessons

Try This Exercises (Student Edition)

Additional Examples (Teacher's Edition)

Help at Home
- Lessons 1-1 to 1-4
- Lesson 1-5 to 1-10
- Available in English and Spanish

Skills Intervention Kit

Innovative resource package for diagnosing students' gaps in basic skills, prescribing an individualized course of study, and monitoring progress. Eight intervention units cover core skills students need to succeed.

After Lessons

Lesson Quiz (Teacher's Edition)

Reteaching Worksheets (Teaching Resources Box)

Daily Cumulative Review Masters

There is a Daily Cumulative Review worksheet for every lesson in this chapter.

ASSESSMENT OPTIONS

Lesson	1-1	1-2	1-3	1-4	1-5	1-6	1-7	1-8	1-9	1-10	End
Try This Exercises	■	■	■	■	■	■	■		■		
Mixed Reviews	■	■	■	■	■	■	■		■		
Quizzes				■			■				
Chapter Assessment											■
Cumulative Review	A Cumulative Review for Chapters 1-4 is found on pp. 198–201.										
Standardized Test Prep	■					■					
	Sample College Entrance Exams are found in Problem Solving Practice Masters.										
Computer Item Generator CD-ROM	Can be used to create custom-made practice pages or assessment pages at any time.										
Student Tutorial CD-ROM	Students can self-assess and access tutorial help at any time.										

Test-Taking Tips on Transparencies

Test-Taking Tips: Overview
- Get plenty of sleep the night before your test.
- Eat a good breakfast the morning of your test.
- Bring a watch. Plan to spend 1–2 minutes per question.
- If you are nervous, stop and take three deep breaths.
- Underline important words or phrases.
- Keep your scratch work neat and organized.
- Do easy computations with pencil and paper. Use a calculator for the rest, if permitted.
- Cross out answer choices you know are wrong.
- Do the easy questions first.
- Do not stop to work on difficult questions. Skip them and return to them later if you have time remaining.
- Change an answer only when you are sure your first choice is wrong.
- Unless you are told not to guess, mark an answer for every question.
- Be careful to mark each answer in the right place, and fill in the mark completely.
- Think positively by telling yourself, "I have studied and I know this. I will do well."

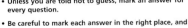

For use with Lesson 1-6

Resources for Chapter 1

TEACHING RESOURCES BOX

	First Five Minutes	Practice	Reteach	Enrichment	Problem Solving	Assessment	Cumulative Review	Lesson Planner		Success-Building	Teaching Transparencies	Help at Home	SE Answers on Transparencies
1-1	■	■	■				■	■		■■■			■
1-2	■	■	■				■	■					■
1-3	■	■	■				■	■					■
1-4	■	■■	■	■■		■	■	■					■
1-5	■	■	■	■			■	■				■	■
1-6	■	■	■		■		■	■		■	■		■
1-7	■	■■	■			■	■	■			■		■
1-8	■		■				■	■			■■		■
1-9	■	■	■				■						■
1-10			■				■	■		■		■	■
End				■		■	5 Forms						■

Also available for use throughout the chapter:

Solution Key
Mathematics Standardized Test Prep
   Student Edition and Teacher's Edition

Overhead Manipulatives Kit
Practice Workbook

Student Manipulatives Kit
Test-Taking Tips on Transparencies

California Assessment Success Kit
Graphing Calculator Handbook

TECHNOLOGY

Computer Item Generator

CD-ROM with an unlimited supply of questions with varying degrees of difficulty for customized practice sheets, quizzes, and tests.

Secondary Math Toolkit™ with Integrated Math Labs

Integrated software package with linkable math tools for exploring key concepts.

Student Tutorial

Test preparation software for students on CD-ROM with management system for teachers; includes Secondary Math Lab Toolkit.

Resource Pro® with Planning Express®

CD-ROM with complete classroom planning tool and teaching resources for customizing and planning lessons.

Web Extension
www.phschool.com

For Students
• Chapter Support with Internet Links
• Internet Activities

For Teachers
• Curriculum Support
• Professional Development
• Product Information
• Regional Information

Also available for use throughout the chapter:

• Algebra Instructional Videos: A Step by Step Guide to Key Concepts

Key Terms

Glossary pages 651–657

You may wish to preteach some of the key terms used in this chapter. Particularly for English Language Learners (ELL), presenting the vocabulary before the chapter or lesson begins gives students a head start into understanding the new material. Writing new words on poster paper, pointing to the words as you say them, then displaying the poster for a period of time is a useful technique.

additive identity (p. 10)
algebraic expression (p. 4)
associative properties (p. 20)
base (p. 15)
commutative properties (p. 9)
counterexample (p. 14)
dimensional analysis (p. 41)
distributive property (p. 24)
equation (p. 33)
equivalent (p. 35)
equivalent expressions (p. 9)
evaluate (p. 4)
exponent (p. 15)
exponential notation (p. 15)
factor (p. 12)
formula (p. 40)
grouping symbols (p. 5)
identity properties (p. 10)
like terms (p. 26)
multiplicative identity (p. 10)
natural numbers (p. 5)
open sentence (p. 33)
power (p. 15)
rational numbers (p. 5)
replacement set (p. 34)
simplest form (p. 12)
simplifying (p. 12)
solution (p. 34)
solution set (p. 34)
solve (p. 34)
substitute (p. 13)
substituting (p. 4)
terms (p. 26)
variable (p. 4)
whole numbers (p. 5)

CHAPTER

What You'll Learn in Chapter 1

- How to evaluate algebraic expressions

- How to use exponential notation

- How to use properties of numbers in algebra

- How to write expressions and evaluate formulas

Skills & Concepts You Need for Chapter 1

Add or subtract. Simplify answers if possible.

1. $\frac{3}{7} + \frac{2}{7}$ **2.** $\frac{3}{8} + \frac{1}{6}$ **3.** $6\frac{3}{4} + 9\frac{5}{8}$ **4.** $3\frac{1}{2} + 4\frac{2}{3} + 7\frac{1}{4}$

5. $\frac{5}{9} - \frac{2}{9}$ **6.** $\frac{5}{6} - \frac{2}{5}$ **7.** $1\frac{7}{8} - \frac{3}{4}$ **8.** $7 - \frac{5}{8}$

Multiply. Simplify answers if possible.

9. $\frac{3}{4} \times \frac{3}{4}$ **10.** $\frac{5}{8} \times 18$ **11.** $4\frac{1}{5} \times 3\frac{5}{7}$ **12.** $2\frac{3}{10} \times 3\frac{1}{3}$

Divide. Simplify answers if possible.

13. $\frac{7}{12} \div \frac{7}{12}$ **14.** $\frac{3}{4} \div 2$ **15.** $3\frac{1}{3} \div 1\frac{1}{4}$ **16.** $3 \div \frac{1}{3}$

Add.

17. $0.5 + 0.35 + 1.5$ **18.** $14 + 3.75 + 8.6$ **19.** $1 + 0.02 + 0.2$

Subtract.

20. $7 - 4.38$ **21.** $11.2 - 6.09$ **22.** $8.9 - 0.76$

Multiply.

23. $\begin{array}{r} 8.75 \\ \times\ \ \ 6 \\ \hline \end{array}$ **24.** $\begin{array}{r} 0.75 \\ \times 0.003 \\ \hline \end{array}$ **25.** $\begin{array}{r} 7.82 \\ \times\ \ 7.9 \\ \hline \end{array}$ **26.** $\begin{array}{r} 0.0004 \\ \times\ \ \ \ \ 57 \\ \hline \end{array}$

Divide. Round answers to the nearest hundredth, if necessary.

27. $7\overline{)8.1}$ **28.** $0.08\overline{)396.7}$ **29.** $1.1\overline{)0.44}$

30. $\frac{5.82}{0.6}$ **31.** $0.065\overline{)333}$ **32.** $8\overline{)0.91}$

2

Skills & Concepts You Need for Chapter 1

1. $\frac{5}{7}$
2. $\frac{13}{24}$
3. $16\frac{3}{8}$
4. $15\frac{5}{12}$
5. $\frac{1}{3}$
6. $\frac{13}{30}$
7. $1\frac{1}{8}$
8. $6\frac{3}{8}$

9. $\frac{9}{16}$
10. $\frac{45}{4}$ or $11\frac{1}{4}$
11. $15\frac{3}{5}$
12. $7\frac{2}{3}$
13. 1
14. $\frac{3}{8}$
15. $2\frac{2}{3}$
16. 9
17. 2.35
18. 26.35
19. 1.22

20. 2.62
21. 5.11
22. 8.14
23. 52.5
24. 0.00225
25. 61.778
26. 0.0228
27. 1.16
28. 4958.75
29. 0.4
30. 9.7
31. 5123.08
32. 0.11

Introduction to Algebra

The memory of a personal computer is measured in bytes. In Lesson 1-3, you will learn how to use exponential notation to express the number of different characters each byte can represent.

3

1-1 TIME-FOCUS METER

1. FOCUS

FIRST FIVE MINUTES
What number goes in the blank?
1. ___ + 5 = 6 1
2. 9 − ___ = 7 2
3. 2 times ___ = 10 5
4. 3 · ___ + 1 = 10 3

2. TEACH the Mathematics

1 Algebraic Expressions

The value of an expression that contains a variable depends on the value we assign the variable. We determine the exact value of the expression when we substitute and evaluate the expression.

Also, point out that of the different ways to show multiplication, the form $3a$ is the most common.

Key Questions
- In an expression such as $3 + m − 2 + m$, can the first $m = 6$ and the second $m = 4$? No
- In $a + b − 7$, can $a = 4$ and $b = 4$? Yes
- In $x + 9$ can x equal either 7 or 8? Yes

Chalkboard Examples
Evaluate each expression.
1. $3x$ for $x = 2$
   $3 \cdot 2 = 6$
2. $3(a)$ for $a = 2$
   $3(2) = 6$
3. $3 \cdot b$ for $b = 2$
   $3 \cdot 2 = 6$
4. $3 \cdot b$ for $b = 5$
   $3 \cdot 5 = 15$
5. $\frac{21}{n}$ for $n = 7$
   $\frac{21}{7} = 3$
6. $z + 5$ for $z = 4$
   $4 + 5 = 9$

 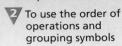

1-1 ▷ Symbols and Expressions

What You'll Learn
1 To evaluate algebraic expressions
2 To use the order of operations and grouping symbols

...And Why
To prepare for evaluating formulas

Math in Action

The time for a high-speed train to travel 396 km from Paris, France to Lyon, France is determined by the velocity of the train.

Velocity (km/h)	Time (hours)
180	$396 \div 180$, or 2.2
200	$396 \div 200$, or 1.98
220	$396 \div 220$, or 1.8
v	$396 \div v$

The average velocity of a high-speed train for the 396-km trip from Paris to Lyon is 198 km/h. What is the average time for the trip?

PART 1 Algebraic Expressions

Objective: Evaluate algebraic expressions.

In algebra we use symbols to stand for various numbers. One type of symbol used is a **variable.** A variable is a letter, such as v or x or m, that represents one or more numbers. In the last line of the table above, we let the letter v stand for the velocity of the train.

An expression may be a number, or two or more numbers involving operation signs. An expression, such as $396 \div v$, that contains at least one variable is called an **algebraic expression.** We can replace a variable with a number. This is called **substituting** for the variable. To **evaluate** an algebraic expression, substitute a number for each variable and calculate.

EXAMPLE 1 Evaluate $n − 7$ for $n = 15$.
$$n − 7 = 15 − 7 \quad \text{Substituting 15 for the variable } n$$
$$= 8$$

Try This Evaluate.

a. $y + 8$ for $y = 9$ **b.** $2 + x$ for $x = 6$ **c.** $t + 3 + t$ for $t = 4$

4 Chapter 1 *Introduction to Algebra*

Photo Caption
2h

Try This
a. 17
b. 8
c. 11

Algebraic expressions involving multiplication can be written in several ways. For example, "3 times a" can be written as $3 \times a$, $3 \cdot a$, $3(a)$, or simply $3a$. Algebraic expressions involving division can also be written in several ways. For example, "m divided by 4" can be written as $m \div 4$ or simply as $\frac{m}{4}$. The fraction bar is a division symbol.

EXAMPLE 2   Evaluate $5y$ for $y = 6$.

$5y = 5(6)$ Substituting 6 for the variable y
$\quad = 30$

Try This   Evaluate.

d. $\frac{x}{12}$ for $x = 36$ **e.** $6m$ for $m = 3$ **f.** $\frac{18}{g}$ for $g = 2$

EXAMPLE 3   Evaluate $\frac{x}{y}$ for $x = 10$ and $y = 5$.

$\frac{x}{y} = \frac{10}{5}$ Substituting 10 for x and 5 for y and dividing

$\quad = 2$

Try This   Evaluate.

g. $a + b$ for $a = 3$ and $b = 7$ **h.** mn for $m = 2$ and $n = 6$

We also use several different sets of numbers in algebra. Here are two you already know.

- **Natural numbers** are the numbers used for counting: 1, 2, 3, and so on.
- **Whole numbers** are the natural numbers and zero: 0, 1, 2, 3, and so on.

We will also work with numbers of the form $\frac{a}{b}$, where $b \neq 0$. Some examples are $\frac{2}{3}$, $\frac{6}{3}$, and $\frac{4}{1}$. These numbers, which include natural and whole numbers, are contained in a set of numbers called **rational numbers.** Rational numbers are explored further in Chapter 2.

PART 2   Order of Operations

> **Objective: Evaluate expressions using grouping symbols and the order of operations.**

Parentheses are called **grouping symbols.** When an expression contains parentheses, any operation inside the parentheses should be done first. The fraction bar is also a grouping symbol. In expressions containing a fraction bar, do all computations above and below the bar before dividing.

$$\frac{4 + 6}{2 \cdot 1} = \frac{10}{2} = 5$$

Try This
d. 3
e. 18
f. 9
g. 10
h. 12

Teach the Mathematics (continued)

2 Order of Operations

Illustrate how the value of the expression
$$3 + 5 \cdot 2$$
depends on the order in which the operations are completed.

(3 1 5) ?2 5 16
3 1 (5 ?2) 5 13

A complete listing of the order of operations is given in Lesson 1-3.

Avoiding Common Errors

Students may rewrite $\frac{4 \ 1 \ 3}{7}$ as $4 + 3 \div 7$. Remind them that the fraction bar is a grouping symbol, and $\frac{4 \ 1 \ 3}{7}$ 5 (4 1 3) 4 7. Students may also tend to evaluate expressions from left to right, disregarding the order of operations. They may, for example, write
$$14 + 8 \div 2 = 11$$
Emphasize the need to scan through an entire expression before computing.

Key Question

- How many different answers can you get by inserting parentheses into the following expression?
$$2 \cdot 4 + 3 \cdot 5$$
$(2 \cdot 4) + (3 \cdot 5) = 23$
$2 \cdot (4 + 3) \cdot 5 = 70$
$2 \cdot (4 + (3 \cdot 5)) = 38$
$((2 \cdot 4) + 3) \cdot 5 = 55$

Chalkboard Examples

1. Evaluate $\frac{m \ 1 \ n}{3}$ for $m = 6$ and $n = 3$.
3

2. Simplify $\frac{16}{2}$ 1 4 ?2.16

3. Evaluate $2x$ 1 $\frac{y}{4}$ for $x = 6$ and $y = 4$.
13

LESSON ENRICHMENT

Rewrite these expressions by removing as many sets of parentheses as possible without changing the value of the expression.

1. $(9 + (3 \cdot 7))$
$9 + 3 \cdot 7$

2. $(3 \cdot 5) + (4 \cdot x)$
$3 \cdot 5 + 4 \cdot x$ or $3 \cdot 5 + 4x$

3. $(5 - ((3 \cdot 2) + 1))$
$5 - (3 \cdot 2 + 1)$
The remaining set of parentheses can't be removed without changing the value of the expression.

4. $((5 + (3)))$
$5 + 3$
The parentheses have no effect because there is only one operation.

Evaluate each expression.

1. $x + 7$ for $x = 2$
   $2 + 7 = 9$
2. $7z$ for $z = 3$
   $7 \cdot 3 = 21$
3. $u - v$ for $u = 7$, $v = 4$
   $7 - 4 = 3$
4. $\left(\frac{12 - x}{3}\right)$ for $x = 6$
   $\left(\frac{12 - 6}{3}\right) = \frac{6}{3} = 2$

Simplify.

5. $\frac{20}{4} \cdot 3$
   $\left(\frac{20}{4}\right) \cdot 3 = 5 \cdot 3 = 15$
6. $4 + 3 \cdot 5$
   $4 + (3 \cdot 5) = 4 + 15 = 19$
7. $12 + \frac{6}{3} - 1$
   $12 + \left(\frac{6}{3}\right) - 1 = 12 + 2 - 1 = 13$

Assignment Guide

To provide flexible scheduling, this lesson can be split into parts.
▼ Core 1–22
  Extension 49
▼ Core 23–45
  Extensions 46–48, 50

Use Mixed Review to maintain skills.

EXAMPLE 4   Evaluate $a(3 + b)$ for $a = 5$ and $b = 2$.

$$\begin{aligned}
a(3 + b) &= 5(3 + 2) && \text{Substituting 5 for } a \text{ and 2 for } b\\
&= 5(5) && \text{Working inside parentheses}\\
&= 25
\end{aligned}$$

Try This   Evaluate.

i. $14 - (b + 5)$ for $b = 3$ **j.** $\frac{x + 5}{2 \cdot 3}$ for $x = 7$

k. $3 + (6x)$ for $x = 2$ **l.** $s(t - 4)$ for $s = 4$ and $t = 8$

We need a rule for the order in which the operations should be done.

Order of Operations

1. Compute within grouping symbols.
2. Multiply and divide in order from left to right.
3. Add and subtract in order from left to right.

EXAMPLE 5   Simplify.

$$\begin{aligned}
8 \cdot 4 + \frac{16}{2} &= 32 + 8 && \text{Multiplying and dividing first}\\
&= 40 && \text{Adding}
\end{aligned}$$

Try This   Simplify.

m. $36 \div (4 + 5)$ **n.** $24 - (12 + 3) \div 5$ **o.** $4 \times 3 + 6 \div 2$

EXAMPLE 6   Evaluate $\frac{2m}{n}$ for $m = 6$ and $n = 3$.

$$\begin{aligned}
\frac{2m}{n} &= \frac{2 \cdot 6}{3} && \text{Substituting 6 for } m \text{ and 3 for } n\\
&= \frac{12}{3}\\
&= 4
\end{aligned}$$

Try This   Evaluate.

p. $3x + y$ for $x = 2$ and $y = 5$ **q.** $\frac{2a + b}{5}$ for $a = 4$ and $b = 2$

Try This
i. 6
j. 2
k. 15
l. 16
m. 4
n. 21
o. 15
p. 11
q. 2

Order of Operations

You should determine whether or not your calculator follows the Order of Operations. Calculate $3 + 4(2)$.

| 3 | + | 4 | × | 2 | = | →? |

If your calculator displays 11, the correct answer, your calculator is programmed to follow the Order of Operations.

If your calculator displays 14, you must always enter the operations in the correct order to get the correct answer.

| 4 | × | 2 | + | 3 | = | →11 |

1-1 Exercises

Extra Help On the Web
Look for worked-out examples at the Prentice Hall Web site.
www.phschool.com

A

Mental Math   Evaluate.

1. $x + 6$ for $x = 7$
2. $3 + y$ for $y = 9$
3. $m - 2$ for $m = 12$
4. $9 - h$ for $h = 3$
5. $t + 24$ for $t = 11$
6. $18 + x$ for $x = 30$
7. $12 - x$ for $x = 5$
8. $k - 6$ for $k = 15$
9. $4 - x - x$ for $x = 1$
10. $k + 8 - k$ for $k = 10$
11. $4h$ for $h = 12$
12. $8m$ for $m = 3$
13. $3t$ for $t = 9$
14. $6y$ for $y = 12$
15. $\frac{12}{y}$ for $y = 2$
16. $\frac{p}{5}$ for $p = 30$
17. $\frac{h}{7}$ for $h = 63$
18. $\frac{x}{y}$ for $x = 16$ and $y = 4$
19. $a - b$ for $a = 12$ and $b = 3$
20. mn for $m = 3$ and $n = 7$
21. $p + q$ for $p = 7$ and $q = 9$
22. $\frac{m}{n}$ for $m = 36$ and $n = 9$

Simplify.

23. $13 + 54 \div 9$
24. $64 \div 16 + 8$
25. $12 + 3 - 7 \cdot 2 + 8$
26. $12 \div 2 \times 3 \div 9$
27. $4 + 12 \times 2 - 8 \div 4$
28. $15 \div 5 \times 5 \times 0$
29. $32 \div 8 + 4 \times 3$
30. $18 \times 2 \div 9 - 3$

Exercises
1. 13
2. 12
3. 10
4. 6
5. 35
6. 48
7. 7
8. 9
9. 2
10. 8
11. 48
12. 24
13. 27
14. 72
15. 6
16. 6
17. 9
18. 4
19. 9
20. 21
21. 16
22. 4
23. 19
24. 12
25. 9
26. 2
27. 26
28. 0
29. 16
30. 1

Evaluate.

31. $2x + y$ for $x = 5$ and $y = 4$ **32.** $x + 4y$ for $x = 2$ and $y = 3$

33. $3m + 4n$ for $m = 2$ and $n = 6$ **34.** $\frac{x + y}{4}$ for $x = 4$ and $y = 8$

35. $\frac{a + 3b}{5}$ for $a = 4$ and $b = 2$ **36.** $\frac{4p}{3q}$ for $p = 6$ and $q = 8$

B

Evaluate.

37. $\frac{n}{3m}$ for $n = 12$ and $m = 4$ **38.** $\frac{ab}{8}$ for $a = 5$ and $b = 8$

39. $\frac{3x}{2y + 1}$ for $x = 7$ and $y = 3$ **40.** $\frac{a + b}{2a}$ for $a = 5$ and $b = 15$

41. $2x + 3x - 4x$ for $x = 5$ **42.** $\frac{24}{2x} + \frac{36}{3x} + \frac{6}{x}$ for $x = 6$

43. $\frac{x + y}{4} + \frac{x - y}{4}$ for $x = 12$ and $y = 8$

44. $\frac{4y}{4y} + (2x + y) - 3z$ for $x = 3$, $y = 2$, and $z = 1$

45. $\frac{y + x}{2} + \frac{3y}{x}$ for $x = 2$ and $y = 4$

46. *Critical Thinking* Use each of the numbers 2, 4, 6, 8, and 10 exactly once, with any operation signs and grouping symbols, to write an expression equal to 0.

47. *Error Analysis* When Rob simplified the expression $72 \div 6 + 3$, his answer was 8. What was Rob's error?

48. **TEST PREP** For what value of x will $\frac{4x + 2}{2} - x$ equal 7?

 A. 4 **B.** 5 **C.** 6 **D.** 7

Challenge

49. The sum of two numbers, $a + b$, is 17, and the product of these numbers, ab, is 60. What numbers do a and b represent?

50. Write as many of the whole numbers from 0 to 10 as you can, using only the digit 4 with operation signs and grouping symbols as many or as few times as you need to. For example, $\frac{(4 + 4)}{4} = 2$.

Calculate. **51.** $251 - 179$ **52.** $307 + 94$ **53.** $1824 \div 32$

54. $2.66 - 0.93$ **55.** $5.74 + 8.36$ **56.** $(4.9)(3.04)$ **57.** $\frac{3}{4} + \frac{2}{7}$

58. $\frac{5}{8} - \frac{1}{3}$ **59.** $2\frac{5}{6} - \frac{2}{3}$ **60.** $4 \div \frac{1}{2}$ **61.** $1\frac{1}{4} \div 2\frac{1}{3}$ *Pre-Course*

Math Point

For Error Analysis exercises, encourage students to consider what specific misuse of either the number properties or the order of operations could lead to the incorrect results.

For a complete list of Error Analysis exercises, see the Index.

Exercises

31. 14
32. 14
33. 30
34. 3
35. 2
36. 1
37. 1
38. 5
39. 3
40. 2
41. 5
42. 5
43. 6

44. 6
45. 9
46. Answers may vary.
 Ex: $10(2 + 8 - 4 - 6) = 0$
47. Rob did not use the order of operations. He added before dividing.
48. C
49. 12 and 5

50. $4 - 4 = 0$
 $\frac{4}{4} = 1$
 $\frac{4 + 4}{4} = 2$
 $4 - \frac{4}{4} = 3$
 $4 = 4$
 $4 + \frac{4}{4} = 5$
 $4 + \frac{4 + 4}{4} = 6$
 $4 + 4 - \frac{4}{4} = 7$
 $4 + 4 = 8$
 $4 + 4 + \frac{4}{4} = 9$
 $4 + 4 + \frac{4 + 4}{4} = 10$

Mixed Review

51. 72
52. 401
53. 57
54. 1.73
55. 14.1
56. 14.896
57. $1\frac{1}{28}$
58. $\frac{7}{24}$
59. $2\frac{1}{6}$
60. 8
61. $\frac{15}{28}$

The Commutative and Identity Properties

In this lesson you will begin to study number properties as they apply to algebraic expressions. You already know that the order in which you add two numbers does not affect the sum.

$$3 + 4 = 7 \quad \text{and} \quad 4 + 3 = 7$$

You also know that the order in which you multiply two numbers does not affect the product.

$$8 \cdot 2 = 16 \quad \text{and} \quad 2 \cdot 8 = 16$$

You will now see how these relationships apply to algebraic expressions.

 **Commutative Properties**

> **Objective: Use the commutative properties for addition and multiplication of whole numbers.**

The expressions $x + 2$ and $2 + x$ have the same value for every replacement for the variable x. Similarly, the expressions $3y$ and $y(3)$ have the same value for every replacement for the variable y. The **commutative properties** state that these relationships will always be true.

Commutative Properties

Addition

For any numbers a and b, $a + b = b + a$. (We can change the order when adding without affecting the sum.)

Multiplication

For any numbers a and b, $ab = ba$. (We can change the order when multiplying without affecting the product.)

Expressions such as $2 + x$ and $x + 2$, which always result in the same number when we substitute any value for their variables, are called **equivalent expressions.**

EXAMPLE 1 Write an expression equivalent to $y + 5$ using a commutative property.

$y + 5 = 5 + y$ using the commutative property of addition.

 CA: 1.0

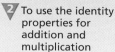 **TIME-FOCUS METER**

What You'll Learn

1 To use the commutative properties for addition and multiplication

2 To use the identity properties for addition and multiplication

3 To simplify expressions

. . . And Why

To write equivalent expressions

1. FOCUS

FIRST FIVE MINUTES

1. Which, if either, has the greater value, 321 + 987 or 987 + 321?
   They are equal.
2. Which, if either, has the greater value, 21 · 98 or 98 · 21? They are equal.

2. TEACH the Mathematics

1 Commutative Properties

Introduce the commutative properties by using numerical cases like those in the *First Five Minutes.* Have students state the generalization that the order does not matter when the only operation is addition or multiplication.

Have students evaluate Examples 1–3 for specific values to show that the commutative properties are true.

Key Questions

- For which operations does the commutative property apply? **Addition and multiplication**
- Is subtraction commutative? No; 1 − 3 does not equal 3 − 1.
- Is division commutative? No; 1 ÷ 3 ≠ 3 ÷ 1.

Chalkboard Examples

Use the commutative property to write an equivalent expression for each of the following.

1. 7 + 11
   11 + 7
2. 3 + x
   x + 3
3. 14 · 32
   32 · 14
4. 5y
   y(5)

2 Identity Properties

Point out that when you add any number to 0 you get that identical number; and when you multiply any number by 1, you get that identical number. Thus we call 0 and 1 the identity numbers for addition and multiplication respectively.

Use numerical examples to show how any nonzero number or expression divided by itself equals 1.

Key Questions

- What is a numerical example of the identity property of addition? Answers may vary. $2 + 0 = 2$; $0 + 7 = 7$.
- What are some expressions that are equivalent to 1? Answers may vary. $\frac{2}{2}$, $\frac{987}{987}$, $\frac{x}{x}$ if $x \neq 0$

Chalkboard Examples

Write an equivalent expression using the indicated expression for 1.

1. $\frac{6}{7}$ using $\frac{3}{3}$ for 1

   $\frac{6}{7} \cdot \frac{3}{3} = \frac{6 \cdot 3}{7 \cdot 3} = \frac{18}{21}$

2. $\frac{2}{3}$ using $\frac{5}{5}$ for 1

   $\frac{2}{3} \cdot \frac{5}{5} = \frac{2 \cdot 5}{3 \cdot 5} = \frac{10}{15}$

3. $\frac{x}{2}$ using $\frac{a}{a}$ for 1

   $\frac{x}{2} \cdot \frac{a}{a} = \frac{x \cdot a}{2 \cdot a} = \frac{xa}{2a}$

EXAMPLES Write an expression equivalent to each using a commutative property.

2 xy An equivalent expression is yx by the commutative property of multiplication.

3 $5 + ab$ An equivalent expression is $ab + 5$ by the commutative property of addition.

Another is $5 + ba$ by the commutative property of multiplication.

Another is $ba + 5$ by both commutative properties.

Try This   Use a commutative property to write an equivalent expression.

a. $x + 9$ **b.** pq **c.** $xy + t$

PART 2 Identity Properties

Objective: Use the identity properties for addition and multiplication of whole numbers.

When 0 is added to any number, the sum is the number. We call 0 the **additive identity.** When any number is multiplied by 1, the product is that number. We call 1 the **multiplicative identity.**

Identity Properties

Addition

For any number a, $a + 0 = a$ and $0 + a = a$. (Adding 0 to any number gives that number.)

Multiplication

For any number a, $1 \cdot a = a$ and $a \cdot 1 = a$. (Multiplying a number by 1 gives that number.)

Recall that the bar in expressions written as $\frac{a}{b}$ means to divide.

Using this idea, we see that the expressions $\frac{5}{5}$, $\frac{3}{3}$, and $\frac{26}{26}$ all name the number 1.

Dividing a Number by Itself

For any number a, $a \neq 0$, $\frac{a}{a} = 1$.

---

10   Chapter 1   *Introduction to Algebra*

Try This

a. $9 + x$
b. qp
c. $yx + t$, $t + xy$, or $t + yx$

Here are some algebraic expressions that have the value 1 for all replacements, except those that would make the denominator zero. (In Chapter 2 we will discuss why division by zero is not allowed.)

$$\frac{n}{n} \qquad \frac{m+3}{m+3} \qquad \frac{5y+4}{5y+4}$$

We can use the identity property for multiplication to write equivalent expressions. If we multiply a fraction by 1, written in the form $\frac{a}{a}(a \neq 0)$, we get a fraction equivalent to the original one.

EXAMPLE 4 Write an equivalent expression for $\frac{2}{3}$ by multiplying by 1. Use $\frac{5}{5}$ for 1.

$\frac{2}{3} = \frac{2}{3} \cdot 1$ Multiplying by the identity

$\quad = \frac{2}{3} \cdot \frac{5}{5}$ Substituting $\frac{5}{5}$ for 1

$\quad = \frac{10}{15}$ Multiplying numerators and denominators

Quick Review

If a number has two different names, such as 1 and $\frac{5}{5}$, then either can be substituted in place of the other.

Try This

d. Write an equivalent expression for $\frac{7}{5}$ by multiplying by 1. Use $\frac{4}{4}$ for 1.

e. Write an equivalent expression for $\frac{3}{8}$ by multiplying by 1. Use $\frac{5}{5}$ for 1.

We can also use the identity property for multiplication to write equivalent algebraic expressions. In this lesson we will assume that all variables in the denominator are nonzero.

EXAMPLE 5 Write an expression equivalent to $\frac{x}{2}$ by multiplying by 1. Use $\frac{y}{y}$ for 1.

$\frac{x}{2} = \frac{x}{2} \cdot \frac{y}{y}$ Multiplying by 1

$\quad = \frac{xy}{2y}$

The expressions $\frac{x}{2}$ and $\frac{xy}{2y}$ have the same value for all replacements for x and y, $y \neq 0$. The expressions $\frac{x}{2}$ and $\frac{xy}{2y}$ are equivalent.

Try This

f. Write an expression equivalent to $\frac{y}{2x}$ by multiplying by 1. Use $\frac{z}{z}$ for 1.

g. Write an expression equivalent to $\frac{2m}{n}$ by multiplying by 1. Use $\frac{p}{p}$ for 1.

Try This

d. $\frac{28}{20}$

e. $\frac{15}{40}$

f. $\frac{yz}{2xz}$

g. $\frac{2mp}{np}$

3 Simplifying Expressions

Review the concept of factoring by having students factor several whole numbers. Point out that it is not necessary to factor completely if common factors are identified, as in Example 7.

You may wish to introduce "canceling" at this point.

$$\frac{10}{15} = \frac{2 \cdot 5}{3 \cdot 5} = \frac{2}{3}$$

It is important that students understand, however, that canceling is a shortcut for the steps shown in the examples.

Key Questions

■ Can all fractions and expressions be simplified? No
■ Why are common factors needed above and below the fraction bar to simplify expressions? Because a factor of 1 can be removed

Chalkboard Examples

Simplify.

1. $\frac{21}{14} = \frac{3 \cdot 7}{2 \cdot 7}$
   $= \frac{3}{2} \cdot \frac{7}{7}$
   $= \frac{3}{2} \cdot 1$
   $= \frac{3}{2}$

2. $\frac{40}{60} = \frac{10 \cdot 4}{10 \cdot 6}$
   $= \frac{10 \cdot 2 \cdot 2}{10 \cdot 2 \cdot 3}$
   $= \frac{2}{3}$

3. $\frac{4ab}{8a} = \frac{4 \cdot a \cdot b}{4 \cdot a \cdot 2}$
   $= \frac{b}{2}$

4. $\frac{y}{3xy} = \frac{y}{y \cdot 3 \cdot x}$
   $= \frac{y \cdot 1 \cdot 1}{y \cdot 3 \cdot x}$
   $= \frac{1}{3x}$

LESSON ENRICHMENT

What value for x will make the denominator zero?

1. $\frac{x + y}{3 - x}$ 3
2. $\frac{7x}{4x}$ 0
3. $\frac{2}{x - 5}$ 5

Objective: Simplify expressions.

When two or more numbers are multiplied to form a product, each number is called a **factor** of the product. For example, $3 \times 5 = 15$, so 3 and 5 are factors of 15. When the only common factor of the numerator and the denominator of a fraction is 1, the fraction is in **simplest form.** The process of finding the simplest form is called **simplifying.**

EXAMPLES   Simplify.

6 $\frac{10}{15} = \frac{2 \cdot 5}{3 \cdot 5}$ Factoring the numerator and denominator

   $= \frac{2}{3} \cdot 1$ Substituting 1 for $\frac{5}{5}$

   $= \frac{2}{3}$ Using the identity property of multiplication

7 $\frac{36}{24} = \frac{6 \cdot 6}{4 \cdot 6}$ Factoring the numerator and denominator

   $= \frac{3 \cdot 2 \cdot 6}{2 \cdot 2 \cdot 6}$ Further factoring

   $= \frac{3}{2} \cdot 1$ Substituting 1 for $\frac{2 \cdot 6}{2 \cdot 6}$

   $= \frac{3}{2}$

Try This   Simplify.

h. $\frac{18}{27}$ **i.** $\frac{48}{18}$ **j.** $\frac{56}{49}$

The number of factors of the numerator and denominator may not always "match." If they do not, you can always use the factor 1.

EXAMPLES   Simplify.

8 $\frac{18}{72} = \frac{2 \cdot 9}{4 \cdot 2 \cdot 9}$

   $= \frac{1 \cdot 2 \cdot 9}{4 \cdot 2 \cdot 9}$ Using the identity property (inserting a factor of 1)

   $= \frac{1}{4} \cdot \frac{2 \cdot 9}{2 \cdot 9}$ Factoring the fraction

   $= \frac{1}{4}$

Try This

h. $\frac{2}{3}$

i. $\frac{8}{3}$

j. $\frac{8}{7}$

9 $\frac{72}{9} = \frac{8 \cdot 9}{1 \cdot 9}$ Factoring and inserting a factor of 1 in the denominator

$$= \frac{8}{1} \cdot \frac{9}{9}$$

$$= \frac{8}{1}$$

$$= 8$$

Try This   Simplify.

k. $\frac{27}{54}$ **l.** $\frac{48}{12}$

We can simplify algebraic expressions using the identity property for multiplication and procedures like those used above with numbers. Note that whenever two algebraic expressions are equivalent, we can **substitute** one for the other. In Example 11, substituting $1 \cdot x$ for x helps us simplify the fractions.

EXAMPLES   Simplify.

10 $\frac{xy}{3y} = \frac{x \cdot y}{3 \cdot y}$ Factoring numerator and denominator

$$= \frac{x}{3} \cdot \frac{y}{y}$$ Factoring the fraction

$$= \frac{x}{3}$$ Using the identity property (removing a factor of 1)

11 $\frac{x}{5xy} = \frac{1 \cdot x}{5 \cdot x \cdot y}$ Substituting $1 \cdot x$ for x.

$$= \frac{1}{5y} \cdot \frac{x}{x}$$ Using the commutative property and factoring the fractional expression

$$= \frac{1}{5y}$$

12 $\frac{4cd}{2c} = \frac{4 \cdot c \cdot d}{2 \cdot c \cdot 1}$

$$= \frac{4 \cdot d}{2 \cdot 1} \cdot \frac{c}{c}$$

$$= \frac{2d}{1}$$

$$= 2d$$

Try This   Simplify.

m. $\frac{5xy}{3x}$ **n.** $\frac{m}{8mn}$ **o.** $\frac{14ab}{7b}$

Try This

k. $\frac{1}{2}$

l. 4

m. $\frac{5y}{3}$

n. $\frac{1}{8n}$

o. $2a$

3. PRACTICE/ASSESS

LESSON QUIZ

Use the commutative property to write an equivalent expression for each.

1. $u + v$ $v + u$

2. $1 + xy$
$xy + 1$ or $1 + yx$ or $yx + 1$

3. Multiply $\frac{5}{s}$ by 1 to get an equivalent expression. Use $\frac{3}{3}$ for 1.
$\frac{5}{s} \cdot \frac{3}{3} = \frac{15}{s \cdot 3} = \frac{15}{3s}$

4. Simplify $\frac{18}{15}$.
$\frac{18}{15} = \frac{3 \cdot 6}{3 \cdot 5} = \frac{6}{5}$

5. Simplify $\frac{4x}{2y}$.
$\frac{4x}{2y} = \frac{2 \cdot 2 \cdot x}{1 \cdot 2 \cdot y} = \frac{2x}{y}$

6. Simplify $\frac{x}{9x}$.
$\frac{x}{9x} = \frac{1 \cdot x}{9 \cdot x} = \frac{1}{9}$

7. Simplify $\frac{2abx}{4acx}$.
$\frac{2abx}{4acx} = \frac{2ax \cdot b}{2ax \cdot 2c} = \frac{b}{2c}$

Assignment Guide

To provide flexible scheduling, this lesson can be split into parts.
▼ Core 1–8
   Extension 30, 31, 40
▼ Core 9–14
   Extension 32–35
▼ Core 15–29
   Extension 36–39

Use Mixed Review to maintain skills.

Math Point

For Exercise 40, urge students to first review the commutative properties on page 9 and then state what they think a commutative property for division would say. Emphasize that, for their assertion to be a property, it would have to be true for *any* numbers *a* and *b*. Thus, to show it is not a property, they need to find *only one* example of two numbers for which the assertion is not true. Such an example is appropriately called a *counter*example.

Exercises

1. $8 + y$
2. $3 + x$
3. nm
4. ba
5. $9 + yx$ or $yx + 9$ or $xy + 9$
6. $ab + 11$ or $ba + 11$ or $11 + ba$
7. $c + ab$ or $c + ba$ or $ba + c$

8. $t + rs$
   $t + sr$
   $sr + t$
9. $\frac{40}{48}$
10. $\frac{99}{110}$
11. $\frac{600}{700}$
12. $\frac{yz}{10z}$
13. $\frac{st}{20t}$
14. $\frac{mp}{3np}$
15. $\frac{1}{8}$

16. 8
17. 12
18. y
19. $\frac{a}{9}$
20. $\frac{1}{9y}$
21. $\frac{1}{8p}$
22. $\frac{8}{3b}$
23. $\frac{9}{17q}$
24. $\frac{p}{2}$
25. $\frac{3}{s}$

26. $\frac{9z}{19t}$
27. $\frac{13r}{3h}$
28. $3c$
29. 8
30. No
31. No
32. Yes
33. No
34. No
35. Yes
36. $\frac{3sb}{2}$
37. $\frac{8r}{3g}$

38. $\frac{5}{2}$
39. Answers may vary.
   $\frac{8ab}{2c}$, $\frac{4abd}{cd}$
40. No, $12 \div 4 \neq 4 \div 12$

Mixed Review
41. 16
42. 1
43. 42
44. $\frac{31}{40}$
45. $\frac{15}{16}$
46. 0.062
47. 0.48

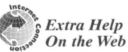

Extra Help On the Web

Look for worked-out examples at the Prentice Hall Web site.
www.phschool.com

1-2 Exercises

A

Write an equivalent expression using a commutative property.

1. $y + 8$ 2. $x + 3$ 3. mn 4. ab
5. $9 + xy$ 6. $11 + ab$ 7. $ab + c$ 8. $rs + t$

Write an equivalent expression. Use the indicated expression for 1.

9. $\frac{5}{6}$ Use $\frac{8}{8}$ for 1.   10. $\frac{9}{10}$ Use $\frac{11}{11}$ for 1.   11. $\frac{6}{7}$ Use $\frac{100}{100}$ for 1.

12. $\frac{y}{10}$ Use $\frac{z}{z}$ for 1.   13. $\frac{s}{20}$ Use $\frac{t}{t}$ for 1.   14. $\frac{m}{3n}$ Use $\frac{p}{p}$ for 1.

Simplify.

15. $\frac{13}{104}$ 16. $\frac{56}{7}$ 17. $\frac{132}{11}$ 18. $\frac{5y}{5}$ 19. $\frac{ab}{9b}$

20. $\frac{x}{9xy}$ 21. $\frac{q}{8pq}$ 22. $\frac{8a}{3ab}$ 23. $\frac{9p}{17pq}$ 24. $\frac{3pq}{6q}$

25. $\frac{51d}{17sd}$ 26. $\frac{9nz}{19tn}$ 27. $\frac{13rv}{3vh}$ 28. $\frac{9abc}{3ab}$ 29. $\frac{32prq}{4qrp}$

B

Tell whether each pair of expressions is equivalent.

30. $3t + 5$ and $3 \cdot 5 + t$ 31. $4x$ and $x + 4$
32. $bxy + bx$ and $yxb + bx$ 33. $ab + bc$ and $ac + db$
34. $a + c + e + g$ and $ea + cg$ 35. $abc \cdot de$ and $a \cdot b \cdot c \cdot ed$

Simplify.

36. $\frac{33sba}{2 \cdot (11a)}$ 37. $\frac{36 \cdot 2rh}{3 \cdot (9hg)}$ 38. $\frac{3 \cdot (4xy) \cdot (5)}{2 \cdot (3x) \cdot (4y)}$

39. **Critical Thinking**   Find two expressions that simplify to $\frac{4ab}{c}$.

Challenge

40. **Mathematical Reasoning**   Is there a commutative property for division of whole numbers? If not, give a counterexample. A **counterexample** is one case where a rule is false.

Mixed Review

Simplify.   41. $12 + 8 \div 2$ 42. $16 \div 8 \cdot 2 \div 4$ 43. $(3 + 4)6$ *1-1*

Calculate.   44. $\frac{2}{5} + \frac{3}{8}$ 45. $\frac{5}{8} \div \frac{2}{3}$ 46. $(3.1)(0.02)$ 47. $\frac{4.8}{10}$ *Pre-Course*

Exponential Notation

 1-3

Math in Action

In a computer, information is read in units called "bits" and "bytes." A bit is like an on-off switch and is read by the computer as 1 (on) or 0 (off). A byte is a group of 8 bits, put together to represent one unit of data such as a letter, digit, or special character. Each byte, therefore, can represent $2 \times 2 \times 2 \times 2 \times 2 \times 2 \times 2 \times 2$ or 256 different characters.

This book was edited on a personal computer with 2^7 megabytes of built-in memory. If the prefix *mega-* means one million, how many bytes of built-in memory does this computer have?

What You'll Learn

1 To express numbers with exponents

2 To evaluate expressions with exponents

...And Why

To use exponential notation to simplify expressions with repeated factors

---

1-3 TIME-FOCUS METER

1. FOCUS

FIRST FIVE MINUTES
1. $3 \cdot 3 \cdot 3 = ?$ 27
2. $2 \cdot 2 \cdot 2 \cdot 2 \cdot 2 = ?$ 32
3. $1 \cdot 1 \cdot 1 \cdot 1 \cdot 1 = ?$ 1
4. $10 \cdot 10 \cdot 10 = ?$ 1000

2. TEACH the Mathematics

1 **Using Exponents**

Emphasize that the exponent tells you how many times the base is used as a factor. You may want to reinforce this with a diagram.

$$\text{exponent} \searrow 3^5 = 3 \cdot 3 \cdot 3 \cdot 3 \cdot 3$$
$$\text{base} \nearrow \qquad \text{Five factors}$$

Key Questions

In the expression 4^8,
- what is the 8 called? The exponent
- what is the 4 called? The base
- How do you read this expression? Four to the eighth

Chalkboard Examples

Write without exponential notation.
1. 2^4
   $2 \cdot 2 \cdot 2 \cdot 2 = 16$
2. x^5
   $x \cdot x \cdot x \cdot x \cdot x$
3. $6t^2$
   $6 \cdot t \cdot t$
4. $3^2 x^3$
   $3 \cdot 3 \cdot x \cdot x \cdot x$

Write using exponential notation.
5. $3 \cdot 3 \cdot 3 \cdot 3 \cdot 3 \cdot 3$
   3^6
6. $c \cdot c \cdot c$
   c^3
7. $2 \cdot y \cdot y \cdot y$
   $2y^3$
8. $3 \cdot 3 \cdot x \cdot x \cdot y \cdot y \cdot y$
   $3^2 x^2 y^3$

  PART 1 Using Exponents

Objective: Express numbers using exponential notation.

A product in which the factors are the same is called a **power.** We can write $2 \times 2 \times 2 \times 2 \times 2 \times 2 \times 2 \times 2$ as 2^8. The number 8 is called the **exponent,** and 2 is called the **base.** The exponent tells how many times the base is used as a factor. Similarly, we can write $a \cdot a \cdot a = a^3$. Here the exponent is 3 and the base is a. When an expression is written with exponents, we say the expression is written using **exponential notation.**

$$\text{Exponent} \longrightarrow$$
$$\text{Base} \longrightarrow b^n$$

We read b^n as the "nth power of b," or simply "b to the nth," or "b to the n." We may also read b^2 as "b squared" and b^3 as "b cubed."

EXAMPLES What is the meaning of each expression?

1 2^2 2^2 means $2 \cdot 2$

2 3^5 3^5 means $3 \cdot 3 \cdot 3 \cdot 3 \cdot 3$

3 n^4 n^4 means $n \cdot n \cdot n \cdot n$

4 $2y^3$ $2y^3$ means $2 \cdot y \cdot y \cdot y$

Try This What is the meaning of each expression?
a. 5^4 **b.** b^3 **c.** $2x^3$ **d.** $12y^4$

Photo Caption

128,000,000

Try This

a. $5 \cdot 5 \cdot 5 \cdot 5$
b. $b \cdot b \cdot b$
c. $2 \cdot x \cdot x \cdot x$
d. $12 \cdot y \cdot y \cdot y \cdot y$

Teach the Mathematics (continued)

2 Evaluating Expressions

This lesson extends the order of operations to include powers.

Use Teaching Transparency T6 to illustrate the order of operations.

Avoiding Common Errors

Students often assume that $2 \cdot 3^2$ means 6^2, not $2 \cdot 9$. Remind students that the exponent only affects the number it follows unless it follows parentheses. Use the following example.

$$2 \cdot 3^2 = 2 \cdot 9 = 18$$
$$(2 \cdot 3)^2 = 6^2 = 36$$

Key Questions

What number does the exponent 2 affect?
- $3 \cdot 4^2$ 4
- $(3 \cdot 4)^2$ $3 \cdot 4$, or 12

Chalkboard Examples

Evaluate.
1. x^3 for $x = 4$
   $4^3 = 4 \cdot 4 \cdot 4 = 64$
2. a^4 for $a = 2$
   $2^4 = 2 \cdot 2 \cdot 2 \cdot 2 = 16$
3. z^{100} for $z = 1$
   $1 \cdot 1 \cdot \ldots \cdot 1 = 1$
4. w^2 for $w = 0$
   $0^2 = 0 \cdot 0 = 0$
5. $a^2 + 1$ for $a = 3$
   $3^2 + 1 = 9 + 1 = 10$
6. $z^4 - 1$ for $z = 1$
   $1^4 - 1 = 1 - 1 = 0$
7. $(4x)^2$ for $x = 2$
   $(4 \cdot 2)^2 = (8)^2 = 8^2 = 64$
8. $(6r)^5$ for $r = 0$
   $(6 \cdot 0)^5 = (0)^5 = 0^5 = 0$

LESSON ENRICHMENT

A particular kind of amoeba is found in a sample of swamp water. This amoeba splits into two amoebas after exactly one hour. After another hour, each of the two amoebas splits into two more amoebas. How many amoebas are there after 5 hours? How many after 10 hours? 32; 1024

Practice Multiple Choice

Choose the best answer.

1. Which property is shown by this equation?

$$5 + (3 + 6) = 5 + (6 + 3)$$

A Identity property of multiplication

B Commutative property of addition

C Identity property of addition

D Commutative property of multiplication

2. Evaluate $2a^2$ for $a = 3$.

F 6

G 12

H 18

J 36

1. B; Algebra 1.0
2. H; Algebra 2.0

Try This

e. 9^3
f. y^5
g. $4n^5$
h. $15x^4$
i. $10b^3$
j. 100
k. 32
l. 0

EXAMPLES   Write using exponential notation.

5 $7 \cdot 7 \cdot 7 \cdot 7$ can be written as 7^4

6 $n \cdot n \cdot n \cdot n \cdot n \cdot n$ can be written as n^6

7 $3 \cdot x \cdot x$ can be written as $3x^2$

8 $2 \cdot y \cdot y \cdot y \cdot y$ can be written as $2y^4$

Try This   Write using exponential notation.

e. $9 \cdot 9 \cdot 9$ **f.** $y \cdot y \cdot y \cdot y \cdot y$ **g.** $4 \cdot n \cdot n \cdot n \cdot n \cdot n$

h. $15 \cdot x \cdot x \cdot x \cdot x$ **i.** $10 \cdot b \cdot b \cdot b$

Here are some definitions for exponents.

Definitions

b^1 means b for any number b.

If n is a whole number greater than 1, b^n means $\overset{n \text{ factors}}{\overbrace{b \cdot b \cdot b \cdot b \cdot \ldots \cdot b}}$.

PART 2   Evaluating Expressions

Objective: Evaluate expressions containing exponents.

EXAMPLES   Evaluate each expression.

9 x^4 for $x = 2$
    $x^4 = 2^4$ Substituting
       $= 2 \cdot 2 \cdot 2 \cdot 2$
       $= 16$

10 y^2 for $y = 5$
    $y^2 = 5^2$ Substituting
       $= 5 \cdot 5$
       $= 25$

Try This   Evaluate each expression.

j. a^2 for $a = 10$ **k.** y^5 for $y = 2$ **l.** x^4 for $x = 0$

We now extend the rules for the order of operations to include exponents.

Order of Operations—Extended

1. Compute within grouping symbols first.
2. Compute powers.
3. Multiply and divide in order from left to right.
4. Add and subtract in order from left to right.

EXAMPLES Evaluate each expression.

11 $y^4 + 3$ for $y = 2$
$y^4 + 3 = 2^4 + 3$
$= 2 \cdot 2 \cdot 2 \cdot 2 + 3$
$= 16 + 3$
$= 19$

12 $m^3 + 5$ for $m = 4$
$m^3 + 5 = 4^3 + 5$
$= 4 \cdot 4 \cdot 4 + 5$
$= 64 + 5$
$= 69$

Try This Evaluate each expression.

m. $x^3 + 2$ for $x = 3$ **n.** $n^5 + 8$ for $n = 2$

When an expression inside parentheses is raised to a power, everything inside the parentheses is the base. Compare $3a^3$ and $(3a)^3$.

$3a^3$ means $3 \cdot a \cdot a \cdot a$ *a* is the base
$(3a)^3$ means $(3a)(3a)(3a)$ *3a* is the base

EXAMPLES Evaluate.

13 $(3a)^3$ for $a = 2$
$(3a)^3 = (3a)(3a)(3a)$
$= (3 \cdot 2)(3 \cdot 2)(3 \cdot 2)$
$= 6 \cdot 6 \cdot 6$
$= 216$

14 $3a^3$ for $a = 2$
$3a^3 = 3 \cdot a \cdot a \cdot a$
$= 3 \cdot 2 \cdot 2 \cdot 2$
$= 24$

Try This Evaluate.

o. $(2x)^2$ for $x = 4$ **p.** $(5y)^3$ for $y = 2$ **q.** $3x^2$ for $x = 3$

Evaluating Expressions Involving Exponents

You can evaluate expressions like $y^3 + 3$ for $y = 2$ on a calculator with an exponent key. Calculate $2^3 + 3$.

2 y^x 3 = + 3 = → 11

1-3 Exercises

A
What is the meaning of each expression?

1. 2^4 **2.** 5^3 **3.** 3^1 **4.** 1^3 **5.** a^3 **6.** $5y^4$

Write using exponential notation.

7. $10 \cdot 10 \cdot 10 \cdot 10 \cdot 10 \cdot 10$ **8.** $6 \cdot 6 \cdot 6 \cdot 6$ **9.** $x \cdot x \cdot x \cdot x \cdot x$
10. $4 \cdot y \cdot y \cdot y$ **11.** $5 \cdot m \cdot m \cdot m \cdot m$ **12.** $2 \cdot n \cdot n \cdot n \cdot n \cdot n$

Extra Help On the Web
Look for worked-out examples at the Prentice Hall Web site.
www.phschool.com

3. PRACTICE/ASSESS

LESSON QUIZ
Write an equivalent expression without exponents.
1. 5^3
   $5 \cdot 5 \cdot 5$
2. $2a^3$
   $2 \cdot a \cdot a \cdot a$
3. Write using exponential notation.
   $t \cdot t \cdot t \cdot t$
   t^4
4. Write using exponential notation.
   $3 \cdot 3 \cdot a \cdot a \cdot b$
   $3^2 a^2 b$
5. Simplify to a form without parentheses. $(3z)^2$
   $(3z) \cdot (3z) = 3z \cdot 3z = 3 \cdot z \cdot 3 \cdot z = 3 \cdot 3 \cdot z \cdot z = 9z^2$.
6. Evaluate s^6 for $s = 2$.
   $2^6 = 2 \cdot 2 \cdot 2 \cdot 2 \cdot 2 \cdot 2 = 64$
7. Evaluate $u^2 + 1$ for $u = 4$.
   $4^2 + 1 = 16 + 1 = 17$

Assignment Guide
To provide flexible scheduling, this lesson can be split into parts.
▼ Core 1–12, 30–33
   Extension 36, 37, 40
▼ Core 13–29, 34, 35
   Extensions 38, 39, 41

Use Mixed Review to maintain skills.

Try This
m. 29
n. 40
o. 64
p. 1000
q. 27

Exercises
1. $2 \cdot 2 \cdot 2 \cdot 2$
2. $5 \cdot 5 \cdot 5$
3. 3
4. $1 \cdot 1 \cdot 1$
5. $a \cdot a \cdot a$
6. $5 \cdot y \cdot y \cdot y \cdot y$
7. 10^6
8. 6^4
9. x^5
10. $4y^3$
11. $5m^4$
12. $2n^6$

Evaluate each expression.

13. m^3 for $m = 3$ **14.** x^6 for $x = 2$ **15.** p^1 for $p = 19$

16. x^{19} for $x = 0$ **17.** $x^4 - 8$ for $x = 4$ **18.** $y^{15} + 4$ for $y = 1$

19. $x^3 + 2$ for $x = 4$ **20.** $y^2 - 3$ for $y = 5$ **21.** $3m^3$ for $m = 1$

22. $4x^2$ for $x = 3$ **23.** $2n^4$ for $n = 2$ **24.** $(4x)^3$ for $x = 2$

25. $(2a)^4$ for $a = 3$ **26.** $(5n)^2$ for $n = 6$ **27.** $(6y)^4$ for $y = 2$

B

28. Evaluate $(2ab)^3$ for $a = 2$ and $b = 4$.

29. Evaluate $(3mn)^3$ for $m = 2$ and $n = 0$.

Write with a single exponent.

For example, $\dfrac{3^5}{3^3} = \dfrac{3 \cdot 3 \cdot 3 \cdot 3 \cdot 3}{3 \cdot 3 \cdot 3} = 3 \cdot 3 = 3^2$

30. $\dfrac{10^5}{10^3}$ **31.** $\dfrac{10^7}{10^2}$ **32.** $\dfrac{5^4}{5^2}$ **33.** $\dfrac{8^6}{8^2}$

34. Evaluate $x^3 y^2 + zx$ for $x = 2$, $y = 1$, $z = 3$.

35. *Critical Thinking*   Does $x^y = y^x$ for all whole numbers x and y? If yes, justify your answer. If no, provide a counterexample.

36. *Mathematical Reasoning*   Square any number, then double the result. Is your answer *always, sometimes,* or *never* greater than the result of doubling the number, then squaring it? Justify your answer.

37. *Error Analysis*   Elaine wrote in her math journal "The square of any number is always greater than the number." Find a counterexample to show that Elaine's statement is incorrect.

Challenge

38. Find yx^{149} for $x = 13$ and $y = 0$.

39. Find $x^{410} y^2$ for $x = 1$ and $y = 3$.

40. 10^{127} is 1 followed by how many zeros?

41. Find $(x^2)^2$ if $x = 3$.

Mixed Review

Calculate.   **42.** $8\frac{1}{3} + 2\frac{2}{3}$ **43.** $1\frac{5}{8} - \frac{3}{4}$ **44.** $\frac{3}{8} \div 3$ **45.** $5 \times 2\frac{1}{2}$ *Pre-Course*

Evaluate.   **46.** $2(m + n)$ for $m = 7$, $n = 1$ **47.** $(3 + n)n$ for $n = 2$ *1-1*

Simplify.   **48.** $\frac{7}{56}$ **49.** $\frac{96}{12}$ **50.** $\frac{r}{8rs}$ **51.** $\frac{18x}{2xy}$ **52.** $\frac{3ab}{12b}$ *1-2*

Math Point

In Exercise 36 students must decide whether a mathematical relationship
(in this case, $2x^2 = (2x)^2$)
a) is true for *all* values of x,
b) is true for *some* values of x and false for *some* other values of x, or
c) is true for *no* values of x.
You may wish to point out that justifying "always true" or "never true" requires a convincing argument about all possible cases. Justifying "sometimes true," requires only one true example and one true counterexample.

For a complete list of "sometimes, always, never" exercises, see the Index.

Exercises

13. 27
14. 64
15. 19
16. 0
17. 248
18. 5
19. 66
20. 22
21. 3
22. 36
23. 32
24. 512
25. 1296
26. 900
27. 20,736
28. 4096
29. 0
30. 10^2
31. 10^5
32. 5^2
33. 8^4
34. 14
35. No; for example, $2^3 = 8$ and $3^2 = 9$.
36. Never; $(2x)^2 = 4x^2$ and $4x^2 \geq 2x^2$ for all x.
37. Answers may vary. Sample: 1; $1^2 = 1$.
38. 0
39. 9
40. 127
41. 81

Mixed Review

42. 11
43. $\frac{7}{8}$
44. $\frac{1}{8}$
45. $12\frac{1}{2}$
46. 16
47. 10
48. $\frac{1}{8}$
49. 8
50. $\frac{1}{8s}$
51. $\frac{9}{y}$
52. $\frac{a}{4}$

The Associative Properties

 CA: 1.0

 PART 1 — Parentheses

Objective: Evaluate expressions involving parentheses.

You have learned to calculate within parentheses first. You also know that you simplify powers before doing other operations.

EXAMPLES Calculate.

1 $(3 \cdot 4)^2 = 12^2$ Working within parentheses first
$= 144$

2 $3 \cdot 4^2 = 3 \times 16$ There are no parentheses, so we find 4^2 first.
$= 48$

Try This   Calculate.

a. $(3 \cdot 5)^2$ **b.** $3 \cdot 5^2$ **c.** $4 \cdot 2^3$ **d.** $(4 \cdot 2)^3$
e. $4 + 2^2$ **f.** $(4 + 2)^2$ **g.** $(5 - 1)^2$ **h.** $5 - 1^2$

EXAMPLES Evaluate each expression.

3 $(3x)^3 - 2$ for $x = 2$
$(3x)^3 - 2 = (3 \cdot 2)^3 - 2$ Substituting
$= 6^3 - 2$ Multiplying within parentheses first
$= 216 - 2$
$= 214$

4 $(2 + x)(y - 1)$ for $x = 3$ and $y = 5$
$(2 + x)(y - 1) = (2 + 3)(5 - 1)$
$= 5 \cdot 4$ Working within parentheses first
$= 20$

Try This   Evaluate each expression.

i. $(4y)^2 - 5$ for $y = 3$ **j.** $6(x + 12)$ for $x = 8$

k. $t + \dfrac{6}{5t^2}$ for $t = 2$ **l.** $(x - 4)^3$ for $x = 6$

m. $(4 + y) \cdot (x - 3)$ for $y = 3$ and $x = 12$

1-4 *The Associative Properties*   **19**

What You'll Learn

1 To evaluate expressions involving parentheses

2 To use the associative properties of addition and multiplication

3 To write equivalent expressions using properties

. . . And Why

To use the associative properties to make calculations easier

---

1-4 TIME-FOCUS METER

1. FOCUS

FIRST FIVE MINUTES
Simplify.
1. $(3 + 2) + 1$
   6
2. $(1 + 2) - 3$
   0
3. $(1 + 2) \cdot 3$
   9
4. $3 \cdot (2 + 1)$
   9

2. TEACH the Mathematics

1 Parentheses

Stress that operations in parentheses are evaluated first, and that the order of operations is followed within the parentheses.
    Remind students that -1^2 means $-(1^2)$, *not* $(-1)^2$.

Key Question
■ How many different values can you get by inserting parentheses into the following expression?
$4 + 3 \cdot 2^2$
$4 + 3 \cdot 2^2 = 16$
$(4 + 3) \cdot 2^2 = 28$
$4 + (3 \cdot 2)^2 = 40$
$(4 + 3 \cdot 2)^2 = 100$
$((4 + 3) \cdot 2)^2 = 196$

Try This
   a. 225
   b. 75
   c. 32
   d. 512
   e. 8
   f. 36
   g. 16
   h. 4
   i. 139
   j. 120
   k. $2\frac{3}{10}$
   l. 8
   m. 63

Chalkboard Examples

Calculate.

1. $(2 \cdot 3)^2$
   $= 6^2 = 36$

2. $2 \cdot 3^2$
   $= 2 \cdot 9 = 18$

3. $8 - 2^2$
   $= 8 - 4 = 4$

Evaluate.

4. $(5a)^2 - 1$ for $a = 2$
   $(5 \cdot 2)^2 - 1 = 10^2 - 1 = 99$

5. $(2 + c)(3 - c)$ for $c = 1$
   $(2 + 1)(3 - 1) = (3)(2) = 6$

6. $(x - 1)(x - 2)$ for $x = 2$
   $(2 - 1)(2 - 2) = (1)(0) = 0$

7. $(y - 5)^3$ for $y = 7$
   $(y - 5)^3 = (2)^3 = 8$

 Using the Associative Properties

You may wish to show that subtraction does not have the associative property.

$$8 - (5 - 2) \neq (8 - 5) - 2$$
$$8 - 3 \quad \neq \quad 3 - 2$$
$$5 \quad \neq \quad 1$$

Avoiding Common Errors

Students often assume that when a pair of equivalent expressions have parentheses in them, the associative property is being used. Stress that the associative property allows a different *association* of numbers and that the commutative property allows a different *ordering* of the numbers.

Key Questions

Can the parentheses be removed from the following expressions without changing their values?

- $(x + 3) + (3 + x)$
  Yes

- $(x + 3) + 3 + x$
  Yes

- $(3x)(3x)$
  Yes

Evaluating Expressions

You can use a calculator to evaluate algebraic expressions.

Evaluate $\frac{x + 2y}{3}$ for $x = 9$ and $y = 3$.

Key sequence for scientific calculators, which follow the Order of Operations:

| (| 9 | + | 2 | × | 3 |) | ÷ | 3 | = | → 5 |

Key sequence for arithmetic calculators, which do not follow the Order of Operations:

| 2 | × | 3 | + | 9 | = | ÷ | 3 | = | → 5 |

PART 2

Using the Associative Properties

Objective: Write equivalent expressions using the associative properties.

When addition is the only operation in an expression, the parentheses can be moved without affecting the value of the expression. For example, the expressions $3 + (7 + 5)$ and $(3 + 7) + 5$ are equivalent.

$$
\begin{array}{cc}
3 + (7 + 5) & (3 + 7) + 5 \\
3 + 12 & 10 + 5 \\
15 & 15
\end{array}
$$

When multiplication is the only operation in an expression, parentheses can be moved without affecting the value of the expression. For example, the expressions $3 \cdot (4 \cdot 2)$ and $(3 \cdot 4) \cdot 2$ are equivalent.

$$
\begin{array}{cc}
3 \cdot (4 \cdot 2) & (3 \cdot 4) \cdot 2 \\
3 \cdot 8 & 12 \cdot 2 \\
24 & 24
\end{array}
$$

The **associative properties** state that this will always be true.

Reading Math

You read the expression $3 + (7 + 5)$ as "3 plus the quantity 7 plus 5."

Associative Property of Addition

For any numbers a, b, and c,

$$a + (b + c) = (a + b) + c$$

(Numbers can be grouped in any order for addition.)

Associative Property of Multiplication

For any numbers a, b, and c,

$$a \cdot (b \cdot c) = (a \cdot b) \cdot c$$

(Numbers can be grouped in any order for multiplication.)

EXAMPLES Use an associative property to write an equivalent expression.

5 $y + (z + 3) = (y + z) + 3$ Using the associative property of addition

6 $5 \cdot (x \cdot y) = (5 \cdot x) \cdot y$ Using the associative property of multiplication

Try This Use an associative property to write an equivalent expression.

n. $a + (b + 2)$ **o.** $3 \cdot (v \cdot w)$

PART 3 Using the Properties Together

Objective: Write equivalent expressions using the commutative and associative properties.

If addition or multiplication is the only operation in an expression, then the associative and commutative properties allow us to group and change order as we please. For example, in a calculation like $(5 + 2) + (3 + 5) + 8$, addition is the only operation. Therefore, we can change the grouping and order to make our calculations easier.

$$(5 + 5) + (2 + 8) + 3 = 10 + 10 + 3 = 23$$

In algebra we often need to change the order or grouping of an expression. The associative and commutative properties allow us to do this.

EXAMPLE 7 Use the commutative and associative properties to write three expressions equivalent to $(x + 5) + y$.

$(x + 5) + y = x + (5 + y)$ Using the associative property first
$\qquad\qquad = x + (y + 5)$ and then the commutative property

$(x + 5) + y = y + (x + 5)$ Using the commutative property and
$\qquad\qquad = y + (5 + x)$ then the commutative property again

$(x + 5) + y = 5 + (x + y)$ Using the commutative property first
   and then the associative property

1-4   *The Associative Properties*   **21**

Try This
n. $(a + b) + 2$
o. $(3 \cdot v) \cdot w$

Teach the Mathematics (continued)

Chalkboard Examples
Use the associative properties to write an equivalent expression.
1. $(3 + 2) + 5$
   $3 + (2 + 5)$
2. $(x + 3) + z$
   $x + (3 + z)$
3. $a + (b + c)$
   $(a + b) + c$
4. $(3 \cdot c) \cdot d$
   $3 \cdot (c \cdot d)$
5. $u(vw)$
   $(uv)w$

3 Using the Properties Together

Chalkboard Examples
Tell which property, commutative or associative, is used at each step.
1. $(x + 5) \cdot (2 \cdot y)$
   a. $= (5 + x) \cdot (2 \cdot y)$
     Commutative
   b. $= (5 + x) \cdot (y \cdot 2)$
     Commutative
   c. $= (y \cdot 2) \cdot (5 + x)$
     Commutative
   d. $= y \cdot (2 \cdot (5 + x))$
     Associative
2. $(a + b) + cd$
   a. $= a + (b + cd)$
     Associative
   b. $= a + (cd + b)$
     Commutative
   c. $= (a + cd) + b$
     Associative
   d. $= (a + dc) + b$
     Commutative

3. PRACTICE/ASSESS

LESSON QUIZ

Calculate.

1. $3 \cdot 5^2$
   $3 \cdot 25 = 75$

2. $(3 - 1)^3$
   $2^3 = 8$

Evaluate.

3. $5(a + 2)$ for $a = 4$
   $5 \cdot (4 + 2) = 5 \cdot 6 = 30$

4. $(x - 3)(x - 5)$ for $x = 7$
   $(7 - 3)(7 - 5) = 4 \cdot 2 = 8$

5. $\frac{x^2 + 3}{2x}$ for $x = 4$
   $\frac{4^2 + 3}{2 \cdot 4} = \frac{16 + 3}{8} = \frac{19}{8}$

Use the associative property to write an equivalent expression.

6. $a + (3 + c)$
   $(a + 3) + c$

7. $(5x)y$
   $5(xy)$

Assignment Guide

To provide flexible scheduling, this lesson can be split into parts.

▼ Core 1–16, 17–29 odd
  Extension 50–53

▼ Core 18–30 even, 31–34
  Extension 55, 56

▼ Core 35–49
  Extension 54, 57

Use Mixed Review to maintain skills.

EXAMPLE 8   Use the commutative and associative properties to write three expressions equivalent to $(3 \cdot x) \cdot y$.

$(3 \cdot x) \cdot y = 3 \cdot (x \cdot y)$ Using the associative property first
$\qquad\qquad\quad = 3 \cdot (y \cdot x)$ and then the commutative property

$(3 \cdot x) \cdot y = y \cdot (x \cdot 3)$ Using the commutative property twice

$(3 \cdot x) \cdot y = x \cdot (y \cdot 3)$ Using the commutative property, then the associative property, and then the commutative property again

Try This   Use the commutative and associative properties to write three equivalent expressions.

p. $4 \cdot (t \cdot u)$ **q.** $r + (2 + 5)$

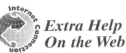

Extra Help On the Web
Look for worked-out examples at the Prentice Hall Web site.
www.phschool.com

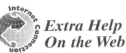

1-4 Exercises

A

Mental Math   Calculate.

1. $(5 \cdot 4)^2$	**2.** $(6 \cdot 3)^2$	**3.** $5 \cdot 4^2$	**4.** $6 \cdot 3^2$
5. $7 + 2^2$	**6.** $5 + 3^2$	**7.** $(7 + 2)^2$	**8.** $(5 + 3)^2$
9. $(5 - 2)^2$	**10.** $(3 - 2)^2$	**11.** $10 - 3^2$	**12.** $16 - 4^2$
13. $12 - 2^3$	**14.** $30 - 3^3$	**15.** $(2 + 3)^3$	**16.** $3 \cdot 2^3$

Evaluate each expression.

17. $5x^2 - 4$ for $x = 4$
18. $3a^3 + 2$ for $a = 1$
19. $(5y)^3 - 75$ for $y = 2$
20. $(7x)^2 + 59$ for $x = 3$
21. $3(a + 10)$ for $a = 12$
22. $b(7 + b)$ for $b = 5$
23. $(t + 3)^3$ for $t = 4$
24. $(12 - w)^3$ for $w = 7$
25. $(x + 5)(12 - x)$ for $x = 7$
26. $(y - 4)(y + 6)$ for $y = 10$
27. $\frac{y + 3}{2y}$ for $y = 5$
28. $\frac{(4x) + 2}{2x}$ for $x = 5$
29. $\frac{w^2 + 4}{5w}$ for $w = 4$
30. $\frac{b^2 + b}{2b}$ for $b = 5$

Use the associative properties to write an equivalent expression.

31. $(a + b) + 3$ 32. $(5 + x) + y$ 33. $3 \cdot (a \cdot b)$ 34. $(6 \cdot x) \cdot y$

Use the commutative and associative properties to write three equivalent expressions.

35. $(a + b) + 2$ 36. $(3 + x) + y$ 37. $5 + (v + w)$
38. $6 + (x + y)$ 39. $(x \cdot y) \cdot 3$ 40. $(a \cdot b) \cdot 5$
41. $7 \cdot (a \cdot b)$ 42. $5 \cdot (x \cdot y)$ 43. $2 \cdot c \cdot d$

Try This

p. Ex. $4 \cdot (u \cdot t)$ or $u \cdot (4 \cdot t)$ or $t \cdot (4 \cdot u)$

q. Ex. $r + (5 + 2)$ or $(2 + 5) + r$ or $(r + 5) + 2$

Exercises

1. 400
2. 324
3. 80
4. 54
5. 11
6. 14
7. 81
8. 64
9. 9
10. 1
11. 1
12. 0
13. 4
14. 3
15. 125
16. 24
17. 76
18. 5
19. 925
20. 500
21. 66
22. 60
23. 343
24. 125
25. 60
26. 96
27. $\frac{4}{5}$
28. $\frac{11}{5}$
29. 1
30. 3
31. $a + (b + 3)$
32. $5 + (x + y)$
33. $(3 \cdot a) \cdot b$
34. $6 \cdot (x \cdot y)$

B

Use the commutative and associative properties to write two expressions equivalent to each expression.

44. $(4a + 2) + b$ **45.** $(7 \cdot m) \cdot n + 3$ **46.** $(5x^3 + 2) + 6$

47. $(6m)(np)$ **48.** $2(x + 3)y$ **49.** $5 + (3 + 7y) + 4$

Find a replacement for the variable for which the two expressions are *not* equivalent.

50. $3x^2; (3x)^2$ **51.** $(a + 2)^3; a^3 + 2^3$

52. $\frac{x + 2}{2}; x$ **53.** $\frac{y^6}{y^3}; y^2$

54. *Critical Thinking*   If it is true that $A + B = 25$ and $(A + C) + B = 85$, what is the value of $A + (C + B)$? of C?

Challenge

55. *Mathematical Reasoning*   Evaluate $a - (b - c)$ and $(a - b) - c$ for $a = 12, b = 7, c = 4$. Is there an associative property for subtraction?

56. *Mathematical Reasoning*   Evaluate $a \div (b \div c)$ and $(a \div b) \div c$ for $a = 32, b = 8$, and $c = 4$. Is there an associative property for division?

57. *Mathematical Reasoning*   Suppose we define a new operation @ on the set of whole numbers as follows: $a @ b = 2a + b$. For example, $4 @ 5 = 2(4) + 5 = 13$.
   a. Determine whether @ is commutative for whole numbers. That is, does $a @ b = b @ a$ for all whole numbers a and b?
   b. Determine whether @ is associative for whole numbers. That is, does $(a @ b) @ c = a @ (b @ c)$ for all whole numbers a, b, and c?

Mixed Review

Calculate.   **58.** $12\frac{1}{4} + 7\frac{3}{8}$ **59.** $3\frac{3}{5} + 5\frac{1}{2}$ **60.** $8\frac{1}{3} + 3\frac{3}{5}$

61. $3\frac{3}{4} - 2\frac{1}{3}$ **62.** $\frac{7}{8} \times \frac{2}{3}$ **63.** $1\frac{1}{5} \times 1\frac{1}{3}$ **64.** 3.75×0.3 *Pre-Course*

Simplify.   **65.** $\frac{6x}{7xy}$ **66.** $\frac{12t}{24t}$ **67.** $\frac{6mn}{11mt}$ **68.** $\frac{14n}{28ny}$ *1-2*

Evaluate.   **69.** $(3a^3)$ for $a = 5$ **70.** $4y^2$ for $y = 7$

71. $2w^3 - 9$ for $w = 2$ **72.** $4r + \frac{3t}{6}$ for $r = 4$ and $t = 8$

73. $3(m + 2n)$ for $m = 4$ and $n = 3$ **74.** $2a + 5b$ for $a = 2$ and $b = 6$

75. $\frac{3s + 7}{t}$ for $s = 1$ and $t = 5$ **76.** $\frac{x + x}{7}$ for $x = 7$

77. $\frac{w + 2z}{z}$ for $w = 6$ and $z = 3$ **78.** $\frac{6 + 3x}{6y}$ for $x = 4$ and $y = 1$ *1-3*

1-4   *The Associative Properties*   **23**

Math Point

Use Exercises 55 and 56 to reinforce the idea of "counterexample" (see p. 14, Exercise 40). Remind students that to be a "property," an assertion must be true for *all* possible examples. A single counterexample proves that the assertion is false.

Self-Test On the Web

Check your progress. Look for a self-test at the Prentice Hall Web site. www.phschool.com

51. Any number except 0 or −2
52. Any number except 2
53. Any number except 1. 0 is not acceptable.
54. 85, 60
55. 9; 1; No, 9 ≠ 1
56. 16; 1; No, 16 ≠ 1
57. a. No; 2 @ 3 = 7 and 3 @ 2 = 8
   b. No; (1 @ 2) @ 3 = (4 @ 3)
   = 11 and 1 @ (2 @ 3)
   = 1 @ 7 = 9

Mixed Review

58. $19\frac{5}{8}$
59. $9\frac{1}{10}$
60. $11\frac{14}{15}$
61. $1\frac{5}{12}$
62. $\frac{7}{12}$
63. $\frac{8}{5}$ or $1\frac{3}{5}$
64. 1.125
65. $\frac{6}{7y}$
66. $\frac{1}{2}$
67. $\frac{6n}{11t}$
68. $\frac{1}{2y}$
69. 375
70. 196
71. 7
72. 20
73. 30
74. 34
75. 2
76. 2
77. 4
78. 3

Exercises

35. $(2 + b) + a$
   $(2 + a) + b$
   $b + (a + 2)$
36. $(y + 3) + x$
   $3 + (y + x)$
   $x + (3 + y)$
37. $v + (w + 5)$
   $(5 + w) + v$
   $w + (5 + v)$
38. $x + (y + 6)$
   $y + (6 + x)$
   $(x + 6) + y$

39. $(y \cdot 3) \cdot x$
   $x \cdot (3 \cdot y)$
   $y \cdot (x \cdot 3)$
40. $(5 \cdot a) \cdot b$
   $b \cdot (a \cdot 5)$
   $a \cdot (5 \cdot b)$
41. $a \cdot (b \cdot 7)$
   $(a \cdot 7) \cdot b$
   $b \cdot (7 \cdot a)$
42. $(x \cdot 5) \cdot y$
   $(5 \cdot y) \cdot x$
   $y \cdot (5 \cdot x)$
43. $c \cdot (2 \cdot d)$
   $d \cdot (c \cdot 2)$
   $2 \cdot (d \cdot c)$

44. $(a \cdot 4 + b) + 2$
   $(b + 4a) + 2$
45. $7 \cdot (n \cdot m) + 3$
   $3 + m \cdot (7 \cdot n)$
46. $(2 + 6) + 5x^3$
   $2 + (5x^3 + 6)$
47. $6(mp)n$
   $m(6n)p$
48. $(x + 3)2y$
   $(x + 3)y \cdot 2$
49. $(3 + 5) + 7y + 4$
   $5 + 3 + (4 + 7y)$
Answers may vary.
50. Any number except 0

1-4   *The Associative Properties*   **23**

1-5

 TIME-FOCUS METER

1. FOCUS

FIRST FIVE MINUTES

Calculate.

1. $3 \cdot (2 + 6)$
   $3 \cdot 8 = 24$
2. $3 \cdot 2 + 3 \cdot 6$
   $6 + 18 = 24$
3. $2 \cdot (1 + 2 + 3)$
   $2 \cdot 6 = 12$
4. $2 \cdot 1 + 2 \cdot 2 + 2 \cdot 3$
   $2 + 4 + 6 = 12$
5. $5 \cdot (6 + 8) - (5 \cdot 6 + 5 \cdot 8)$
   $5 \cdot 14 - (30 + 40)$
   $= 70 - 70 = 0$

Introducing the Concept:
The Distributive Property

Have students calculate the perimeter of a rectangle that is 8 in. long and 5 in. wide using both formulas. Then have them calculate the perimeter of several different rectangles using both formulas. They should quickly see that the formulas give the same result.

2. TEACH the Mathematics

1 Using the Distributive Property

In Example 2, remind students that the commutative property tells us that $s \cdot 6 = 6 \cdot s$. Tell them it is usual notation to write $6s$.

Avoiding Common Errors

Students will often write $3 \cdot x + y$ for the expression $3 \cdot (x + y)$. Remind students that in the first expression only the x is multiplied by 3, and in the second expression both the x and the y are multiplied by 3.

Key Questions

Use two methods to evaluate each expression.

- $3(7 + 4)$
  $3(11) = 33$
  $21 + 12 = 33$
- $6(8 + 3)$
  $6(11) = 66$
  $48 + 18 = 66$

What You'll Learn

1 To use the distributive property to write equivalent expressions

2 To use the distributive property to factor expressions

3 To use the distributive property to collect like terms

...And Why

To simplify expressions by collecting like terms

 CA 1.0, 4.0, 10.0: Use arithmetic properties of numbers. Simplify expressions. Add monomials (by collecting like terms).

1-5 ▷ The Distributive Property of Multiplication Over Addition

Introducing the Concept:
The Distributive Property

Formulas for the perimeter of a rectangle are used often by surveyors in designing land plots. One surveyor used Formula A; another used Formula B. Do both formulas give the same number for the perimeter?

Formula A: $P = 2l + 2w$
$P = (2 \cdot 8) + (2 \cdot 5)$

Formula B: $P = 2(l + w)$
$P = 2 \cdot (8 + 5)$

 PART 1 Using the Distributive Property

Objective: Use the distributive property to write equivalent expressions.

The activity above shows that expressions like $2 \cdot (8 + 5)$ and $(2 \cdot 8) + (2 \cdot 5)$ are equivalent. The **distributive property of multiplication over addition** states that this will always be true.

The Distributive Property of Multiplication Over Addition
For any numbers a, b, and c, $a(b + c) = ab + ac$. For any numbers a, b, and c, $(b + c)a = ba + ca$.

We can omit the parentheses in expressions like $(4 \cdot 5) + (3 \cdot 7)$ and just write $4 \cdot 5 + 3 \cdot 7$, since this will not change the order of the operations. If we omit the parentheses in expressions like $2(3 + 5)$, however, we will no longer have equivalent expressions.

$$2(3 + 5) = 2(8) = 16 \qquad 2 \cdot 3 + 5 = 6 + 5 = 11$$

The distributive property must be used to remove the parentheses.

$$2(3 + 5) = 2 \cdot 3 + 2 \cdot 5 = 6 + 10 = 16$$

24 Chapter 1 *Introduction to Algebra*

The following diagram illustrates the distributive property.

2(3 + 5)   2 × 3   2 × 5

EXAMPLES Use the distributive property to write an equivalent expression.

1 $3(x + 2) = 3x + 3 \cdot 2 = 3x + 6$

2 $(s + t + w)6 = s(6) + t(6) + w(6)$
$= 6s + 6t + 6w$ Using the commutative property

3 $4(2s + 5) = 4(2s) + 4(5)$
$= 8s + 20$

Try This Use the distributive property to write an equivalent expression.

a. $4(x + y + z)$ **b.** $(y + 3)5$
c. $(8a + 3)2$ **d.** $6(x + 2y + 5)$

PART 2 Factoring

Objective: Factor expressions.

If the statement of the distributive property is reversed, we have the basis of a process called factoring: $ab + ac = a(b + c)$. To factor an expression, write an equivalent expression as a product of the factors.

EXAMPLES Factor.

4 $3x + 3y = 3(x + y)$ Look for a common factor. Then use the distributive property.

5 $5x + 5y + 5z = 5(x + y + z)$ The common factor is 5.

6 $7y + 14 + 21z = 7 \cdot y + 7 \cdot 2 + 7 \cdot 3z$ The common factor is 7.
$= 7(y + 2 + 3z)$

7 $9x + 27y + 9 = 9 \cdot x + 9 \cdot 3y + 9 \cdot 1$ The common factor is 9.
$= 9(x + 3y + 1)$

Try This Factor.

e. $5x + 10$ **f.** $12 + 3x$
g. $6x + 12 + 9y$ **h.** $5x + 10y + 5$

1-5 *The Distributive Property of Multiplication Over Addition* **25**

Chalkboard Examples
Use the distributive property to write an equivalent expression.
1. $6(x + y)$
   $6 \cdot x + 6 \cdot y = 6x + 6y$
2. $a(3 + b)$
   $a \cdot 3 + a \cdot b$
3. $2(x + y + z)$
   $2x + 2y + 2z$
4. $(u + v) \cdot 3$
   $u \cdot 3 + v \cdot 3$ or $3u + 3v$
5. $4(2x + 1)$
   $4 \cdot 2x + 4 \cdot 1 = 8x + 4$

2 Factoring

Using the distributive property to rewrite the expression
$3(x + y)$ as $3x + 3y$
can be described as "multiplying through by 3." Using the distributive property to rewrite the expression
$3x + 3y$ as $3(x + y)$
is described as "factoring out the 3."

You can also demonstrate visually how factoring relates to the distributive property.

3x   +   3y   =   3(x + y)

Remind students that the first step in factoring is to factor out the *greatest* common factor.

Key Questions
Find the common factor.
■ $9x + 9$
   9
■ $9x + 27$
   9

Chalkboard Examples
1. $3a + 3b$
   $3(a + b)$
2. $6x + 12y$
   $6(x + 2y)$

Try This
a. $4x + 4y + 4z$
b. $5y + 15$
c. $16a + 6$
d. $6x + 12y + 30$
e. $5(x + 2)$
f. $3(4 + x)$
g. $3(2x + 4 + 3y)$
h. $5(x + 2y + 1)$

EXAMPLE 8   Factor and check by multiplying.

$$5x + 10 = 5(x + 2) \qquad \text{Check: } 5(x + 2) = 5x + 5 \cdot 2$$
$$= 5x + 10$$

Try This   Factor and check by multiplying.

i. $9x + 3y$ **j.** $5 + 10x + 15y$

PART
3   Collecting Like Terms

Objective: Collect like terms.

In an expression like $6s + 6t + 6w$, $6s$, $6t$, and $6w$ are called **terms.**

Terms such as $5x$ and $4x$, whose variable factors are exactly the same, are called **like terms.** Similarly, $3y^2$ and $9y^2$ are like terms. Terms such as $4y$ and $5y^2$ are not like terms. We often simplify expressions using the distributive property to collect like terms.

EXAMPLES   Collect like terms.

9 $3x + 4x = (3 + 4)x$ Using the distributive property
$$= 7x$$

10 $x + x = 1 \cdot x + 1 \cdot x$ Using the identity property
$$= (1 + 1)x \qquad \text{Using the distributive property}$$
$$= 2x$$

11 $2x + 3y + 5x + 2y = 2x + 5x + 3y + 2y$ Using the commutative property
$$= (2 + 5)x + (3 + 2)y \qquad \text{Using the distributive property}$$
$$= 7x + 5y$$

12 $5x^2 + x^2 = 5x^2 + 1 \cdot x^2$ Using the identity property
$$= (5 + 1)x^2 \qquad \text{Using the distributive property}$$
$$= 6x^2$$

Try This   Collect like terms.

k. $6y + 2y$ **l.** $7x + 3y + 5y + 4x$
m. $10p + 8q + 4p + 5q$ **n.** $7x^2 + x^2$

---

3 Collecting Like Terms

Emphasize that there is no number property that allows the addition or subtraction of unlike terms such as x and x^2, or $3y^3$ and $2y^2$.

Key Questions

How many terms are in the following expressions?
- $2x + y$
  Two
- $2xy$
  One
- $x - \frac{1}{4}$
  Two

Chalkboard Examples

Use the distributive property to collect like terms.

1. $y + y$
   $1y + 1y = (1 + 1)y = 2y$
2. $2 \cdot a + 3 \cdot a$
   $(2 + 3) \cdot a = 5a$
3. $3c + 2c$
   $(3 + 2)c = 5c$
4. $4x + 6y + 3x + 1y$
   $4x + 3x + 6y + 1y$
   $(4 + 3)x + (6 + 1)y$
   $7x + 7y$
5. $7a^2 + 3a^2$
   $(7 + 3)a^2 = 10a^2$

Collect like terms mentally and write only the answer.

6. $3x + x + 4x$ $8x$
7. $2u + 4u + 5u$ $11u$
8. $5y^2 + 7y^2 + y^2$ $13y^2$

3. PRACTICE/ASSESS

LESSON QUIZ

Use the distributive property to write an equivalent expression.

1. $7(x + y)$
   $7x + 7y$
2. $3(2u + 5v)$
   $6u + 15v$

Factor.

3. $6r + 6s$
   $6(r + s)$ or $(r + s) \cdot 6$
4. $2p + 6q$
   $2(p + 3q)$
5. $8a + 6b + 2c$
   $2(4a + 3b + c)$

Mentally collect like terms.

6. $8d + 2d$
   $10d$
7. $2e^2 + 5e^2$
   $7e^2$
8. $2u^2 + t + u^2 + t^2$
   $3u^2 + t^2 + t$

Try This

i. $3(3x + y)$
j. $5(1 + 2x + 3y)$
k. $8y$
l. $11x + 8y$
m. $14p + 13q$
n. $8x^2$

A

Use the distributive property to write an equivalent expression.

1. $2(b + 5)$ **2.** $4(x + 3)$ **3.** $(1 + t)7$

4. $6(v + 4)$ **5.** $3(x + 1)$ **6.** $(x + 8)7$

7. $4(1 + y)$ **8.** $9(s + 1)$ **9.** $6(5x + 2)$

10. $9(6m + 7)$ **11.** $7(x + 4 + 6y)$ **12.** $(5x + 8 + 3p)4$

Factor.

13. $2x + 4$ **14.** $5y + 20$ **15.** $30 + 5y$

16. $7x + 28$ **17.** $14x + 21y$ **18.** $18a + 24b$

19. $5x + 10 + 15y$ **20.** $9a + 27b + 81$ **21.** $14c + 63d + 7$

22. $4y + 10 + 8x$ **23.** $9r + 27s + 18$ **24.** $24x + 72y + 8$

Factor and check by multiplying.

25. $9x + 27$ **26.** $6x + 24$

27. $9x + 3y$ **28.** $15x + 5y$

29. $8a + 16b + 64$ **30.** $5 + 20x + 35y$

31. $11x + 44y + 121$ **32.** $7 + 14b + 56w$

33. $5x + 10y + 45z$ **34.** $9p + 3q + 27r$

Collect like terms.

35. $9a + 10a$ **36.** $12x + 2x$

37. $10a + a$ **38.** $16x + x$

39. $2x + 9z + 6x$ **40.** $3a + 5b + 7a$

41. $7x + 6y^2 + 9y^2$ **42.** $12m^2 + 6q + 9m^2$

43. $41a + 90 + 60a + 2$ **44.** $42x + 6 + 4x + 2$

45. $8a + 8b + 3a + 3b$ **46.** $100y + 200z + 190y + 400z$

47. $8u^2 + 3t + 10t + 6u^2 + 2$ **48.** $5 + 6h + t + 8 + 9h$

49. $23 + 5t + 7y + t + y + 27$ **50.** $45 + 90d + 87 + 9d + 3 + 7d$

51. $\frac{1}{2}b + \frac{1}{2}b$ **52.** $\frac{2}{3}x + \frac{1}{3}x$

53. $2y + \frac{1}{4}y + y$ **54.** $\frac{1}{2}a + a + 5a$

Simplify each expression. Collect like terms as needed.

55. $4x + 5y + 6x$ **56.** $6z + 3k + 9z$

57. $4p^2 + 2p + 4p + 8p^2$ **58.** $2m + 3mn + 2m + mn$

59. $7xy + 3y + 6x + 2xy$ **60.** $6tp + 3t^2 + 9t^2 + 2tp$

Extra Help On the Web

Look for worked-out examples at the Prentice Hall Web site.
www.phschool.com

Practice Multiple Choice

Choose the best answer.

1. Which property is shown by this equation?
$5 \cdot (3 \cdot 4) = (5 \cdot 3) \cdot 4$

A Commutative property of multiplication

B Associative property of multiplication

C Commutative property of addition

D Associative property of addition

2. Simplify the expression $3(2x + 7) + 7(5x + 2)$.

F $17x + 24$

G $41x + 35$

H $41x + 9$

J $76x$

1. B; Algebra 1.0
2. G; Algebra 1.0

Exercises

1. $2b + 10$
2. $4x + 12$
3. $7 + 7t$
4. $6v + 24$
5. $3x + 3$
6. $7x + 56$
7. $4 + 4y$
8. $9s + 9$
9. $30x + 12$
10. $54m + 63$
11. $7x + 28 + 42y$
12. $20x + 32 + 12p$
13. $2(x + 2)$

14. $5(y + 4)$
15. $5(6 + y)$
16. $7(x + 4)$
17. $7(2x + 3y)$
18. $6(3a + 4b)$
19. $5(x + 2 + 3y)$
20. $9(a + 3b + 9)$
21. $7(2c + 9d + 1)$
22. $2(2y + 5 + 4x)$
23. $9(r + 3s + 2)$
24. $8(3x + 9y + 1)$
25. $9(x + 3)$
26. $6(x + 4)$
27. $3(3x + y)$

28. $5(3x + y)$
29. $8(a + 2b + 8)$
30. $5(1 + 4x + 7y)$
31. $11(x + 4y + 11)$
32. $7(1 + 2b + 8w)$
33. $5(x + 2y + 9z)$
34. $3(3p + q + 9r)$
35. $19a$
36. $14x$
37. $11a$
38. $17x$
39. $8x + 9z$
40. $10a + 5b$
41. $7x + 15y^2$

42. $21m^2 + 6q$
43. $101a + 92$
44. $46x + 8$
45. $11a + 11b$
46. $290y + 600z$
47. $14u^2 + 13t + 2$
48. $13 + 15h + t$
49. $50 + 6t + 8y$
50. $135 + 106d$
51. $1b$ or b
52. $1x$ or x
53. $\frac{13}{4}y$ or $3\frac{1}{4}y$
54. $\frac{13}{2}a$ or $6\frac{1}{2}a$
55. $10x + 5y$
56. $15z + 3k$
57. $12p^2 + 6p$
58. $4mn + 4m$
59. $9xy + 6x + 3y$
60. $8pt + 12t^2$

B

Simplify each expression.

61. $4(x + 3) + 5(x + 3)$ **62.** $7(m^2 + 2) + 7(m^2 + 2)$

63. $8(a + b) + 4(a + 2b)$ **64.** $4(5x + 6y + 3) + 2(x + 2y)$

65. a. The money you deposit in a bank is called the principal. When you deposit money in a bank and earn interest, the new principal is given by the expression $P + Prt$, where P is the principal, r is the rate of interest, and t is the time. Factor the expression $P + Prt$.
    b. If \$400 is invested at 3% interest, find the new principal at the end of one year by substituting $P = 400$, $r = 0.03$, and $t = 1$ in the expression in part (a).

66. a. Factor $17x + 34$. Then evaluate both expressions when $x = 10$.
    b. Do you get the same answer for both expressions? Why?

67. *Critical Thinking*   Does $(x + y)^2 = x^2 + y^2$ for all whole numbers? When are the expressions equal? Explain.

68. *Critical Thinking*   You know that $a(b + c) = ab + ac$ for any numbers $a, b,$ and c. Use this fact and the properties introduced earlier to write a paragraph explaining why $(b + c)a = ba + ca$ is also true for any numbers $a, b,$ and c.

69. *Mathematical Reasoning*   A student factored $ax + ay + bx + by$ as $a(x + y) + b(x + y)$. Another student factored the same expression as $x(a + b) + y(a + b)$. Are both answers correct, or is one of them incorrect? Justify your answer.

Challenge

70. Find a simpler expression equivalent to $\dfrac{3a + 6}{2a + 4}$.

71. Find a simpler expression equivalent to $\dfrac{4x + 12y}{3x + 9y}$.

Collect like terms, if possible, and factor the result.

72. $x + 2x^2 + 3x^3 + 4x^2 + 5x$

73. $q + qr + qrs + qrst$

74. $21x + 44xy + 15y - 16x - 8y - 38xy + 2x + xy$

75. Simplify $a\{1 + b[1 + c(1 + d)]\}$. (Hint: Begin with $c(1 + d)$ and work outwards.)

Mixed Review

Calculate.   **76.** $(4 \cdot 3)^2$ **77.** $6 \cdot 2^3$ **78.** $(3 - 2)^3$ **79.** $8 - 2^3$ *1-4*

Simplify.   **80.** $\dfrac{8xy}{2x}$ **81.** $\dfrac{6b}{18ab}$ **82.** $\dfrac{15c}{30c}$ **83.** $\dfrac{24xy}{3y}$ *1-2*

Evaluate.   **84.** $6(t + 4)$ for $t = 2$ **85.** $w(5 + w)$ for $w = 3$

86. k^1 for $k = 5$ **87.** $(x + 3) \cdot (5 - x)$ for $x = 2$ *1-1*

Exercises

61. $9x + 27$

62. $14m^2 + 28$

63. $12a + 16b$

64. $22x + 28y + 12$

65. a. $P(1 + rt)$
   b. \$412

66. a. $17(x + 2)$;
   $17(10 + 2) = 17(12) = 204$;
   $17(10) + 34 = 170 + 34 = 204$
   b. Yes; distributive property

67. No; when either x or y is 0.

68. $(b + c)a = a(b + c)$ by the commutative property of multiplication;

$a(b + c) = ab + ac$ by the distributive property;
$ab + ac = ba + ca$ by the commutative property of multiplication. Thus,
$(b + c)a = ba + ca$.

69. Both answers are correct.
$ax + ay + bx + by =$
$a(x + y) + b(x + y)$ and
$ax + ay + bx + by =$
$ax + bx + ay + by =$
$xa + xb + ya + yb =$
$x(a + b) + y(a + b)$.

70. $\dfrac{3}{2}$

71. $\dfrac{4}{3}$

72. $6x + 6x^2 + 3x^3 =$
   $3x(2 + 2x + x^2)$

73. $q(1 + r + rs + rst)$

74. $7x + 7xy + 7y = 7(x + xy + y)$

75. $a + ab + abc + abcd$

Mixed Review

76. 144

77. 48

78. 1

79. 0

80. $4y$

81. $\dfrac{1}{3a}$

82. $\dfrac{1}{2}$

83. $8x$

84. 36

85. 24

86. 5

87. 15

Writing Expressions

1-6

Objective: Write algebraic expressions involving one operation.

Many problems can be solved by translating data given with words into algebraic expressions. To do this, you must know which phrases suggest each of the operations (addition, subtraction, multiplication, and division).

EXAMPLES   Write as an algebraic expression.

1   5 more than a number

$n + 5$ Think of a specific number, say 3. "5 more than 3" would be 3 + 5, so "5 more than a number" would be $n + 5$.

2   3 less than a number

$n - 3$ Think of a specific number, say 5. "3 less than 5" would be 5 − 3, so "3 less than a number" would be $n - 3$.

3   3 times a number

$3n$ Think of a specific number, say 6. "3 times 6" would be 3 · 6, so "3 times a number" would be $3n$.

4   a number divided by 5

$\frac{n}{5}$ Think of a specific number, say 20. "20 divided by 5" would be $\frac{20}{5}$, so "a number divided by 5" would be $\frac{n}{5}$.

Try This   Write as an algebraic expression.

a. the sum of a number and 7   **b.** the product of a number and 4
c. 4 less than y **d.** 6 fewer than x
e. the difference of m and n **f.** twice y
g. a less than b **h.** 7 times a number

EXAMPLES

5   Let L be the amount of money Lila earned. Glenn earned twice as much as Lila. Write an expression for the amount Glenn earned.

$2L$ "Twice as much" suggests multiplying by 2.

6   Let h be the number of hits John had in a baseball game. John had 2 more walks than hits. Write an expression for the number of walks.

$h + 2$ "2 more walks than hits" suggests adding 2 to the number of hits.

1-6   *Writing Expressions*   **29**

Try This
   a. $n + 7$
   b. $4n$
   c. $y - 4$
   d. $x - 6$
   e. $m - n$
   f. $2y$
   g. $b - a$
   h. $7n$

CA: Building toward 5.0

1-6   TIME-FOCUS METER

1. FOCUS

FIRST FIVE MINUTES

Use the distributive property to write an equivalent expression.
   1. $5(x + y)$
      $5x + 5y$
   2. $a(b + c)$
      $ab + ac$
   3. $3(2u + v)$
      $6u + 3v$
Factor.
   4. $7a + 7b$
      $7(a + b)$
   5. $14c + 21d$
      $7(2c + 3d)$
   6. $ax + ay + az$
      $a(x + y + z)$

2. TEACH the Mathematics

Use the punch-outs of Teaching Transparency T7 to illustrate algebraic expressions.

   The first and most important task of problem solving is to identify and name the numeric quantities in the problem so that statements can be made about them. Encourage students to use any single letter that reminds them of the quantity. For example, n is a good variable name for an unknown number, h is good for the height of a tree, and t for temperature.

Avoiding Common Errors

Students often translate expressions involving subtraction in the wrong order. Since subtraction is not commutative, the order is important.

   Point out that statements such as "the difference of 5 and n" are translated in the order in which they are stated: $5 - n$. Statements that use the word "than," such as "less than" and "fewer than," are translated in reverse order. The algebraic expression for "5 less than n" is $n - 5$.

Key Question

■ Write an algebraic expression for "5 more than n." $5 + n$ or $n + 5$
Why can we write this expression both ways? Since addition is commutative, $5 + n$ and $n + 5$ are equivalent.

Chalkboard Examples

Write as an algebraic expression.

1. the sum of x and 2
   x + 2
2. the sum of a number and 3
   n + 3
   Other variables could be used instead of n.
3. six more than a number
   n + 6
4. nine less than a number
   n − 9
5. twice a number
   2n
6. half of a number
   $\frac{1}{2}n$ or $\frac{n}{2}$
7. the product of u and v
   uv
8. Let d be the number of dimes. There are 7 fewer nickels than dimes. Write an expression for the number of nickels.
   d − 7
9. Let w be the width of the table. The length is three times the width. Write an expression for the length.
   3w

3. PRACTICE/ASSESS

LESSON QUIZ

Write as an algebraic expression.

1. five more than x
   x + 5
2. seven less than a number
   n − 7
3. five times a number
   5n
4. a number divided by 2
   $\frac{n}{2}$
5. Let m be the number of miles Malia ran. Laurel ran 3 miles further than Malia. Write an expression for the distance Laurel ran.
   m + 3

Assignment Guide

▼ Core 1–51
   Extension 52–63

Use Mixed Review to maintain skills.

Try This

i. Let *a* be the amount of money Barbara has. Barbara divides her money among 7 people. Write an expression for the amount each person receives.

j. Let *c* be the number of coins. Ilene has 24 fewer stamps than coins. Write an expression for the number of stamps she has.

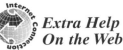

Extra Help On the Web

Look for worked-out examples at the Prentice Hall Web site.
www.phschool.com

1-6 Exercises

A

Write as an algebraic expression.

1. 6 more than *b*	**2.** 8 more than *t*
3. 9 less than *c*	**4.** 4 less than *d*
5. 6 greater than *q*	**6.** 11 greater than *z*
7. *b* more than *a*	**8.** *c* more than *d*
9. *x* less than *y*	**10.** *c* less than *h*
11. *x* added to *w*	**12.** *s* added to *t*
13. *m* subtracted from *n*	**14.** *p* subtracted from *q*
15. the sum of *r* and *s*	**16.** the sum of *d* and *f*
17. twice *x*	**18.** three times *p*
19. 5 multiplied by *t*	**20.** 9 multiplied by *d*
21. the product of 3 and *b*	**22.** *x* divided among 5
23. double *h*	**24.** half of *x*
25. *y* fewer than *x*	**26.** *n* more than 6
27. 5 less than *m*	**28.** *q* less than *p*

29. Let *a* be Connie's age. Robin is 5 years older than Connie. Write an expression for Robin's age.

30. Let *p* be the number of points the Tigers scored. The Lions scored double the number of points the Tigers scored. Write an expression for the number of points the Lions scored.

31. Let *m* be the amount of money Bob had before he went shopping. Bob spent $4.50 while shopping. Write an expression for the amount Bob had left after shopping.

32. Let *t* be the total amount Rosalie spent for blouses. Each of the 5 blouses cost the same. Write an expression for the cost of each blouse.

33. Let *a* be the amount Greg earned last week. Greg earned $45 more this week than last week. Write an expression for the amount he earned this week.

Try This

i. $\frac{a}{7}$

j. c − 24

Exercises

1. b + 6
2. t + 8
3. c − 9
4. d − 4
5. q + 6
6. z + 11
7. a + b
8. d + c
9. y − x
10. h − c
11. w + x
12. t + s
13. n − m
14. q − p
15. r + s
16. d + f
17. 2x
18. 3p
19. 5t
20. 9d
21. 3b
22. $\frac{x}{5}$
23. 2h
24. $\frac{x}{2}$
25. x − y
26. n + 6
27. m − 5
28. p − q
29. a + 5
30. 2p
31. m − $4.50
32. $\frac{t}{5}$
33. a + $45

34. Let n be the number of magazines Scotty sold. Sherry sold half as many magazines as Scotty. Write an expression for the number of magazines that Sherry sold.

35. Let w be Tom's weight last week. Tom lost 2 pounds this week. Write an expression for Tom's weight this week.

36. Let a be the amount Gil has left after buying a record. The record cost $8. Write an expression for the amount he had before buying the record.

37. Let K be the amount Kelly earns. Geri earns three times as much as Kelly. Write an expression for the amount Geri earns.

38. Let w be the width of a racing-eight crew shell. A racing-eight shell is 32 times as long as it is wide. Write an expression for the length of a racing-eight crew shell.

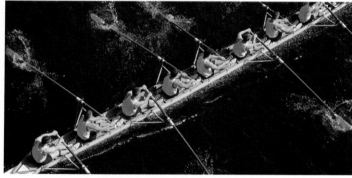

39. Let t be the total amount of money collected. The total amount was divided evenly among 4 charities. Write an expression for the amount received by each charity.

40. Let d be the distance Paul ran. Steve ran a third as far as Paul. Write an expression for the distance Steve ran.

A racing-eight shell is 32 times as long as it is wide. How long is a 22 in.-wide shell? (See Exercise 38.)

41. Let R be Randy's age 3 years from now. Write an expression for Randy's age now.

B

Write as an algebraic expression.

42. a number x increased by three times y

43. a number y increased by twice x

44. a number a increased by 2 more than b

45. a number that is 3 less than twice x

46. a number x increased by itself

47. the area of a rectangle with length l and width w

48. the perimeter of a square with side s

Evaluate.

49. $\frac{256y}{32x}$ for $y = 1$ and $x = 4$

50. $\frac{y + x}{2} + \frac{3 \cdot y}{x}$ for $x = 2$ and $y = 4$

51. $\frac{a + b}{4} + \frac{a \cdot b}{2}$ for $a = 3$ and $b = 4$

Exercises

34. $\frac{n}{2}$

35. $w - 2$

36. $a + \$8$

37. $3K$

38. $32w$

Photo caption: 58 ft 8 in.

39. $\frac{1}{4}t$ or $\frac{t}{4}$

40. $\frac{1}{3}d$ or $\frac{d}{3}$

41. $R - 3$

42. $x + 3y$

43. $y + 2x$

44. $a + (b + 2)$

45. $2x - 3$

46. $x + x$ or $2x$

47. lw

48. $4s$

49. 2

50. 9

51. $\frac{31}{4}$

Evaluate $\frac{x + y}{4}$ when

52. $y = 2$ and x is 14. **53.** $x = 9$ and y is three times x.

54. $y = 8$ and x is twice y. **55.** $x = 64$ and y is half of x.

56. *Critical Thinking* Describe a real-world situation that could be translated to the expression $25a + 10b$.

57. *Multi-Step Problem* Let x be the number of students in the art club.

   a. All but 6 students in the club went on a field trip. Write an expression for the number of students on the field trip.

   b. When the students got to the museum, they were divided into three groups of equal size. Write an expression for the number of students in each group.

   c. Four students from another school joined the group that Ed was in. Write an expression for the number of students in Ed's group.

   d. Before lunch, some students (not including Ed) left Ed's group to go to a special exhibit. The number of students that left was equal to one-ninth of the number of students in the art club. Write an expression for the number of students that remained in Ed's group.

   e. There are 27 students in the art club. How many students were in Ed's group at lunchtime?

58. *Critical Thinking* Let n be a whole number. Tell whether each expression always represents an odd number. Justify your answers.

   a. $2(n + 1)$ **b.** $2n + 1$ **c.** $10n - 1$ **d.** $11n$

Challenge

59. Let $w + 3$ represent a whole number. Give an expression for the next whole number after it.

60. Let $d + 2$ represent an odd whole number. Give an expression for the preceding odd number.

61. The difference between two numbers is 3. One number is t. What are two possible values for the other number?

62. Two numbers are $v + 2$ and $v - 2$. What is their sum?

63. Two numbers are $2 + w$ and $2 - w$. What is their sum?

Mixed Review

Evaluate. **64.** $4c^2$ for $c = 6$ **65.** $3t^4$ for $t = 2$ **66.** $(4x)^2$ for $x = 3$ *1-3*

Factor. **67.** $3x + 6$ **68.** $20a + 30b$ **69.** $8 + 16x + 40y$ *1-5*

Collect like terms. **70.** $14c + 8c$ **71.** $4a + 7b + 8a$ **72.** $\frac{1}{3}c + \frac{2}{3}c$

73. $3y + 7y + y$ **74.** $\frac{1}{4}d + \frac{3}{4}d$ **75.** $5 + 7c + 4$ *1-5*

32 Chapter 1 *Introduction to Algebra*

Exercises

52. 4
53. 9
54. 6
55. 24
56. Answers may vary. Sample: The total cost in cents of a items at 25¢ each and b items at 10¢ each.

57. a. $x - 6$
   b. $\frac{x - 6}{3}$
   c. $\frac{x - 6}{3} + 4$
   d. $\frac{x - 6}{3} + 4 - \frac{x}{9}$
   e. 8 students

58. a. No; let $n = 9$; $2(9 + 1) = 20$
   b. Yes; $2n$ is always even because it has a factor of 2, so $2n + 1$ is always odd.
   c. Yes; $10n$ is always even, so $10n - 1$ is always odd.
   d. No; let $n = 10$; $11(10) = 110$

59. $w + 4$
60. d
61. $t + 3$, $t - 3$
62. $2v$
63. 4

Mixed Review

64. 144
65. 48
66. 144
67. $3(x + 2)$
68. $10(2a + 3b)$
69. $8(1 + 2x + 5y)$
70. $22c$
71. $12a + 7b$
72. c
73. $11y$
74. d
75. $9 + 7c$

Solving Equations: An Introduction

  **1-7**

Introducing the Concept: Equations

A block and two marbles balance six marbles on a scale. The marbles each weigh one ounce. How much does the block weigh?

Which of the following scales balance?

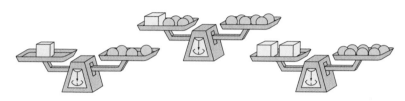

Much of your work in algebra will involve solving equations. In this lesson we introduce solving simple equations. An **equation** is a mathematical sentence that uses an equal sign to state that two expressions represent the same number or are equivalent. Here are some examples.

$$3 + 2 = 5 \qquad 7 - 2 = 4 \qquad x + 15 = 12$$

 PART 1 True, False, and Open Equations

Objective: Determine whether an equation is true, false, or open.

An equation that contains only numbers may be either true or false. For example, $3 + 2 = 5$ is true, but $7 - 2 = 4$ is false. An equation containing a variable may be neither true nor false. For example, $x + 5 = 12$ is neither true nor false because you do not know the value of the variable. An equation that contains at least one variable is called an **open sentence.**

EXAMPLES State whether each sentence is true, false, or open.

1 $18 + 32 = 50$ True

2 $42 - 15 = 25$ False

3 $12 = 4 + x$ Open

 1–7 *Solving Equations: An Introduction* **33**

Introducing the Concept: Equations

4 oz
No
Yes
Yes

What You'll Learn

1 To determine whether an equation is true, false, or open

2 To find solution sets of an equation

3 To recognize equivalent equations

. . . And Why

To prepare for solving equations algebraically

1-7 TIME-FOCUS METER

1. FOCUS

FIRST FIVE MINUTES

Write as an algebraic expression.
1. three more than z
   $z + 3$
2. twice as big as w
   $2w$
3. seven fewer than x
   $x - 7$
4. Let s be the distance from Los Angeles to New York. The distance to Omaha is half of the distance from Los Angeles to New York. Write an expression for the distance to Omaha.
   $\frac{s}{2}$
5. half the sum of a and b
   $\frac{a + b}{2}$

Introducing the Concept: Equations

Use Teaching Transparency T8 for a balance scale.

Remind students of some facts about scales. In order to balance, each side must have the same weight. If you add or remove the same amount of weight from each side of a balanced scale, the scale will remain balanced. By removing 2 marbles from each side of the first scale, students should be able to determine that a block has the same weight as 4 marbles, or 4 ounces. They should then be able to add weights to each side to determine which of the other three scales balance.

2. TEACH the Mathematics

1 **True, False, and Open Equations**

Emphasize that when an equation contains a variable, you may be unable to tell whether the equation is true or false.

> **Math Point**
>
> An equation that contains only numbers cannot be open; it must be true or false. An equation that contains a variable can be true, false **or** open. For example, $x = x$ is true, $x = x + 5$ is false, and $x = 14$ is open.

Try This   State whether each sentence is true, false, or open.

a. $3 \cdot 5 + 2 = 13$ **b.** $4 \cdot 2 - 3 = 5$ **c.** $y + 5 = 6$

PART 2   Equations and Solutions

Objective: Find solution sets of an equation.

The set of numbers from which you can select replacements for the variable is called the **replacement set.** A replacement for a variable that makes an equation true is called a **solution.** To **solve** an equation means to find all of its solutions. The collection of all the solutions is called the **solution set.**

When the replacement set contains a small number of elements, one way to solve the equation is to substitute each element in the set to see if it makes a true sentence.

EXAMPLE 4

Solve $2x = x + 3$ for the replacement set $\{0, 1, 2, 3\}$.

$$2x = x + 3$$

Replace the variable with each number in the replacement set.

$2(0) = 0 + 3$
$0 = 3$ False

$2(1) = 1 + 3$
$2 = 4$ False

$2(2) = 2 + 3$
$4 = 5$ False

$2(3) = 3 + 3$
$6 = 6$ True

The solution to the equation is 3. The solution set is $\{3\}$.

Try This

d. Solve $x^2 + 3 = 12$ for $\{0, 3, 9\}$.

e. Solve $\frac{12}{x} = 3x$ for $\{2, 4, 12\}$.

If the replacement set is large, trying numbers is not a good method for solving an equation. If an equation contains small numbers and one operation, the equation can often be solved mentally.

Try This
a. False
b. True
c. Open
d. $\{3\}$
e. $\{2\}$

EXAMPLES Solve mentally. The replacement set is all whole numbers.

5 $x + 6 = 13$
$\qquad x = 7$ Think: What number added to 6 gives 13?

6 $4y = 32$
$\qquad y = 8$ Think: What number multiplied by 4 gives 32?

Try This   Solve mentally. The replacement set is all whole numbers.

f. $x + 4 = 10$ **g.** $\frac{y}{6} = 4$

h. $14 = y + 9$ **i.** $x - 5 = 12$

PART 3 Equivalent Equations

Objective: Recognize equivalent equations.

Two equations are **equivalent** if one can be obtained from the other by a sequence of the folowing steps:

You can
add the same number to both sides of an equation,
subtract the same number from both sides of an equation,
multiply both sides of an equation by the same nonzero number, or
divide both sides of an equation by the same nonzero number.
Equivalent equations have the same solution set.

Equivalent Equations		*Nonequivalent Equations*	
	Solution Set		Solution Set
$x + 4 = 10$	{6}	$x + 8 = 10$	{2}
$x + 6 = 12$	{6}	$x + 8 = 14$	{6}

An equation is like a balanced scale. If you add the same weight to both sides of the scale, it will remain balanced. Likewise, if you add the same quantity to both sides of an equation, the equations will be equivalent.

$x + 4 = 10$
$x + 4 + 2 = 10 + 2$ Adding 2 to both sides
$x + 6 = 12$

The equation $x + 4 = 10$ is equivalent to the equation $x + 6 = 12$.

EXAMPLE 7   Each pair of equations is equivalent. What was done to the first equation to get the second one?

$x + 2 = 5$
$x + 5 = 8$ $x + 2 + 3 = 5 + 3$

Three was added to both sides of the first equation to get the second equation.

Try This
f. $x = 6$
g. $y = 24$
h. $y = 5$
i. $x = 17$

Teach the Mathematics (continued)

3 Equivalent Equations

Students can determine if two equations are equivalent by solving both and comparing the solution sets. Since there may be cases where the solution sets are different sizes, students should not merely check that each member of the solution set of one also solves the other.

Math Point
Two equations are equivalent if and only if they have the same solution set.

Chalkboard Examples
Each pair of equations is equivalent. What was done to the first equation to get the second one?
1. $3x + 1 = x$
   $3x + 2 = x + 1$
   1 was added to both sides of the equation.
2. $x + 5 = 7 - x$
   $2(x + 5) = 2(7 - x)$
   Both sides of the equation were multiplied by 2.

LESSON ENRICHMENT
1. Solve $4x - 9 = x$ for the replacement set {5, 6, 7}.
   There is no solution.
2. Solve $4x - 9 = x$ for the replacement set {1, 2, 3}.
   The solution set is {3}.
3. Can an equation have different solutions if you use different replacement sets?
   Yes
4. What must be true about the solution?
   The solution must be contained in the replacement set.

LESSON QUIZ

State whether the following sentences are true, false, or open.

1. $\frac{5}{x} = 20$
   Open
2. $5(4 + 2) = 20$
   False
3. Solve $3x - 7 = \frac{20}{x}$ for the replacement set $\{2, 4, 5\}$.
   The solution set is $\{4\}$.

Solve mentally. The replacement set is all whole numbers.

4. $x + 6 = 8$ $x = 2$
5. $6x = 36$ $x = 6$
6. $2x + 1 = 3$ $x = 1$
7. This pair of equations is equivalent. What was done to the first equation to get the second one?
   $x^2 - 3 = x$
   $x^2 - 3 - 3 = x - 3$
   3 was subtracted from both sides.

Assignment Guide

To provide flexible scheduling, this lesson can be split into parts.
▼ Core 1–3
   Core 4–18, 28–36
▼ Extension 45–49
   Core 19–27, 37–42
▼ Extension 43, 44

Use Mixed Review to maintain skills.

Extra Help On the Web

Look for worked-out examples at the Prentice Hall Web site.
www.phschool.com

EXAMPLES Each pair of equations is equivalent. What was done to the first equation to get the second one?

8 $4x = 20$
    $x = 5$ $\frac{4x}{4} = \frac{20}{4}$

Both sides of the first equation were divided by 4 to get the second equation.

9 $\frac{1}{3}x = 8$
    $\frac{2}{3}x = 16$ $2 \cdot \frac{1}{3}x = 2 \cdot 8$

Both sides of the first equation were multiplied by 2 to get the second equation.

Try This Each pair of equations is equivalent. What was done to the first equation to get the second one?

j. $x + 8 = 20$
   $x + 12 = 24$

k. $2x - 4 = 56$
   $2x - 9 = 51$

l. $6x = 42$
   $3x = 21$

1-7 Exercises

A

State whether each sentence is true, false, or open.

1. $2 + 3 \cdot 5 = 25$ **2.** $3a - 4 = 5$ **3.** $2^3 + 8 = 16$

Solve for the given replacement set.

4. $3n + 2 = 23 \{5, 7, 9\}$ **5.** $6u - 2 = 46 \{5, 6, 8\}$

6. $2m^2 - 1 = 7 \left\{1, \frac{3}{2}, 2\right\}$ **7.** $x^2 + x = 0 \{0, 100, 1000\}$

8. $8 - n = 2n \{1, 2, 4\}$ **9.** $t - 8 = 4t - 44 \{8, 12, 18\}$

Mental Math Solve mentally. The replacement set is all whole numbers.

10. $x + 10 = 20$ **11.** $m + 7 = 30$ **12.** $x - 7 = 12$

13. $y - 8 = 19$ **14.** $6a = 54$ **15.** $8y = 72$

16. $\frac{x}{6} = 5$ **17.** $\frac{c}{8} = 6$ **18.** $d + 98 = 100$

Each pair of equations is equivalent. Tell what was done to the first equation to get the second equation.

19. $3x - 5 = 12$ **20.** $4r + 3 = 12$ **21.** $x + 5 = 12$
    $3x = 17$ $4r = 9$ $x - 5 = 2$

Try This

j. 4 was added to both sides of the equation.
k. 5 was subtracted from both sides of the equation.
l. Both sides of the equation were divided by 2.

Exercises

1. False
2. Open
3. True
4. $\{7\}$
5. $\{8\}$
6. $\{2\}$
7. $\{0\}$
8. No solution
9. $\{12\}$
10. $x = 10$
11. $m = 23$
12. $x = 19$
13. $y = 27$
14. $a = 9$
15. $y = 9$
16. $x = 30$
17. $c = 48$
18. $d = 2$
19. 5 was added to both sides.
20. 3 was subtracted from both sides.
21. 10 was subtracted from both sides.

22. $12x = 36$
$4x = 12$

23. $\frac{r}{4} = 6$
$r = 24$

24. $\frac{3y}{5} = 3$
$3y = 15$

25. $\frac{x}{8} = 4$
$x = 32$

26. $5 = \frac{n}{3}$
$15 = n$

27. $7 = \frac{2y}{4}$
$28 = 2y$

B

Mental Math   Simplify; then solve mentally. The replacement set is all whole numbers.

28. $5x + 3x = 24$

29. $9y + 4y = 26$

30. $6t + 3t = 0$

31. $\frac{y}{2} + \frac{y}{2} = 31$

32. $\frac{2}{3}y + \frac{1}{3}y = 2$

33. $20x - 6x = 7$

34. $\frac{10d}{5} = 10$

35. $\frac{20k}{4} = 10$

36. $4t^2 = 0$

What can be done to each side of the equation to get the variable alone on one side of the equal sign?

37. $x - 12 = 34$

38. $g + 34 = 60$

39. $3x = 23$

40. $5v = 35$

41. $\frac{t}{8} = 12$

42. $\frac{m}{5} = 14$

Error Analysis   A student made the claim that each pair of equations below is equivalent. Explain why the student is incorrect.

43. $n - 5 = 21$
$n - 5 + 5 = 21 - 5$

44. $\frac{x}{6} = 12$
$12 \cdot \frac{x}{6} = 6 \cdot 12$

45.   **TEST PREP**   For which replacement set does the equation $25 = \frac{n}{5}$ have a solution?

   A. $\{5, 25\}$ **B.** $\{25, 75\}$ **C.** $\{\frac{1}{5}, 5\}$ **D.** $\{10, 125\}$

46. *Critical Thinking*   Write an equation with no solution if the replacement set is the set of all odd whole numbers.

Challenge

47. Write an equation that has *no* whole number solution.

48. Write an equation for which *every* whole number is a solution.

49. Write an equation of the type $ax = b$ where $x = 0$ is a solution.

Mixed Review

Write using exponential notation. **50.** $m \cdot m \cdot m$ **51.** $n \cdot n \cdot 5 \cdot n \cdot n \cdot n$ *1-3*

Calculate. **52.** $(3 \cdot 2)^2$ **53.** $(4 + 4)^2$ **54.** $9 + 3^2$ **55.** $(9 - 6)^3$ *1-4*

Factor.   **56.** $4x + 12$ **57.** $13t + 52$ **58.** $10t + 25m$

59. $16 + 8y$ **60.** $8a + 16b$ **61.** $9x + 3$ **62.** $8 + 24c$ *1-5*

Exercises

22. Both sides were divided by 3.
23. Both sides were multiplied by 4.
24. Both sides were multiplied by 5.
25. Both sides were multiplied by 8.
26. Both sides were multiplied by 3.
27. Both sides were multiplied by 4.
28. $x = 3$
29. $y = 2$
30. $t = 0$
31. $y = 31$
32. $y = 2$
33. $x = \frac{1}{2}$
34. $d = 5$
35. $k = 2$
36. $t = 0$
37. Add 12 to both sides.
38. Subtract 34 from both sides.
39. Divide both sides by 3.
40. Divide both sides by 5.
41. Multiply both sides by 8.
42. Multiply both sides by 5.
43. 5 was added to the left side, but subtracted from the right side.
44. The left side was multiplied by 12, but the right side was multiplied by 6.
45. D
46. Ex. $x + 2 = 8$
47. Ex. $3x = 2$
48. Ex. $x - x = 0$
49. Ex. $12x = 0$

Mixed Review

50. m^3
51. $5n^5$
52. 36
53. 64
54. 18
55. 27
56. $4(x + 3)$
57. $13(t + 4)$
58. $5(2t + 5m)$
59. $8(2 + y)$
60. $8(a + 2b)$
61. $3(3x + 1)$
62. $8(1 + 3c)$

1-8

1. FOCUS

FIRST FIVE MINUTES

1. Joel got 87 points on his first test. That was 12 points more than Winston got. Write an algebraic expression for the number of points that Joel got.
   $W + 12$

2. A dozen donuts costs $3.24. Write an expression for the cost of 1 donut.
   $3.24 \div 12$

3. Corliss has $5 less than Zelma. Zelma has $38. Write an expression for how much Corliss has.
   $\$38 - \$5$

2. TEACH the Mathematics

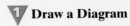

Draw a Diagram

Use Teaching Transparency T9.
Read the Problem-Solving Guidelines with students and discuss each phase. These guidelines are also on Overhead Transparency 1. The guidelines lead students through the problem-solving process and provide a systematic way of approaching the problem.

Many of the problem-solving strategies that will be introduced can be used to help students write an equation for solving. It is also important, however, for students to experience problems that cannot be solved by writing and solving equations and to know other strategies that can be used to solve problems.

Emphasize that drawing a diagram can be very helpful in understanding the problem. Demonstrate with the example how drawing a diagram helps you sort out and visualize the information in the problem.

KEY QUESTIONS

- How long is the tunnel at the end of the first day of work?
  500 ft
- How long is the tunnel at the beginning of the second day of work? 300 ft
- How long is the tunnel at the end of the second day of work? 800 ft

---

What You'll Learn

1 To solve nonroutine problems using the strategy *Draw A Diagram*

. . . And Why

To increase efficiency in solving problems by applying reasoning skills

---

1-8 ▷ Reasoning Strategies

CA 24.0: Use and know simple aspects of a logical argument.

PART 1 Draw a Diagram

Objective: Solve nonroutine problems using the strategy *Draw a Diagram*.

You can use the Problem-Solving Guidelines below to help you solve problems.

PROBLEM-SOLVING GUIDELINES
■ **Phase 1: UNDERSTAND the problem** What am I trying to find? What data am I given? Have I ever solved a similar problem?
■ **Phase 2: Develop and carry out a PLAN** What strategies might I use to solve the problem? How can I correctly carry out the strategies I selected?
■ **Phase 3: Find the ANSWER and CHECK** Does the proposed solution check? What is the answer to the problem? Does the answer seem reasonable? Have I stated the answer clearly?

The planning phase involves selecting and carrying out one or more *strategies* for solving problems. One of the most useful strategies is to *draw a diagram* of the situation.

EXAMPLE

A mining company estimates that it needs to tunnel about 2000 ft into a mountain to reach the mineral deposits. Each day the company is able to tunnel about 500 ft into the mountain. Each night, when equipment is removed for maintenance, about 200 ft of the tunnel refills with rocks. At this rate, estimate how many days it will take the company to reach the mineral deposits.

■ **UNDERSTAND the problem**

Question: How many days will the company need to tunnel?
Data: Each day it gains 500 ft; each night it loses 200 ft.

38 Chapter 1   *Introduction to Algebra*

B

The formula below gives the approximate stopping distance (d) in feet for an automobile driving at x miles per hour (mi/h). Find the approximate stopping distance for each speed given.

$$d = x + \frac{x^2}{20}$$

17. $x = 25$ mi/h   **18.** $x = 10$ mi/h   **19.** 55 mi/h   **20.** 50 mi/h

The formula below gives the area of a trapezoid. As shown in the picture, h is the height, b is the length of one base, and c is the length of the other base. Use this formula to find the area for the different values given below.

$$A = \tfrac{1}{2}h\,(b + c)$$

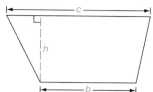

21. $h = 2$ ft, $b = 5$ ft, $c = 12$ ft

22. $h = 10$ in., $b = 8$ in., $c = 14$ in.

23. $h = 4$ m, $b = \frac{1}{2}$ m, $c = \frac{3}{4}$ m

24. *Critical Thinking*   The length and width of a rectangle are each whole numbers. Find possible areas for this rectangle if its perimeter is 14 cm. Use the formulas $A = lw$ and $P = 2l + 2w$.

25. *Error Analysis*   A rectangular field is 150 m wide and 0.5 km long. To find the area, Andrew and Marie each used the formula $A = lw$. Andrew found the area of the field to be 75 m². Marie found the area of the field to be 75 km². Both of these answers are incorrect.
   a. Identify each student's error.
   b. Find the actual area of the field.

Challenge

26. Find the length of a rectangle (l) with area (A) 64 cm² and width (w) 16 cm. Use the formula $A = lw$.

Write a formula for the area of each figure.

27.

28.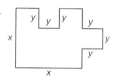

Write as an algebraic expression.   **29.** 5 more than t

30. the sum of x and y **31.** 3 times k **32.** 3 less than m *1-6*

Collect like terms.   **33.** $15c + c$ **34.** $3x + 4 + 5x$ *1-5*

Solve mentally.   **35.** $x + 6 = 15$ **36.** $6m = 42$ *1-7*

Exercises

17. 56.25 ft
18. 15 ft
19. 206.25 ft
20. 175 ft
21. 17 ft²
22. 110 in.²
23. $2\frac{1}{2}$ m²

24. $P = 2(l + w)$, so $l + w = 7$ cm. The dimensions of the rectangle could be 1 cm × 6 cm, 2 cm × 5 cm, or 3 cm × 4 cm. Thus, the area could be 6 cm², 10 cm², or 12 cm².

25. a. Andrew did not convert 0.5 km to meters. Marie did not convert 150 m to kilometers.
   b. 75,000 m² or 0.075 km²
26. 4 cm
27. Answers may vary. Ex: $a^2 - b^2$.
28. Answers may vary. Ex: $x^2 + y^2 - y^2 = x^2$.

Mixed Review

29. $t + 5$
30. $x + y$
31. $3k$
32. $m - 3$
33. $16c$
34. $8x + 4$
35. 9
36. 7

 CA: 24.0

1-10

1. FOCUS

FIRST FIVE MINUTES

1. Play the game Hi-Lo. Think of a number for students to guess. The only clues you should give are "high" or "low." The first student to guess the correct number wins. Suggested numbers to use are 54, 5480, −34, 3.8.

2. Use the Hi-Lo method to approximate the square root of 200. That is, try to find a number that when multiplied by itself gives 200.

   $\sqrt{200} \approx 14.1421$

2. TEACH the Mathematics

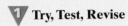 Try, Test, Revise

Every day, problems are solved by the *Try, Test, Revise* method. Emphasize that the key is to make intelligent tries. That is, first make a "ballpark" try based on the data in the problem, then evaluate the accuracy of that try and use this information to make increasingly "educated" tries and focus in on a correct answer.

Key Question

■ In Example 1, if the sum is too great, what should you do?
Guess a lower number.

Chalkboard Examples

Use the *Try, Test, Revise* strategy to solve the following problems.

1. $\dfrac{13 + \square \cdot 5}{3} = 16$

   Try 5 and check.
   $\dfrac{13 + 5 \cdot 5}{3} = \dfrac{13 + 25}{3}$
   $\qquad\qquad = \dfrac{38}{3}$

   $\dfrac{38}{3} = 12\frac{2}{3}$: less than 16

   Try 8 and check.
   $\dfrac{13 + 8 \cdot 5}{3} = \dfrac{53}{3}$

   $\dfrac{53}{3} = 17\frac{2}{3}$: greater than 16

   Try 7 and check.
   $\dfrac{13 + 7 \cdot 5}{3} = \dfrac{48}{3}$

   $\dfrac{48}{3} = 16$ Correct

What You'll Learn

▼ To solve problems using the strategy *Try, Test, Revise*

. . . And Why

To increase efficiency in solving problems by applying reasoning skills

PART 1 Try, Test, Revise

Objective: Solve problems using the strategy *Try, Test, Revise* and other strategies.

PROBLEM-SOLVING GUIDELINES
■ UNDERSTAND the problem
☐ Develop and carry out a PLAN
■ Find the ANSWER and CHECK

Some problems can be solved by choosing a possible solution, testing it, and, if necessary, using information gained from the test to revise the possible solution.

This strategy for solving problems is called *Try, Test, Revise.*

EXAMPLE 1 Use the *Try, Test, Revise* strategy to find the missing number.

$$\dfrac{3 \cdot \square + 7}{2} = 11$$

■ Try 8 for ☐. Test. $\dfrac{3 \cdot 8 + 7}{2} = \dfrac{24 + 7}{2}$

$\qquad\qquad\qquad\qquad = \dfrac{31}{2} = 15\frac{1}{2}$

Since $15\frac{1}{2}$ is greater than 11, 8 was too large. Try 4.

■ Try 4 for ☐. Test. $\dfrac{3 \cdot 4 + 7}{2} = \dfrac{12 + 7}{2}$

$\qquad\qquad\qquad\qquad = \dfrac{19}{2} = 9\frac{1}{2}$

Since $9\frac{1}{2}$ is less than 11, 4 is too small. Try 5.

■ Try 5 for ☐. Test. $\dfrac{3 \cdot 5 + 7}{2} = \dfrac{15 + 7}{2}$

$\qquad\qquad\qquad\qquad = \dfrac{22}{2} = 11$ Correct.

The missing number is 5.

The missing number in the example was found using the *Try, Test, Revise* strategy. The missing number also could have been found using equation-solving techniques that you will learn in later chapters. *Many problems in mathematics can be solved correctly in more than one way.*

Use the *Try, Test, Revise* strategy to solve the following problem.

EXAMPLE 2 One number is 12 more than another number. The sum of the two numbers is 48. What are the two numbers?

- Try 5 for the first number. $5 + 12 = 17$, the second number

    $17 + 5 = 22$ Too low, try a higher first number.

- Try 20 for the first number. $20 + 12 = 32$, the second number

    $20 + 32 = 52$ Too high but close. Try a lower number.

- Try 18 for the first number. $18 + 12 = 30$

    $18 + 30 = 48$ Correct.

    The two numbers are 18 and 30.

Reasoning Strategies

Draw a Diagram	Try, Test, Revise	Write an Equation
Make an Organized List	Use Logical Reasoning	Make a Table
Look for a Pattern	Simplify the Problem	Work Backward

1-10 Problems

Extra Help
On the Web
Look for worked-out examples at the Prentice Hall Web site.
www.phschool.com

Solve using the *Try, Test, Revise* strategy.

1. $\dfrac{4 \cdot \square - 12}{2} = 8$

2. $\dfrac{2 \cdot \square + 18}{4} = 6$

3. $\dfrac{\square \cdot 3 + 19}{2} = 20$

4. $\dfrac{5 \cdot 8 + \square}{4} = 12$

5. $\dfrac{30}{2 + \square} = 3$

6. $\dfrac{12}{2 + \square} = 2$

7. $7(14 - \square) = 35$

8. $5(3 + \square) = 40$

9. $2 \cdot \square - 1 = 4 + \square$

10. $6 \cdot \square + 3 = 2 \cdot \square + 11$

11. One number is 4 times larger than another number. Their sum is 60. What are the two numbers?

12. Consecutive numbers are numbers that follow each other when counting. For example, 5, 6, and 7 are consecutive numbers. Find three consecutive numbers whose sum is 72.

13. The length of a rectangle is twice as long as the width. The perimeter of the rectangle is 72 in. What are the length and width of this rectangle?

1-10   *Reasoning Strategies*   **45**

---

3. PRACTICE/ASSESS

Hints for Problems

11–19. Use the strategy try, test, and revise.

20. Use the table to record tries and the results of each try.

21. Make a guess for regular hours. If she works 20 regular hours, how will you find the number of overtime hours?

22. Draw a diagram to represent the 8-day expedition. Could one person make the trip? two people?

23. Try an amount for the first week. Test. Revise your try.

24. Try a number of 4-wheel lawnmowers. Check. Revise your try. Can you find another solution?

Assignment Guide
▼ Core 1–19
   Extension 20–24

Problems

1. 7
2. 3
3. 7
4. 8
5. 8
6. 4
7. 9
8. 5
9. 5
10. 2
11. The numbers are 12 and 48.
12. 23, 24, and 25
13. 24 in., 12 in.

Practice Multiple Choice

Choose the best answer.

1. Robin worked x hours on Saturday and 3 times as many hours on Monday. Write an expression for the total number of hours she worked.

A $x + 3$ hours

B $x + 4x$ hours

C 4 hours

D $4x$ hours

2. What was done to the first equation to get the second equation?

$4x - 16 = 20;$
$4x = 36$

F Added 20 to both sides

G Subtracted 16 from both sides

H Added 14 to both sides

J Added 16 to both sides

1. D; Algebra 5.0
2. J; Algebra 4.0

14. The length of a rectangle is 8 more than the width. The area is 308 square units. What are the dimensions of the rectangle?

15. The sum of the interior angles of a triangle is 180°. Two angles are the same. The other angle is two times as large as one of the smaller angles. What are the angles of the triangle?

16. One angle of a triangle is twice as large as the smallest. Another is three times as large as the smallest. What are the three angles?

17. The sum of two numbers is 33. Their product is 242. What are the numbers?

18. The product of two numbers is 800. Their difference is 7. What are the two numbers?

19. The sum of the digits of a two-digit number is 14. If the digits are reversed, the new number is 36 greater than the original number. What is the original two-digit number?

20. The sum of three numbers is 47. The second number is 5 more than the smallest number. The third number is 5 times larger than the smallest number. What are the three numbers? Copy and complete a table like the one below to record your tests.

	1st Number	2nd Number	3rd Number	Sum
1st test				
2nd test				
3rd test				

Solve using one or more of the strategies.

21. Eunpyo worked a total of 33 hours in 1 week. She worked half as many overtime hours as she worked regular hours. How many overtime hours did she work?

22. A photography expedition planned an 8-day crossing of an animal preserve. Each person can carry at most a 5-day supply of water. What is the smallest number of people that must start the trip in order for one member of the group to cross the preserve and the others to return safely to the starting point?

23. Peter earned $45.75 in the second week of his new job. This amount was 3 times what he earned the first week. How much did Peter earn the first week?

24. *Write a Convincing Argument*   Solve the problem below. Then write an argument that would convince a classmate that your solution is correct.

Juanita installs wheels on lawnmowers. She works on 4-wheel and 5-wheel lawnmowers. One day she installed 98 wheels. She earns $6 for each lawnmower. How much money could she have earned that day?

46   Chapter 1   *Introduction to Algebra*

Problems

14. 14×22

15. 45°, 45°, 90°

16. 30°, 60°, 90°

17. 22 and 11

18. 32 and 25

19. 59

20. 6, 11, and 30

21. Eunpyo worked 11 hours of overtime.

22. Four people are needed to start the journey.

23. Peter earned $15.25 the first week.

24. Juanita could have earned $120, $126, $132, $138, or $144 for her workday.

Chapter Wrap Up

1-1

To evaluate an **algebraic expression, substitute** a number for each variable and calculate the results. When an expression contains grouping symbols, any operation inside the grouping symbols must be done first. When an expression contains a fraction bar, all computations above and below the bar must be done before dividing. When no grouping symbols are used, follow the **Order of Operations.**

Evaluate.

1. $y + 7$ for $y = 4$

2. $n - 6$ for $n = 15$

3. $\frac{30}{x}$ for $x = 6$

4. $4t$ for $t = 8$

5. ab for $a = 8$ and $b = 9$

6. $x - y$ for $x = 19$ and $y = 11$

7. $\frac{a}{3b}$ for $a = 18$ and $b = 3$

8. $p(6 + q)$ for $p = 3$ and $q = 5$

Simplify.

9. $15 \div 3 + 6 \cdot 8$

10. $2 \cdot 10 \div 5 + 6$

Evaluate.

11. $\frac{4a}{2b + 3}$ for $a = 7$ and $b = 2$

12. $6x + \frac{3y}{2}$ for $x = 8$ and $y = 4$

1-2

The **commutative properties,** $a + b = b + a$ and $ab = ba$, and **identity properties,** $1 \cdot a = a$ and $0 + a = a$, are used to write **equivalent expressions** and to **simplify** expressions.

Write an equivalent expression using a commutative property.

13. $x + 8$

14. $11 + ab$

Write an equivalent expression. Use the indicated expression for 1.

15. $\frac{4}{5}$ Use $\frac{9}{9}$ for 1.

16. $\frac{2x}{y}$ Use $\frac{z}{z}$ for 1.

Simplify.

17. $\frac{6}{18}$

18. $\frac{56}{16}$

19. $\frac{35ab}{105bc}$

20. $\frac{96z}{24xyz}$

21. $\frac{mn}{6m}$

22. $\frac{9pq}{72p}$

Chapter 1 Wrap Up

1. 11
2. 9
3. 5
4. 32
5. 72
6. 8
7. 2
8. 33
9. 53
10. 10
11. 4
12. 54
13. $8 + x$
14. $ab + 11$, $ba + 11$, or $11 + ba$
15. $\frac{36}{45}$
16. $\frac{2xz}{yz}$
17. $\frac{1}{3}$
18. $\frac{7}{2}$
19. $\frac{a}{3c}$
20. $\frac{4}{xy}$
21. $\frac{n}{6}$
22. $\frac{q}{8}$

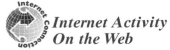
1-3

We write $10 \times 10 \times 10 \times 10$ using **exponential notation as** 10^4. The **exponent,** 4, tells how many times the **base,** 10, is used as a factor. When an expression inside parentheses is raised to a power, everything inside the parentheses is the base.

Write using exponential notation.

23. $6 \cdot 6 \cdot 6 \cdot 6 \cdot 6$ **24.** $3 \cdot y \cdot y \cdot y \cdot y$

Evaluate each expression.

25. y^3 for $y = 4$ **26.** $2x^2$ for $x = 6$

27. $a^2 - 2$ for $a = 8$ **28.** $b^4 + 3$ for $b = 2$

29. $(2a)^3$ for $a = 3$ **30.** $(5t)^5$ for $t = 2$

1-4

The **associative properties,** $(a + b) + c = a + (b + c)$ and $(ab)c = a(bc)$, are used to write equivalent expressions. When evaluating an expression, you must use the order of operations correctly.

Calculate.

31. $(4 \cdot 5)^2$ **32.** $6 + 7^2$

Evaluate.

33. $6 + (4y)^2$ for $y = 2$ **34.** $(6 + a) \cdot (b - 4)$ for $a = 8$ and $b = 6$

Use an associative property to write an equivalent expression.

35. $(a + b) + 6$ **36.** $(7 \cdot y) \cdot x$

Use the commutative and associative properties to write three equivalent expressions.

37. $(1 + m) + n$ **38.** $4 \cdot (x \cdot y)$

1-5

The **distributive property of multiplication over addition,** $a(b + c) = ab + ac$, is used to write equivalent expressions and to collect like terms. We can multiply: $3(4x + 3) = 12x + 9$; factor expressions: $3xy + 9 = 3(xy + 3)$; and collect like terms: $4y + 7y = 11y$.

Use the distributive property to write an equivalent expression.

39. $7(y + 5)$ **40.** $(6m + 4n + 5)3$

Factor.

41. $18x + 6y$ **42.** $4 + 12b + 36a$

Collect like terms.

43. $3a + 2b + 5a + 7b$ **44.** $15m^2 + 12m + 4m^2$

48   Chapter 1   *Introduction to Algebra*

Chapter 1 Wrap Up

23. 6^5
24. $3y^4$
25. 64
26. 72
27. 62
28. 19
29. 216
30. 100,000
31. 400
32. 55
33. 70
34. 28

35. $a + (b + 6)$
36. $7 \cdot (y \cdot x)$
37. $1 + (n + m)$
     $n + (m + 1)$
     Answers may vary.
     $m + (1 + n)$
38. $4 \cdot (y \cdot x)$
     $y \cdot (x \cdot 4)$
     $x(y \cdot 4)$
     Answers may vary.
39. $7y + 35$

40. $18m + 12n + 15$
41. $6(3x + y)$
42. $4(1 + 3b + 9a)$
43. $8a + 9b$
44. $19m^2 + 12m$

1-6

It is often necessary to translate data given in words into algebraic expressions. We use a variable to represent each unknown number.

Write as an algebraic expression.

45. fives times a number

46. seven less than a number

47. four more than a number

48. twice a number

49. Suppose x is the amount of money Jenny earned on Monday, and she earned twice that amount on Tuesday. Write an expression for the amount Jenny earned on those two days.

50. Suppose a was Robert's age 12 years ago. Write an expression for Robert's age now.

1-7

An equation that contains only numbers may be either true or false. An equation that contains at least one variable is called an **open sentence.** A replacement for a variable that makes an equation true is called a **solution.** The collection of all the solutions is called the **solution set.** Two equations are **equivalent** if one can be obtained from the other by a sequence of steps listed on page 35. Equivalent equations have the same solution set.

Solve for the given replacement set.

51. $3n + 7 = 16$ {1, 3, 5}

52. $x^2 - x = 0$ {0, 1, 10}

Solve mentally. The replacement set is all whole numbers.

53. $5a = 35$

54. $\frac{c}{4} = 6$

Each pair of equations is equivalent. What was done to the first equation to get the second one?

55. $2x - 8 = 20$
$2x - 13 = 15$

56. $\frac{r}{5} = 10$
$2r = 100$

1-9

To evaluate a **formula,** substitute the given numerical values for the variables and calculate the results.

57. Find the area (A) of a figure with base (b) of 12.5 cm and height (h) of 7.5 cm using the formula $A = bh$.

58. Find the approximate area (A) of a circle with radius (r) of 3 ft using the formula $A = 3.14r^2$.

1-8, 1-10

There are many strategies involved in solving all kinds of problems. You will use a variety of reasoning strategies throughout your study of algebra.

Chapter 1 Wrap Up

45. $5n$

46. $n - 7$

47. $n + 4$

48. $2n$

49. $x + 2x$ or $3x$

50. $a + 12$

51. {3}

52. {0, 1}

53. $a = 7$

54. $c = 24$

55. 5 was subtracted from both sides.

56. Both sides were multiplied by 10.

57. 93.75 cm^2

58. 28.26 ft^2

Assessment Item Analysis

Item	Lesson
1–8	1-1
9–16	1-2
17–26	1-3
27–32	1-4
33–39	1-5
40–45	1-6
46–48	1-7
49, 50	1-7
51, 52	1-9

Evaluate.

1. $p - 11$ for $p = 25$

2. $\frac{40}{x}$ for $x = 8$

3. $\frac{3x}{y}$ for $x = 10$ and $y = 5$

4. $a - 2b$ for $a = 16$ and $b = 3$

Simplify.

5. $16 \div 8 + 8$

6. $3 \cdot 4 + 2 \cdot 8$

Evaluate.

7. $3(2a + b)$ for $b = 4$ and $a = 2$

8. $\frac{2x + y}{4}$ for $x = 3$ and $y = 6$

Write an equivalent expression using a commutative property.

9. $xy + 3$

10. $a + 6$

Write an equivalent expression. Use the indicated expression for 1.

11. $\frac{3}{7}$ Use $\frac{4}{4}$ for 1.

12. $\frac{6}{3y}$ Use $\frac{x}{x}$ for 1.

Simplify.

13. $\frac{16}{24}$

14. $\frac{81}{45}$

15. $\frac{xy}{12x}$

16. $\frac{9xy}{15yz}$

What is the meaning of each expression?

17. 2^4

18. $5x^3$

Write in exponential notation.

19. $7 \cdot 7 \cdot 7 \cdot 7$

20. $8 \cdot x \cdot x \cdot x \cdot x \cdot x$

Evaluate each expression.

21. $(5x)^2$ for $x = 4$

22. $(3y)^4$ for $y = 0$

23. x^3 for $x = 3$

24. $3y^2$ for $y = 4$

25. $b^2 - 5$ for $b = 7$

26. $(4t)^3$ for $t = 2$

Calculate.

27. $(3 \cdot 6)^2$

28. $6 + 3^3$

Evaluate.

29. $(3x)^3 + 4$ for $x = 2$

30. $(r + 5)(s - 4)$ for $r = 5$ and $s = 10$

50   Chapter 1   *Introduction to Algebra*

Chapter 1 Assessment

1. 14
2. 5
3. 6
4. 10
5. 10
6. 28
7. 24
8. 3
9. $3 + xy, 3 + yx, yx + 3$
10. $6 + a$
11. $\frac{12}{28}$
12. $\frac{6x}{3yx}$
13. $\frac{2}{3}$
14. $\frac{9}{5}$
15. $\frac{y}{12}$
16. $\frac{3x}{5z}$
17. $2 \cdot 2 \cdot 2 \cdot 2$
18. $5 \cdot x \cdot x \cdot x$
19. 7^4
20. $8x^5$
21. 400
22. 0
23. 27
24. 48
25. 44
26. 512
27. 324
28. 33
29. 220
30. 60

Use an associative property to write an equivalent expression.

31. $(x + y) + 5$

Use the commutative and associative properties to write three equivalent expressions.

32. $3 \cdot (a \cdot b)$

Use the distributive property to write an equivalent expression.

33. $6(4y + 3)$

Factor.

34. $8a + 12b$

35. $18x + 6y + 12$

36. $3 + 12b + 36a$

37. $8a + 4 + 12c$

Collect like terms.

38. $7a + 3b + 8a + 4b$

39. $6m + 9m^2 + 3m + 7m^2$

Write as an algebraic expression.

40. 11 fewer than x

41. half of a number

42. twice a number

43. six more than a number

44. Suppose w was Lisa's weight last year. Lisa lost 7 pounds this year. Write an expression for Lisa's weight this year.

45. Suppose t is the total amount of tickets sold to the dance. If each of the ninth, tenth, and eleventh grades sold the same number of tickets, write an expression for the number of tickets sold by each grade.

Solve for the given replacement set.

46. $5n - 4 = 11$ $\{2, 3, 4\}$

47. $x^2 - x = 2$ $\{0, 2, 4\}$

48. $7.2y = 36$ $\{5, 50, 500\}$

Each pair of equations is equivalent. What was done to the first equation to get the second one?

49. $\frac{2}{5}m = 3$

$\frac{4}{5}m = 6$

50. $2x = 10$

$2x + 4 = 14$

Evaluate.

51. Find the distance (d) traveled by a train moving at the rate (r) of 50 mi/h for the time (t) of 3 h using the formula $d = rt$.

52. Find the temperature in degrees Celsius (C) given a temperature of 77° Fahrenheit (F) using the formula $C = \frac{5}{9}(F - 32)$.

Chapter 1 Assessment

31. $x + (y + 5)$

32. $3 \cdot (b \cdot a)$

$b \cdot (a \cdot 3)$

$a \cdot (b \cdot 3)$

33. $24y + 18$

34. $4(2a + 3b)$

35. $6(3x + y + 2)$

36. $3(1 + 4b + 12a)$

37. $4(2a + 3c + 1)$

38. $15a + 7b$

39. $9m + 16m^2$

40. $x - 11$

41. $\frac{n}{2}$

42. $2n$

43. $6 + n$

44. $w - 7$

45. $\frac{t}{3}$

46. $\{3\}$

47. $\{2\}$

48. $\{5\}$

49. Both sides were multiplied by 2.

50. 4 was added to both sides.

51. 150 mi

52. 25°C

CHAPTER 2 ▷ Integers and Rational Numbers

CHAPTER AT A GLANCE

PACING OPTIONS

This chart suggests pacing only for the lessons and their parts. It is provided as a possible guide.
It will help you determine how much time you have in your schedule to cover other features, such as the Chapter Wrap Up and Assessment.

	Day 1	Day 2	Day 3	Day 4	Day 5	Day 6	Day 7	Day 8	Day 9	Day 10	Day 11
Traditional (40–45 min. class periods)	2-1 ▽▽▽	2-2 ▽▽▽	2-3 ▽▽▽	2-4 ▽▽	2-5 ▽	2-6 ▽▽▽	2-7 ▽▽	2-7 ▽ 2-8 ▽	2-8 ▽▽	2-9 ▽	2-10 ▽▽
Algebra 1 Over 2 Years (40–45 min. class periods)	2-1 ▽▽	2-1 ▽	2-2 ▽▽	2-2 ▽	2-3 ▽	2-3 ▽▽	2-4 ▽	2-4 ▽	2-5 ▽	2-5 ▽	2-6 ▽
Block Scheduling (90 min. class periods)	2-1 ▽▽▽ 2-2 ▽▽▽	2-3 ▽▽▽ 2-4 ▽▽▽	2-5 ▽ 2-6 ▽▽▽	2-7 ▽▽▽ 2-8 ▽	2-8 ▽▽ 2-9 ▽	2-10 ▽▽▽					

SKILLS TRACE

SKILL	FOUNDATION	DEVELOPED IN LESSONS	REVIEWED/REINFORCED/EXTENDED
Comparing integers	previous course	**2-1**	4-1
Comparing and graphing rational numbers	previous course	**2-2**	4-1
Adding and subtracting rational numbers	previous course	**2-3, 2-4**	4-2
Multiplying and dividing rational numbers	previous course	**2-5, 2-6**	4-3
Applying the distributive property to expressions using integers	1-5	**2-7**	5-9
Finding the inverse of a sum	1-5	**2-8**	5-9
Simplifying expressions involving grouping symbols	1-1	**2-8**	5-11
Writing equations to solve problems	1-6	**2-9**	Used throughout the text
Using number properties in proofs	1-2, 1-4	**2-10**	7-9, 10-11, 13-3

CORRELATION TO STANDARDIZED TESTS

 YOUR LOCAL TEST*

Lesson		CAT5	CTBS/5 TerraNova™	ITED	MAT7	SAT9		CA Algebra
2-1	Integers and the Number Line							2.0
2-2	Rational Numbers			■		■		1.0
2-3	Addition of Rational Numbers		■		■			1.0
2-4	Subtraction of Rational Numbers				■			1.0
2-5	Multiplication of Rational Numbers				■			1.0
2-6	Division of Rational Numbers	■			■			1.0, 2.0
2-7	Using the Distributive Property							1.0, 4.0, 10.0
2-8	Inverse of a Sum and Simplifying							1.0, 2.0, 4.0, 10.0
2-9	Writing Equations		■		■			5.0
2-10	Number Properties and Proofs				■			1.0, 1.1, 25.0, 25.1, 25.2

CAT5 California Achievement Test, 5th Edition
CTBS/5 Comprehensive Test of Basic Skills, 5th Edition
ITED Iowa Test of Educational Development
    Level 15, Complete Battery, Form M

MAT7 Metropolitan Achievement Test, 7th Edition
SAT 9 Stanford Achievement Test/Task 1

For other standardized test correlations, follow the link to your state at **www.phschool.com**.

*See pp. T34–T39 for the California Standards.

ay 12	Day 13	Day 14	Day 15	Day 16	Day 17	Day 18	Day 19	Day 20	Day 21	Day 22	Day 23	Day 24
0 ▽	2-6 ▽	2-7 ▽	2-7 ▽	2-7 ▽	2-8 ▽	2-8 ▽	2-8 ▽	2-9 ▽	2-9 ▽	2-10 ▽	2-10 ▽	2-10 ▽

Math Background

Chapter Overview

Integers and rational numbers are defined, discussed, and compared using the order relations *is less than* and *is greater than*. The operations of addition, subtraction, multiplication, and division are practiced with integers and rational numbers throughout the chapter. All four operations are then used to simplify expressions. The distributive property is emphasized for its future usefulness, and absolute value is introduced both geometrically and algebraically.

Translation of phrases into algebraic notation is discussed, and word problems are translated into equations using the reasoning strategy *Write an Equation*.

2-1 Integers and the Number Line

Integers are typically shown on a horizontal line with positive numbers to the right of 0 and negative numbers to the left. This sort of number line gives sense to the distance concept of absolute value.

The photo on page 55 shows integers on an arc. The Celsius and Fahrenheit scales illustrate the fact that the choice of unit measure and placement of the 0 point are arbitrary. Also, many thermometers are displayed with the number line vertical and "up" the positive direction.

2-2 Rational Numbers

Showing a Number Is Rational

Example 1 points out the fact that 1 is also the identity for division; students may have discussed this in Lesson 1-2. They should be aware that the equivalent expressions $\frac{a}{1}$ and a are often substituted for each other.

Graphing Rational Numbers

Students may be interested to know that the root meaning of *coordinate* is "to set in order" or "to arrange." They have probably experienced *coordinating* schedules. They may also have heard of map *coordinates*.

In discussing the density property with Exercises 31–34, make sure students recognize that, while it is true that every rational number can be associated with a point on the number line (Key Question 2), the converse is not true. Not every point on the number line is associated with a *rational* number.

Students have had experience rewriting fractions as repeating or terminating decimals. (See Lesson 2-6.) Many students will have worked with $\sqrt{2}$, or π, and have probably been told that such a number is irrational—a non-repeating, non-terminating decimal. Such numbers also have places on the number line.

2-3 Addition of Rational Numbers

Be certain students are clear that, when adding on the number line, positive numbers are associated with "right arrows" and negative numbers with "left arrows." Emphasize that the answer is the number associated with the point under the arrowhead—but could also be represented by an arrow from the 0 to the point.

Students may enjoy being able to now prove the assertion in Lesson 2-2: that $\frac{-3}{4}$ equals the additive inverse of $\frac{3}{4}$, that is $\frac{-3}{4} = -\frac{3}{4}$. Since

$$\frac{3}{4} + \frac{-3}{4} = \frac{3 + (-3)}{4} = \frac{0}{4} = 0,$$

by definition, $\frac{-3}{4}$ is the additive inverse of $\frac{3}{4}$. Point out that the argument depends on the uniqueness of an additive inverse (there is one and only one).

2-4 Subtraction of Rational Numbers

Emphasize the importance of using precise language to distinguish a negative number from the operation of subtraction. Urge students not to refer to a negative number, such as -67, as "minus 67." Either "negative 67" or "the opposite of 67" is more precise. As pointed out in the text, the best way to read an algebraic expression such as $-x$ is "the opposite of x," since the value of $-x$ might be positive or negative. "Minus" is correctly used only in reading an expression such as $3y - 6$.

Point out to students that, in subtracting on a number line, the answer is the directed arrow from the subtrahend to the minuend. For $10 - 12$, "What are the direction and distance to 10 from 12?" or "Start at 12; what are the direction and the distance to 10?" are questions that might make this clear.

It may be helpful to compare the related number line additions. (For $10 - 12 = -2$, also draw $10 = -2 + 12$.) After learning that subtraction can be interpreted as addition of the opposite, students might then want to redo Examples 1 and 2 by drawing number line additions. (Draw $10 + -12 = -2$.) Then they should compare the three number line representations of the same problem.

2-5 Multiplication of Rational Numbers

Students can now prove the assertion from Lesson 2-2 that $\frac{3}{-4} = -\frac{3}{4}$.

$$\frac{3}{-4} = \frac{3}{-4} \cdot \frac{-1}{-1} = \frac{3(-1)}{-4(-1)} = \frac{-3}{4}$$

and we have already shown that $\frac{-3}{4}$ is the additive inverse of $\frac{3}{4}$.

Some students have difficulty understanding that the empty set is a subset of every set. You might use the definition of subset and ask "Is every element of the empty set in the given set?"

2-6 Division of Rational Numbers

Students sometimes do not recognize the validity of the substitutions based on $\frac{a}{b} = a \cdot \frac{1}{b}$. Warn them to watch for it, particularly in factoring and simplifying expressions.

Students who doubt that $\frac{0}{x} = 0$, where $x \neq 0$, might write $\frac{0}{x} = 0 \cdot \frac{1}{x}$ and use the multiplicative property of zero from the last lesson.

2-7 Using the Distributive Property

Here is a proof of the first equation given in The Distributive Property of Multiplication Over Subtraction.

$a(b - c)$	$= a(b + (-c))$	To subtract, add the opposite.
	$= ab + a(-c)$	distributive property of multiplication over addition
	$= ab + (-ac)$	See Math Point, page 77.
	$= ab - ac$	To add the opposite, subtract.

Emphasize that multiplying can always check factoring. Some students will undoubtedly factor

$6xy + 2y - 12y^2$ as $2y(3x - 6y)$

instead of as $\quad 2y(3x + 1 - 6y)$.

Remind them to use the multiplicative identity, that is, to substitute $1 \cdot 2y$ for $2y$.

Also point out to them that, whenever a monomial is factored out of an algebraic expression, the remaining factor will have the same number of terms as the original expression. This is another way to check their work.

2-8 Inverse of a Sum and Simplifying

The substitution $-a = -1 \cdot a$ may help students factor correctly.

2-9 Writing Equations

The strategy *Writing Equations* is of vital importance, and students should know that there are problems for which this is, by far, the easiest strategy. They also may want to *Draw a Diagram* and use their experience from Lesson 1-6 to help them write the equations.

2-10 Number Properties and Proofs

Number Properties and Definitions

Closure is the only field axiom not previously presented in the text. Additional examples for students to consider are the negative integers and the nonpositive integers (closed only under addition) and the set $\{-1,0\}$ (closed under multiplication). They might also consider the existence of identities and inverses in such sets. The nonpositive integers have 0 as the additive identity. $\{1, 0, -1\}$ has 0 as the additive inverse, 1 as the multiplicative identity, 1 and -1 are additive inverses, and 1 is its own multiplicative inverse, as is -1.)

Properties of Equality

Students often think the Properties of Equality are not of much use, since they seem so obvious. However, many difficulties with equations stem from forgetting the symmetric and transitive properties. To become more familiar with the concepts, students might consider the relations "subset of" (reflexive and transitive), "child of" (none of the three), and "ancestor of" (transitive).

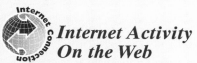

Internet Activity
On the Web

For professional development tips visit our Web site.
www.phschool.com

Monitoring Progress

UNIVERSAL ACCESS

▶ Preventing a Student from Falling Behind

These resources are particularly helpful in preventing a student from falling behind his or her appropriate math level. For a complete list of resources for this chapter, see page 52F.

Before Lessons

Skills You Need for Chapter 2 (p. 52)
- Simplify fractions
- Evaluating expressions
- Collecting like terms and factoring

Preteaching Math Vocabulary
- List of Key Terms (p. 52 and p. 107)
- Reading Math (p. 82)
- Writing Math (p. 102)

Skills Intervention Kit With CD-ROM

With Lesson	Use this Unit
2-2, 2-3, 2-4, 2-5, 2-6	Decimals
2-2, 2-3, 2-4, 2-5, 2-6	Operations with Fractions
2-1, 2-9	Pre-Algebra Basics

During Lessons

Try This Exercises (Student Edition)

Additional Examples (Teacher's Edition)

Help at Home
- Lessons 2-1 to 2-4
- Lessons 2-5 to 2-9
- Available in English and Spanish

After Lessons

Lesson Quiz (Teacher's Edition)

Reteaching Worksheets (Teaching Resources Box)

Daily Cumulative Review Masters

There is a Daily Cumulative Review worksheet for every lesson in this chapter.

Skills Intervention Kit

Innovative resource package for diagnosing students' gaps in basic skills, prescribing an individualized course of study, and monitoring progress. Eight intervention units cover core skills students need to succeed.

ASSESSMENT OPTIONS

Lesson	2-1	2-2	2-3	2-4	2-5	2-6	2-7	2-8	2-9	2-10	End
Try This Exercises	■	■	■	■	■	■	■	■		■	
Mixed Reviews	■	■	■	■	■	■	■	■		■	
Quizzes				■				■			
Chapter Assessment											■
Cumulative Review	A Cumulative Review for Chapters 1–4 is found on pp. 198–201.										
Standardized Test Prep	■	■		■		■		■			
	Sample College Entrance Exams are found in Problem Solving Practice Masters.										
Computer Item Generator CD-ROM	Can be used to create custom-made practice pages or assessment pages at any time.										
Student Tutorial CD-ROM	Students can self-assess and access tutorial help at any time.										

Test-Taking Tips on Transparencies

Test-Taking Tip: Use a Variable

Sometimes you can use a variable to solve a problem.

Example A taxi ride costs a flat fee of $1.75 plus $.80 per mile. What is the fare for traveling 5 miles?

A. $4.00   B. $1.75   C. $5.75   D. $41.75   E. $4.75

Choose variables: Let m = miles traveled and c = cost.

Describe the situation in words:

Cost = flat fee + cost for traveling m miles

Use variables to express the cost: $c = 1.75 + 0.80m$

Substitute $m = 5$: $c = 1.75 + 0.80(5)$

$= 1.75 + 4$

$= 5.75

The answer is $5.75, or choice C.

Use a variable to find the answer. Explain your reasoning.

1. The measures of the angles of a triangle are in the ratio 2 : 4 : 6. Find the measure of the smallest angle.

A. 15°   B. 20°   C. 30°   D. 60°   E. 90°

2. One side of a rectangle is 3 times the other side. The perimeter is 16 cm. How long is the long side?

F. 8 cm   G. 2 cm   H. 3 cm   J. 6 cm   K. 16 cm

For use with Lesson 2-9

Resources for Chapter 2

TEACHING RESOURCES BOX

	First Five Minutes	Practice	Reteach	Enrichment	Problem Solving	Assessment	Cumulative Review	Lesson Planner	Success-Building	Teaching Transparencies	Help at Home	SE Answers on Transparencies
2-1	■	■	■	■			■	■		■		■
2-2	■	■	■				■	■				■
2-3	■	■	■		■		■	■		■		■
2-4	■	■■				■	■	■			■	■
2-5	■	■	■				■	■				■
2-6	■	■	■				■	■				■
2-7	■	■■	■	■		■	■	■		■		■
2-8	■	■	■				■	■				■
2-9	■	■	■	■			■	■	■			■
2-10	■						■	■				■
End				■	■	5 Forms	■				■	■
												■

Also available for use throughout the chapter:

Solution Key
Mathematics Standardized Test Prep
   Student Edition and Teacher's Edition

Overhead Manipulatives Kit
Practice Workbook

Student Manipulatives Kit
Test-Taking Tips on Transparencies

California Assessment Success Kit
Graphing Calculator Handbook

TECHNOLOGY

Computer Item Generator
CD-ROM with an unlimited supply of questions with varying degrees of difficulty for customized practice sheets, quizzes, and tests.

Secondary Math Toolkit™ with Integrated Math Labs
Integrated software package with linkable math tools for exploring key concepts.

Student Tutorial
Test preparation software for students on CD-ROM with management system for teachers; includes Secondary Math Lab Toolkit.

Resource Pro® with Planning Express®
CD-ROM with complete classroom planning tool and teaching resources for customizing and planning lessons.

Web Extension
www.phschool.com

For Students
- Chapter Support with Internet Links
- Internet Activities

For Teachers
- Curriculum Support
- Professional Development
- Product Information
- Regional Information

Also available for use throughout the chapter:
- Algebra Instructional Videos: A Step by Step Guide to Key Concepts

Key Terms

Glossary pages 651–657

You may wish to preteach some of the key terms used in this chapter. Particularly for English Language Learners (ELL), presenting the vocabulary before the chapter or lesson begins gives students a head start into understanding the new material. Writing new words on poster paper, pointing to the words as you say them, then displaying the poster for a period of time is a useful technique.

absolute value (p. 56)
additive inverse (p. 66)
axiom (p. 102)
braces (p. 95)
brackets (p. 95)
closed (p. 103)
coordinate (p. 59)
density property (p. 62)
difference (p. 71)
distributive properties (p. 89)
field (p. 102)
field axioms (p. 102)
graph of a number (p. 59)
inequality (p. 55)
integers (p. 54)
inverse of a sum property
    (p. 94)
irrational number (p. 86)
multiplicative inverse (p. 82)
multiplicative property of zero
    (p. 78)
negative integers (p. 54)
opposites (p. 54)
parentheses (p. 95)
positive integers (p. 54)
property of –1 (p. 93)
property of additive
    inverses (p. 66)
property of multiplicative
    inverses (p. 82)
quotient (p. 81)
rational numbers (p. 59)
real numbers (p. 61)
reciprocal (p. 82)
repeating decimal (p. 86)
terminating decimal (p. 86)
terms (p. 90)
theorem (p. 102)

What You'll Learn in Chapter 2

- How to use integers and rational numbers to model real situations

- How to add, subtract, multiply, and divide rational numbers and how to use these operations in solving problems

- How to use the distributive property to simplify algebraic expressions

- How to apply the properties of numbers, axioms and theorems, to algebraic expressions

CHAPTER 2

Skills & Concepts You Need for Chapter 2

1-2 Simplify.

1. $\frac{12}{27}$ **2.** $\frac{a}{4ab}$ **3.** $\frac{13xy}{xy}$ **4.** $\frac{18cd}{15d}$

1-3 Evaluate.

5. $(4n)^2$ for $n = 2$ **6.** p^1 for $p = 24$ **7.** $3x^3$ for $x = 2$

1-5 Multiply.

8. $5(a + b + d)$ **9.** $11(w + 4)$ **10.** $7(3z + y + 2)$

1-5 Factor.

11. $45 + 9y$ **12.** $3a + 12b$ **13.** $4x + 10 + 8y$

1-5 Collect like terms.

14. $5x + 3y + 2x$ **15.** $b^2 + 3a + 4b^2$ **16.** $5t + 2 + 3t + 7$

Solve for the given replacement set.
17. $4x + 2 = 30$ $\{3, 5, 7\}$ **18.** $8a = 4$ $\{0.5, 5, 50\}$

52

Skills & Concepts You Need for Chapter 2

1. $\frac{4}{9}$
2. $\frac{1}{4b}$
3. 13
4. $\frac{6c}{5}$
5. 64
6. 24
7. 24
8. $5a + 5b + 5d$
9. $11w + 44$
10. $21z + 7y + 14$
11. $9(5 + y)$
12. $3(a + 4b)$
13. $2(2x + 5 + 4y)$
14. $7x + 3y$
15. $5b^2 + 3a$
16. $8t + 9$
17. $\{7\}$
18. $\{0.5\}$

Integers and Rational Numbers

In Death Valley National Park, the elevation ranges from 282 feet below sea level at the valley floor to 14,494 feet at the peak of Mt. Whitney. What is the difference in elevation?

Photo Caption
14,776 ft

1. FOCUS

FIRST FIVE MINUTES

True or false?
1. 0 is a positive number. F (Zero is neither positive nor negative.)
2. −8, 0, and 4 are all integers. T
3. The set of whole numbers includes all positive integers, negative integers, and 0. F

2. TEACH the Mathematics

▼1 The Set of Integers

Illustrate that the set of integers includes the set of whole numbers, just as the set of students in the classroom includes the set of girls in the classroom. Have students think of other pairs of sets in which one set includes another.

Key Questions

To which of the following sets does each number belong: integers, positive integers, negative integers, whole numbers?

- 2
  Integers, positive integers, whole numbers
- −9
  Integers, negative integers
- 0
  Integers, whole numbers

Chalkboard Examples

Name the integer suggested by each situation.
1. 1000 B.C. −1000
2. You walk forward 9 steps. 9
3. The temperature is 15 degrees above 0. 15
4. Acme Lint Company is 10 million dollars in debt. −10,000,000
5. The treasure was buried 50 feet deep. −50
6. The balloon was up 1000 feet. 1000
7. The picnic was two days ago. −2

What You'll Learn

1 To give an integer that corresponds to a real-world situation

2 To compare integers using > or <

3 To find the absolute value of a number

. . . And Why

To learn how integers can model real-world situations

CA 2.0: Understand and use such operations as taking the opposite.

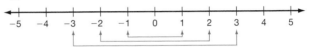

2-1 ▷ Integers and the Number Line

Math in Action

Some computer spreadsheets show amounts of money less than zero using parentheses. You can also write amounts less than zero using a "negative sign." ($35,000) is the same as −$35,000.

	A	B
1		October
2	Income	$129,000
3	Expenses	($164,000)
4	Balance	($35,000)

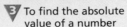

PART 1 The Set of Integers

Objective: Give an integer that corresponds to a real-world situation.

We know that the set of whole numbers consists of 0, 1, 2, 3, 4, and so on. On a number line we can match each whole number with another number that is the same distance from 0 but on the opposite side of 0. Numbers such as 3 (read "positive three" or just "three") and −3 (read "negative three") that are the same distance from 0, but on opposite sides of 0, are called **opposites.** Zero is its own opposite. The set of **integers** consists of the whole numbers and their opposites. On the number line, the **positive integers** are to the right of 0, and the **negative integers** are to the left of 0. Zero is neither positive nor negative. The number line below shows some examples of opposites.

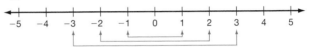

Definition

The set of **integers** consists of the positive integers, negative integers, and zero. {. . . −4, −3, −2, −1, 0, 1, 2, 3, 4, . . .}

EXAMPLES Name the integer that is suggested by each situation.

1 Death Valley is 282 ft below sea level.

−282   Below sea level suggests a negative integer.

2 The temperature is 3° below 0.

−3 Below 0 suggests a negative integer.

3 Mickey's juice stand made an $18 profit on Monday.

18 A profit suggests a positive integer.

Try This Name the integer that is suggested by each situation.

a. Julia has a debt of $12.

b. The halfback made a gain of 8 yd.

c. The quarterback lost 5 yd.

d. Ignition occurs 3 seconds before liftoff.

Order on the Number Line

Objective: Compare integers using > or <.

We use the symbol < to mean *is less than*. For example, 6 < 8 means "6 is less than 8." The symbol > means *is greater than*. For example, 2 > −4 means "2 is greater than −4." The symbols > and < are called inequality symbols. A mathematical sentence that contains an inequality symbol is called an **inequality.** We can read an inequality in two ways. For example, the sentence 5 < 7 means "5 is less than 7." This sentence can also be reversed and read as "7 is greater than 5." An inequality can be true or false. The sentence 12 > 2 is true. The sentence 5 > 16 is false.

On the number line, numbers increase as we move from left to right. For any two numbers, the one farther to the right is the greater and the one to the left is the lesser. This means that all negative numbers are less than 0 and all positive numbers are greater than 0.

EXAMPLES Write a true sentence using > or <.

4 2 < 9 Since 2 is to the left of 9, 2 is less than 9.

5 −7 < 3 Since −7 is to the left of 3, −7 is less than 3.

6 6 > −12 Since 6 is to the right of −12, 6 is greater than −12.

7 −18 < −5 Since −18 is to the left of −5, −18 is less than −5.

Try This Write a true sentence using > or <.

e. 14 ☐ 7   **f.** 11 ☐ −2   **g.** −15 ☐ −5

This thermometer has both Fahrenheit (F) and Celsius (C) scales. The temperature is about 0°F. What is the temperature in degrees Celsius? For what temperature are the Fahrenheit and Celsius readings the same?

Teach the Mathematics (continued)

② Order on the Number Line

The **less than** symbol, <, and the **greater than** symbol, >, can be thought of as little "funnels." The small number is at the small end of the funnel. The big number is at the big end of the funnel.

Emphasize that a negative number is always less than a positive number.

Key Questions

True or false?

- 3 > −1
  True
- 3 < 1
  False
- −1 < 3
  True
- −3 > 1
  False

Chalkboard Examples

Insert the proper symbol, < or >, to get a true statement.

1. 8 ☐ 128   <
2. 13 ☐ 713   <
3. −5 ☐ 7 − 5   <
4. 14 ☐ −814   >
5. −10 ☐ −5 − 10   >
6. −4 ☐ −11 − 4   >

Use Teaching Transparency T1 to compare numbers on a number line.

2-1 *Integers and the Number Line* **55**

Try This
a. −12
b. 8
c. −5
d. −3
e. >
f. >
g. <

Try This
about −18°C;
−40°C = −40°F

Absolute Value

Emphasize that the absolute value of a number is never negative, just as the distance between two points is never negative. It is always a positive number or zero. Also point out that −*n*, or the opposite of *n*, is a positive number if *n* is a negative number.

Key Questions

- What is the distance on the number line from 0 to 6?
  6
- What is the distance on the number line from 0 to −9?
  9
- What is the opposite of 12?
  −12
- What is the opposite of −23?
  23
- Is |15| greater than, less than or equal to |−15|?
  |15| = |−15|

Chalkboard Examples

Find the absolute value.

1. |3| 3
2. |−3| 3
3. |0| 0
4. |−27| 27

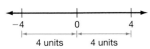

Absolute Value

Objective: Find the absolute value of an integer.

The integers 4 and −4 are both the same distance, 4 units, from 0 on the number line.

$$\xleftarrow{\quad} \underset{-4}{+} \quad \underset{0}{+} \quad \underset{4}{+} \xrightarrow{\quad}$$

4 units   4 units

The **absolute value** of a number is its distance from 0 on the number line. We use the symbol |*n*| to represent "the absolute value of *n*." The absolute value of a number is either positive or zero. The number line above shows that |4| = 4 and |−4| = 4. The absolute value of 0 is 0.

> **Definition**
>
> **Absolute Value**
>
> For any number *n*,
> |*n*| = *n* if *n* is a positive number or 0, and
> |*n*| = −*n* if *n* is a negative number.

Note that −*n* means the opposite of *n*. It does not necessarily stand for a negative number. For instance, the opposite of −8, written −(−8), is 8. And 8 is a positive number.

EXAMPLES   Find the absolute value.

8 |12| = 12   12 is 12 units from 0.

Using the definition of absolute value, |12| = 12 since 12 is a positive number.

9 |−7| = 7   −7 is 7 units from 0.

Using the definition of absolute value, |−7| = the opposite of −7 = 7. Notice that the absolute value is always nonnegative.

10 |−3.04| = 3.04   −3.04 is 3.04 units from 0.

Using the definition of absolute value, |−3.04| = the opposite of −3.04 = 3.04.

Try This   Find the absolute value.

h. |17| **i.** |−8| **j.** |−14|

k. |21| **l.** |0| **m.** |−21|

Try This
h. 17
i. 8
j. 14
k. 21
l. 0
m. 21

2-1 Exercises

Extra Help On the Web
Look for worked-out examples at the Prentice Hall Web site.
www.phschool.com

A

Name the integer that is suggested by each situation.

1. In one game Carlos lost 12 marbles.
2. Jana won 5 marbles in her first game.
3. The temperature Wednesday was 18° above zero.
4. Ramona has a debt of $17.
5. Jane's business had a profit of $2500 in one week.
6. The Dead Sea, between Jordan and Israel, is 1299 feet below sea level.
7. On Friday, Vicki withdrew $125 from her savings account.
8. Terry's bowling team won by 34 pins.
9. In foreign trade, the U.S. had an excess of $3 million.

Write a true sentence using < or >.

10. 5 □ 0	**11.** 9 □ 0	**12.** −9 □ 5	**13.** 8 □ −8
14. −6 □ 6	**15.** 0 □ −7	**16.** −8 □ −5	**17.** −4 □ −3
18. −5 □ −11	**19.** −3 □ −4	**20.** −6 □ −5	**21.** −10 □ −14

Find the absolute value.

22. $|-3|$	**23.** $|-7|$	**24.** $|10|$	**25.** $|11|$
26. $|0|$	**27.** $|-4|$	**28.** $|-24|$	**29.** $|325|$
30. $|-125|$	**31.** $|5.5|$	**32.** $|-4.2|$	**33.** $|-120.2|$
34. $|755|$	**35.** $|-340|$	**36.** $|-5.8|$	**37.** $|-0.3|$
38. $|12.75|$	**39.** $|-0.07|$	**40.** $|-80|$	**41.** $|-3.75|$

B

Evaluate.

42. $|-5| + |-6|$	**43.** $|17| + |-17|$	**44.** $|12| \cdot |-3|$
45. $|-5| \cdot |-6| \cdot |0|$	**46.** $|-3| \cdot |-7| + |-4|$	**47.** $|8| \cdot |-2| - |5|$

Write the following integers in order from least to greatest.

48. 13, −12, 5, −17
49. −23, 4, 0, −17
50. −24, −26, −18, −32, −5, −16
51. 15, −24, −5, −16, 12, −13, −14

Evaluate each expression.

52. $|x| + 24$ for $x = -7$
53. $|t| - 15$ for $t = -36$

LESSON QUIZ

What integer is suggested by each situation?

1. The temperature is 60 degrees above zero.
   60
2. Dorealea lost 2 pounds.
   −2
3. The hole was 20 feet deep.
   −20
4. The tree grew 5 feet.
   5

Insert either < or > to make a true statement.

5. 4 □ 9   <
6. −8 □ 7   <
7. −14 □ −20   >
8. −12 □ −10   <
9. 4 □ −2   >

Find the absolute value.

10. $|-9|$ 9
11. $|12|$ 12

Assignment Guide

To provide flexible scheduling, this lesson can be split into parts.
▼ Core 1–9
   Extension 57
▼ Core 10–21
   Extension 48–51
▼ Core 22–47, 52–56
   Extension 58–72

Use Mixed Review to maintain skills.

Exercises

1. −12	14. <	28. 24	42. 11
2. 5	15. >	29. 325	43. 34
3. 18	16. <	30. 125	44. 36
4. −17	17. <	31. 5.5	45. 0
5. 2500	18. >	32. 4.2	46. 25
6. −1299	19. >	33. 120.2	47. 11
7. −125	20. <	34. 755	48. −17, −12, 5, 13
8. 34	21. >	35. 340	49. −23, −17, 0, 4
9. 3,000,000	22. 3	36. 5.8	50. −32, −26, −24, −18, −16, −5
10. >	23. 7	37. 0.3	51. −24, −16, −14, −13, −5, 12, 15
11. >	24. 10	38. 12.75	52. 31
12. <	25. 11	39. 0.07	53. 21
13. >	26. 0	40. 80	
	27. 4	41. 3.75	

54. $|a| + |b|$ for $a = -5$ and $b = -12$

55. $2|x| + |y|$ for $x = 8$ and $y = 15$

56. $3a - |b| + |c|$ for $a = 5, b = -4, c = -12$

57. *Critical Thinking*   Find the next three numbers in each pattern by thinking about integers and the number line.

    a. $13, 9, 5, 1,$ ____, ____, ____

    b. $6, 5, 3, 0,$ ____, ____, ____

    c. $-3, -5, -8, -12,$ ____, ____, ____

    d. $-1, -3, -4, -7,$ ____, ____, ____

TEST PREP   Compare the boxed quantity in column A with the boxed quantity in column B. Choose the best answer.

A. The quantity in column A is greater.
B. The quantity in column B is greater.
C. The two quantities are equal.
D. The relationship cannot be determined with the information supplied.

	column A	column B		column A	column B
58.	5.3	$|5.3|$	**59.**	-3.1	$|-3.1|$
60.	0	$|0|$	**61.**	2.7	$-|2.7|$
62.	x	$|x|$	**63.**	$|x|$	$-|x|$

Challenge

Use $<$, $>$, or $=$ to write a true sentence.

64. $|-3| \square 5$ **65.** $2 \square |-4|$ **66.** $-2 \square |-1|$ **67.** $0 \square |0|$

68. $|-5| \square |-2|$ **69.** $|4| \square |-7|$ **70.** $|x| \square -1$ **71.** $|-8| \square |8|$

72. List in order from least to greatest. $7^1, -5, |-6|, 4, |3|, -100, 0, 1, \frac{14}{4}$

Mixed Review

Collect like terms.   **73.** $6m + 11m + 4m$ **74.** $\frac{1}{2}a + \frac{1}{2}a$

75. $8x^2 + 3x^2 + 7x$ **76.** $4c^2 + 7c + 2c^2$ *1-5*

Factor.   **77.** $4m + 24c$ **78.** $7b + 14$ **79.** $14x + 28y + 7$ *1-5*

Solve for the given replacement set.   **80.** $y + 3 = 42$ $\{14, 39, 45\}$

81. $w + 3911 = 4272$ $\{361, 7183, 8183\}$ **82.** $14t = 42$ $\{2, 3, 28\}$

83. $c + 9.7 = 12.4$ $\{2.7, 3.3, 22.1\}$ **84.** $2.6n = 7.8$ $\{3, 5.2, 10.4\}$ *1-7*

Mental Math   **85.** $x - 4 = 18$ **86.** $c - 25 = 30$

87. $y - 80 = 10$ **88.** $\frac{a}{4} = 20$ **89.** $\frac{x}{10} = 2.4$ **90.** $\frac{d}{7} = 20$ *1-7*

Exercises

54. 17
55. 31
56. 23
57. a. $-3, -7, -11$
    b. $-4, -9, -15$
    c. $-17, -23, -30$
    d. $-11, -18, -29$ (*Ans. may vary*)
58. C
59. B
60. C
61. A
62. D
63. D
64. $<$

65. $<$
66. $<$
67. $=$
68. $>$
69. $<$
70. $>$
71. $=$
72. $-100, -5, 0, 1, |3|, \frac{14}{4}, 4, |-6|, 7^1$

Mixed Review

73. $21m$
74. a
75. $11x^2 + 7x$

76. $6c^2 + 7c$
77. $4(m + 6c)$
78. $7(b + 2)$
79. $7(2x + 4y + 1)$
80. $\{39\}$
81. $\{361\}$
82. $\{3\}$
83. $\{2.7\}$
84. $\{3\}$
85. $x = 22$
86. $c = 55$
87. $y = 90$
88. $a = 80$
89. $x = 24$
90. $d = 140$

Rational Numbers

Objective: Show a number is rational.

Much of your work in algebra will involve rational numbers. The word "rational" comes from the word *ratio*.

Definition

Any number that can be expressed as the ratio of two integers, $\frac{a}{b}$, where $b \neq 0$, is called a **rational number.**

There are three ways to write a negative rational number. You can write "negative three fourths" as follows.

$$-\frac{3}{4} \qquad \frac{-3}{4} \qquad \frac{3}{-4}$$

To show that a number is rational, we only have to find one way of naming it as a ratio of two integers.

 EXAMPLES Show that each can be written as the ratio of two integers.

1 $3 = \frac{3}{1}$

2 $-9.2 = -\frac{92}{10}$

Try This Show that each can be written as the ratio of two integers.

a. 4.5 **b.** -10 **c.** -14.3 **d.** -0.01

Objective: Graph rational numbers.

There is a point on the number line for every rational number. The number is called the **coordinate** of the point. The point is the **graph** of the number. When we draw a point for a number on a number line, we say that we have graphed the number.

 Try This

a. $\frac{45}{10}$ or $\frac{9}{2}$

b. $-\frac{10}{1}$

c. $-\frac{143}{10}$

d. $-\frac{1}{100}$

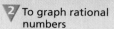 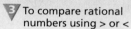

1 To show that a number is rational

2 To graph rational numbers

3 To compare rational numbers using > or <

. . . And Why

To learn how rational numbers can model real-world situations

---

1. FOCUS

FIRST FIVE MINUTES

Simplify.

1. $\frac{4}{2}$ 2

2. $\frac{8}{16}$ $\frac{1}{2}$

3. Which is larger, $\frac{1}{2}$, or $\frac{1}{3}$? $\frac{1}{2}$

4. Write 0.1 as a fraction. $\frac{1}{10}$

5. Write 0.5 as a fraction. $\frac{1}{2}$

2. TEACH the Mathematics

1 **Showing a Number Is Rational**

Point out that all integers are rational numbers, but not all rational numbers are integers.

Key Questions

True or false?

- $-\frac{3}{4} = \frac{3}{-4}$
  True
- -2 is a rational number.
  True

Chalkboard Examples

Show that each number can be written as the ratio of two integers.

1. 7
   $\frac{7}{1}$ or $\frac{14}{2}$

2. 0
   $\frac{0}{1}$ or $\frac{0}{2}$

3. 0.7
   $\frac{7}{10}$

4. 81.54
   $\frac{8154}{100}$

5. -5.7
   $-\frac{57}{10}$

6. -0.001
   $-\frac{1}{1000}$

2 **Graphing Rational Numbers**

When graphing rational numbers, it is important that students divide the number line carefully into the units needed.

Key Questions

- On a number line, does $-\frac{1}{2}$ lie between -1 and -2? No
- Can any rational number be graphed on the number line? Yes

Teach the Mathematics (continued)

Chalkboard Examples

Graph each rational number.

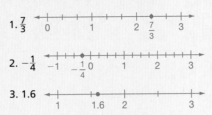

1. $\frac{7}{3}$

2. $-\frac{1}{4}$

3. 1.6

3 Order of the Rational Numbers

Often, the order relation between two rational numbers is not readily apparent. For example, which is smaller, $\frac{18}{33}$ or $\frac{44}{81}$? The answer is not obvious. Stress to students that in such cases they should convert the numbers to decimals.

$$\frac{18}{33} = 0.545\ldots \qquad \frac{44}{81} = 0.543\ldots$$

We observe that

$$\frac{44}{81} < \frac{18}{33}$$

Key Question

■ What should you do to determine the order relation of a set of fractions?
Convert to common denominator or to decimals

Chalkboard Examples

Insert either $<$ or $>$ to make a true statement.

1. 0.5 □ 0.1 $>$
2. -2.81 □ 1.73 $<$
3. -7.3 □ -1.5 $<$
4. $\frac{7}{5}$ □ $\frac{9}{5}$ $<$
5. $\frac{7}{5}$ □ $\frac{34}{25}$

   Convert to common denominator

   $\frac{35}{25} > \frac{34}{25}$; so $\frac{7}{5} > \frac{34}{25}$

6. $-\frac{3}{8}$ □ $-\frac{1}{3}$

   Convert to common denominator

   $-\frac{9}{24} < -\frac{8}{24}$ so $-\frac{3}{8} < -\frac{1}{3}$

EXAMPLES   Graph each of these numbers.

3 $\frac{5}{2}$ The number $\frac{5}{2}$ can be named $2\frac{1}{2}$.
Its graph is halfway between 2 and 3.

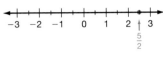

Divide the units of the number line into halves.

4 -1.2

Divide the units of the number line into tenths.

5 $\frac{7}{4}$

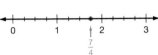

Divide the units of the number line into fourths.

Try This   Graph each rational number.

e. $\frac{12}{5}$ **f.** -4.8 **g.** $-\frac{18}{4}$ **h.** 0.5

PART 3 Order of the Rational Numbers

Objective: Compare rational numbers using > or <.

The relations $<$ (is less than) and $>$ (is greater than) are the same for rational numbers as they are for integers. Recall that numbers on the number line increase from left to right.

EXAMPLES   Use either $<$ or $>$ to write a true sentence.

6 $1.38 < 1.83$ 38 hundredths is less than 83 hundredths.

7 $-3.45 < 1.32$ Negative rational numbers are always less than positive rational numbers.

8 $-4.23 > -5.2$ –4 is farther to the right on the number line than –5, so $-4 > -5$.

9 $\frac{3}{4}$ □ $\frac{5}{8}$

   $\frac{6}{8}$ □ $\frac{5}{8}$ Find a common denominator. $\frac{3}{4} = \frac{6}{8}$

   $\frac{6}{8} > \frac{5}{8}$ $\frac{6}{8}$ is farther to the right on the number line than $\frac{5}{8}$.

   $\frac{3}{4} > \frac{5}{8}$

60   Chapter 2   *Integers and Rational Numbers*

Try This

e.

f.

g.

h.

10 $-\frac{2}{3}$ □ $-\frac{5}{8}$

$-\frac{16}{24}$ □ $-\frac{15}{24}$ Find a common denominator. $-\frac{2}{3} = -\frac{16}{24}$ $-\frac{5}{8} = -\frac{15}{24}$

$-\frac{16}{24} < -\frac{15}{24}$ $-\frac{16}{24}$ is farther to the left on the number line than $-\frac{15}{24}$.

$-\frac{2}{3} < -\frac{5}{8}$

Try This   Use either $<$ or $>$ to write a true sentence.

i. 4.62 □ 4.26   **j.** -3.11 □ -3.22 **k.** $\frac{5}{6}$ □ $\frac{7}{8}$ **l.** $-\frac{2}{3}$ □ $-\frac{4}{5}$

Rational numbers are part of a larger set of numbers called the **real numbers.** Real numbers also include irrational numbers, about which you will learn more in Chapter 11. The diagram below shows the relationships among these sets of numbers.

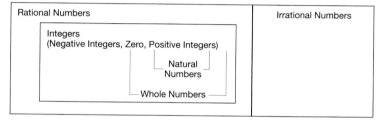

2-2 Exercises

A

Show that each number can be written as the ratio of two integers.

1. 14   **2.** -7 **3.** 4.2   **4.** 1.5

5. -0.5 **6.** -0.03 **7.** 3.444   **8.** -5.333

9. -0.68 **10.** -4 **11.** $7\frac{1}{2}$ **12.** $1\frac{2}{3}$

Graph each rational number.

13. $\frac{10}{3}$ **14.** $-\frac{17}{5}$ **15.** -4.3 **16.** 6.4

17. **TEST PREP**   To which sets of numbers does $\frac{-10}{2}$ belong?

I. Integers   II. Rational numbers   III. Whole numbers

a. I only   **b.** II only   **c.** I and II   **d.** II and III

Extra Help On the Web

Look for worked-out examples at the Prentice Hall Web site.
www.phschool.com

LESSON QUIZ

Graph each rational number

1. $\frac{3}{4}$

2. $\frac{7}{2}$

3. $-\frac{5}{4}$

Insert either $<$ or $>$ to make a true statement.

4. 4.7 □ 3.5 $4.7 > 3.5$

5. -2.5 □ -1.6 $-2.5 < -1.6$

6. $\frac{2}{3}$ □ $\frac{5}{6}$ $\frac{2}{3} < \frac{5}{6}$

7. $-\frac{3}{7}$ □ $-\frac{4}{5}$ $-\frac{3}{7} > -\frac{4}{5}$

Show that each number can be written as a ratio.

8. 14 $\frac{14}{1}$ **9.** 1.7 $\frac{17}{10}$

10. -3.17 $-\frac{317}{100}$

Assignment Guide

To provide flexible scheduling, this lesson can be split into parts.
▼ Core 1–12
   Extension 17, 41
▼ Core 13–16
▼ Core 18–29
   Extension 30–40

Use Mixed Review to maintain skills.

Try This
i. $>$
j. $>$
k. $<$
l. $>$

Exercises
1. $\frac{14}{1}$
2. $-\frac{7}{1}$
3. $\frac{42}{10}$ or $\frac{21}{5}$
4. $\frac{15}{10}$ or $\frac{3}{2}$
5. $-\frac{5}{10}$ or $-\frac{1}{2}$
6. $-\frac{3}{100}$
7. $\frac{3444}{1000}$ or $\frac{861}{250}$
8. $-\frac{5333}{1000}$
9. $-\frac{68}{100}$ or $-\frac{17}{25}$
10. $-\frac{4}{1}$
11. $\frac{15}{2}$
12. $\frac{5}{3}$

13.
14.
15.
16.
17. c

Use either $<$ or $>$ to write a true sentence.

18. $2.14 \ \square \ 1.24$ **19.** $-3.3 \ \square \ -2.2$ **20.** $7.075 \ \square \ 7.750$

21. $-14.5 \ \square \ 0.011$ **22.** $17.2 \ \square \ -1.67$ **23.** $-345 \ \square \ -354$

24. $-12.88 \ \square \ -13$ **25.** $-14.34 \ \square \ -17.88$ **26.** $-0.606 \ \square \ -0.660$

27. $\frac{4}{10} \ \square \ -\frac{1}{2}$ **28.** $-\frac{5}{12} \ \square \ -\frac{3}{8}$ **29.** $-\frac{5}{3} \ \square \ -\frac{7}{5}$

30. *Mathematical Reasoning* Show that $\frac{1}{3} > 0.33$ and that $-\frac{1}{3} < -0.33$.

B

The **density property** of rational numbers states that between any two rational numbers, there is another rational number. Find a number between the following pairs of numbers.

31. $\frac{1}{2}, \frac{1}{4}$ **32.** $\frac{1}{5}, \frac{2}{5}$ **33.** $0.45, 0.46$ **34.** $0.012, 0.013$

Write these rational numbers in order from least to greatest.

35. $\frac{3}{8}, \frac{7}{8}, \frac{1}{8}, -\frac{4}{8}, \frac{5}{8}, -\frac{8}{8}$ **36.** $\frac{6}{5}, -\frac{4}{5}, -\frac{2}{5}, \frac{4}{5}, -\frac{7}{5}, -\frac{1}{5}$

37. $\frac{4}{5}, \frac{4}{3}, \frac{4}{8}, \frac{4}{6}, \frac{4}{9}, \frac{4}{2}$ **38.** $-\frac{2}{3}, \frac{1}{2}, -\frac{3}{4}, -\frac{5}{6}, \frac{3}{8}, \frac{1}{6}$

39. *Critical Thinking* Find five ways the numbers 2, 3, 4, 5, and 7 can be placed in the boxes to make a true statement.

$$\frac{\square}{\square} > \frac{\square}{\square}$$

Challenge

40. *Mathematical Reasoning* Show that for any positive rational numbers, $\frac{a}{b}$ and $\frac{c}{d}$, if $\frac{a}{b} < \frac{c}{d}$, then $ad < cb$. (*Hint*: Find a common denominator.)

41. *Reasoning* Is the following generalization always, sometimes, or never true? $\frac{a}{b} = \frac{a+c}{b+c}$, where $b \neq 0$ and $c \neq 0$. Explain.

Mixed Review

Write as an algebraic expression. **42.** 11 less than m

43. y divided among x **44.** the sum of 9 and t **45.** 4 times w *1-6*

Find the absolute value. **46.** $|0.06|$ **47.** $|-2.3|$ **48.** $|-41|$ *2-1*

Solve. **49.** $y + \frac{3}{5} = \frac{4}{5}$ **50.** $a - \frac{1}{7} = \frac{6}{7}$ **51.** $x + \frac{2}{3} = \frac{5}{6}$

52. $\frac{a}{7} = 8$ **53.** $\frac{c}{6} = 12$ **54.** $\frac{y}{4} = 32$ **55.** $\frac{y}{3} = 7 + \frac{1}{3}$ *1-7*

Mental Math Evaluate. **56.** $D = r \cdot k$ for $r = 45$ and $k = 3$ **57.** $A = bh$ for $b = 10.2$ and $h = 5$ **58.** $P = 2w + 2l$ for $w = 17$ and $l = 2.5$ *1-1*

Exercises

18. $>$
19. $<$
20. $<$
21. $<$
22. $>$
23. $>$
24. $>$
25. $>$
26. $>$
27. $>$
28. $<$
29. $<$
30. $\frac{1}{3} \approx 0.333 > 0.330 = 0.33$
   $-\frac{1}{3} \approx -0.333 < -0.330 = -0.33$

31–34. Answers may vary.
   Examples are given.
31. $\frac{3}{8}$
32. $\frac{3}{10}$
33. 0.455
34. 0.0125
35. $-\frac{8}{8}, -\frac{4}{8}, \frac{1}{8}, \frac{3}{8}, \frac{5}{8}, \frac{7}{8}$
36. $-\frac{7}{5}, -\frac{4}{5}, -\frac{2}{5}, -\frac{1}{5}, \frac{4}{5}, \frac{6}{5}$
37. $\frac{4}{9}, \frac{4}{8}, \frac{4}{6}, \frac{4}{5}, \frac{4}{3}, \frac{4}{2}$
38. $-\frac{5}{6}, -\frac{3}{4}, -\frac{2}{3}, \frac{1}{6}, \frac{3}{8}, \frac{1}{2}$

39. Answers may vary.
   $\frac{2}{3} > \frac{4}{7}, \frac{3}{2} > \frac{5}{7}, \frac{3}{2} > \frac{4}{5}, \frac{4}{5} > \frac{2}{7}, \frac{7}{2} > \frac{5}{4}$
40. $\frac{a}{b} < \frac{c}{d}$
   $\frac{ad}{bd} < \frac{cb}{bd}$
   $\therefore \ ad < cb$
41. Sometimes; true when $a = b$.

Mixed Review
42. $m - 11$
43. $\frac{y}{x}$
44. $9 + t$
45. $4w$

46. 0.06
47. 2.3
48. 41
49. $\frac{1}{5}$
50. 1
51. $\frac{1}{6}$
52. 56
53. 72
54. 128
55. 22
56. 135
57. 51
58. 39

CA 1.0: Identify and use arithmetic properties of rational numbers.

Addition of Rational Numbers

 2-3

Math in Action

The school refreshment stand started selling popcorn during lunch and after school. They kept a record of profits and losses for the first five days of operation. What was the total profit or loss?

Monday	Tuesday	Wednesday	Thursday	Friday
$18 profit	$7 loss	$5 loss	$11 profit	$2 loss

Profit and loss statements often involve the addition of integers. This problem can be solved by finding this sum.

$$18 + (-7) + (-5) + 11 + (-2)$$

 PART 1 Addition Using a Number Line

Objective: Add rational numbers using a number line.

Addition of whole numbers can be shown by moves on a number line. To add 2 and 5, we start at 2, the first number. Then we move a distance of 5 units to the right. We end up at 7, the sum.

We can also add any two rational numbers using moves on the number line. When we add a negative number, however, we must move to the left. Recall that 0 plus any number is that number.

EXAMPLES Add using the number line.

1 $3 + (-5)$

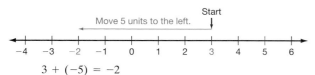

$$3 + (-5) = -2$$

 **CA: 1.0**

What You'll Learn

1 To add rational numbers using a number line

2 To add rational numbers without using a number line

3 To give the additive inverse of a number

...And Why

To learn how to operate with rational numbers so that you will be able to use them to solve real-world problems

---

2-3 TIME-FOCUS METER

1. FOCUS

FIRST FIVE MINUTES

In each case, tell how many jumps backward or forward would accomplish the same result.

1. forward 2, backward 1
   Forward 1
2. backward 1, forward 3
   Forward 2
3. forward 2, forward 3
   Forward 5
4. backward 3, backward 5
   Backward 8
5. backward 8, forward 2
   Backward 6

MATH IN ACTION

The problem posed in the opening paragraph is solved in Example 9.

2. TEACH the Mathematics

1 **Addition Using a Number Line**

Adding rational numbers on a number line provides a valuable illustration prior to learning rules for the addition of rational numbers.

You may wish to have students add Examples 1–4 in reverse order and then compare their answers.

Key Questions

Is starting at 5 and moving 2 to the left equivalent to
- starting at -2 and moving 5 to the right?
  Yes
- starting at 2 and moving 5 to the left?
  No

Chalkboard Examples

Add using the number line.

1. $2 + (-1)$

$2 + (-1) = 1$

2. $-5 + 7$

$-5 + 7 = 2$

3. $-4 + (-5)$

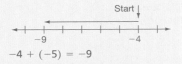

$-4 + (-5) = -9$

Use Teaching Transparency T11 to present Chalkboard Examples 1–3.

Teaching Option

The following activity provides a model that will help students gain an understanding of how to add positive and negative numbers.

Provide students with two-color counters or improvise using cardboard or buttons. Let yellow counters represent positive integers, and red counters represent negative integers. When red and yellow counters are paired, they cancel each other and both are removed.

Have students make two piles of counters, each pile consisting of only one color. They should then combine the piles, and remove pairs of counters when possible.

Students can complete several rows of a table like the one below by repeating this process several times and writing an equation that describes their actions.

First Pile
Ⓨ Ⓨ Ⓨ Ⓨ
Ⓨ Ⓨ Ⓨ Ⓨ

Second Pile
Ⓡ Ⓡ Ⓡ Ⓡ

First Pile	Second Pile	Combined Pile	Equation
8	−4	4	$8 + (-4) = 4$

Encourage students to come up with rules for adding integers and list them on the blackboard.

---

2 $-4 + (-3)$

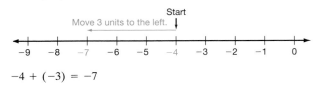

$-4 + (-3) = -7$

3 $-4 + 9$

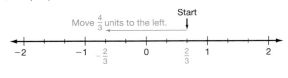

$-4 + 9 = 5$

4 $\frac{2}{3} + \left(-\frac{4}{3}\right)$

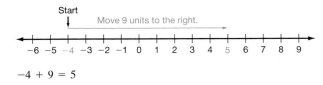

$\frac{2}{3} + \left(-\frac{4}{3}\right) = -\frac{2}{3}$

Try This   Add using the number line.

a. $4 + 3$ **b.** $-5 + 2$ **c.** $3 + (-5)$ **d.** $-4 + (-2)$ **e.** $-\frac{3}{4} + \frac{7}{4}$

PART 2 — Addition Without a Number Line

Objective: Add rational numbers without a number line.

We can use the number line to suggest how to add rational numbers.

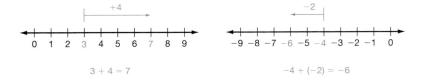

$3 + 4 = 7$ $-4 + (-2) = -6$

64   Chapter 2   *Integers and Rational Numbers*

Try This
a. 7
b. −3
c. −2
d. −6
e. $\frac{4}{4}$ or 1

These illustrations suggest the following.

Adding Two Positive or Two Negative Numbers

Add the absolute values. The sum has the same sign as the addends.

In these illustrations, we add a positive number and a negative number.

 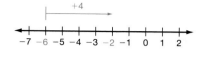

$$5 + (-2) = 3$$

$$-6 + 4 = -2$$

These illustrations suggest the following.

Adding a Positive and a Negative Number

Subtract the absolute values. The sum has the sign of the addend with the greater absolute value.

EXAMPLES   Add without using the number line.

5 $-12 + (-7) = -19$ Since both addends are negative, the sum is negative.

6 $-1.4 + 8.5 = 7.1$ The difference of the absolute values is 7.1. The positive addend has the greater absolute value, so the sum is positive.

7 $21 + (-36) = -15$ The difference of the absolute values is 15. The negative addend has the greater absolute value, so the sum is negative.

8 $-\frac{2}{3} + \frac{4}{5} = -\frac{10}{15} + \frac{12}{15}$

$= \frac{2}{15}$ The difference of the absolute values is $\frac{2}{15}$. The positive addend has the greater absolute value, so the sum is positive.

Try This   Add without using a number line.

f. $-17 + 17$ **g.** $-13 + (-7)$ **h.** $-15 + (-10)$

i. $-0.17 + 0.7$ **j.** $-12 + 25$ **k.** $14 + (-21)$

l. $\frac{3}{4} + \left(-\frac{5}{4}\right)$ **m.** $-\frac{5}{8} + \left(-\frac{1}{4}\right)$ **n.** $-\frac{4}{5} + \frac{5}{7}$

Teach the Mathematics (continued)

2 Addition Without a Number Line

Mention to students that parentheses around negative numbers are sometimes not necessary and may be omitted when the meaning is clear. For example, (-5) can be written -5.

Key Questions

- Will the sum $-3 + -4$ be positive or negative?
  Negative
- Will the sum $-3 + 4$ be positive or negative?
  Positive
- Will the sum $3 + -4$ be positive or negative?
  Negative

Chalkboard Examples

Add without using the number line.

1. $-6 + (-5) = ?$
   -11
2. $-2.3 + (-1.4) = ?$
   -3.7
3. $7.3 + (-9.7) = ?$
   -2.4
4. $-4.6 + 9.9 = ?$
   5.3
5. $12 + (-15) = ?$
   -3
6. $-\frac{2}{7} + \left(-\frac{3}{7}\right) = ?$
   $-\frac{5}{7}$
7. $-\frac{4}{9} + \frac{1}{3} = ?$
   $-\frac{4}{9} + \frac{3}{9} = -\frac{1}{9}$

Try This

f. 0
g. -20
h. -25
i. 0.53
j. 13
k. -7
l. $-\frac{2}{4}$ or $-\frac{1}{2}$
m. $-\frac{7}{8}$
n. $-\frac{3}{35}$

3 Additive Inverses

Stress that it is preferable to read −*a* as "the additive inverse of *a*" or "the opposite of *a*." This avoids the misconception that −*a* is necessarily a negative number.

Key Questions

■ How many additive inverses does −3 have?
One
■ What is the additive inverse of 0?
0
■ Is the additive inverse of a number always negative? No

Chalkboard Examples

Find the additive inverse of each.
1. −7   7
2. 34.7   −34.7
3. −4.81   4.81
4. −$\frac{3}{7}$ $\frac{3}{7}$
5. Find −*x* and −(−*x*) when *x* is 5.
   −*x* = −5
   −(−*x*) = −(−5) = 5
6. Find −*x* and −(−*x*) when *x* is −2.
   −*x* = −(−2) = 2
   −(−*x*) = −(−(−2)) = −2
7. Find −*x* and −(−*x*) when *x* is 0.
   −*x* = −0 = 0
   −(−*x*) = −(−(0)) = 0
8. Maria made $13 baby sitting, paid $11.50 for a scarf, received a $10 bill for her birthday, and bought a snack for $2.25. How much money does she now have?
   13 + (−11.50) + 10 + (−2.25)
   = 13 + 10 + (−11.50) + (−2.25)
   =   23   + (−13.75)
   =   9.25
   Maria now has $9.25.

The commutative and associative properties hold for rational numbers, so we can group and order addends as we please. One way is to group the positive numbers together and group the negative numbers together.

EXAMPLE 9   Add.

18 + (−7) + (−5) + 11 + (−2)
  = (18 + 11) + [(−7) + (−5) + (−2)]   *Grouping the positive and the negative numbers together*

  = 29   +   (−14)   *Adding the results*
  = 15

Try This   Add.

o. (−15) + (−37) + 25 + 42 + (−59) + (−14)
p. 42 + (−81) + (−28) + 24 + 18 + (−31)

PART 3   Additive Inverses

Objective: Give the additive inverse.

When opposites such as 6 and −6 are added, the sum is 0. Number pairs such as 6 and −6 are also called additive inverses.

Definition

Two rational numbers whose sum is 0 are called **additive inverses** of each other.

Every rational number has an additive inverse.

Property of Additive Inverses

For each rational number *a*, there is one and only one rational number −*a* such that *a* + (−*a*) = 0.

EXAMPLES   Find the additive inverse of each.

10   34
         The additive inverse is −34.   34 + (−34) = 0

11   −2.96
         The additive inverse is 2.96.   −2.96 + 2.96 = 0

Try This
o. −58
p. −56

12 $-\frac{5}{4}$

The additive inverse is $\frac{5}{4}$. $\qquad -\frac{5}{4} + \frac{5}{4} = 0$

Try This   Find the additive inverse of each.

q. -19 **r.** 54 **s.** 0 **t.** -7.4 **u.** $-\frac{8}{3}$

The symbol -8 is usually read "negative 8." It could also be read "the additive inverse of 8" or "the opposite of 8" because the additive inverse of 8 is negative. A symbol like $-x$ should be read "the additive inverse of x" or "the opposite of x," and not "negative x," however, because we do not know if $-x$ represents a negative number, a positive number, or 0 until we know the value of x.

Inverse of the Inverse

The inverse of the inverse of a rational number is the number itself.
$$-(-n) = n$$

EXAMPLES

13 Find $-x$ and $-(-x)$ when x is 16.

$$\begin{aligned} \text{If } x = 16, \text{ then } -x &= -(16) \qquad &\text{Replacing } x \text{ with } 16\\ &= -16 \\ -(-x) &= -(-16) \qquad &\text{Replacing } x \text{ with } 16 \\ &= 16 \end{aligned}$$

14 Find $-x$ and $-(-x)$ when x is -3.

$$\begin{aligned} \text{If } x = -3, \text{ then } -x &= -(-3) \qquad &\text{Replacing } x \text{ with } -3\\ &= 3 \\ -(-x) &= -(-(-3)) \qquad &\text{Replacing } x \text{ with } -3 \\ &= -3 \end{aligned}$$

Try This   Find $-x$ and $-(-x)$ when x is each of the following.

v. 14 **w.** 1 **x.** -19

EXAMPLE 15

A submarine is cruising at a depth of 30 m. It climbs 12 m, then dives 21 m, and then climbs 13 m. At what depth is the submarine?

$$-30 + 12 + (-21) + 13 = -26 \qquad \text{We can represent depth with a negative number. Use a positive number to represent climbing.}$$

The submarine is at a depth of -26 m.

2-3   *Addition of Rational Numbers*   **67**

Try This

q. 19

r. -54

s. 0

t. 7.4

u. $\frac{8}{3}$

v. -14, 14

w. -1, 1

x. 19, -19

LESSON QUIZ

Add.
1. $-4 + 7$
   3
2. $-7 + (-4)$
   -11
3. $-3.8 + (-4.1)$
   -7.9
4. $\frac{3}{8} + \left(-\frac{7}{8}\right)$
   $-\frac{4}{8} = -\frac{1}{2}$
5. $-\frac{1}{3} + \left(-\frac{5}{6}\right)$
   $-\frac{2}{6} + \left(-\frac{5}{6}\right) = -\frac{7}{6}$
6. $-4 + 7 + (-6) + 8$
   $-4 + (-6) + 7 + 8$
   $= -10 + 15 = 5$
7. $-12 + 8 + (-16) + (-9)$
   $-12 + (-16) + (-9) + 8$
   $= -37 + 8 = -29$

Find the additive inverse of each.
8. -14
   The additive inverse is 14.
9. $\frac{7}{3}$
   The additive inverse is $-\frac{7}{3}$.
10. Find $-x$ when x is -4.
    $-(-4) = 4$
11. A blimp rose 500 ft, fell 700 ft, fell
    1300 ft, and rose 300 ft. How much did
    it rise or fall all together?
    $5 + (-7) + (-13) + 3$
    $= 5 + 3 + (-7) + (-13)$
    $= 8 + (-20) = -12$
    It fell 1200 feet.
12. For what number x is $-x$ equal to x?
    $-0 = 0$

Assignment Guide

To provide flexible scheduling, this
lesson can be split into parts.
▼ Core 1–8
   Extension 51–53, 70
▼ Core 9–34, 57–63
   Extension 55–56, 72–75
▼ Core 35–50, 64–69
   Extension 54, 71, 76

Use Mixed Review to maintain skills.

Try This   Solve.

y. Rico carried the ball six times in the third quarter of a football game. Here
are his gains and losses: 11-yd gain, 4-yd loss, 6-yd loss, 5-yd gain, 8-yd gain,
2-yd loss. What was the total number of yards he gained (or lost)?

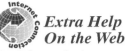
*Extra Help
On the Web*

Look for worked-out
examples at the Prentice
Hall Web site.
www.phschool.com

2-3 Exercises

A

Add using a number line.
1. $-9 + 2$	**2.** $2 + (-5)$	**3.** $-10 + 6$	**4.** $8 + (-3)$
5. $-8 + 8$	**6.** $6 + (-6)$	**7.** $-3 + (-5)$	**8.** $-4 + (-6)$

Add without using a number line.
9. $-7 + 0$	**10.** $-13 + 0$	**11.** $0 + (-27)$
12. $0 + (-35)$	**13.** $17 + (-17)$	**14.** $-15 + 15$
15. $-17 + (-25)$	**16.** $-24 + (-17)$	**17.** $-14 + (-29)$
18. $-\frac{5}{8} + \frac{1}{4}$	**19.** $-\frac{5}{6} + \frac{2}{3}$	**20.** $-\frac{3}{7} + \left(-\frac{2}{5}\right)$
21. $-\frac{5}{8} + \left(-\frac{1}{3}\right)$	**22.** $-\frac{3}{5} + \left(-\frac{2}{15}\right)$	**23.** $-\frac{5}{9} + \left(-\frac{1}{18}\right)$

24. $-44 + \left(-\frac{3}{8}\right) + 95 + \left(-\frac{5}{8}\right)$

25. $\frac{-3}{12} + \frac{3}{18} + \frac{-7}{6} + 2$

26. $24 + 3.1 + (-44) + (-8.2) + 63$

27. $-17 + 28 + (-12) + (-20.5) + 16.5$

28. $24 + (-36) + 75 + (-75) + 82 + (-63)$

29. $98 + (-54) + 113 + (-998) + 44 + (-612) + (-18) + 334$

30. $-455 + (-123) + 1026 + (-919) + 213 + 111 + (-874)$

Estimation   Which of the two numbers is greater? Use estimation
to decide.
31. $14 + (-36)$ or $14 + (-35)$	**32.** $-32 + (-9)$ or $-32 + (-8)$
33. $-\frac{3}{5} + \frac{2}{5}$ or $-\frac{3}{5} + \frac{3}{5}$	**34.** $-16 + 9$ or $-16 + (-9)$

Find the additive inverse of each.
35. 24	**36.** -64	**37.** -9	**38.** $\frac{7}{2}$	**39.** -26.9	**40.** 48.2

Find $-x$ when x is
41. 9	**42.** -26	**43.** $-\frac{14}{3}$	**44.** $\frac{1}{328}$	**45.** 0.101	**46.** 0

Try This
y. 12 yd gained

Exercises
1. -7
2. -3
3. -4
4. 5
5. 0
6. 0
7. -8
8. -10
9. -7
10. -13

11. -27
12. -35
13. 0
14. 0
15. -42
16. -41
17. -43
18. $-\frac{3}{8}$
19. $-\frac{1}{6}$
20. $-\frac{29}{35}$
21. $-\frac{23}{24}$
22. $-\frac{11}{15}$

23. $-\frac{11}{18}$
24. 50
25. $\frac{3}{4}$
26. 37.9
27. -5
28. 7
29. -1093
30. -1021
31. $14 + (-35)$
32. $-32 + (-8)$
33. $-\frac{3}{5} + \frac{3}{5}$
34. $-16 + 9$

35. -24
36. 64
37. 9
38. $-\frac{7}{2}$
39. 26.9
40. -48.2
41. -9
42. 26
43. $\frac{14}{3}$
44. $-\frac{1}{328}$
45. -0.101
46. 0

Find $-(-x)$ when x is

47. -65 **48.** 29 **49.** $\frac{5}{3}$ **50.** -9.1

Mathematical Reasoning Use *sometimes*, *always*, or *never* to make the statement true.

51. The sum of two negative numbers is ___?___ positive.

52. The sum of two positive numbers is ___?___ positive.

53. The sum of a positive and a negative number is ___?___ positive.

54. The additive inverse of a number is ___?___ negative.

55. The sum of two numbers is ___?___ greater than either number.

56. The sum of two numbers is ___?___ less than either number.

Solve.

57. The barometric pressure at Omaha was 1012 millbars (mb). The pressure dropped 6 mb, then it rose 3 mb. After that it dropped 14 mb and then rose 4 mb. What was the pressure then?

58. In a football game, the quarterback attempted passes with the following results. Find the total gain (or loss).

first try	13-yd gain
second try	incomplete
third try	12-yd loss (tackled behind the line)
fourth try	21-yd gain
fifth try	14-yd loss

Barometric pressure is also measured in inches of mercury (the length of a column of mercury that is supported by the atmosphere). A pressure of 1012 mb is equivalent to 29.88 in. of mercury. How many inches of mercury are equivalent to 999 mb?

59. The average attendance at a soccer game last year was 1755 people. The table below shows the attendance for each game this year compared to last year's average. By how much was the total attendance for all 6 games above or below last year's?

Game 1	Game 2	Game 3	Game 4	Game 5	Game 6
+357	−144	−250	+347	+420	−188

60. The business class kept a record of the change in a stock market for a period of 5 weeks. After 5 weeks, how many points had the market gained or lost?

Week 1	Week 2	Week 3	Week 4	Week 5
down 120 pts	down 150 pts	up 350 pts	down 100 pts	up 180 pts

61. In a board game, Alice started with $1475. After these transactions how much did Alice have?

purchased properties	1700
collected rents	1640
purchased houses	900
passed start (collected money)	1200

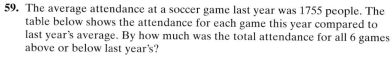

Exercises

47. -65

48. 29

49. $\frac{5}{3}$

50. -9.1

51. never

52. always

53. sometimes

54. sometimes

55. sometimes

56. sometimes

57. 999 mb

Photo caption: 29.50 in. of mercury

58. 8-yd gain

59. 542 above last year's

60. Up 160 points

61. $1715

62. The table below shows the profits and losses of a company over a six-year period. Find the total profit or loss for this period of time.

Year	Profit or loss ($)
1994	+32,056
1995	−2,925
1996	+81,429
1997	−19,365
1998	−13,875
1999	+384

63. Francine received an allowance of $5.00, bought a pen for $0.59, gave $1.75 to Pat, made $10.50 baby sitting, and spent $6.75 at a movie. How much did she have left?

B

64. For what numbers x is $-x$ negative?

65. For what numbers x is $-x$ positive?

Mathematical Reasoning   Tell whether the sum is *positive*, *negative*, or *zero*. Explain your answers.

66. n is positive, m is negative. $n + (-m)$ is _____.

67. n is positive, m is negative. $-n + m$ is _____.

68. $n = m$, n and m are negative. $-n + (-m)$ is _____.

69. $n = m$, n and m are negative. $n + (-m)$ is _____.

70. Name the largest negative integer.

71. *Write a Convincing Argument*   Write an argument to convince a classmate that $-(-n) = n$.

Challenge

Solve.

72. $x + x = 0$

73. $x + (-5) = x$

74. $3y + (-2) = 7$

75. $x + (-5) = 16$

76. Does $x - y = x + (-y)$ for all numbers x and y?

Mixed Review

Solve.   **77.** $2.6n = 6.24$ **78.** $w - 1.07 = 3.24$ **79.** $7r = 84$ *1-7*

Use either $<$ or $>$ to write a true sentence.   **80.** $-9 \square 2$

81. $-4 \square -6$ **82.** $-1 \square 0$ **83.** $3.62 \square 3.26$ **84.** $0 \square 0.001$ *2-1*

Find the absolute value.   **85.** $|2|$ **86.** $|-4|$ **87.** $|-2.03|$ **88.** $|0|$ *2-1*

89. Each of the members of Miss Odell's class read 8 books. If the class read 104 books in all, how many members are in the class?   *1-10*

70 Chapter 2 Integers and Rational Numbers

Exercises

62. 77,704 profit
63. $6.41
64. When x is positive
65. When x is negative
66. Positive; n is positive and $-m$ is positive, so their sum is positive.
67. Negative; $-n$ is negative and m is negative, so their sum is negative.
68. Positive; $-n$ is positive and $-m$ is positive, so their sum is positive.
69. Zero; $-m$ is the additive inverse of n, so their sum is zero.
70. -1
71. Answers may vary, but should include the idea that since $-n + n = 0$, the additive inverse of $-n$ is n.
72. 0
73. No value
74. 3
75. 21
76. Yes

Mixed Review

77. 2.4
78. 4.31
79. 12
80. $<$
81. $>$
82. $<$
83. $>$
84. $<$
85. 2
86. 4
87. 2.03
88. 0
89. 13

CA 1.0: Identify and use arithmetic properties of rational numbers.

Subtraction of Rational Numbers

The floor of Death Valley, California, can be seen betweeen the two mountain ranges.

Math in Action

The lowest point in Asia is the Dead Sea, 396 meters below sea level. The lowest point in the United States is Death Valley, 86 meters below sea level. How much higher is Death Valley than the Dead Sea?

Drawing a diagram can help you understand the problem.

Let *d* be the difference between the altitude of Death Valley and the Dead Sea. You can solve this problem by subtracting rational numbers.

$$d = -86 - (-396)$$

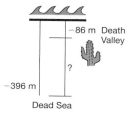

PART 1

Subtraction on a Number Line

Objective: Subtract rational numbers using a number line.

We can subtract rational numbers by using the definition of subtraction and a number line.

Definition

For all rational numbers *a* and *b*, the **difference** $a - b$ is the number *c*, such that $c + b = a$.

2-4   *Subtraction of Rational Numbers*   **71**

What You'll Learn

1 To subtract rational numbers using a number line

2 To subtract rational numbers without using a number line

... And Why

To learn how to operate with rational numbers so that you will be able to use them to solve real-world problems

---

  CA: 1.0

 TIME-FOCUS METER

2-4

1. FOCUS

FIRST FIVE MINUTES

Add.
1. $5 + (-7)$ -2
2. $-3 + (-4)$ -7
3. $-3.9 + 2.1$ -1.8
4. What is the additive inverse of -12?
   12
5. What is the additive inverse of $-(-12)$?
   -12
6. Simplify $-(-3)$. $-(-3) = 3$
7. Add.

   $\frac{2}{7} + \left(-\frac{3}{14}\right)$

   $\frac{4}{14} + \left(-\frac{3}{14}\right) = \frac{1}{14}$

MATH IN ACTION

In the introductory problem,
   $d = -86 - (-396)$
   $\quad = 310$
Death Valley is 310 meters higher than the Dead Sea.

You may want to show students the following alternate solution.
   $d = -396 - (-86)$
   $d = -396 + 86$
   $d = -310$
The Dead Sea is 310 meters *lower* than Death Valley.

Stress that both methods are correct, but since the question asked how much higher Death Valley is, the answer should be given in that form.

2. TEACH the Mathematics

1 **Subtraction on a Number Line**

After solving $10 - 12$ in Example 1, show students that the number line solution of $10 + (-12)$ gives the same answer.

Key Question

- In Example 1, how far and in which direction would you go to move from 12 to 10?

  Move 2 in the negative direction (to the left).

Chalkboard Examples

Subtract using a number line.

1. **−3 − 7**

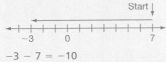

−3 − 7 = −10

2. **− 9 − (−5)**

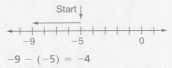

−9 − (−5) = −4

3. **10 − 7**

10 − 7 = 3

4. **− 4 − (−6)**

−4 − (−6) = 2

Teaching Option

The following cooperative learning activity models subtraction of positive and negative numbers.

Divide the class into groups of 4 or 5 students. Remind students that yellow counters represent positive numbers and that red counters represent negative numbers. Provide each group with 9 chips, including at least one of each color. Give groups the following instructions.

Your set of counters represents an integer. Determine the value of that integer. Then, beginning with your original set, show the values you can make:

- if you remove 1 counter
- if you remove 2 counters
- if you remove 3 counters

Draw a diagram to represent each action and record the value of each.

Example:

  Value: −1

EXAMPLE 1   Subtract.

$$10 - 12$$

From the definition of subtraction, the number that can be added to 12 to get 10 will be the answer. On a number line we start at 12 and move to 10.

We moved 2 units in the negative direction. The answer is −2. Therefore, $10 - 12 = -2$. We can check by adding, $12 + (-2) = 10$.

EXAMPLE 2   Subtract.

$$-1 - (-5)$$

We read this "negative 1 minus negative 5." From the definition of subtraction, the number that can be added to −5 to get −1 will be the answer. Start at −5 and move to −1.

We moved 4 units in the positive direction. The answer is 4. Therefore, $-1 - (-5) = 4$. Check by adding, $-5 + 4 = -1$.

Try This   Subtract using a number line.

a. $-2 - 6$ **b.** $4 - 10$ **c.** $-9 - (-4)$

PART 2   Subtraction Without a Number Line

Objective: Subtract rational numbers without using a number line.

The examples below show that adding the opposite of a rational number gives the same result as subtracting the rational number.

$8 - 3 = 5$	$8 + (-3) = 5$
$4 - 7 = -3$	$4 + (-7) = -3$
$-4.5 - 2 = -6.5$	$-4.5 + (-2) = -6.5$

These examples suggest the following rule.

Subtracting Numbers

For all rational numbers a and b, $a - b = a + (-b)$.
(To subtract a rational number, add its additive inverse or opposite.)

Try This

a. −8
b. −6
c. −5

EXAMPLES Subtract.

3 $2 - 6 = 2 + (-6)$ Writing as addition; adding the opposite of 6
      $= -4$ Adding

4 $-86 - (-400) = -86 + 400$
               $= 314$

5 $-4.2 - (-3.6) = -4.2 + 3.6$
              $= -0.6$

6 $-\frac{1}{2} - \frac{3}{4} = -\frac{1}{2} + \left(-\frac{3}{4}\right) = -\frac{5}{4}$

Try This   Subtract.

d. $4 - 9$ **e.** $6 - (-4)$ **f.** $-4 - 17$

g. $-3 - (-12)$ **h.** $\frac{3}{8} - \left(-\frac{1}{4}\right)$

When addition and subtraction occur several times, we can use the rule for subtracting rational numbers to make them all additions.

EXAMPLE 7   Simplify.

     $8 - (-4) - 2 - (-4) + 2 = 8 + 4 + (-2) + 4 + 2$
                           $= 16$

EXAMPLE 8   Simplify.

     $-4 - (-2x) + x - (-5) = -4 + 2x + x + 5$
                          $= 3x + 1$ Combining like terms

Try This   Simplify.

i. $-6 - (-2) - (-4) - 12 + 3$
j. $3 - (-7.1) + 6.3 - (-5.2)$
k. $-8 - (-3x) + 2x - (-13)$

EXAMPLE 9

Mr. Casper had $75.50 in his checking account. He wrote a check for $95.00. By how much has he overdrawn his checking account? Let $c =$ the amount in his checking account.

     $c = 75.50 - 95.00$
     $c = -19.50$

He has overdrawn his checking account by $19.50.

Try This
   d. -5
   e. 10
   f. -21
   g. 9
   h. $\frac{5}{8}$
   i. -9
   j. 21.6
   k. $5x + 5$

Removing 2 counters:

     Value: -3

     Value: -1

     Value: $+1$

Have each group present its results to the class, then encourage students to make generalizations.

2 **Subtraction Without a Number Line**

It is helpful to have students practice saying "add the opposite" as you work through the chalkboard examples. Stress that in the first chalkboard example, $5 - 8$, both the 5 and the 8 are positive numbers. You may want to write $+5 - (+8)$.

Key Question

- Using the numbers 5 and 8, addition, subtraction, and additive inverses, how many different numbers can you write?
     $5 + 8 = 13$
     $5 - 8 = -3$
     $-5 + 8 = 3$
     $-5 - 8 = -13$
There are many other equations, but only these 4 numbers.

Chalkboard Examples
Subtract.
   1. $5 - 8$
     $5 + (-8) = -3$
   2. $-8 - (-5)$
     $-8 + (-(-5)) = -8 + 5 = -3$
   3. $-6.7 - 9.1$
     $-6.7 + (-9.1) = -15.8$
   4. $-\frac{1}{3} - \left(\frac{5}{3}\right)$
     $-\frac{1}{3} + \left(-\frac{5}{3}\right) = -\frac{6}{3} = -2$
Simplify.
   5. $4 - 5 + (-3) + 1$
     $4 + (-5) + (-3) + 1$
     $= 4 + 1 + (-5) + (-3)$
     $= 5 + (-8) = -3$
   6. $9.1 - (-4.2) + 3.7$
     $9.1 + (-(-4.2)) + 3.7$
     $= 9.1 + 4.2 + 3.7 = 17.0$
   7. $-6 - (-3x) + 5x + 2$
     $-6 + (-(-3x)) + 5x + 2$
     $= -6 + 2 + 3x + 5x$
     $= -4 + 8x$

8. Ace Drilling is digging a well. The ground level at the surface is 112 feet above sea level. They drill down 250 feet. How far below sea level is the bottom of the well?
Ground level is 112.
The well depth is −250.
112 + (−250) = −138
The bottom of the well is 138 ft below sea level.

LESSON ENRICHMENT

Magic Squares with Integers

Use each of the integers −4, −3, −2, −1, 0, 1, 2, 3, and 4 exactly once to fill in a three by three table so that all the rows, columns, and diagonals add up to 0. Get students started by drawing the table and putting a −1 in the top left-hand corner and a 3 in the bottom left-hand corner. Note that answers for magic squares may vary.

−1	4	−3
−2	0	2
3	−4	1

3. PRACTICE/ASSESS

LESSON QUIZ

Add or subtract.
1. 5 − 9 −4
2. −11 + 3 −8
3. −13 − 5 −18
4. 12 − (−3)
   12 + 3 = 15
5. $-\frac{6}{9} - \left(-\frac{2}{3}\right)$
   $= -\frac{6}{9} + \frac{2}{3}$
   $= -\frac{6}{9} + \frac{6}{9} = 0$

Simplify.
6. 14 − (−5) + 3 − 9
   = 14 + 5 + 3 − 9
   = 22 − 9 = 13
7. −6 − (−5x) + 4x + 3
   = −6 + 3 + 5x + 4x
   = −3 + 9x
8. The temperature was −12° at dusk and fell to −23° at midnight. How much and in what direction did the temperature change?
   −23 − (−12)
   = −23 + 12 = −11
   It fell 11°.

Try This   Solve.

I. Juan has saved $35 toward a new stereo system. The total cost of the system is $125. How much more money does Juan need?

Extra Help On the Web
Look for worked-out examples at the Prentice Hall Web site.
www.phschool.com

2-4 Exercises

A

Subtract using a number line.
1. $3 - 7$ 2. $4 - 9$ 3. $0 - 7$ 4. $0 - 10$
5. $5 - (-2)$ 6. $-6 - (-8)$ 7. $-10 - (-10)$ 8. $-8 - (-8)$

Subtract.
9. $7 - 7$ 10. $0.9 - 0.9$ 11. $7 - (-7)$
12. $4 - (-4)$ 13. $8 - (-3)$ 14. $-7 - 4$
15. $-6 - 8$ 16. $6 - (-10)$ 17. $-4 - (-9)$
18. $15 - (-6)$ 19. $0 - 5$ 20. $0 - 0.6$
21. $-51 - (-2)$ 22. $-39 - (-41)$ 23. $-79 - 114$
24. $-197 - 216$ 25. $0 - (-500)$ 26. $500 - (-1000)$
27. $-2.8 - 0$ 28. $6.04 - 1.1$ 29. $7 - 10.53$
30. $8 - (-9.3)$ 31. $\frac{1}{6} - \frac{2}{3}$ 32. $-\frac{3}{8} - \left(-\frac{1}{2}\right)$
33. $\frac{12}{5} - \frac{12}{5}$ 34. $-\frac{4}{7} - \left(-\frac{10}{7}\right)$ 35. $-\frac{7}{10} - \frac{10}{15}$
36. $-\frac{4}{18} - \left(-\frac{2}{9}\right)$ 37. $\frac{1}{13} - \frac{1}{12}$ 38. $-\frac{1}{7} - \left(-\frac{1}{6}\right)$

Simplify.
39. $18 - (-15) - 3 - (-5) + 2$
40. $22 - (-18) + 7 + (-42) - 27$
41. $-31 + (-28) - (-14) - 17$
42. $-43 - (-19) - (-21) + 25$
43. $-34 - 28 + (-33) - 44$
44. $39 + (-88) - 29 - (-83)$
45. $84 + (-99) + 44 - (-18) - 43$
46. $-5 - (-3x) + 3x + 4x - (-12)$
47. $14 + (-5x) + 2x - (-32)$
48. $13x - (-2x) + 45 - (-21)$
49. $8x - (-2x) - 14 - (-5x) + 53$
50. **Error Analysis**   A student claims that $-12 - (-3)$ equals -15. How would you convince the student that the answer is incorrect?

Try This
I. $90

Exercises
1. −4
2. −5
3. −7
4. −10
5. 7
6. 2
7. 0
8. 0
9. 0
10. 0
11. 14
12. 8
13. 11
14. −11
15. −14
16. 16
17. 5
18. 21
19. −5
20. −0.6
21. −49
22. 2
23. −193
24. −413
25. 500
26. 1500
27. −2.8
28. 4.94
29. −3.53
30. 17.3
31. $-\frac{1}{2}$
32. $\frac{1}{8}$
33. 0
34. $\frac{6}{7}$
35. $-\frac{41}{30}$
36. 0
37. $-\frac{1}{156}$
38. $\frac{1}{42}$
39. 37
40. −22
41. −62
42. 22
43. −139
44. 5
45. 4
46. 10x + 7
47. −3x + 46
48. 15x + 66
49. 15x + 39

Solve.

51. Mrs. Kang has $619.46 in her checking account. She wrote a check for $950.00. By how much did she overdraw her checking account?

52. Omar had $137.40 in his checking account. He wrote a check for $225.20. By how much has he overdrawn his checking account?

53. On a winter night the temperature dropped from −5°C to −12°C. How many degrees did the temperature drop?

54. The temperature at 6 P.M. was 5°C. At 9 P.M. the temperature had dropped to −5°C. How many degrees did the temperature fall?

55. There are 47 females in the band. If there is a total of 163 band members, how many males are in the band?

56. Sarah had a balance of $45 in her checking account. She wrote two checks totaling $12. How much money does she have in her checking account now?

57. The lowest point in Africa is Lake Assal, which is 156 m below sea level. The lowest point in South America is the Valdes Peninsula, which is 40 m below sea level. How much lower is Lake Assal than the Valdes Peninsula?

58. The deepest point in the Pacific Ocean is the Marianas Trench, which is 10,415 m deep. The deepest point in the Atlantic Ocean is the Puerto Rico Trench, which is 8,648 m deep. How much deeper is the Marianas Trench than the Puerto Rico Trench?

TEST PREP   Compare the boxed quantity in column A with the boxed quantity in column B. Choose the best answer.
  A. The quantity in column A is greater.
  B. The quantity in column B is greater.
  C. The two quantities are equal.
  D. The relationship cannot be determined with the information supplied.

	column A	column B			column A	column B
59.	$10 - 1$	$10 - 5$	60.		$10 - (-1)$	$10 - (-5)$
61.	$-10 - 1$	$-10 - 5$	62.		$-10 - (-1)$	$-10 - (-5)$
63.	$x - 1$	$x - 5$	64.		$x - (-1)$	$x - (-5)$

B

65. Evaluate each expression using the values from the table.

a	b	x	y	z
5	−8	−2.3	4.1	0

  a. $(a + x) - b$ b. $z - (b - x)$
  c. $(x - y) + (a - b)$ d. $(y - x) - (b - a)$
  e. $b - |x - a|$ f. $|x| - a - (|b| + y)$

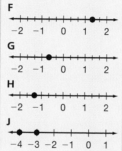

Practice
Multiple Choice

Choose the best answer.

1. Evaluate $|a| - |b|$ when a = −15 and b = 8.

  A −23
  B 7
  C −7
  D 23

2. Which graph shows $-\frac{4}{3}$ on a number line?

F
  −2 −1 0 1 2

G
  −2 −1 0 1 2

H
  −2 −1 0 1 2

J
  −4 −3 −2 −1 0 1

1. B; Algebra 3.0
2. H; Algebra 2.0

Assignment Guide
To provide flexible scheduling, this lesson can be split into parts.
▼ Core 1–8, 50, 53–56
  Extension 59–64, 66
▼ Core 9–49, 51–52, 57–58
  Extension 65, 67–76

Use Mixed Review to maintain skills.

Exercises

50. Sample answer: If 12 red counters represent −12 and you remove 3 of them to represent subtracting −3, the result is 9 red counters which represent −9.
51. $330.54
52. $87.80
53. 7°
54. 10°
55. 116 males
56. $33
57. 116 m

58. 1767 m
59. A
60. B
61. A
62. B
63. A
64. B
65. a. 10.7
    b. 5.7
    c. 6.6
    d. 19.4
    e. −15.3
    f. −14.8

66. *Critical Thinking* Study the first scale and then add items to the right side of the second scale so it will balance.

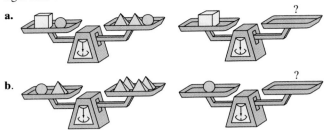

a.

b.

Challenge

Mathematical Reasoning If a statement is not true for all integers m and n, give a counterexample.

67. $n - 0 = 0 - n$

68. $0 - n = n$

69. If $m \neq n$, then $m - n \neq 0$.

70. If $m = -n$, then $m + n = 0$.

71. If $m + n = 0$, then m and n are additive inverses.

72. If $m - n = 0$, then $m = -n$.

73. Do the commutative and associative properties hold for subtraction of integers?

74. Simplify $-[-(-5)]$ and $-\{-[-(-5)]\}$. Give a rule for determining the sign of expressions like these, which involve any number of negative signs.

75. Is $a - 1 \leq a$ for all, some, or no rational numbers? Explain.

76. Does $|a| \cdot (b + c) = |a| \cdot b + |a| \cdot c$ for all integers a, b, and c?

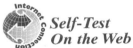
Self-Test On the Web
Check your progress. Look for a self-test at the Prentice Hall Web site. www.phschool.com

Mixed Review

Evaluate. **77.** $(n + 3)^2$ for $n = 4$ **78.** $(3n)^3 - 100$ for $n = 2$

79. t^4 for $t = 3$ **80.** n^5 for $n = 2$ **81.** $9y^3$ for $y = 3$

82. m^3 for $m = 0$ **83.** $3t^2 + 6$ for $t = 2$ **84.** $2|m|$ for $m = -3$ *1-3*

Mental Math Solve. **85.** $3y = 3$ **86.** $\frac{a}{2} = 4$ **87.** $4y = 1$ *1-7*

Combine like terms.

88. $3x + 5x^2 + 5x + 2x^2$ **89.** $2a + 3b + 4c + 5b$ *1-5*

Factor. **90.** $3c^2 + 5c$ **91.** $6x + 24y - 18z$ **92.** $6m + 9p$ *1-5*

76 Chapter 2 Integers and Rational Numbers

76 Chapter 2 *Integers and Rational Numbers*

Exercises

66. a.

b.

67. False; $3 - 0 \neq 0 - 3$

68. False; $0 - 3 \neq 3$

69. True

70. True

71. True

72. False; $3 - 3 = 0, 3 \neq -3$

73. No

74. $-[-(-5)] = -5$
$-\{-[-(-5)]\} = 5$
A term with an even number of negative signs is positive. A term with an odd number of negative signs is negative.

75. All; $a - 1$ is to the left of a on the number line.

76. Yes

Mixed Review

77. 49

78. 116

79. 81

80. 32

81. 243

82. 0

83. 18

84. 6

85. $y = 1$

86. $a = 8$

87. $y = \frac{1}{4}$

88. $7x^2 + 8x$

89. $2a + 8b + 4c$

90. $c(3c + 5)$

91. $6(x + 4y - 3z)$

92. $3(2m + 3p)$

Multiplication of Rational Numbers

Objective: Multiply rational numbers.

Introducing the Concept: Multiplication of Integers

We know that one interpretation of multiplication is as repeated addition. For example, $5 \cdot 3$ can be written as $3 + 3 + 3 + 3 + 3 = 15$. Therefore, $5 \cdot 3 = 15$. Use this interpretation of multiplication to copy and complete the table below. What patterns do you see?

Factor	Factor	Repeated Addition	Product
5	4	$4 + 4 + 4 + 4 + 4$	20
5	3	$3 + 3 + 3 + 3 + 3$	15
5	2		
5	1		
5	0		
5	−1		
5	−2		
5	−3		

The table above suggests the following rule.

Multiplying a Positive Number and a Negative Number

To multiply a positive number and a negative number, multiply their absolute values. The sign of the product is negative.

EXAMPLES Multiply.

1 $8(-5) = -40$ **2** $-\frac{1}{3} \cdot \frac{5}{7} = -\frac{5}{21}$ **3** $(-7.2)5 = -36.0$ or -36

Try This Multiply.

a. $(-3)6$ **b.** $20(-5)$ **c.** $4.5(-20)$ **d.** $-\frac{2}{3}\left(\frac{9}{4}\right)$

How do we multiply two negative numbers? Since -3 is the opposite of 3, it seems reasonable that $-3(-5)$ would be the opposite of $3(-5)$. You saw above that $3(-5) = -15$. So, $-3(-5) = 15$ (the opposite of -15). This example suggests the following rule.

2-5 *Multiplication of Rational Numbers* **77**

What You'll Learn

▼ To multiply rational numbers

...And Why

To learn how to operate with rational numbers so that you will be able to use them to solve real-world problems

---

1. FOCUS

FIRST FIVE MINUTES

Subtract.
1. $3 \cdot 5 - (3 \cdot 5)$ 0

Factor. Simplify, if possible.
2. $2 \cdot a + 2 \cdot b$ $2 \cdot (a + b)$
3. $2 \cdot 5 + 2 \cdot (-5)$
   $2 \cdot (5 + (-5)) = 2 \cdot 0 = 0$
4. $2 \cdot y + 2 \cdot (-y)$
   $2 \cdot (y + (-y)) = 2 \cdot 0 = 0$
5. $x \cdot y + x \cdot (-y)$
   $x \cdot (y + (-y)) = x \cdot 0 = 0$
6. What number is its own inverse?
   $0 = -0$

2. TEACH the Mathematics

INTRODUCING THE CONCEPT

Ask students to make a chart like the one to the left and fill it in. Then have them complete a similar chart as follows.

$2 \cdot (-3) = -3 + (-3) = -6$
$1 \cdot (-3) =$
$0 \cdot (-3) =$
$-1 \cdot (-3) =$

The students should be able to use the pattern to determine that the product of two negative numbers is a positive number.

Once students understand the rules for determining the sign of a product, you may wish to present the following:

+ times + = +
+ times − = −
− times + = −
− times − = +

Math Point

Factor and simplify the expression
$2(5) + 2(-5) = 2(5 + -5)$
$= 2(0)$
$= 0$

Hence
$2 \cdot 5 + 2(-5) = 0$
$2(-5) = -(2 \cdot 5)$
This argument works for any two numbers x and y and shows the general principle that
$x \cdot (-y) = -(x \cdot y)$
for any numbers x and y.

Introducing the Concept: Multiplication of Integers		Try This
$2 + 2 + 2 + 2 + 2$	10	a. −18
$1 + 1 + 1 + 1 + 1$	5	b. −100
$0 + 0 + 0 + 0 + 0$	0	c. −90
$-1 + (-1) + (-1) + (-1) + (-1)$	−5	d. $-\frac{3}{2}$
$-2 + (-2) + (-2) + (-2) + (-2)$	−10	
$-3 + (-3) + (-3) + (-3) + (-3)$	−15	

78 Chapter 2 *Integers and Rational Numbers*

Key Questions

Which products are positive?

- $-1 \cdot 1$ No
- $-1 \cdot -1$ Yes
- $1 \cdot -1$ No
- $1 \cdot 1$ Yes

Chalkboard Examples

Multiply.

1. $3 \cdot (-2)$ -6
2. $-5 \cdot 3$ -15
3. $\left(-\frac{1}{3}\right) \cdot \left(\frac{2}{5}\right)$ $-\frac{2}{15}$
4. $3.5 \cdot (-4)$ -14
5. $876 \cdot 0$ 0
6. $\left(-\frac{3}{7}\right) \cdot \left(-\frac{4}{2}\right)$
   $\left(\frac{3}{7}\right) \cdot \left(\frac{4}{2}\right) = \frac{12}{14}$ or $\frac{6}{7}$
7. $(-4)(-2)(3)$
   $8 \cdot 3 = 24$
8. $-7 \cdot 3(-5)$
   $(-21)(-5) = 105$
9. $-2(-6)(3)(-1)$
   $12(3)(-1) = 36(-1) = -36$

Multiplying Two Negative Numbers

To multiply two negative numbers, multiply their absolute values. The sign of the product is positive.

We already know how to multiply two positive numbers. The only case we have not considered is multiplying by 0.

Multiplicative Property of Zero

For any rational number n, $n \cdot 0 = 0$.
(The product of 0 and any rational number is 0.)

EXAMPLES Multiply.

4 $\quad -3(-4) = 12$ **5** $\quad -1.6(-2) = 3.2$ **6** $\quad -\frac{5}{6}\left(-\frac{1}{9}\right) = \frac{5}{54}$

Try This Multiply.

e. $-5(-4)$ **f.** $-8(0)$ **g.** $-4.2(-3)$ **h.** $-\frac{3}{8}\left(-\frac{1}{7}\right)$

The commutative and associative properties of multiplication hold for rational numbers. We can, therefore, choose the order and grouping.

EXAMPLES Multiply.

7 $\quad -8(2)(-3) = -16(-3)$ Multiplying the first two numbers
$\qquad\qquad\qquad\quad = 48$ Multiplying the results

8 $\quad -8(2)(-3) = 24 \cdot 2$ Multiplying the negative numbers
$\qquad\qquad\qquad\quad = 48$

9 $\quad -\frac{1}{2}(8)\left(-\frac{2}{3}\right)(-6) = (-4)4$
$\qquad\qquad\qquad\qquad\qquad = -16$

Try This Multiply.

i. $-5(-6)(-3)$
j. $-4(5)(-3)(2)$
k. $(-7)\left(-\frac{2}{3}\right)\left(-\frac{1}{7}\right)(9)$

Try This
e. 20
f. 0
g. 12.6
h. $\frac{3}{56}$
i. -90
j. 120
k. -6

A

Multiply.

1. $-8 \cdot 2$ **2.** $-2 \cdot 5$ **3.** $-7 \cdot 6$ **4.** $-9 \cdot 2$

5. $8(-3)$ **6.** $9(-5)$ **7.** $-9 \cdot 8$ **8.** $-10 \cdot 3$

9. $-8(-2)$ **10.** $-2(-5)$ **11.** $-7(-6)$ **12.** $-9(-2)$

13. $15(-8)$ **14.** $-12(-10)$ **15.** $-14(17)$ **16.** $-13(-15)$

17. $-25(-48)$ **18.** $39(-43)$ **19.** $-3.5(-28)$ **20.** $97(2.1)$

21. $\frac{1}{5}\left(\frac{-2}{9}\right)$ **22.** $-\frac{3}{5}\left(-\frac{2}{7}\right)$

23. $-7(-21)(13)$ **24.** $-14 \cdot 34 \cdot 12$

25. $-4(-1.8)(7)$ **26.** $-8(-1.3)(-5)$

27. $-\frac{1}{9}\left(\frac{-2}{3}\right)\left(\frac{5}{7}\right)$ **28.** $-\frac{7}{2}\left(\frac{-5}{7}\right)\left(\frac{-2}{5}\right)$

29. $4(-4)(-5)(-12)$ **30.** $-2(-3)(-4)(-5)$

31. $0.07(-7)(6)(-6)$ **32.** $80(-0.8)(-90)(-0.09)$

33. $-\frac{5}{6}\left(\frac{1}{8}\right)\left(-\frac{3}{7}\right)\left(-\frac{1}{7}\right)$ **34.** $\frac{4}{5}\left(\frac{-2}{3}\right)\left(-\frac{15}{7}\right)\left(\frac{1}{2}\right)$

35. $(-14)(-27)(0)$ **36.** $7(-6)(5)(-4)(3)(-2)(1)(0)$

37. $0.02(-4)(1.3)$ **38.** $-5.1(0.03)(-1.1)$

B

Simplify.

39. $-6[(-5) + (-7)]$ **40.** $7[(-16) + 9]$

41. $-3[(-8) + (-6)]\left(-\frac{1}{7}\right)$ **42.** $8[17 - (-3)]\left(-\frac{1}{4}\right)$

43. $-(3^5) \cdot [-(2^3)]$ **44.** $4(2^4) \cdot [-(3^3)] \cdot 6$

45. $(-2)^5$ **46.** $(-1)^{23}$

Evaluate for $x = -2$, $y = -4$, and $z = 5$.

47. $xy + z$ **48.** $-4y + 3x + z$

49. $-6(3x - 5y) + z$ **50.** $(-9z)(-5x)(-7y)$

51. $y(x^4) - z$ **52.** $3z^2 - xy$

53. *Critical Thinking*   Find a pair of integers with a product of -84 and a sum of 5.

54. **TEST PREP**   Which of these numbers is the least?

   A. $-1.08\left(-\frac{4}{3}\right)$ B. $-1.08\left(\frac{4}{3}\right)$ C. $-1.08\left(-\frac{2}{3}\right)$ D. $-1.08\left(\frac{2}{3}\right)$

3. PRACTICE/ASSESS

LESSON QUIZ

Multiply.

1. $-7 \cdot 6$
   -42
2. $8 \cdot (-7)$
   -56
3. $(-9)(-10)$
   90
4. $\left(-\frac{1}{7}\right)\left(-\frac{3}{4}\right)$
   $\left(\frac{1}{7}\right)\left(\frac{3}{4}\right) = \frac{3}{28}$
5. $5 \cdot (-3)(-2)(4)$
   $-15 \cdot (-2)(4)$
   $= 30 \cdot 4 = 120$
6. $(-13)(-35) \cdot 0$
   0

Assignment Guide

▼ Core 1–54
   Extension 55–59

Use Mixed Review to maintain skills.

Exercises

1. -16
2. -10
3. -42
4. -18
5. -24
6. -45
7. -72
8. -30
9. 16
10. 10
11. 42
12. 18
13. -120
14. 120
15. -238
16. 195
17. 1200
18. -1677
19. 98
20. 203.7
21. $\frac{-2}{45}$
22. $\frac{6}{35}$
23. 1911
24. -5712
25. 50.4
26. -52
27. $\frac{10}{189}$
28. -1
29. -960
30. 120
31. 17.64
32. -518.4
33. $-\frac{5}{784}$
34. $\frac{4}{7}$
35. 0
36. 0
37. -0.104
38. 0.1683
39. 72
40. -49
41. -6
42. -40
43. 1944
44. $-10,368$
45. -32
46. -1
47. 13
48. 15
49. -79
50. $-12,600$
51. -69
52. 67
53. $12, -7$
54. B

Challenge

55. What must be true of m and n if $-mn$ is positive?

56. What must be true of m and n if $-mn$ is negative?

57. For any rational numbers a and b, is it *sometimes*, *always*, or *never* true that $|ab| = |-a||-b|$? Explain.

58. What must be true of x if $x(x - 2) < 0$?

59. What must be true of z if $|z| \cdot z < 0$?

Mixed Review

Add or subtract. **60.** $4 - 9$ **61.** $3 - (-1)$ **62.** $0 + (-4)$
63. $-8 + 8$ **64.** $6 - (-2)$ **65.** $-37 + 52$ **66.** $67 + (-8)$ *2-3, 2-4*
Use $<$, $>$, or $=$ to write a true sentence. **67.** $-1.01 \square -1$

68. $2.5 \square -2.4$ **69.** $\frac{7}{2} \square 4$ **70.** $|-3| \square |3|$ *2-1*

Factor. **71.** $4x + 10 + 8y$ **72.** $10a + 15b + 5$ *1-5*

Evaluate. **73.** $3x^3$ for $x = 2$. **74.** $5x^3$ for $x = 1$ *1-3*

Subsets of the Rational Numbers

We can use the diagram on page 61 and set notation to write subsets of the rational numbers. Consider these sets:
Natural numbers or positive integers
$$N = \{1, 2, 3, \ldots\}$$
Whole numbers
$$W = \{0, 1, 2, 3, \ldots\}$$
Integers
$$I = \{\ldots, -3, -2, -1, 0, 1, 2, 3, \ldots\}$$
Consider these definitions: Each number in a set is called an element or member of the set. The symbol $\in$ is read "is an element of." We write: $-3 \in I$. Set A is a subset of set B if every element of set A is an element of set B. The symbol $\subset$ is read "is a subset of." We write: $A \subset B$.

The following are true statements.
$N \subset W$ The natural numbers are a subset of the whole numbers.
$W \subset I$ The whole numbers are a subset of the integers.
$I \subset R$ (rational numbers) The integers are a subset of the rational numbers.

1. Write at least five subset statements using the sets shown in the diagram on page 61.
2. The empty set or null set, symbolized $\emptyset$, is a set with no elements. Is $\emptyset$ a subset of the rational numbers?

Exercises

55. Either m or n is negative and the other is positive.
56. Both m and n are positive or both are negative.
57. Always; for all values of a and b, $|ab| \geq 0$, $|-a| \geq 0$, and $|-b| \geq 0$. Both sides of the given equation equal $|a| \cdot |b|$.
58. $0 < x < 2$
59. $z < 0$

Mixed Review

60. -5
61. 4
62. -4
63. 0
64. 8
65. 15
66. 59
67. $<$
68. $>$
69. $<$
70. $=$
71. $2(2x + 5 + 4y)$
72. $5(2a + 3b + 1)$

73. 24
74. 5

Subsets of the Rational Numbers

1. Answers may vary.
2. Yes

Division of Rational Numbers

CA: 1.0, 2.0

PART 1 | Division

Objective: Divide rational numbers.

To divide rational numbers, we can use the definition of division.

Definition

For all rational numbers a and b, the **quotient** $\frac{a}{b}$ (or $a \div b$), where $b \neq 0$, is the number c such that $cb = a$.

EXAMPLES Divide. Check your answers.

1 $14 \div (-7) = -2$ Check: $(-2)(-7) = 14$

2 $\frac{-32}{-4} = 8$ Check: $8(-4) = -32$

3 $\frac{-10}{2} = -5$ Check: $-5(2) = -10$

These examples suggest the following rule.

Dividing Positive and Negative Numbers

To divide positive and negative numbers, divide their absolute values. Use the following rules to determine the sign of the quotient.

- When we divide a positive number by a negative number or a negative number by a positive number, the quotient is negative.
- When we divide two positive numbers or two negative numbers, the quotient is positive.

Try This   Divide. Check your answer.

a. $15 \div (-3)$ **b.** $-21 \div (-7)$ **c.** $\frac{-44}{-11}$ **d.** $\frac{35}{-5}$

e. $\frac{-8}{-4}$ **f.** $\frac{45}{-9}$ **g.** $-24 \div -8$ **h.** $\frac{105}{-5}$

Try This
a. -5
b. 3
c. 4
d. -7
e. 2
f. -5
g. 3
h. -21

What You'll Learn

1 To divide rational numbers

2 To find the reciprocal of a rational number

... And Why

To learn how to operate with rational numbers so that you will be able to use them to solve real-world problems

---

2-6

TIME-FOCUS METER

1. FOCUS

FIRST FIVE MINUTES

Simplify.
1. $4 \cdot 5$ 20
2. $-4 \cdot 5$ -20
3. $4 \cdot (-15)$ -60
4. $-14 \cdot (-5)$ 70
5. $\frac{20}{4}$ 5
6. $\frac{20}{5}$ 4
7. $20 \cdot \frac{1}{4}$ 5
8. $\frac{0}{1}$ 0

2. TEACH the Mathematics

1 Division

Point out that the rules to determine the sign of a quotient are similar to those for multiplication.
- $+$ divided by $+$ $=$ $+$
- $+$ divided by $-$ $=$ $-$
- $-$ divided by $+$ $=$ $-$
- $-$ divided by $-$ $=$ $+$

Remind students that $a \div b$, $\frac{a}{b}$, and $a \cdot \frac{1}{b}$ are all equivalent expressions.

Key Questions
- Does $\frac{0}{-1} = \frac{0}{1}$?   Yes
- Does $\frac{1}{-1} = \frac{1}{1}$?   No

Chalkboard Examples
Divide.
1. $\frac{21}{-3}$ -7
2. $\frac{-12}{-4}$ 3
3. $\frac{-8}{2}$ -4

2 Reciprocals

You may wish to use the following illustration of the property of multiplicative inverses.

$$a \cdot \frac{1}{a}$$
$$= \frac{a}{1} \cdot \frac{1}{a}$$
$$= \frac{a}{a}$$
$$= 1$$

Key Questions

- How many reciprocals of 3 are there?
  One
- What is the reciprocal of 0?
  There is none.
- Is the reciprocal of a negative number positive or negative?
  Negative

Chalkboard Examples

Find the reciprocal.

1. $\frac{3}{7}$

   The reciprocal is $\frac{7}{3}$ because
   $$\frac{3}{7} \cdot \frac{7}{3} = 1$$

2. -8

   The reciprocal is $\frac{1}{-8}$ because
   $$-8 \cdot \frac{1}{-8} = 1$$

3. 4.5

   The reciprocal is $\frac{2}{9}$ because
   $$4.5 = \frac{9}{2} \text{ and } \frac{9}{2} \cdot \frac{2}{9} = 1$$

4. $\frac{x}{y}$

   The reciprocal is $\frac{y}{x}$ because
   $$\frac{x}{y} \cdot \frac{y}{x} = 1$$

5. $-\frac{2}{3}$

   The reciprocal is $-\frac{3}{2}$ because
   $$-\frac{2}{3} \cdot -\frac{3}{2} = 1$$

We can show why we cannot divide any nonzero number by 0. For $\frac{a}{0}$, $a \neq 0$, we look for a number which, when multiplied by 0, gives a. There is no such number because the product of 0 and any number is 0. If we divide $\frac{0}{0}$, we look for a number r such that $r \cdot 0 = 0$. But $r \cdot 0 = 0$ for any number r. Thus $\frac{0}{0}$ could be any number we choose. Since for any operation there must be only one answer, we agree that we shall not divide 0 by 0. In general, we cannot divide by 0.

PART 2 Reciprocals

Objective: Find the reciprocal of a rational number.

When pairs of numbers like $-\frac{1}{8}$ and -8 are multiplied, their product is 1. Number pairs such as $-\frac{1}{8}$ and -8, whose product is 1, are called multiplicative inverses or reciprocals.

Definition

Two rational numbers whose product is 1 are called **multiplicative inverses** or **reciprocals** of each other.

Any nonzero rational number has a reciprocal.

Property of Multiplicative Inverses

For each nonzero rational number a, there is one and only one rational number $\frac{1}{a}$ such that $a \cdot \frac{1}{a} = 1$.

If a nonzero rational number is named with fractional notation $\frac{a}{b}$, then its reciprocal can be named $\frac{b}{a}$. Also, the reciprocal of a positive number is positive, and the reciprocal of a negative number is negative.

Reading Math

Since we cannot divide by 0, assume that any variable in the denominator of a rational expression represents a nonzero number.

EXAMPLES Find the reciprocal.

4. $\frac{7}{8}$ The reciprocal of $\frac{7}{8}$ is $\frac{8}{7}$ because $\frac{7}{8} \cdot \frac{8}{7} = 1$.

5. -5 The reciprocal of -5 is $\frac{1}{-5}$ because $-5\left(\frac{1}{-5}\right) = 1$.

6. 0.8   The reciprocal of $0.8 = \frac{8}{10}$ is $\frac{10}{8}$ because $\frac{8}{10} \cdot \frac{10}{8} = 1$.

7. $\frac{m}{n}$ The reciprocal of $\frac{m}{n}$ is $\frac{n}{m}$ because $\frac{m}{n} \cdot \frac{n}{m} = 1$.

Try This   Find the reciprocal.

i. $\frac{3}{6}$ **j.** -4 **k.** -0.5 **l.** $1\frac{1}{3}$ **m.** $\frac{x}{y}$

PART
3   **Division and Reciprocals**

Objective: Divide by multiplying by the reciprocal.

We know we can subtract a rational number by adding its inverse. Similarly, we can divide by a rational number by multiplying by its reciprocal.

Dividing Numbers

For all rational numbers a and b $(b \neq 0)$,
$$\frac{a}{b} = a \cdot \frac{1}{b}$$

EXAMPLES   Rewrite each division as multiplication.

8 $-4 \div 3 = -4 \cdot \frac{1}{3}$

9 $\frac{x + 2}{5} = (x + 2) \cdot \frac{1}{5}$ Parentheses are necessary here.

10 $\frac{-17}{\frac{1}{b}} = -17 \cdot b$

11 $\frac{3}{5} \div \left(-\frac{9}{7}\right) = \frac{3}{5}\left(-\frac{7}{9}\right)$

Try This   Rewrite each division as multiplication.

n. $-6 \div \frac{1}{5}$ **o.** $\frac{-5}{7}$ **p.** $\frac{x^2 - 2}{3}$ **q.** $\frac{x}{y}$

r. $\frac{-15}{\frac{1}{x}}$ **s.** $-\frac{4}{7} \div -\frac{3}{5}$ **t.** $\frac{13}{\frac{2}{3}}$ **u.** $\frac{a}{\frac{1}{b}}$

When doing division calculations, we sometimes multiply by a reciprocal and we sometimes divide directly. With fractional notation, it is usually easier to multiply by a reciprocal. With decimal notation, it is usually easier to divide directly.

3 **Division and Reciprocals**

You may want to have students try to divide a number by zero on a calculator. Then discuss why the result is "ERROR."

According to the definition of division, if $1 \div 0 = a$, then $0 \cdot a = 1$. Since any number multiplied by 0 is 0, it is impossible to divide by 0.

Chalkboard Examples
Rewrite each division as multiplication.

1. $\frac{7}{3}$ $7 \cdot \frac{1}{3}$
2. $-\frac{5}{2}$ $-5 \cdot \frac{1}{2}$
3. $\frac{6}{-7}$ $6 \cdot \frac{1}{-7}$
4. $\frac{a + 7}{4}$ $(a + 7) \cdot \frac{1}{4}$

The parentheses are necessary.
Divide.

5. $\frac{9}{8} \div \frac{5}{3} = \frac{9}{8} \cdot \frac{3}{5}$
   $= \frac{27}{40}$
6. $\frac{1}{2} \div \frac{-5}{7} = \frac{1}{2} \cdot \frac{7}{-5}$
   $= \frac{7}{-10}$ or $-\frac{7}{10}$
7. $-\frac{2}{5} \div -\frac{7}{3} = -\frac{2}{5} \cdot -\frac{3}{7}$
   $= \frac{6}{35}$

Try This

i. $\frac{6}{3}$ or 2
j. $-\frac{1}{4}$
k. -2
l. $\frac{3}{4}$
m. $\frac{y}{x}$
n. $-6(5)$
o. $-5\left(\frac{1}{7}\right)$
p. $(x^2 - 2)\frac{1}{3}$
q. $x\left(\frac{1}{y}\right)$

r. $-15x$
s. $-\frac{4}{7}\left(-\frac{5}{3}\right)$
t. $13\left(\frac{3}{2}\right)$
u. ab

LESSON QUIZ

Divide.

1. $42 \div -7$ -6

2. $\frac{-8}{-2}$ 4

3. $\frac{0}{-5}$ 0

Find the reciprocal.

4. $\frac{13}{17}$ $\frac{17}{13}$

5. 4.2 $\frac{1}{4.2}$

6. -18 $-\frac{1}{18}$

7. $-\frac{3}{7}$ $-\frac{7}{3}$

Rewrite each division as multiplication.

8. $\frac{3}{7}$ $3 \cdot \frac{1}{7}$

9. $\frac{1}{3} \div \frac{2}{7}$ $\frac{1}{3} \cdot \frac{7}{2}$

Divide.

10. $-\frac{2}{7} \div -\frac{3}{5}$

$-\frac{2}{7} \cdot -\frac{5}{3}$

$= \frac{2}{7} \cdot \frac{5}{3} = \frac{10}{21}$

Assignment Guide

To provide flexible scheduling, this lesson can be split into parts.

▼ Core 1–15, 52–57
Extension 68, 70–71,
Terminating and Repeating
Decimals 1–9

▼ Core 16–31
Extension 58–61, 66–67, 69, 72–73

▼ Core 32–51
Extension 62–65

Use Mixed Review to maintain skills.

Extra Help On the Web

Look for worked-out examples at the Prentice Hall Web site.
www.phschool.com

EXAMPLES   Divide.

12 $\frac{4}{3} \div \left(-\frac{9}{7}\right) = \frac{4}{3}\left(-\frac{7}{9}\right)$

$= -\frac{4 \cdot 7}{3 \cdot 9} = -\frac{28}{27}$

13 $-27.9 \div (-3) = \frac{-27.9}{-3} = 9.3$

Try This   Divide.

v. $-\frac{3}{5} \div \left(-\frac{12}{11}\right)$ **w.** $-\frac{8}{5} \div \frac{2}{3}$ **x.** $-64.8 \div 4$ **y.** $78.6 \div (-3)$

2-6 Exercises

A

Divide. Check your answer.

1. $36 \div (-6)$ 2. $\frac{28}{-7}$ 3. $\frac{-16}{8}$

4. $-22 \div (-2)$ 5. $\frac{-48}{-12}$ 6. $-63 \div (-9)$

7. $\frac{-50}{25}$ 8. $-100 \div (-50)$ 9. $\frac{-200}{8}$

10. $-108 \div 9$ 11. $\frac{-63}{-7}$ 12. $\frac{200}{-25}$

13. $(-300) \div (0)$ 14. $\frac{75}{5}$ 15. $\frac{0}{-5}$

Find the reciprocal. Recall that all variables represent nonzero rational numbers.

16. $\frac{15}{7}$ 17. $\frac{3}{8}$ 18. $\frac{47}{13}$ 19. $-\frac{31}{12}$

20. 13 21. -10 22. 0.3 23. -0.4

24. $1\frac{1}{2}$ 25. $2\frac{2}{3}$ 26. $\frac{p}{q}$ 27. $\frac{s}{t}$

28. $\frac{1}{4y}$ 29. $\frac{-1}{8a}$ 30. $\frac{2a}{3b}$ 31. $\frac{-4y}{3x}$

Rewrite each division as multiplication.

32. $3 \div 19$ 33. $4 \div (-9)$ 34. $\frac{6}{-13}$ 35. $-\frac{12}{41}$

36. $\frac{13.9}{-1.5}$ 37. $\frac{x}{\frac{1}{y}}$ 38. $\frac{3x + 4}{5}$ 39. $\frac{5a - b}{5a + b}$

Try This

v. $\frac{11}{20}$

w. $-\frac{12}{5}$

x. -16.2

y. -26.2

Exercises

1. -6
2. -4
3. -2
4. 11
5. 4
6. 7

7. -2
8. 2
9. -25
10. -12
11. 9
12. -8
13. None
14. 15
15. 0
16. $\frac{7}{15}$
17. $\frac{8}{3}$
18. $\frac{13}{47}$

19. $-\frac{12}{31}$
20. $\frac{1}{13}$
21. $-\frac{1}{10}$
22. $\frac{10}{3}$
23. $-\frac{5}{2}$
24. $\frac{2}{3}$
25. $\frac{3}{8}$
26. $\frac{q}{p}$
27. $\frac{t}{s}$
28. $4y$

29. $-8a$
30. $\frac{3b}{2a}$
31. $-\frac{3x}{4y}$
32. $3\left(\frac{1}{19}\right)$
33. $4\left(\frac{-1}{9}\right)$
34. $6\left(-\frac{1}{13}\right)$
35. $-12\left(\frac{1}{41}\right)$
36. $13.9\left(-\frac{1}{1.5}\right)$
37. $x \cdot y$

Divide.

40. $\frac{3}{4} \div \left(-\frac{2}{3}\right)$ **41.** $\frac{7}{8} \div \left(-\frac{1}{2}\right)$ **42.** $-\frac{5}{4} \div \left(-\frac{3}{4}\right)$

43. $-\frac{5}{9} \div \left(-\frac{5}{6}\right)$ **44.** $-\frac{2}{7} \div \left(-\frac{4}{9}\right)$ **45.** $-\frac{3}{5} \div \left(-\frac{5}{8}\right)$

46. $-44.1 \div (-6.3)$ **47.** $-42.3 \div 0$ **48.** $0 \div -2.5$

49. $-\frac{1}{3} \div \frac{1}{3}$ **50.** $-\frac{1}{4} \div \frac{1}{2}$ **51.** $-\frac{5}{6} \div \frac{3}{4}$

TEST PREP   Compare the boxed quantity in column A with the boxed quantity in column B. Choose the best answer.

A. The quantity in column A is greater.
B. The quantity in column B is greater.
C. The two quantities are equal.
D. The relationship cannot be determined with the information supplied.

	column A	column B			column A	column B
52.	$\frac{20}{10}$	$\frac{20}{5}$	**53.**		$\frac{-20}{10}$	$\frac{-20}{5}$
54.	$\frac{20}{-10}$	$\frac{20}{-5}$	**55.**		$\frac{-20}{-10}$	$\frac{-20}{-5}$
56.	$\frac{x}{10}$	$\frac{x}{5}$	**57.**		$\frac{x}{-10}$	$\frac{x}{-5}$

B

Simplify.

58. $\frac{(-9)(-8) + (-3)}{25}$ **59.** $\frac{-3(-9) + 7}{-4}$ **60.** $\frac{(-2)^7}{(-4)^2}$ **61.** $\frac{(-3)^4}{-9}$

62. $5\frac{3}{7} \div 4\frac{2}{5}$ **63.** $\frac{10}{7} \div 1\frac{3}{4}$ **64.** $2\frac{2}{3} \div \frac{40}{15}$ **65.** $\frac{(-4)^3}{(-8)^3}$

66. Use a calculator to find the reciprocal of -10.5.

67. Use a calculator to find the reciprocal of 4.2.

68. What should happen if you enter a number on a calculator and press the reciprocal key twice? Why?

69. *Critical Thinking*   Is it possible for a number to be its own reciprocal? Explain.

Challenge

Write a Convincing Argument   Write a convincing argument or give a counterexample.

70. Is division of rational numbers commutative? That is, does $a \div b = b \div a$ for all rational numbers a and b?

71. Is division of rational numbers associative? That is, does $(a \div b) \div c = a \div (b \div c)$ for all rational numbers a, b, and c?

72. Is it possible for the additive inverse of a number to be its reciprocal?

1. **A; Algebra 1.0, 2.0**
2. **J; Algebra 1.0, 2.0**

Exercises

38. $\frac{1}{5}(3x + 4)$

39. $(5a - b)\left(\frac{1}{5a + b}\right)$

40. $-\frac{9}{8}$

41. $-\frac{7}{4}$

42. $\frac{5}{3}$

43. $\frac{2}{3}$

44. $\frac{9}{14}$

45. $\frac{24}{25}$

46. 7

47. None
48. 0
49. -1
50. $-\frac{1}{2}$
51. $-\frac{10}{9}$
52. B
53. A
54. A
55. B
56. D
57. D
58. $\frac{69}{25}$

59. $\frac{-17}{2}$
60. -8
61. -9
62. $\frac{95}{77}$
63. $\frac{40}{49}$
64. 1
65. $\frac{1}{8}$
66. $-0.095238095238\ldots$
67. 0.238095238
68. You get the original number.
69. Yes, this is true for 1 and also for -1.

70. No, $\frac{4}{2} \neq \frac{2}{4}$.
71. No, $(12 \div 6) \div 2 = 2 \div 2 = 1$ but $12 \div (6 \div 2) = 12 \div 3 = 4$.
72. No. A reciprocal has the same sign as the number. (Zero has no reciprocal.)

TERMINATING AND REPEATING DECIMALS

The calculator is useful for converting fractions to decimals. If calculators are used, however, it should be noted that many calculators round off the last digit.

The decimal conversion for $\frac{3}{11}$ is displayed on many calculators as 0.2727273. Point out to students that this is the rounded answer and that 27 is the repeating decimal part. (They may need to work a few problems without the calculator to be convinced.)

---

73. Are both $\frac{b}{a}$ and $\frac{1}{\left(\frac{a}{b}\right)}$ reciprocals of a nonzero rational number $\frac{a}{b}$?

Mixed Review

Simplify. **74.** $6 + (-3) - 5 - (-9)$ **75.** $12 - 7 - (-4) + (-2)$
76. $9 + (11) + (-8) - 4$ **77.** $8 + (-15) - 4 - (-18)$ *2-3, 2-4*

Write as an algebraic expression. **78.** 5 more than t **79.** twice m
80. 36 divided among y **81.** x less than 25 **82.** m times n *1-1*
Solve. **83.** $12 = 24p$ **84.** $20n = 5$ **85.** $42x = 14$ **86.** $3 = 6y$ *1-7*

Terminating and Repeating Decimals

We have learned that a rational number can be expressed as the ratio of two integers. A rational number can also be expressed as either a **terminating decimal** or a **repeating decimal.** When we divide the integer a by the integer b in the rational number $\frac{a}{b}$, the resulting decimal will either terminate or repeat.

$\frac{3}{8} = 0.375$ The decimal ends or terminates in the thousandths place.

$\frac{3}{11} = 0.272727 = 0.\overline{27}$ The digits 27 repeat. We use a bar to indicate which digits repeat.

A decimal that neither terminates nor repeats, such as 2.35335333533335 . . . names an **irrational number.**

Exercises

Write as a decimal. If the decimal repeats, use a bar for the repeating decimal part.

1. $\frac{4}{11}$ **2.** $\frac{7}{20}$ **3.** $\frac{23}{9}$ **4.** $\frac{5}{18}$ **5.** $\frac{4}{9}$ **6.** $\frac{2}{13}$

To find the decimal equivalent to $\frac{1}{7}$, you can divide 1 by 7. Several steps of the long division are shown at the right. In the first three subtractions, the remainders are 1, 3, and 2.

7. Continue the long division to find a repeating pattern of remainders. How many digits are in this pattern?
8. What repeating decimal equals $\frac{1}{7}$? How many digits repeat?
9. *Write a Convincing Argument* What is the greatest number of digits that can repeat in the repeating decimal for $\frac{1}{17}$? Explain.

```
       0.14
   7)1.00
      0
      10
       7
      30
      28
       2
```

Exercises

73. Yes; $\frac{1}{\left(\frac{a}{b}\right)} \cdot \frac{\left(\frac{b}{a}\right)}{\left(\frac{b}{a}\right)} = \frac{\left(\frac{b}{a}\right)}{1} = \frac{b}{a}$

Mixed Review
74. 7
75. 7
76. 8
77. 7
78. $t + 5$
79. $2m$
80. $\frac{36}{y}$
81. $25 - x$

82. mn
83. $\frac{1}{2}$
84. $\frac{1}{4}$
85. $\frac{1}{3}$
86. $\frac{1}{2}$

Terminating and Repeating Decimals

1. $0.\overline{36}$
2. 0.35
3. $2.\overline{5}$
4. $0.2\overline{7}$
5. $0.\overline{4}$

6. $0.\overline{153846}$
7. There are 6 numbers in the repeating pattern of remainders: 1, 3, 2, 6, 4, 5, . . .
8. $0.\overline{142857}$, 6 digits repeat
9. For the divisor 17, the 16 possible remainders are 1, 2, . . . , 16. As soon as any remainder repeats, the digits in the quotient repeat. So there can be no more than 16 digits in the quotient that repeat.

Lever Problems

The principles that allow small forces to lift heavy bridges and provide for movement on playground teeter-totters also provide ways for small forces to move heavy loads. Consider the problem of lifting a 1500-pound bale of hay. If a farmer uses a tower boom crane to lift the bale of hay, how many pounds of force are needed to lift the bale with the crane?

The problem is like the problem of lifting a person off the ground on a seesaw. A force needs to be applied to the opposite side of the seesaw or to the opposite side of the boom on the crane.

A "square" bale of hay with dimensions 14" × 18" × 36" weighs 50 to 60 lb. This rolled bale weighs about 1500 lb. How many square bales are equivalent to the rolled bale?

You can use integers to predict what will happen when forces are applied to a seesaw or boom. Both of these situations are examples of **levers**. The diagram represents the physical situation involved.

The 0 point, where the lever pivots, is called the fulcrum. The moment, or torque, for both the load and the force, is the product of the force each exerts and its distance from the fulcrum: Moment = (force)(distance). Downward forces, such as weight or force applied, are negative. Distances to the left of the fulcrum can be thought of as negative, and distances to the right can be thought of as positive, as on a number line.

The farmer uses a hydraulic jack to pull on the end of the other side of the boom to lift the bale. He notes that the force required was 750 pounds to lift and balance the bale. This force caused the moments of the two sides to be equal.

Farmer's moment: $(-750)(-20) = 15,000$
Bale's moment: $(-1500)(10) = -15,000$
Sum of the two moments: $15,000 + (-15,000) = 0$

When the sum of the moments is 0, the boom balances.

Application **87**

Photo Caption

25 to 30 bales

Discuss the unlimited potential of the lever: The greater the distance from the fulcrum, the less is the force required to shift a given weight. The Greek mathematician Archimedes (287–212 B.C.) analyzed the principle of the lever. Fascinated by its potential, he said, "Give me a place to stand and I will move the world."

Equilibrium is derived from the Latin "equal weights." Any system under stress of forces is in equilibrium when the forces cancel each other out. Discuss this concept and its application to moment problems.

Mechanics is the branch of physics dealing with motions and forces. The study of forces in equilibrium is *statics*, from the Greek, "to cause to stand."

Use a doorknob to demonstrate advantageous uses of leverage. The door is a lever, with the hinge as its fulcrum. What happens when a doorknob is placed in the center of the door? What would happen if it were placed just an inch from the hinge?

The Principle of Moments

When several parallel forces act on an object, it will be in balance if the sum of the moments is 0.

To move an object using a lever and fulcrum, the moment on one side of the fulcrum has to exceed the moment created by the load to be moved. Exact solutions of such problems must also take into account the mass of the lever.

EXAMPLE

To lift a heavy load, one end of an eight-foot pry bar is placed two feet beyond a pivot point and inserted into a chain link. How many pounds of force are needed to balance the chain link if 200 pounds of force are placed on the other end of the pry bar?

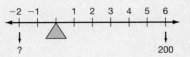

The force of 200 pounds acting downward at a distance of 6 feet from the fulcrum creates a moment of $(-200)(6)$ or -1200. The chain link end is acting through a distance of 2 feet on the negative side of the fulcrum. If f represents the force exerted here, we have a moment of $-2f$ being in balance with the moment on the other side of -1200. Hence, f must equal 600 pounds.

Problems

Solve. Use the conditions in the hay bale problem for Problems 1–3.

1. Show two other places the farmer could hook the jack to the boom and lift the hay bale. Give the force required to balance the bale for each of these points.

2. How long a boom on the farmer's side would be required to balance the bale with a force of 125 pounds?

3. Suppose the hay bale was attached at a point 8 feet from the fulcrum. How much force 20 feet from the fulcrum would be required to balance the bale?

4. One end of a 10-foot pry bar is inserted under a 420-pound rock. If the fulcrum is 3 feet from the rock, how many pounds of force have to be exerted on the other end of the bar to balance the rock?

5. A meter bar has a 10-kg weight on one end and a 15-kg weight on the other end. Where would the fulcrum have to be placed to balance the loads?

Problems

1. Answers may vary. Some examples are 15 ft, 1000 lb; and 30 ft, 500 lb.
2. 120 ft
3. 600 lb
4. 180 lb
5. The fulcrum would have to be 60 cm from the 10-kg weight and 40 cm from the 15-kg weight.

CA 1.0, 4.0, 10.0: Use the arithmetic properties of rational numbers. Simplify expressions. Add and subtract monomials (like terms).

Using the Distributive Property

 PART 1 The Distributive Property Over Subtraction

Objective: Multiply using the distributive property over subtraction.

In Chapter 1 you learned how to use the distributive property over addition with whole numbers. The distributive property over addition applies to all rational numbers.

The Distributive Property of Multiplication Over Addition

For any rational numbers a, b, and c, $a(b + c) = ab + ac$, and
$$(b + c)a = ba + ca$$

We can use the basic properties and previous definitions to show that the distributive property holds for subtraction as well.

The Distributive Property of Multiplication Over Subtraction

For any rational numbers a, b, and c, $a(b - c) = ab - ac$, and
$$(b - c)a = ba - ca$$

We refer to this property as the **distributive property over subtraction.**

EXAMPLES Multiply.

1 $9(x - 5) = 9x - 9(5)$
$ = 9x - 45$

2 $-3(y - 3) = -3y - (-3)(3)$
$ = -3y + 9$

3 $\frac{4}{3}(s - t + w) = \frac{4}{3}s - \frac{4}{3}t + \frac{4}{3}w$

4 $-4(x - 2y + 3z) = -4 \cdot x - (-4)(2y) + (-4)(3z)$
$ = -4x - (-8y) + (-12z) = -4x + 8y - 12z$

Try This Multiply.

a. $8(y - 7)$ **b.** $\frac{5}{6}(x - y + 7z)$ **c.** $-5(x - 3y + 8z)$

Try This
a. $8y - 56$
b. $\frac{5}{6}x - \frac{5}{6}y + \frac{35}{6}z$
c. $-5x + 15y - 40z$

 **CA: 1.0, 4.0, 10.0**

What You'll Learn

1 To multiply using the distributive property of multiplication over subtraction

2 To factor expressions

3 To collect like terms in an expression

...And Why

To be able to simplify algebraic expressions

1. FOCUS

FIRST FIVE MINUTES
Use the distributive property to multiply.
1. $3(x + 1)$ $3x + 3$
2. $a(b + 2)$ $ab + 2a$
3. $x(y + z)$ $xy + xz$
4. $5(x + (-2))$ $5x + 5(-2) = 5x - 10$
Use the distributive property to factor.
5. $2a + 2b$ $2(a + b)$
6. $ax + ay$ $a(x + y)$
7. $3x + 3(-y)$
$\quad 3[x + (-y)] = 3(x - y)$

2. TEACH the Mathematics

1 **The Distributive Property Over Subtraction**

You may wish to illustrate the distributive property over subtraction with an arithmetic example. For instance,
$7(8 - 3) = 7 \cdot 8 - 7 \cdot 3 = 35$
$7(8 - 3) = 7(5) = 35$

> **Math Point**
> The distributive property is the *only* property that relates addition and subtraction to multiplication.

Chalkboard Examples
Multiply.
1. $7(a - 2)$ $7a - 14$
2. $-5(u - v)$
$\quad -5u - (-5)v = -5u + 5v$
3. $\frac{1}{2}(r + s - t)$
$\quad \frac{1}{2}r + \frac{1}{2}s - \frac{1}{2}t$
4. $-6(2e - 3f - g)$
$\quad (-6)2e - (-6)3f - (-6)g$
$\quad = -12e + 18f + 6g$

▼2 Factoring

Illustrate that factoring is the reverse of the distributive property. For instance, Example 5:

Factor $5x - 5y$.
$5(x - y)$
Multiply $5(x - y)$.
$5x - 5y$

Chalkboard Examples

Factor.
1. $3z - 3y$
   $3(z - y)$
2. $10u - 30$
   $10(u - 3)$
3. $ua - ub - uc$
   $u(a - b - c)$
4. $5x - 35y - 10$
   $5(x) - 5(7y) - 5(2)$
   $= 5(x - 7y - 2)$
5. $-6u - 4v - 8w$
   $-2(3u + 2v + 4w)$
6. $14u - 21w - 28$
   $7(2u - 3w - 4)$
7. $\frac{2}{3}p - \frac{1}{3}q + \frac{5}{3}r$
   $\frac{1}{3}(2p - q + 5r)$

▼3 Collecting Like Terms

Chalkboard Examples

What are the terms of each expression?
1. $4a - 2b - 5c$
   The terms are $4a$, $-2b$, $-5c$.
2. $-8x + y - 7z$
   The terms are $-8x$, y, $-7z$.
3. $\frac{1}{7}a - \frac{3}{5}b$
   The terms are $\frac{1}{7}a$, $-\frac{3}{5}b$.

Collect like terms.
4. $-7x + 2x - 3x$
   $(-7 + 2 - 3)x$
   $= -8x$
5. $5x - 2y - 2x + 6y$
   $5x - 2x - 2y + 6y$
   $= (5 - 2)x + (-2 + 6)y$
   $= 3x + 4y$
6. $3.4a - 2.1a + 1.0a$
   $(3.4 - 2.1 + 1.0)a$
   $= 2.3a$
7. $-6a + 5b + 4a - b$
   $-6a + 4a + 5b - b$
   $= (-6 + 4)a + (5 - 1)b$
   $= -2a + 4b$
Use Teaching Transparency T12 for more examples of collecting like terms.

Objective: Factor expressions.

Recall that we can use the distributive properties to **factor** an expression.

$$ab + ac = a(b + c)$$
$$ab - ac = a(b - c)$$

EXAMPLES   Factor.

5 $5x - 5y = 5(x - y)$

6 $8x - 16 = 8 \cdot x - 8 \cdot 2 = 8(x - 2)$

7 $ax - ay + az = a(x - y + z)$

8 $9x - 27y - 9 = 9(x) - 9(3y) - 9(1)$
  $= 9(x - 3y - 1)$

9 $-3x + 6y - 9z = 3(-x + 2y - 3z)$ or $-3(x - 2y + 3z)$

10 $18z - 12x - 24 = 6(3z - 2x - 4)$

11 $\frac{1}{2}x + \frac{3}{2}y - \frac{1}{2} = \frac{1}{2}(x + 3y - 1)$

Try This   Factor.

d. $4x - 8$ **e.** $3x - 6y - 15$ **f.** $bx - by + bz$
g. $-2y + 8z - 2$ **h.** $12z - 16x - 4$

Objective: Collect like terms.

If there are subtractions in an expression, we can think of an equivalent expression without subtraction signs. Then the terms are separated by addition signs.

EXAMPLE 12

What are the terms of $3x - 4y + 2z$?

The terms are $3x$, $-4y$, and $2z$.   Think $3x + (-4y) + 2z$.

In the first term, $3x$, 3 and x are the factors. In the second term, $-4y$, -4 and y are the factors. In the last term, $2z$, 2, and z are the factors.

Try This   What are the terms of each expression?

i. $5a - 4b + 3$ **j.** $-5y - 3x + 5z$

Try This

d. $4(x - 2)$
e. $3(x - 2y - 5)$
f. $b(x - y + z)$
g. $-2(y - 4z + 1)$ or
   $2(-y + 4z - 1)$
h. $4(3z - 4x - 1)$
i. $5a$, $-4b$, 3
j. $-5y$, $-3x$, $5z$

We can collect like terms by using the distributive property of multiplication over addition or subtraction to factor.

EXAMPLES Collect like terms.

13 $2k + 7k = (2 + 7)k = 9k$

14 $2x + 3y - 5x - 2y = 2x - 5x + 3y - 2y$
$\qquad\qquad\qquad\qquad = (2 - 5)x + (3 - 2)y$ Factoring
$\qquad\qquad\qquad\qquad = -3x + y$

15 $3x - x = (3 - 1)x = 2x$

16 $x - 0.24x = 1 \cdot x - 0.24x = (1 - 0.24)x = 0.76x$

17 $x - 6x = 1 \cdot x - 6x = (1 - 6)x = -5x$

Try This   Collect like terms.

k. $6x - 3x$
l. $7y - y$
m. $m - 0.44m$
n. $5x + 4y - 2x - y$
o. $3x - 7x - 11 + 8y - 4 - 13y$

2-7 Exercises

Extra Help On the Web
Look for worked-out examples at the Prentice Hall Web site.
www.phschool.com

A
Multiply.

1. $7(x - 2)$
2. $5(x - 8)$
3. $-7(y - 2)$
4. $-9(y - 7)$
5. $-9(-5x - 6y + 8)$
6. $-7(-2x - 5y + 9)$
7. $-4(x - 3y - 2z)$
8. $8(2x - 5y - 8z)$
9. $3.1(-1.2x + 3.2y - 1.1)$
10. $-2.1(-4.2x - 4.3y - 2.2)$
11. $\frac{2}{3}(3a - 6b + 9)$
12. $\frac{1}{2}(4c + 5d - 6)$
13. $-\frac{4}{5}\left(-\frac{1}{2}x + \frac{2}{3}y - 1\right)$
14. $-\frac{7}{8}\left(\frac{2}{3}x - \frac{1}{2}y - 8\right)$

Factor.

15. $8x - 24$
16. $-10x - 50$
17. $32 - 4y$
18. $24 - 6m$
19. $8x + 10y - 22$
20. $-9a + 6b - 15$
21. $ax - 7a$
22. $by - 9b$
23. $ax - ay - az$
24. $cx + cy - cz$
25. $\frac{3}{4}x - \frac{1}{4}y - \frac{1}{4}$
26. $\frac{2}{3}x - \frac{1}{3}y + \frac{1}{3}$

3. PRACTICE/ASSESS

LESSON QUIZ
Multiply.
 1. $8(a - 3)$ $8a - 24$
 2. $-2(x - 7)$
$\quad -2x - (-2)7$
$\quad = -2x + 14$
 3. $4(3z - 2w)$ $12z - 8w$
 4. $-7(3x - 2y - w)$
$\quad -21x + 14y + 7w$
Factor.
 5. $7x - 21y$ $7(x - 3y)$
 6. $af - ag - ah$ $a(f - g - h)$
Collect like terms.
 7. $9x - 2x + x$ $(9 - 2 + 1)x = 8x$
 8. $3a - 7b - 2a + 12b$
$\quad 3a - 2a - 7b + 12b$
$\quad = (3 - 2)a + (-7 + 12)b$
$\quad = a + 5b$

Assignment Guide
To provide flexible scheduling, this lesson can be split into parts.
▼ Core 1–14
 Extension 53–59
▼ Core 15–26
▼ Core 27–52

Use Mixed Review to maintain skills.

Try This
k. $3x$
l. $6y$
m. $0.56m$
n. $3x + 3y$
o. $-4x - 5y - 15$

Exercises
1. $7x - 14$
2. $5x - 40$
3. $-7y + 14$
4. $-9y + 63$
5. $45x + 54y - 72$
6. $14x + 35y - 63$
7. $-4x + 12y + 8z$
8. $16x - 40y - 64z$
9. $-3.72x + 9.92y - 3.41$
10. $8.82x + 9.03y + 4.62$
11. $2a - 4b + 6$
12. $2c + \frac{5}{2}d - 3$
13. $\frac{2}{5}x - \frac{8}{15}y + \frac{4}{5}$
14. $-\frac{7}{12}x + \frac{7}{16}y + 7$
15. $8(x - 3)$
16. $-10(x + 5)$ or $10(-x - 5)$
17. $4(8 - y)$
18. $6(4 - m)$
19. $2(4x + 5y - 11)$
20. $-3(3a - 2b + 5)$ or $3(-3a + 2b - 5)$
21. $a(x - 7)$
22. $b(y - 9)$
23. $a(x - y - z)$
24. $c(x + y - z)$
25. $\frac{1}{4}(3x - y - 1)$
26. $\frac{1}{3}(2x - y + 1)$

What are the terms of each expression?

27. $4x + 3z$ **28.** $8x - 1.4y$

29. $7x + 8y - 9z$ **30.** $8a + 10b - 18c$

31. $12x - 13.2y + \frac{5}{8}z - 4.5$ **32.** $3ab - 4cd$

Collect like terms.

33. $x - 3x$ **34.** $9t - 17t$

35. $6n - n$ **36.** $y - 17y$

37. $9x + 2y - 5x$ **38.** $8y - 3z + 4y$

39. $11x + 2y - 4x - y$ **40.** $13a + 9b - 2a - 4b$

41. $2.7x + 2.3y - 1.9x - 1.8y$ **42.** $6.7a + 4.3b - 4.1a - 2.9b$

43. $5y - 3x - 7y$ **44.** $13m + 5m - 3n - 18m$

45. $-8t + p + 4p - t$ **46.** $q + q + q + 5p$

47. $17a - 17b - 17c + 15a$ **48.** $6m - 3.5n + 2.5m - 7n$

49. $5.5d - 1.2a + 3d + 4.2a$ **50.** $17z + 3x - 2y + y - 5z - 3x$

51. $\frac{1}{5}x + \frac{4}{5}y + \frac{2}{5}x - \frac{1}{5}y$ **52.** $\frac{7}{8}x + \frac{5}{8}y + \frac{1}{8}x - \frac{3}{8}y$

B

Write as an algebraic expression.

53. eight times the difference of x and y

54. nine times the difference of y and z, increased by $3z$

55. three times the sum of a and b, decreased by $7a$

56. the total cost if you buy x cassette tapes at \$2.95 on Monday and y cassettes at the same price on Wednesday

57. *Critical Thinking* For all rational numbers a, b, and c, does $a \cdot (b - c) = a - (b \cdot c)$? Explain.

Challenge

58. If the temperature is C degrees Celsius, it is $\frac{9}{5}C + 32$ degrees Fahrenheit. What is the Fahrenheit temperature if the Celsius temperature drops 5°?

59. Jill has 5420 shares of a stock that she bought at $41\frac{1}{8}$. The stock is now worth $37\frac{3}{4}$. Show two ways of determining how much she has lost. Solve.

Mixed Review

Find the reciprocal. **60.** $\frac{2}{15}$ **61.** $-\frac{6}{11}$ **62.** 4 **63.** $\frac{1}{3c}$ *2-6*

Simplify. **64.** $11 - |-3| + (-9) - 16$ **65.** $4x - (-9x) - x$ *1-5, 2-3, 2-4*

Calculate. **66.** $\frac{4}{5}\left(\frac{2}{3}\right)$ **67.** $-\frac{3}{8}\left(\frac{1}{2}\right)$ **68.** $\frac{2}{3} \div -\frac{1}{2}$ **69.** $\frac{4}{5} \div \frac{2}{5}$ *2-5, 2-6*

Exercises

27. $4x$, $3z$
28. $8x$, $-1.4y$
29. $7x$, $8y$, $-9z$
30. $8a$, $10b$, $-18c$
31. $12x$, $-13.2y$, $\frac{5}{8}z$, -4.5
32. $3ab$, $-4cd$
33. $-2x$
34. $-8t$
35. $5n$
36. $-16y$
37. $4x + 2y$
38. $12y - 3z$
39. $7x + y$
40. $11a + 5b$
41. $0.8x + 0.5y$
42. $2.6a + 1.4b$

43. $-2y - 3x$
44. $-3n$
45. $-9t + 5p$
46. $3q + 5p$
47. $32a - 17b - 17c$
48. $8.5m - 10.5n$
49. $8.5d + 3a$
50. $12z - y$
51. $\frac{3}{5}x + \frac{3}{5}y$
52. $x + \frac{1}{4}y$
53. $8(x - y)$
54. $9(y - z) + 3z$ or $9y - 6z$
55. $3(a + b) - 7a$ or $3b - 4a$

56. $2.95(x + y)$
57. No; $1 \cdot (3 - 2) = 1$, $1 - (3 \cdot 2) = -5$
58. $\frac{9}{5}(C - 5) + 32$ or $\frac{9}{5}C + 23$
59. $5420(41\frac{1}{8} - 37\frac{3}{4})$ or $5420\left(41\frac{1}{8}\right) - 5420\left(37\frac{3}{4}\right)$; \$18,292.50

Mixed Review

60. $\frac{15}{2}$
61. $-\frac{11}{6}$

62. $\frac{1}{4}$
63. $3c$
64. -17
65. $12x$
66. $\frac{8}{15}$
67. $-\frac{3}{16}$
68. $-\frac{4}{3}$
69. 2

CA 1.0, 2.0, 4.0, 10.0: Use the arithmetic properties of rational numbers. Find opposites. Simplify expressions. Add and subtract monomials (like terms).

Inverse of a Sum and Simplifying

 **2-8**

 CA: 1.0, 2.0, 4.0, 10.0

 **TIME-FOCUS METER**

PART 1 **Inverse of a Sum**

Objective: Find the inverse of a sum.

What happens when we multiply a rational number by -1?

$$-1 \cdot 7 = -7 \qquad -1 \cdot (-5) = 5 \qquad -1 \cdot 0 = 0$$

The product is the additive inverse of the number.

The Property of -1

For any rational number a,
$$-1 \cdot a = -a.$$
(Negative one times a is the additive inverse of a.)

The property of -1 enables us to find an equivalent expression for the additive inverse of a sum.

EXAMPLES Rename each additive inverse without parentheses.

1 $\quad -(3 + x) = -1(3 + x)$ Using the property of -1
$\qquad\qquad\quad = -1 \cdot 3 + (-1)x$ Using a distributive property
$\qquad\qquad\quad = -3 + (-x)$ Using the property of -1
$\qquad\qquad\quad = -3 - x$ Using the subtraction rule

2 $\quad -(3x + 2y + 4) = -1(3x + 2y + 4)$
$\qquad\qquad\qquad\quad = -1(3x) + (-1)(2y) + (-1)4$
$\qquad\qquad\qquad\quad = -3x - 2y - 4$

Try This   Rename each additive inverse without parentheses.

a. $-(x + 2)$ **b.** $-(5x + 2y + 8)$
c. $-(a - 7)$ **d.** $-(3c - 4d + 1)$

2-8   *Inverse of a Sum and Simplifying*   **93**

Try This

    a. $-x - 2$
    b. $-5x - 2y - 8$
    c. $-a + 7$
    d. $-3c + 4d - 1$

What You'll Learn

1 To find the inverse of a sum

2 To simplify expressions involving parentheses

3 To simplify expressions containing multiple grouping symbols

...And Why

To learn how to simplify complex expressions and equations that are obtained when modeling real-life situations

---

1. FOCUS

FIRST FIVE MINUTES

1. $(-1)(-1)$ 1
2. $(-1)x$ $-x$
3. $(-1)2y$ $-2y$
4. $(-1)(x + 2)$
   $(-1)x + (-1)2 = -x - 2$
Simplify.
5. $[(3 + 5) + 7] + 1$
   $(8 + 7) + 1 = 15 + 1 = 16$
6. $(2x + 4x) - 4x$
   $6x - 4x = 2x$
7. $2 + 3(5 + 4)$
   $2 + 3 \cdot 9 = 2 + 27 = 29$
8. $[(7x - 3x) - 2x] + 5x$
   $(4x - 2x) + 5x$
   $2x + 5x = 7x$

2. TEACH the Mathematics

1 **Inverse of a Sum**

Point out that the inverse of a sum can be found by changing the sign of each term.

Key Questions

- Is the additive inverse of 3 equal to the additive inverse of -3?
  No
- What is the additive inverse of 0?
  0
- Write the additive inverse of $x \cdot y$ in 3 different ways.
  $-(x \cdot y), (-x) \cdot (y)$, and $(x) \cdot (-y)$

Chalkboard Examples

Multiply.
1. $-1 \cdot 12$ -12
2. $-1 \cdot (-4)$ 4
3. $0(-1)$ 0
Rename each additive inverse without parentheses.
4. $-(2y + 3)$
   $-1(2y + 3)$
   $= (-1)2y + (-1)3$
   $= -2y - 3$
5. $-(a - 2)$
   $-1(a - 2) = -1 \cdot a + (-1)(-2)$
   $= -a + 2$
6. $-(5y - 3z + 4w)$
   $-1(5y - 3z + 4w) =$
   $(-1)5y + (-1)(-3)z + (-1)4w$
   $= -5y + 3z - 4w$

2-8   *Inverse of a Sum and Simplifying*   **93**

2 Simplifying Expressions Involving Parentheses

You may wish to use an arithmetic example to show students that

$$a - (b + c) = a - b - c$$

For example,

$$3 - (2 + 1) = 3 - 3 = 0 \text{ and}$$
$$3 - (2 + 1) = 3 - 2 - 1 = 0$$

Chalkboard Examples

Do the following mentally.

1. $-(8x - 3y - 2z)$
   $-8x + 3y + 2z$
2. $-(-4a + 7b - 3c)$
   $4a - 7b + 3c$
3. $-(4ab - 5ac + 6bc)$
   $-4ab + 5ac - 6bc$

Simplify.

4. $3 - (x + 1)$
   $3 + [-(x + 1)]$
   $= 3 + (-x - 1)$
   $= 3 + (-x) + (-1)$
   $= 2 - x$
5. $x - (2x - 3y)$
   $x - 2x + 3y$
   $= -x + 3y$
6. $3z - 2y - (4z + 5y)$
   $3z - 2y - 4z - 5y$
   $= -z - 7y$
7. $7u - 3(7u + v)$
   $7u - 21u - 3v$
   $= -14u - 3v$
8. $-2(e - f) - (2e + 5f)$
   $= -2e + 2f - 2e - 5f$
   $= -4e - 3f$

Examples 1 and 2 illustrate an important property of rational numbers.

The Inverse of a Sum Property

For any rational numbers a and b,

$$-(a + b) = -a + (-b)$$

(The additive inverse of a sum is the sum of the additive inverses.)

The inverse of a sum property holds for differences as well as sums because any difference can be expressed as a sum. It also holds when there is a sum or difference of more than two terms. When we apply the inverse of a sum property we sometimes say that we "change the sign of every term."

EXAMPLES Rename each additive inverse without parentheses.

3 $-(5 - y) = -5 + y$ Changing the sign of every term

4 $-(2a - 7b - 6) = -2a + 7b + 6$

Try This Rename each additive inverse without parentheses.

e. $-(6 - t)$ **f.** $-(-4a + 3t - 10)$ **g.** $-(18 - m - 2n + 4t)$

PART 2 Simplifying Expressions Involving Parentheses

Objective: Simplifying expressions involving parentheses.

When an expression inside parentheses is added to another expression as in $5x + (2x + 3)$, the associative property allows us to move the parentheses and simplify the expression to $7x + 3$. When an expression inside parentheses is subtracted from another expression as in $3x - (4x + 2)$, we can subtract by adding the inverse. Then we can use the inverse of a sum property and simplify.

EXAMPLE 5 Simplify.

$$\begin{aligned} 3x - (4x + 2) &= 3x + (-(4x + 2)) &&\text{Using the definition of subtraction} \\ &= 3x + (-4x + (-2)) &&\text{Using the inverse of sum property} \\ &= 3x - 4x - 2 \\ &= -x - 2 &&\text{Collecting like terms} \end{aligned}$$

We can combine the first two steps of Example 5 by changing the sign of every term inside the parentheses.

Try This

e. $-6 + t$
f. $4a - 3t + 10$
g. $-18 + m + 2n - 4t$

EXAMPLES Simplify.

6 $5y - (3y + 4) = 5y - 3y - 4$ Changing the sign of the terms inside parentheses

$= 2y - 4$ Collecting like terms

7 $3y - 2 - (2y - 4) = 3y - 2 - 2y + 4$

$= y + 2$

Try This   Simplify.

h. $5x - (3x + 9)$ **i.** $5x - 2y - (2y - 3x - 4)$

Next consider subtracting an expression consisting of several terms preceded by a number.

EXAMPLES Simplify.

8 $x - 3(x + y) = x + (-3(x + y))$ Adding the inverse of $3(x + y)$

$= x + (-3x - 3y)$ Using the distributive property

$= x - 3x - 3y$

$= -2x - 3y$ Collecting like terms

9 $3y - 2(4y - 5) = 3y + (-2(4y - 5))$ Adding the inverse of $2(4y - 5)$

$= 3y + (-8y + 10)$

$= 3y - 8y + 10$

$= -5y + 10$

Try This   Simplify.

j. $y - 9(x + y)$ **k.** $5a - 3(7a - 6)$

PART 3 Grouping Symbols

Objective: Simplify expressions containing multiple grouping symbols.

Some expressions contain more than one grouping symbol. **Parentheses ( )**, **brackets [ ]**, and **braces { }** are all grouping symbols we use in algebra. When an expression contains more than one grouping symbol, the computations in the innermost grouping symbols should be done first.

EXAMPLES Simplify.

10 $[3 - (7 + 3)] = [3 - 10]$ Computing $7 + 3$

$= -7$

11 $\{8 - [9 - (12 + 5)]\} = \{8 - [9 - 17]\}$ Computing $12 + 5$

$= \{8 - [-8]\}$ Computing $9 - 17$

$= 16$

2-8   *Inverse of a Sum and Simplifying*   **95**

Teach the Mathematics (continued)

3 Grouping Symbols

Point out that brackets and braces are used to clarify expressions that require several sets of grouping symbols.

Key Question

- How many different values can you give the expression $9 \cdot 2 + 5 \cdot 4$ by inserting grouping symbols?

$9 \cdot 2 + 5 \cdot 4 = 38$

$9 \cdot (2 + 5) \cdot 4 = 252$

$(9 \cdot 2 + 5) \cdot 4 = 92$

$9 \cdot (2 + 5 \cdot 4) = 198$

Chalkboard Examples

Simplify.

1. $[5 + (3 + 1)]$

$[5 + 4] = 9$

2. $\{6 - [3 + (5 - 2)]\}$

$\{6 - [3 + 3]\}$

$= \{6 - 6\} = 0$

3. $[3(2x - 1) + 1] - (3x + 1)$

$[(6x - 3) + 1] - 3x - 1$

$= 6x - 3 + 1 - 3x - 1$

$= 3x - 3$

Try This

h. $2x - 9$

i. $8x - 4y + 4$

j. $-9x - 8y$

k. $-16a + 18$

LESSON QUIZ

Rename each additive inverse without parentheses.

1. $-(4x + 7)$ $-4x - 7$
2. $-(-6a + 3b - 7c)$
   $6a - 3b + 7c$

Simplify.

3. $12y - (2y - 1)$
   $12y - 2y + 1$
   $= 10y + 1$
4. $(-5x + 2) - (-2x - 3)$
   $-5x + 2 + 2x + 3$
   $= -5x + 2x + 2 + 3$
   $= -3x + 5$

Simplify.

5. $[3 - (5 - 3)]$
   $[3 - 2] = 1$
6. $[3(x + 4) + 1] - (x - 5)$
   $[3x + 12 + 1] - x + 5$
   $= 3x + 12 + 1 - x + 5$
   $= 3x - x + 12 + 1 + 5$
   $= 2x + 18$

Assignment Guide

To provide flexible scheduling, this lesson can be split into parts.
▼ Core 1–12
   Extension 47
▼ Core 13–30
   Extension 41–44
▼ Core 31–40
   Extension 45–46, 48–51

Use Mixed Review to maintain skills.

EXAMPLES   Simplify.

12 $4(2 + 3) - \{7 - [4 - (8 + 5)]\}$
   $= 4 \cdot 5 - \{7 - [4 - 13]\}$ Working with innermost parentheses first
   $= 20 - \{7 - [-9]\}$ Computing $4 \cdot 5$ and $4 - 13$
   $= 20 - 16$ Computing $7 - [-9]$
   $= 4$

13 $[5(x + 2) - 3x] - [3(y + 2) - 7(y - 3)$
   $= [5x + 10 - 3x] - [3y + 6 - 7y + 21]$ Working with innermost parentheses first
   $= [2x + 10] - [-4y + 27]$ Collecting like terms
   $= 2x + 10 + 4y - 27$
   $= 2x + 4y - 17$

Try This   Simplify.

l. $[9 - (6 + 4)]$ **m.** $3(4 + 2) - \{7 - [4 - (6 + 5)]\}$

n. $[3(4 + 2) + 2x] - [4(y + 2) - 3(y - 2)]$

Internet Connection

Extra Help On the Web

Look for worked-out examples at the Prentice Hall Web site.
www.phschool.com

▶ 2-8 Exercises

A

Rename each additive inverse without parentheses.

1. $-(2x + 7)$
2. $-(3x + 5)$
3. $-(5x - 8)$
4. $-(6x - 7)$
5. $-(4a - 3b + 7c)$
6. $-(5x - 2y - 3z)$
7. $-(6x - 8y + 5)$
8. $-(8x + 3y + 9)$
9. $-(3x - 5y - 6)$
10. $-(6a - 4b - 7)$
11. $-(-8x - 6y - 43)$
12. $-(-2a + 9b - 5c)$

Simplify.

13. $9x - (4x + 3)$
14. $7y - (2y + 9)$
15. $2a - (5a - 9)$
16. $11n - (3n - 7)$
17. $2x + 7x - (4x + 6)$
18. $3a + 2a - (4a + 7)$
19. $2x - 4y - 3(7x - 2y)$
20. $3a - 7b - 1(4a - 3b)$
21. $15x - y - 5(3x - 2y + 5z)$
22. $4a - b - 4(5a - 7b + 8c)$
23. $(3x + 2y) - (5x - 4y)$
24. $(-6a - b) - (4b + a)$
25. $6m - n - 4m - (5n - m)$
26. $7p - (q + 8p) - 5p + 3q$
27. $-(7u - 8v) - (8v - 7u)$
28. $7m + 8n - (4n - 5m) + n$
29. $5a - 3b - (-6b + 4a) - (-b)$
30. $-(-4x - 3y) - 6y + 3x - x - y$

Try This

l. -1
m. 4
n. $2x - y + 4$

Exercises

1. $-2x - 7$
2. $-3x - 5$
3. $-5x + 8$
4. $-6x + 7$
5. $-4a + 3b - 7c$
6. $-5x + 2y + 3z$
7. $-6x + 8y - 5$
8. $-8x - 3y - 9$
9. $-3x + 5y + 6$
10. $-6a + 4b + 7$
11. $8x + 6y + 43$
12. $2a - 9b + 5c$
13. $5x - 3$
14. $5y - 9$
15. $-3a + 9$
16. $8n + 7$
17. $5x - 6$
18. $a - 7$
19. $-19x + 2y$
20. $-a - 4b$
21. $9y - 25z$
22. $-16a + 27b - 32c$
23. $-2x + 6y$
24. $-7a - 5b$
25. $3m - 6n$
26. $-6p + 2q$
27. 0
28. $12m + 5n$
29. $a + 4b$
30. $6x - 4y$

Simplify.

31. $[9 - 2(5 - 4)]$ **32.** $[6 - 5(8 - 4)]$

33. $8[7 - 6(4 - 2)]$ **34.** $10[7 - 4(7 - 5)]$

35. $[4(9 - 6) + 11] - [14 - (6 + 4)]$

36. $[7(8 - 4) + 16] - [15 - (7 + 3)]$

37. $[10(x + 3) - 4)] + [2(x - 1) + 6)]$

38. $[9(x + 5) - 7] + [4(x - 12) + 9]$

39. $[7(x + 5) - 19] - [4(x - 6) + 10]$

40. $[6(x + 4) - 12] - [5(x - 8) + 11]$

B

Find an equivalent expression for each of the following by enclosing the last three terms in parentheses preceded by a minus sign.

41. $x - y - a - b$ **42.** $6y + 2x - 3a + c$

43. $6m + 3n - 5m + 4b$ **44.** $3q - 2p + 4q - 5$

Simplify.

45. $3a + 4 - \{-2 - [-3 - (a - 1)]\}$

46. $2s + 2 - \{-3 - [2 - (3 - s)]\}$

47. *Critical Thinking*   If $-(a + b)$ is $-a + (-b)$, what should be the sum of $(a + b)$ and $-a + (-b)$? Show that your answer is correct.

Challenge

Simplify.

48. $z - \{2z - [3z - (4z - 5z) - 6z] - 7z\} - 8z$

49. $\{x - [f - (f - x)] + [x - f]\} - 3x$

50. $x - \{x - 1 - [x - 2 - (x - 3 - \{x - 4 - [x - 5 - (x - 6)]\})]\}$

51. A bar, or vinculum, can be used as a grouping symbol. Simplify the following.
$$\{y - [y + (3 - y)] - \overline{y + 1}\} + 5y$$

Mixed Review

Factor.   **52.** $3x + 12y$ **53.** $2a - 6b + 12$ **54.** $an + 2a$ *2-7*

Evaluate for $x = 3$, $y = 2$, and $z = 5$.   **55.** $2x^3$ **56.** $-3z^2$

57. $6x + 2y^4$ **58.** $2x^2 + 3z$ **59.** $x + 2y - 3z$ *1-4*

Calculate.   **60.** $\frac{2}{3} + \frac{1}{4} - \left(-\frac{3}{8}\right)$ **61.** $\frac{1}{2}\left(\frac{4}{5}\right) + \left(\frac{5}{6}\right)\left(-\frac{2}{3}\right)$ *2-3, 2-4*

Collect like terms.   **62.** $8b + 7b + b$ **63.** $x^2 + x + x^2$ *1-5*

Write as an algebraic expression.   **64.** a number squared plus 3

65. five less than three times a number   *1-1*

Exercises

31. 7
32. −14
33. −40
34. −10
35. 19
36. 39
37. $12x + 30$
38. $13x - 1$
39. $3x + 30$
40. $x + 41$
41. $x - (y + a + b)$
42. $6y - (-2x + 3a - c)$
43. $6m - (-3n + 5m - 4b)$

44. $3q - (2p - 4q + 5)$
45. $2a + 4$
46. $3s + 4$
47. $0; a + b + (-a) + (-b) =$
     $a + (-a) + b + (-b) = 0$
48. $-4z$
49. $-2x - f$
50. $x - 3$
51. $5y - 4$

Mixed Review

52. $3(x + 4y)$
53. $2(a - 3b + 6)$
54. $a(n + 2)$

55. 54
56. −75
57. 50
58. 33
59. −8
60. $\frac{31}{24}$
61. $-\frac{7}{45}$
62. $16b$
63. $2x^2 + x$
64. $x^2 + 3$
65. $3x - 5$

1. FOCUS

FIRST FIVE MINUTES

Write as an algebraic expression.

1. Six less than the product of 5 and *n*.
   $5n - 6$
2. One third the sum of *p* and *q*.
   $\frac{1}{3}(p + q)$
3. Doug is five years more than 3 times Lee's age. Let *L* be Lee's age. Write an expression for Doug's age.
   $3L + 5$
4. Let *d* be the number of miles Jay runs each week. Nina runs 5 less than twice as far as Jay. Write an expression for the distance Nina runs each week.
   $2d - 5$

2. TEACH the Mathematics

▼ Write an Equation

To clarify a problem, it often helps to underline the phrases that refer to quantities, then replace the phrases with variables that suggest the quantities.

Note that if the equation is set up correctly for these easier problems, the solution to the equation is usually the answer to the problem. In later chapters, however, the answer to the problem will not always be the solution to the equation.

This lesson is meant to give students practice in writing equations to solve problem situations. It is not necessary for students to actually solve the equations. It is fine if they do, as long as they have set up the equation properly.

As always, have students check that their answers are reasonable and that they have included units, if any.

What You'll Learn

1 To write an equation that can be used to solve a problem

... And Why

To be able to solve real-world problems using algebraic reasoning skills

---

2-9 ▷ Writing Equations

> **PART**
> **1** Write an Equation

Objective: Write an equation that can be used to solve a problem.

In the past you have been introduced to strategies that you can use to solve mathematical problems. A powerful strategy is *Write an Equation*. Many of the problems you will work with in your study of algebra can be solved by writing and solving an equation.

PROBLEM-SOLVING GUIDELINES
■ UNDERSTAND the problem
□ Develop and carry out a PLAN
■ Find the ANSWER and CHECK

The Problem-Solving Guidelines were introduced in Chapter 1. The three phases can help you solve many kinds of problems.

The planning phase involves selecting and carrying out strategies for solving problems. Here are some tips you can use when your plan involves writing an equation.

PLANNING to write and solve an equation

Can I use a variable to represent an unknown number?
Can I represent other conditions in terms of the variable?
Can I find equivalent expressions?
Can I write and solve an equation?

EXAMPLE 1   Which equation(s) can be used to solve the problem?

Jose's salary this year was $23,400. This is $1700 more than he made last year. What was his salary last year?

(A) $l - 1700 = 23{,}400$ **(B)** $1700 + l = 23{,}400$
(C) $l = 23{,}400 - 1700$

■ **UNDERSTAND the problem**

Question: What was Jose's salary last year?

Clarifying the question and identifying the data given

Data: Jose earned $23,400 this year. This is $1700 more than he made last year.

■ **Develop and carry out a PLAN**

Let l = last year's salary.

Using a variable to represent what you are trying to find

Our data tell us that 23,400 is 1700 more than l. This is the same as equation (B). We can also say that last year's salary was 1700 less than this year's salary. This is the same as equation (C).

Either (B) or (C) are correct equations.

EXAMPLE 2   Write an equation that could be used to solve the problem.

A color television set uses about 420 kilowatt hours (kWh) of electrical energy in a year. That is 3.5 times the amount of energy used by a black-and-white set. How many kWh does a black-and-white set use in a year?

■ **UNDERSTAND the problem**

Question: How many kWh does a black-   Clarifying the question and
and-white set use in 1 year?   identifying the data given

Data: A color set uses 420 kWh a year.
This amount is 3.5 times as much as
the amount used by a black-and-
white set.

■ **Develop and carry out a PLAN**

Let $b =$ number of kWh used by   Using a variable to represent
a black-and-white set.   what you are trying to find

$3.5b =$ number of kWh used by a color set   3.5 times the number of kWh
for a black-and-white TV
equals the amount used by a
color TV.

$(3.5)b = 420$

EXAMPLE 3   Write an equation that could be used to solve the problem.

In baseball, a player's batting average multiplied by the number of times at bat equals the number of hits. A player had 125 at-bats and 36 hits. What was this player's batting average?

■ **UNDERSTAND the problem**

Question: What was this player's   Clarifying the question and
batting average?   identifying the data given

Data: A player had 125 at-bats and 36 hits.

■ **Develop and carry out a PLAN**

Let $b =$ player's batting average.   Using a variable to represent
what you are trying to find

$125b =$ number of player's hits after
125 at-bats

$(125)b = 36$

Avoiding Common Errors

When writing an equation, students often have difficulty determining whether to add or subtract and to which side. In Example 1, students may want to add 1700 to 23,400 rather than to p.

Ask students to visualize the equation as a scale. Since Jose made more this year than last year, the side of the scale showing this year's salary will be heavier. In order to balance the scale, the student must add to the lighter side, so the equation will be $23,400 = p + 1700$.

Math Point

Ordinary language is efficient. The fewest possible words are used to express facts. This is good for ordinary communication, but it can be bad for doing algebra. Word problems often need to be rephrased and expanded to make their meaning clear.

Key Questions

■ In Example 1, is Jose earning more or less than he earned last year?
More

■ In Example 2, does a color television use more or less energy than a black-and-white television?
More

■ What unit is energy measured in?
Kilowatt hours

■ Write a different equation that can be used to solve Example 2.
$b = 420 \div 3.5$

Chalkboard Examples

1. In the year after Anne-Marie bought a used car, she drove 12,500 miles. At the end of the year the mileage of the car was 42,800. Write an equation for the mileage of the car when Anne-Marie bought it.
Let $m =$ mileage when Anne-Marie bought the car.
$m + 12,500 = 42,800$

2. On one tank of gas, Anne-Marie can drive 238 miles. The gas tank in her car holds $9\frac{1}{2}$ gallons. Write an equation for the number of miles per gallon her car gets.
Let $m =$ miles per gallon.
$m = 238$ miles $\div 9\frac{1}{2}$ *gallons*

**Extra Help
On the Web**
Look for worked-out
examples at the Prentice
Hall Web site.
www.phschool.com

2-9 Problems

Assignment Guide
▼ Core 1–24
Extension 25–28

Use Mixed Review to maintain skills.

Which equation(s) can be used to solve each problem?

1. Nita had 25 points on the second quiz. That was 8 more points than she had on the first quiz. How many points did she have on the first quiz?
Let $x =$ number of points on her first quiz.
   (A) $x - 25 = 8$ **(B)** $x + 8 = 25$ **(C)** $x = 25 - 8$

2. A golfer hit two shots for a total of 375 yards. Her first shot was 240 yards. How far was her second shot?
Let $s =$ length of the second shot.
   (A) $240 + s = 375$ **(B)** $s - 240 = 375$ **(C)** $s = 375 + 240$

3. There are 775 dogs and cats in an animal shelter. There are 423 dogs in the shelter. How many cats are there?
Let $c =$ number of cats.
   (A) $775 - 423 = c$ **(B)** $423 + c = 775$ **(C)** $c - 423 = 775$

4. The San Francisco Giants won 39 more games than the St. Louis Cardinals. The Giants won 101 games. How many games did the Cardinals win?
Let $c =$ number of games the Cardinals won.
   (A) $c - 39 = 101$ **(B)** $c + 39 = 101$ **(C)** $101 + 39 = c$

5. A game board has 64 squares. If you win 35 squares, how many does your opponent get?
Let $o =$ number of squares your opponent gets.
   (A) $o - 35 = 64$ **(B)** $35 + o = 64$ **(C)** $o = 64 - 35$

6. A dozen balloons cost \$3.50. How much is each balloon?
Let $b =$ the cost of each balloon.
   (A) $3.50 \div 12 = b$ **(B)** $3.50 - b = 12$ **(C)** $12b = 3.50$

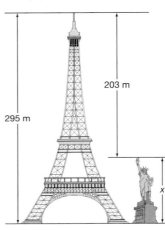

Write an equation that can be used to solve the problem.

7. The height of the Eiffel Tower is 295 m, which is about 203 m higher than the Statue of Liberty. What is the height of the Statue of Liberty?

8. Dennis sold a total of 318 tickets in two days. He sold 127 tickets the second day. How many did he sell the first day?

9. Alberto has \$48 less than Mariana. Mariana has \$115. How much does Alberto have?

10. A bakery charges \$3.12 for a dozen bagels. How much does it cost to buy a single bagel?

100   Chapter 2   *Integers and Rational Numbers*

Problems
1. (B) or (C)
2. (A)
3. (A) or (B)
4. (B)
5. (B) or (C)
6. (A) or (C)
Problems 7–24: Answers may vary.
7. Let $h =$ the height of the Statue of Liberty.
$h + 203 = 295$
8. Let $d =$ the number of tickets sold on the first day.
$127 + d = 318$
9. Let $a =$ the amount of money Alberto has.
$a = 115 - 48$
10. Let $c =$ the cost of a single bagel.
$12c = 3.12$

11. A movie theater took in $438.75 from 117 customers. What was the price of a ticket?

12. A consultant charges $80 an hour. How many hours did the consultant work to make $53,400?

13. The area of Lake Superior is about 4 times the area of Lake Ontario. The area of Lake Superior is 78,114 km^2. What is the area of Lake Ontario?

14. It takes a 60-watt bulb about 16.6 hours to use 1 kWh of electricity. That is about 2.5 times as long as it takes a 150-watt bulb to use 1 kWh. How long does it take a 150-watt bulb to use 1 kWh?

15. The area of Alaska is about 483 times the area of Rhode Island. The area of Alaska is 1,519,202 km^2. What is the area of Rhode Island?

16. The boiling point of ethyl alcohol is 78.3°C. That is 13.5°C higher than the boiling point of methyl alcohol. What is the boiling point of methyl alcohol?

17. The distance from Earth to the sun is about 150,000,000 km. That is about 391 times the distance from Earth to the moon. What is the distance from Earth to the moon?

18. In three-way light bulbs, the highest wattage is the sum of the two lower wattages. If the lowest is 30 watts and the highest is 150 watts, what is the middle wattage?

19. The distance traveled (D) equals the rate of travel (r) times the time traveled (t). How long would it take a boat traveling 50 miles per hour to travel 325 miles, assuming there are no stops?

20. A roll of film costs $3.14 and developing costs $10.39. What is the total cost for each of the 36 prints?

21. The dryers at Franklin Laundry cost a quarter for 7 minutes. How many quarters will you have to use to dry your clothes for 45 minutes?

22. One inch equals 2.54 centimeters. A meter is 100 centimeters. How many inches are there in a meter?

23. Sound travels at 1087 feet per second. How long does it take the sound of an airplane to reach you when it is 10,000 feet overhead?

24. In baseball, a player's batting average multiplied by the number of times at bat equals the number of hits. A player had 125 at-bats and 36 hits. What was this player's batting average?

Write a problem that can be solved using the given equations. Specify what the variable represents.

25. Let x = ?
$x - 2 = 32$

26. Let a = ?
$a + 24 = 42$

27. Let r = ?
$42 - r = 11$

28. Let m = ?
$m + 2m = 18$

Problems

11. Let p = the price of a ticket.
$117p = 438.75$

12. Let c = the amount of hours the consultant worked.
$80c = 53,400$

13. Let a = the area of Lake Ontario.
$4a = 78,114$

14. Let t = the time it takes a 150-watt bulb to use 1 kWh.
$2.5t = 16.6$

15. Let a = the area of Rhode Island.
$483a = 1,519,202$

16. Let b = the boiling point of methyl alcohol.
$b + 13.5 = 78.3$

17. Let d = the distance from Earth to the moon.
$391d = 150,000,000$

18. Let m = the middle wattage of a three-way light bulb.
$m + 30 = 150$

19. Let t = time.
$325 = 50t$

20. Let c = the cost of each print.
$36c = 13.53$

21. Let q = the number of quarters required.
$7q = 45$

22. Let x = the number of inches in a meter.
$x = 2.54 \cdot 100$

23. Let t = the time it takes the sound to reach you.
$1087t = 10,000$

24. Let b = batting average.
$125b = 36$

25–28. Answers will vary.

2-10

Number Properties and Proofs

2-10

TIME-FOCUS METER

1. FOCUS

FIRST FIVE MINUTES

True or false?
1. $10 = 10$
   True; any number equals itself.
2. $(3 + 2) + 1 = 3 + (2 + 1)$
   True, by the associative property.
3. There is a number x such that
   $x + 3 = 1$
   True; $x = -2$.
4. $\frac{a}{0} = 1$
   False; division by 0 is undefined.
5. For all numbers x and y, $x - y = y - x$
   False.
6. There is a number x such that
   $\frac{2}{53} + x = 0$
   True; $x = -\frac{2}{53}$. (Every number has an additive inverse.)

2. TEACH the Mathematics

1 Number Properties and Definitions

Students may have difficulty with the closure properties, as this is probably their first exposure to them. As another example, you may wish to show that the rational numbers do not have the closure property of division: 1 and 0 are rational, but $\frac{1}{0}$ is not.

Key Questions

- Do axioms lead to theorems or do theorems lead to axioms?
  Axioms lead to theorems.
- Do we need to prove an axiom?
  No
- Does the closure property of subtraction hold for whole numbers?
  No; $1 - 2 = -1$, not a whole number
- Does the multiplicative inverse property hold for integers?
  No
- Are the integers a field?
  No

What You'll Learn

1 To identify applications of the number properties

2 To identify the properties of equality

3 To prove number properties

... And Why

To become familiar with the properties of numbers and be able to use them to simplify algebraic expressions

Writing Math

How would you convince a fellow student that the opposite of a number equals the number subtracted from zero?

PART 1 Number Properties and Definitions

Objective: Identify applications of the number properties.

Number properties are important in algebra because they allow us to write equivalent expressions. For example, the associative property allows us to write $(x + 3) + 5$ and $x + (3 + 5)$ and know they are equivalent.

How do we know that the properties we have used so far are true? We accept some number properties as obvious, and then, using these properties, we prove the rest. The properties that we accept without proof are called **axioms.** The properties that we prove are called **theorems.**

Following is a list of properties that we will accept as axioms.

Axioms for Rational Numbers

For any rational numbers a, b, and c

- The Closure Properties
  1. Addition: $a + b$ is a rational number.
  2. Multiplication: ab is a rational number.
- The Commutative Properties
  3. Addition: $a + b = b + a$
  4. Multiplication: $ab = ba$
- The Associative Properties
  5. Addition: $a + (b + c) = (a + b) + c$
  6. Multiplication: $a(bc) = (ab)c$
- The Identity Properties
  7. Addition: $a + 0 = a$
  8. Multiplication: $a \cdot 1 = a$
- The Inverse Properties
  9. Addition: For each a, there is an additive inverse, $-a$, such that $a + (-a) = 0$.
  10. Multiplication: For each a ($a \neq 0$), there is a multiplicative inverse, $\frac{1}{a}$, such that $a \cdot \frac{1}{a} = 1$.
- The Distributive Property of Multiplication over Addition
  11. $a(b + c) = ab + ac$

These axioms hold for rational numbers, and they also hold in some other number systems. Any number system in which these axioms hold is called a **field.** Hence the axioms are known as the **field axioms.**

EXAMPLES Which axiom guarantees the truth of each statement?

1 $2(y + 3) = 2y + 2 \cdot 3$ *Distributive property*

2 $(3m)(n) = 3(mn)$ *Associative property for multiplication*

Try This   Which axiom guarantees the truth of each statement?

a. $4 + (5 + x) = (4 + 5) + x$ **b.** $7\left(\frac{1}{7}\right) = 1$ **c.** $-12 + 12 = 0$

The closure properties for rational numbers guarantee that the sum and product of any two rational numbers are also rational numbers. We say that the set of rational numbers is **closed** for addition and multiplication.

EXAMPLE 3   Is the set $\{0, 1\}$ closed for addition? for multiplication?

No; $1 + 1 = 2$ and 2 is not in $\{0, 1\}$.

Yes; the only possible products of 0 and 1 are 0 and 1.

Try This   **d.** Is the set $\{-1, 0, 1\}$ closed for addition? for multiplication?

Here are some important definitions.

Definitions

Subtraction
The difference $a - b$ is the number c such that $c + b = a$.

Division
The quotient $\frac{a}{b}$, or $a \div b$, where $b \neq 0$, is the number c such that $c \cdot b = a$.

Equality
A sentence $a = b$ states that a and b are expressions for the same number.

PART 2

Properties of Equality

Objective: Identify the properties of equality.

The following are some important properties related to equality.

Properties of Equality

For any rational numbers a, b, and c,

Reflexive Property	**Symmetric Property**	**Transitive Property**
$a = a$ is always true.	If $a = b$, then $b = a$.	If $a = b$ and $b = c$, then $a = c$.

Teach the Mathematics (continued)

Chalkboard Examples
Which axiom guarantees the truth of each statement?

1. $3 \cdot x = x \cdot 3$
   Commutative for multiplication
2. $(2a)b = 2(ab)$
   Associative for multiplication
3. $a(x + b) = ax + ab$
   Distributive
4. $7 + (-7) = 0$
   Inverse for addition
5. $9 \cdot \left(\frac{1}{9}\right) = 1$
   Inverse for multiplication
6. $(-a) + (-b) = (-b) + (-a)$
   Commutative for addition
7. $\frac{1}{2} + \left(\frac{3}{5} + \frac{4}{7}\right) = \left(\frac{1}{2} + \frac{3}{5}\right) + \frac{4}{7}$
   Associative for addition
8. $\left(x + \frac{3}{2}\right) + 0 = \left(x + \frac{3}{2}\right)$
   Identity element for addition

2 Properties of Equality

Chalkboard Examples
Which property of equality guarantees the truth of each statement?

1. $3x + 2 = 3x + 2$
   Reflexive property
2. $x - 3 = 2$, hence $2 = x - 3$
   Symmetric property
3. $a + 2 = b$ and $b = c - 7$, therefore $a + 2 = c - 7$.
   Transitive property
4. $2y + 4x = 16$, therefore $16 = 2y + 4x$.
   Symmetric property
5. $\frac{6}{5}\left(\frac{1}{2}x - \frac{4}{7}\right) = \frac{6}{5}\left(\frac{1}{2}x - \frac{4}{7}\right)$
   Reflexive property

Try This
a. Associative prop. of addition
b. Inverse prop. of multiplication
c. Inverse prop. of addition
d. No; yes

③ Theorems and Proofs

You may wish to explain that algebra is like a game in which the rules are axioms and logic. The axioms and logic allow certain equations to be written down. Other axioms allow expressions to be rewritten in alternate forms. It is not clear at the outset what can and cannot be written down. Every equation that can be derived using the axioms and logic is called a *theorem*.

A proof is a careful record of the "moves" made to show a theorem is true. In the examples on this page, each property is mentioned as it is used. Note that other moves might lead to the same result.

Chalkboard Example

Theorem: $(a + b) - b = a$

Complete the proof of this theorem by supplying the missing reasons.

Proof

1. $(a + b) - b$ $= (a + b) + (-b)$	Subtraction rule
2. $= a + [b + (-b)]$	Associative prop. of addition
3. $= a + 0$	Additive inverses
4. $= a$	Additive identity
5. $(a + b) - b = a$	Transitive prop. of equality

EXAMPLES   Which property of equality justifies each statement?

4 $a(b + c) = ab + ac$, so
$ab + ac = a(b + c)$ Symmetric property

5 $2x^3 = 2x^3$ Reflexive property

6   If $5xy^2 = 5y^2x$ and $5y^2x = 5 \cdot y \cdot y \cdot x$
then $5xy^2 = 5 \cdot y \cdot y \cdot x$.   Transitive property

Try This   Which property of equality justifies each statement?

e. $3a + 5b = 3a + 5b$

f. $(b + c)a = a(b + c)$ and $a(b + c) = ab + ac$. Therefore,
$(b + c)a = ab + ac$.

g. If $a(b - c) = ab - ac$, then $ab - ac = a(b - c)$.

PART 3   Theorems and Proofs

Objective: Prove number properties.

We now consider some number properties that can be proved. The first theorem is a restatement of the distributive property. To prove this theorem, we write a sequence of statements. Each statement must be supported by a reason, which can be an axiom or a definition.

> **Theorem**
>
> For any rational numbers a, b, and c, $(b + c)a = ba + ca$.

EXAMPLE 7   Prove the above theorem.

Statement	Reason
1. $(b + c)a = a(b + c)$	1. Commutative property of multiplication
2. $\quad\quad = ab + ac$	2. Distributive property
3. $\quad\quad = ba + ca$	3. Commutative property of multiplication
4. $(b + c)a = ba + ca$	4. Transitive property of equality

Here is another theorem dealing with the distributive property. It involves three addends.

> **Theorem**
>
> For any rational numbers a, b, c, and d, $a(b + c + d) = ab + ac + ad$.

Try This

e. Reflexive
f. Transitive
g. Symmetric

Try This

h. Complete the following proof by supplying the missing reasons.

Statement	Reason
1. $a(b + c + d) = a[(b + c) + d]$	1. Associative property of addition
2. $\qquad = a(b + c) + ad$	2.
3. $\qquad = ab + ac + ad$	3.
4. $a(b + c + d) = ab + ac + ad$	4. Transitive property of equality

The next theorem was stated on page 78 as the multiplication property of zero.

Theorem

For any rational number a, $a \cdot 0 = 0$.

Try This

i. Complete the following proof by supplying the missing reasons.

1. $a \cdot 0 = a \cdot 0 + 0$	1. Additive identity
2. $\quad = a \cdot 0 + a + (-a)$	2. Additive inverse
3. $\quad = a \cdot 0 + a \cdot 1 + (-a)$	3. Multiplicative identity
4. $\quad = a(0 + 1) + (-a)$	4.
5. $\quad = a \cdot 1 + (-a)$	5. Additive identity
6. $\quad = a + (-a)$	6.
7. $\quad = 0$	7.
8. $a \cdot 0 = 0$	8. Transitive property of equality

 2-10 Exercises

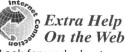 ***Extra Help On the Web***

Look for worked-out examples at the Prentice Hall Web site.
www.phschool.com

A

Which axiom guarantees each statement?

1. $a + b = b + a$

2. $(a + b) + c = c + (a + b)$

3. $x(y + z) = xy + xz$

4. $3(b + c) = 3b + 3c$

5. $y + [x + (-x)] = y + 0$

6. $3x(x + 2) = 3x^2 + 6x$

7. $-(x - 3) = -x + 3$

8. $6x - 3y = 3(2x - y)$

Which axiom or property guarantees the truth of each statement?

9. $(a \cdot b)c = a(b \cdot c)$

10. $(a + b) \cdot 1 = a + b$

11. $17(2b + 1) = 34b + 17$

12. $(2a + 3b) + 19 = 19 + (3b + 2a)$

13. $\dfrac{1}{x + y} \cdot (x + y) = 1$

14. $-(a + b) + (a + b) = 0$

Practice Multiple Choice

Choose the best answer.

1. Which property guarantees the truth of this statement?

$-3(7x + 5y - 4)$
$= -21x - 15y + 12$

A Closure property of addition

B Identity property of multiplication

C Distributive property

D Associative property of multiplication

2. Which operation should be done first to simplify this expression?

$123 - [18 - (14 + 7)]$

F $232 - 18$

G $14 + 7$

H $18 - 7$

J $18 - 14$

Which axiom or property guarantees the truth of each statement?

15. $3x(y + z) = 3x(y + z)$ **16.** $\frac{1}{x} \cdot x = 1$. Thus $1 = \frac{1}{x} \cdot x$

17. $4ab = 4ab$ **18.** $5(a + b) = (a + b)5$

Are the sets closed for addition, subtraction, multiplication, and division (except by 0)? If not, give counterexamples.

19. whole numbers   **20.** rational numbers   **21.** integers

Complete the following proof by supplying the missing reasons.

22. Property of -1. For any number a, $-1 \cdot a = -a$.

1. $-1 \cdot a = -1 \cdot a + 0$	1.
2. $\quad = -1 \cdot a + (a + (-a))$	2. Additive inverse
3. $\quad = (-1 \cdot a + a) + (-a)$	3.
4. $\quad = (-1 \cdot a + 1 \cdot a) + (-a)$	4. Multiplicative identity
5. $\quad = (-1 + 1) \cdot a + (-a)$	5.
6. $\quad = 0 \cdot a + (-a)$	6. Additive inverse
7. $\quad = 0 + -a$	7.
8. $\quad = -a$	8.
9. $-1 \cdot a = -a$	9. Transitive property of equality

B

Write a Convincing Argument   Write a convincing argument or give a counterexample.

23. The set of whole numbers is *closed* for addition. The set of even numbers $\{0, 2, 4, 6, 8, 10, \ldots\}$ consists of numbers of the form $2a$ where a is a whole number. Is the set of even numbers closed for addition?

24. Is the set of odd whole numbers $\{1, 3, 5, 7, 9, \ldots\}$ closed for addition?

25. The set of whole numbers is closed for multiplication. The set $\{0, 3, 6, 9, 12, \ldots\}$ consists of numbers of the form $3a$ where a is a whole number. Is this set closed for multiplication?

Challenge

26. Prove that for any rational numbers a and b, $(-a)b = -ab$.

27. Prove the inverse of a sum property: For any rational numbers a and b, $-(a + b) = -a + (-b)$. (Hint: Use the property of -1 and the distributive property).

Mixed Review

Write an equation.   **28.** A roll of film costs \$4.80 and developing costs \$8.35. What is the total cost for each of the 36 prints?   *2-9*

Factor.   **29.** $16a - 48$ **30.** $8y - 10 + 12x$ **31.** $45 - 15n$ *2-7*

Collect like terms.   **32.** $6a + 9c - 8a$ **33.** $7 + 8c - 25c + 2$ *1-5*

Exercises

15. Reflexive property of equality

16. Symmetric property of equality

17. Reflexive property of equality

18. Commutative property of multiplication

19. Yes; no, $4 - 2$ is not a whole number; yes; no, $1 \div 2$ is not a whole number.

20. Yes; yes; yes; yes

21. Yes; yes; yes; no, $1 \div -2$ is not an integer.

22. 1. Additive identity
3. Associative property of addition
5. Distributive property
7. Multiplication property of zero
8. Additive identity

23. Yes. The sum of two even numbers $2a$ and $2b$ where a and b are whole numbers equals $2(a + b)$ by the distributive property. $2(a + b)$ is even because $a + b$ is a whole number.

24. No. $1 + 3 = 4$. 4 is not in the set of odd whole numbers.

25. Yes. The product of $3a$ and $3b$ where a and b are whole numbers is $(3a)(3b)$ which equals $3(3(ab))$ by the associative and commutative properties of multiplication. ab is a whole number, so $3(ab)$ is a whole number.

1. C; Algebra 1.0, 1.1
2. G; Algebra 1.0

26.

Statement	Reason
1. $(-a)b$ $= (-1 \cdot a)b$	Property of -1
2. $= -1(ab)$	Associative property of multiplication
3. $= -ab$	Property of -1
4. $(-a)b$ $= -ab$	Transitive property of equality

27.

Statement	Reason
1. $-(a + b)$ $= -1(a + b)$	Property of -1
2. $= -1(a) + -1(b)$	Distributive property
3. $= -a + (-b)$	Property of -1
4. $-(a + b)$ $= -a + (-b)$	Transitive property of equality

Mixed Review

28. $c = \frac{4.80 + 8.35}{36}$

29. $16(a - 3)$

30. $2(4y - 5 + 6x)$

31. $15(3 - n)$

32. $9c - 2a$

33. $9 - 17c$

2-1

The set of **integers** consists of the **positive integers,** the **negative integers,** and zero. Numbers that are the same distance from 0, but on opposite sides of 0 on the number line, are called **opposites.** For any two numbers on the number line, the one farther to the right is greater. The **absolute value** of a number is its distance from 0 on the number line.

Name the integer suggested by each situation.
1. Tanya's mom owes $25.
2. Keiko deposited $50 in her savings account.

Find the absolute value.
3. $|-38|$
4. $|91|$
5. $|-0.02|$

2-2

A **rational number** can be expressed as the ratio of two integers, $\frac{a}{b}$, where $b \neq 0$. There is a point on the number line for every rational number. The number is called the **coordinate** of the point, and the point is the **graph** of the number.

Graph each rational number on a number line.
6. -2.5
7. $\frac{4}{3}$
8. $-\frac{16}{5}$

Use $<$ or $>$ to write a true sentence.
9. $-2.5 \ \square \ -4.5$
10. $-\frac{2}{3} \ \square \ -\frac{1}{10}$
11. $-\frac{1}{2} \ \square \ \frac{3}{5}$

Show that each number can be written as the ratio of two integers.
12. -4.2
13. $1\frac{3}{5}$
14. -8

2-3

To add two positive numbers or two negative numbers, add the absolute values; the sum has the same sign as each addend. To add a positive number and a negative number, subtract the absolute values; the sum has the same sign as the addend with the greater absolute value. Number pairs whose sum is 0 are called **additive inverses.**

Add.
15. $-6 + (-13)$
16. $\frac{3}{4} + \left(-\frac{9}{4}\right)$
17. $-3.9 + 7.4$
18. $6 + (-9) + (-8) + 7$
19. $-3.8 + 5.1 + (-12) - (-4.3)$

Key Terms

absolute value (p. 56)
additive inverse (p. 66)
axiom (p. 102)
braces (p. 95)
brackets (p. 95)
closed (p. 103)
coordinate (p. 59)
density property (p. 62)
difference (p. 71)
distributive properties (p. 89)
field (p. 102)
field axioms (p. 102)
graph of a number (p. 59)
inequality (p. 55)
integers (p. 54)
inverse of a sum property (p. 94)
irrational number (p. 86)
multiplicative inverse (p. 82)
multiplicative property of zero (p. 78)
negative integers (p. 54)
opposites (p. 54)
parentheses (p. 95)
positive integers (p. 54)
property of −1 (p. 93)
property of additive inverses (p. 66)
property of multiplicative inverses (p. 82)
quotient (p. 81)
rational numbers (p. 59)
real numbers (p. 61)
reciprocal (p. 82)
repeating decimal (p. 86)
terminating decimal (p. 86)
theorem (p. 102)

Chapter 2 Wrap Up
1. -25
2. $+50$
3. 38
4. 91
5. 0.02

8. 6.   7.
$-4 \ -3 \ -2 \ -1 \quad 0 \quad 1 \quad 2$

9. $>$
10. $<$
11. $<$
12. $-\frac{42}{10}$

13. $\frac{8}{5}$
14. $-\frac{8}{1}$
15. -19
16. $-\frac{6}{4}$ or $-\frac{3}{2}$
17. 3.5
18. -4
19. -6.4

Find the additive inverse of each.

20. 27　　　　　　　**21.** −7.45　　　　　　**22.** $-\frac{7}{3}$

23. Find $-x$ when x is −34.　　　　**24.** Find $-(-x)$ when x is 5.

25. On a first, second, and third down a football team had these gains and losses: a 5-yd gain, a 12-yd loss, and a 15-yd gain. Find the total number of yards gained or lost.

2-4

To subtract a rational number, add its inverse. When addition and subtraction occur several times, use the rule for subtracting rational numbers to make them all additions.

Subtract.

26. $5 - 7$　　　　　　**27.** $-7 - (-3)$　　　　**28.** $-\frac{9}{10} - \frac{1}{2}$

Simplify.

29. $13 - 4 + 8 - (-2)$　　　　　**30.** $4y - 19 - (-7y) + 3$

31. An airplane is 2500 ft above the rim of the Grand Canyon at a point where the Grand Canyon is 1500 ft deep. How high is the plane above the floor of the canyon?

32. Mr. Jones had a balance of $89.00 in his checking account. He wrote a check for $105.95. By how much has he overdrawn his checking account?

2-5

When you multiply a positive number and a negative number, the product is negative. When you multiply two negative numbers or two positive numbers, the product is positive. The product of 0 and a rational number is 0.

Multiply.

33. $6(-4)$　　　　**34.** $\frac{2}{3}\left(-\frac{3}{7}\right)$　　　　**35.** $3(-7)(-2)(5)$

2-6

When you divide a positive number by a negative number or a negative number by a positive number, the quotient is negative. When you divide two negative numbers, the quotient is positive. Two numbers are **multiplicative inverses** or **reciprocals** if their product is 1. To divide by a rational number, multiply by its reciprocal.

Divide.

36. $21 \div (-7)$　　　　**37.** $\frac{-45}{-9}$　　　　**38.** $-\frac{7}{8} \div \frac{5}{4}$

Chapter 2 Wrap Up

20. −27
21. 7.45
22. $\frac{7}{3}$
23. 34
24. 5
25. 8 yd gain
26. −2
27. −4
28. $-\frac{14}{10}$ or $-\frac{7}{5}$
29. 19
30. $11y - 16$
31. 4000 ft
32. $16.95

33. −24
34. $-\frac{2}{7}$
35. 210
36. −3
37. 5
38. $-\frac{7}{10}$

2-7

The **distributive property of multiplication over subtraction** is used to multiply and factor algebraic expressions and to collect like terms.

Multiply.

39. $2(6x - 1)$ **40.** $-7(1 + 4x)$ **41.** $-3(2a - 3b + c)$

Factor.

42. $9a - 9$ **43.** $8x - 32y - 8$ **44.** $42z - 21x + 7$

Collect like terms.

45. $5x + 3x - x$ **46.** $5a - 3a$ **47.** $8m - 6m + 6$

2-8

The property of -1 states that $-1 \cdot a = -a$. The property of -1 and the distributive property allow us to rename the inverse of a sum as the sum of the inverses, $-(a + b) = -a + -b$.

Rename each additive inverse without parentheses.

48. $-(x + 7)$ **49.** $-(7a + 12b + c)$ **50.** $-(6 - z)$

When an expression contains more than one grouping symbol, you must do the computation in the innermost grouping symbols first.

Simplify.

51. $3a - (8a + 3)$ **52.** $7x - 5 - (10x - 4)$

53. $a - 5(a + b)$ **54.** $3p - 4(8p - 3)$

Simplify.

55. $[12 - (8 + 3)]$ **56.** $15 - [9 - (11 + 4)]$

2-9

Write an equation is a powerful strategy for many of the problems you will encounter while studying algebra. You should use the Problem-Solving Guideline, Develop and carry out a PLAN, when you need to write an equation.

Which equation(s) can be used to solve the problem?

57. A dozen roses cost $30. How much does each rose cost?

      Let r = the cost of one rose.

(A) $\frac{30}{12} = r$ **(B)** $30 - r = 12$ **(C)** $12r = 30$

Write an equation that could be used to solve the problem.

58. A professional baseball player made $1,289,196 for the 1999 baseball season. His team played 162 games in the season. How much did the player make per game?

Chapter 2 Wrap Up

39. $12x - 2$

40. $-7 - 28x$

41. $-6a + 9b - 3c$

42. $9(a - 1)$

43. $8(x - 4y - 1)$

44. $7(6z - 3x + 1)$

45. $7x$

46. $2a$

47. $2m + 6$

48. $-x - 7$

49. $-7a - 12b - c$

50. $-6 + z$

51. $-5a - 3$

52. $-3x - 1$

53. $-4a - 5b$

54. $-29p + 12$

55. 1

56. 21

57. (A) or (C)

58. $162a = 1,289,170$

Name the integer suggested by each situation.

1. Ed lost 16 points in a card game.

2. The highest points on the Grand Canyon are 9000 ft above sea level.

Find the absolute value.

3. $|6.5|$

4. $|-105.5|$

Graph each rational number on a number line.

5. $\frac{9}{2}$

6. -2.5

Use $>$ or $<$ to write a true sentence.

7. $-3.2 \ \square \ 1.2$

8. $-\frac{3}{4} \ \square \ -\frac{5}{8}$

Show that each number can be written as the ratio of two integers.

9. -3.5

10. $2\frac{1}{3}$

Add.

11. $3.1 + (-4.7)$

12. $-\frac{3}{5} + \left(-\frac{4}{5}\right)$

13. $-8 + 4 + (-7) + 3$

Find the additive inverse of each.

14. $\frac{2}{3}$

15. -1.4

16. Wendy had $43 in her savings account. She withdrew $25. Then she made a deposit of $30. How much money does she have in her savings account now?

Subtract.

17. $\frac{1}{3} - \frac{2}{3}$

18. $2 - (-8)$

19. $3.2 - 5.7$

Simplify.

20. $6 + 7 - 4 - (-3)$

21. $3y + 16 - (-4y) + 7$

22. On a winter night the temperature dropped from 5°C to −7°C. How many degrees did the temperature drop?

23. Your total assets are $170. You borrow $300 to go on vacation. What is your net worth now?

Multiply.

24. $4(-12)$

25. $\left(-\frac{1}{2}\right)\left(-\frac{3}{8}\right)$

26. $5(-4)(-6)(2)$

Chapter 2 Assessment

1. −16
2. +9000
3. 6.5
4. 105.5

6. / 5. (number line from −3 to 5)

7. $<$
8. $<$
9. $-\frac{35}{10}$
10. $\frac{7}{3}$
11. −1.6
12. $-\frac{7}{5}$
13. −8
14. $-\frac{2}{3}$
15. 1.4
16. $48
17. $-\frac{1}{3}$
18. 10
19. −2.5
20. 12
21. $7y + 23$
22. 12°
23. −$130
24. −48
25. $\frac{3}{16}$
26. 240

Divide.

27. $-35 \div 7$

28. $\frac{-54}{-9}$

29. $\frac{-125}{25}$

Find the reciprocal.

30. $-\frac{8}{7}$

31. $-\frac{24}{7}$

32. $3y$

Divide.

33. $\frac{4}{9} \div \left(\frac{-7}{3}\right)$

34. $\frac{-15}{\frac{1}{x}}$

35. $\frac{-3}{5} \div \left(-\frac{5}{6}\right)$

Multiply.

36. $-7(x + 3)$

37. $\left(\frac{5}{3}\right)(x - 2y + z)$

38. $-7(-3a - 2b - 8)$

Factor.

39. $4x - 12$

40. $4a + 12b - 16$

41. $\frac{2x}{3} - \frac{y}{3}$

Collect like terms.

42. $-5x - 6x + 4x$

43. $q + t - 2t + q$

44. $4m - m + 3$

Multiply.

45. $(-1)(-21)$

46. $-1 \cdot 17$

Rename each additive inverse without parentheses.

47. $-(y - 8)$

48. $-(2a + 5b - c)$

Simplify.

49. $5n - (2n + m)$

50. $4x - 3(y + 2x)$

51. $50 - [12 - (16 + 5)]$

52. $6(9 - 4) - [10 - (6 + 8)]$

Which equation(s) can be used to solve the problem?

53. Saturnina got a 92 on the Chapter 2 test. That was 9 more points than she got on the Chapter 1 test. What was her score on the Chapter 1 test?

(A) $n - 92 = 9$ **(B)** $n = 92 + 9$ **(C)** $n + 9 = 92$

Write an equation that can be used to solve the problem.

54. A museum took in $3456 from 576 patrons. What was the price of admission to the museum?

55. Marta rode her bike 57 miles in two days. She rode 31 miles the first day. How far did she ride the second day?

Chapter 2 Assessment **111**

Chapter 2 Assessment

27. -5
28. 6
29. -5
30. $-\frac{7}{8}$
31. $-\frac{7}{24}$
32. $\frac{1}{3y}$
33. $-\frac{4}{21}$
34. $-15x$
35. $\frac{18}{25}$
36. $-7x - 21$

37. $\frac{5}{3}x - \frac{10}{3}y + \frac{5}{3}z$
38. $21a + 14b + 56$
39. $4(x - 3)$
40. $4(a + 3b - 4)$
41. $\frac{1}{3}(2x - y)$
42. $-7x$
43. $2q - t$
44. $3m + 3$
45. 21
46. -17
47. $-y + 8$
48. $-2a - 5b + c$
49. $3n - m$

50. $-2x - 3y$
51. 59
52. 34
53. C
54. $576p = 3456$ or $p = \frac{3456}{576}$
55. $d + 31 = 57$ or $d = 57 - 31$

Chapter 2 Assessment **111**

CHAPTER

3 ▷ Equations

CHAPTER AT A GLANCE

PACING OPTIONS

This chart suggests pacing only for the lessons and their parts. It is provided as a possible guide.
It will help you determine how much time you have in your schedule to cover other features, such as the Chapter Wrap Up and Assessment.

	Day 1	Day 2	Day 3	Day 4	Day 5	Day 6	Day 7	Day 8	Day 9	Day 10	Day 11
Traditional (40–45 min. class periods)	3-1 ▼▼	3-2 ▼▼	3-3 ▼▼	3-3 ▼	3-4 ▼▼	3-5 ▼	3-5 ▼	3-6 ▼	3-7 ▼	3-8 ▼	3-9 ▼▼
Algebra 1 Over 2 Years (40–45 min. class periods)	3-1 ▼	3-1 ▼	3-2 ▼	3-2 ▼	3-3 ▼	3-3 ▼	3-3 ▼	3-4 ▼	3-4 ▼	3-5 ▼	3-5 ▼
Block Scheduling (90 min. class periods)	3-1 ▼▼ 3-2 ▼▼	3-3 ▼▼▼	3-4 ▼▼ 3-5 ▼	3-5 ▼ 3-6 ▼	3-7 ▼ 3-8 ▼	3-9 ▼▼ 3-10 ▼▼▼	3-11 ▼▼ 3-12 ▼				

SKILLS TRACE

SKILL	FOUNDATION	DEVELOPED IN LESSONS	REVIEWED/REINFORCED/EXTENDED
Using the addition and multiplication properties of equality to solve equations	previous course	**3-1 through 3-3**	Used throughout the text
Solving problems using an equation	2-9	**3-1 through 3-4**	3-12, throughout the text
Solving equations which contain parentheses	2-8	**3-3**	6-8, 10-6, 11-9
Clearing equations of fractions or decimals	previous course	**3-6**	10-3, 10-6, 10-10
Solving equations involving absolute value	2-1, 2-9	**3-8**	9-3
Solving proportions	previous course	**3-9**	12-5
Solving equations using strategies	1-7, 2-9	**3-12**	Used throughout the text, at least once per chapter

CORRELATION TO STANDARDIZED TESTS

YOUR LOCAL TEST*

Lesson		CAT5	CTBS/5 TerraNova™	ITED	MAT7	SAT9		CA Algebra
3-1	The Addition Property of Equality							5.0
3-2	The Multiplication Property of Equality							5.0
3-3	Using the Properties Together							5.0, 25.0
3-4	Expressions and Equations					■		5.0
3-5	More on Solving Equations							5.0
3-6	Clearing an Equation of Fractions or Decimals	■	■					5.0
3-7	Formulas		■					5.0, 25.0
3-8	Solving Equations Involving Absolute Value							3.0, 25.2, 25.3
3-9	Proportions			■				5.0
3-10	Using Percent	■	■	■				5.0
3-11	More Expressions and Equations							5.0
3-12	Reasoning Strategies: Make an Organized List							24.0

CAT5 California Achievement Test, 5th Edition
CTBS/5 Comprehensive Test of Basic Skills, 5th Edition
ITED Iowa Test of Educational Development
　　Level 15, Complete Battery, Form M

MAT7 Metropolitan Achievement Test, 7th Edition
SAT 9 Stanford Achievement Test/Task 1

*See pp. T34–T39 for the California Standards.

For other standardized test correlations, follow the link to your state at **www.phschool.com**.

ay 12	Day 13	Day 14	Day 15	Day 16	Day 17	Day 18	Day 19	Day 20	Day 21	Day 22	Day 23	Day 24
10 ▽▽▿	3-11 ▽▽	3-12 ▽										
▽	3-6 ▽	3-7 ▽	3-7 ▽	3-8 ▽	3-9 ▽	3-9 ▿	3-10 ▽	3-10 ▿	3-10 ▿	3-11 ▽	3-11 ▿	3-12 ▽

Math Background

Chapter Overview

Solving equations in one variable is formally introduced by using the addition and multiplication properties of equality. Skills learned in Chapters 1 and 2 are extended in this chapter to solving equations. Simple equations involving absolute value are introduced and solved. Equations involving proportions and percents are presented.

Translation of phrases into algebraic notation is again discussed, and word problems are translated into equations and solved by using the problem-solving guidelines. The reasoning strategy, *Make an Organized List*, is introduced as another method of solving problems.

3-1, 3-2 The Addition and Multiplication Properties of Equality

There is no need for a subtraction or a division property of equality since subtraction is addition of an additive inverse and division is multiplication by a multiplicative inverse. However, some students may have been previously taught to "undo the operation." That is, they recognize addition and subtraction, and multiplication and division, as inverse operations. To solve $3x + 1 = 7$, such a student may write

$$3x + 1 - 1 = 7 - 1$$

subtracting 1 from each side of the equation since 1 was added to the variable term. Similarly, to solve $7x = 2$, such a student may write

$$\frac{7x}{7} = \frac{2}{7}$$

dividing both sides by 7 since the variable is multiplied by 7. As long as the student's work is correct, this should cause no problem.

3-3 Using the Properties Together

When simplifying an expression such as $12x - 8 + 10x$, students may make the error of combining the 12 and -8 even though they are not in like terms to get $4x + 10x$. Students should again be reminded that collecting like terms is an application of the distributive property. It may help them to use the commutative property of addition, and to always write out the application of the distributive property. So they would write

$$12x - 8 + 10x = 12x + 10x - 8$$
$$= (12 + 10)x - 8$$
$$= 22x - 8$$

3-4 Expressions and Equations

Remind students that checking their answers is an important habit to acquire. In the future, not all problems will be as simple as these are. When a problem involves setting up an equation, it is not sufficient to simply check the answer in the equation because the equation may be incorrect. It is important to analyze the appropriateness of the answer in the original problem.

3-5 More on Solving Equations

Some students have difficulty accepting a solution written as $\frac{2}{3} = x$. Remind them of the symmetric property of equality which makes this equivalent to $x = \frac{2}{3}$.

3-6 Clearing an Equation of Fractions or Decimals

Some students may make the error of multiplying each side of an equation by its own least common denominator. Point out to them that it is the multiplication property of equality (if $a = b$, then $ac = bc$) that requires the same factor to be used to multiply each side of the equation.

Restating this idea as "multiply each *term* of the equation by the same factor" may help these students. Using parentheses to group each side of the equation before multiplying by the equations' least common denominator, and proper use of the distributive property, also help alleviate this problem.

▶ 3-7 Formulas

This is a good opportunity for students to review what they remember about the meaning of various formulas and what the variables represent.

▶ 3-8 Solving Equations Involving Absolute Value

Remind students that solving an equation means to find all the numbers that satisfy the equation. Absolute value equations may have two, one, or no solutions.

$|x| = 1$ has two solutions.

$|x| = 0$ has one solution.

$|x| = -1$ has no solutions.

Remind students again of the value of acquiring the habit of checking their answers.

▶ 3-9 Proportions

Students often make the mistake of trying to "cross multiply" when adding or subtracting fractions. Emphasize that cross multiplication is used *only* for equations that are proportions.

Cross multiplying is just a shortcut for applying the multiplication property of equality. Demonstrate as follows that multiplying both sides of an equation by the product of the denominators gives the same result as cross multiplying.

$$\frac{7.2}{x} = \frac{12}{28}$$

$$28x \cdot \frac{7.2}{x} = 28 \cdot \frac{13}{28}$$

$$28(7.2) = x(13)$$

To check an answer, be sure students understand that they must substitute into the original proportion.

▶ 3-10 Using Percent

When faced with percent problems, some students will agonize over deciding whether to multiply or divide. Point out that they can translate the English sentences into an equation and then simply solve the equation.

▶ 3-11 More Expressions and Equations

This is a good opportunity to review the difference between an expression and an equation. An expression may contain variables, numbers, and operation symbols, but it may not contain an equal sign or an inequality sign. An equation is an algebraic sentence that states that two expressions are equal.

Students should realize that, for an integer n, $2n$ is a common way to represent an even integer. And they should know that $2n + 2$, $2n - 4$, and so on are other representations of even integers. They can use the distributive property to factor out the common factor 2: $2n + 2 = 2(n + 1)$, and so on. It may then be easier for them to see that expressions such as $2n + 1$ or $2n - 3$ represent odd integers.

▶ 3-12 Reasoning Strategies: Make an Organized List

Some students may need to work with a partner to learn ways to *Make an Organized List* and to be certain they have listed all possibilities. This is a good opportunity to begin to discuss the use of patterns, a strategy formally introduced in Lesson 5-12.

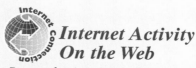

Internet Activity On the Web

For professional development tips visit our Web site.
www.phschool.com

Monitoring Progress

UNIVERSAL ACCESS

▶ Preventing a Student from Falling Behind

These resources are particularly helpful in preventing a student from falling behind his or her appropriate math level. For a complete list of resources for this chapter, see page 112F.

Before Lessons

Skills You Need for Chapter 3 (p. 112)
- Add, subtract, multiply and divide integers
- Factor using integers.
- Simplifying expressions containing grouping symbols

Preteaching Math Vocabulary
- List of Key Terms (p. 112 and p. 165)
- Reading Math (pp. 130, 142)
- Writing Math (p. 143)

Skills Intervention Kit With CD-ROM

With Lesson	Use this Unit
3-6, 3-10	Decimals
3-6	Operations with Fractions
3-9, 3-10	Ratio, Proportion, and Percent
3-1, 3-2, 3-3, 3-4, 3-11	Pre-Algebra Basics

During Lessons

Try This Exercises (Student Edition)

Additional Examples (Teacher's Edition)

Help at Home
- Lessons 3-1 to 3-5
- Lessons 3-6 to 3-11
- Available in English and Spanish

After Lessons

Lesson Quiz (Teacher's Edition)

Reteaching Worksheets (Teaching Resources Box)

Daily Cumulative Review Masters

There is a Daily Cumulative Review worksheet for every lesson in this chapter.

Skills Intervention Kit

Innovative resource package for diagnosing students' gaps in basic skills, prescribing an individualized course of study, and monitoring progress. Eight intervention units cover core skills students need to succeed.

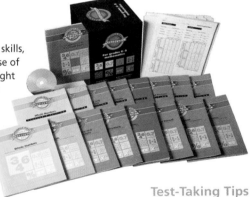

ASSESSMENT OPTIONS

Lesson	3-1	3-2	3-3	3-4	3-5	3-6	3-7	3-8	3-9	3-10	3-11	3-12	End
Try This Exercises	■	■	■	■	■	■	■	■	■	■	■		
Mixed Reviews	■	■	■	■	■	■	■	■	■	■	■	■	
Quizzes				■			■						
Chapter Assessment													■
Cumulative Review	A Cumulative Review for Chapters 1–4 is found on pp. 198–201.												
Standardized Test Prep	■			■		■	Sample College Entrance Exams are found in Problem Solving Practice Masters.						
Computer Item Generator CD-ROM	Can be used to create custom-made practice pages or assessment pages at any time.												
Student Tutorial CD-ROM	Students can self-assess and access tutorial help at any time.												

Test-Taking Tips on Transparencies

Test-Taking Tip: Record Your Response

Learn and practice the proper way to record responses.

Example 1 Answer: $1\frac{1}{2}$

Convert mixed numbers to improper fractions: $1\frac{1}{2} = \frac{3}{2}$

Write answer in boxes. → $\boxed{3\,|\,/\,|\,2}$

Darken matching oval below.

Example 2 Answer: 0.33...

Enter the most accurate value that the grid allows.

Write answer in boxes. → $\boxed{.\,|\,3\,|\,3\,|\,3}$

Darken matching oval below.

Practice recording the following answers.

1. Answer: $x = \$55$

(Can be positioned left, right, or centered.)

2. Answer: $y = \frac{4}{3}$

(Can be recorded as $\frac{4}{3}$ or 1.33. Do not record as $1\frac{1}{3}$ because 11/3 will be interpreted as $\frac{11}{3}$ by the computer.)

For use with Lesson 3-12

Resources for Chapter 3

TEACHING RESOURCES BOX

	First Five Minutes	Practice	Reteach	Enrichment	Problem Solving	Assessment	Cumulative Review	Lesson Planner
3-1	■	■	■		■		■	■
3-2	■	■	■		■		■	■
3-3	■	■	■	■■			■	■
3-4	■	■■	■			■	■	■
3-5	■	■	■				■	■
3-6	■	■	■				■	■
3-7	■	■	■	■	■		■	■
3-8	■	■	■				■	■
3-9	■	■■	■		■		■	■
3-10	■	■	■		■		■	■
3-11	■		■		■		■	■
3-12	■		■				■	■
End				■		■	5 Forms	

	Success-Building	Teaching Transparencies	Help at Home	SE Answers on Transparencies
3-1	■■			■
3-2	■■■			■
3-3	■■			■
3-4	■■■■		■	■
3-5				■
3-6				■
3-7	■			■
3-8				■
3-9				■
3-10				■
3-11		■		■
3-12	■		■	■
End	■			■

Also available for use throughout the chapter:

Solution Key
Mathematics Standardized Test Prep
  Student Edition and Teacher's Edition

Overhead Manipulatives Kit
Practice Workbook

Student Manipulatives Kit
Test-Taking Tips on Transparencies

California Assessment Success Kit
Graphing Calculator Handbook

TECHNOLOGY

Computer Item Generator

CD-ROM with an unlimited supply of questions with varying degrees of difficulty for customized practice sheets, quizzes, and tests.

Secondary Math Toolkit™ with Integrated Math Labs

Integrated software package with linkable math tools for exploring key concepts.

Student Tutorial

Test preparation software for students on CD-ROM with management system for teachers; includes Secondary Math Lab Toolkit.

Resource Pro® with Planning Express®

CD-ROM with complete classroom planning tool and teaching resources for customizing and planning lessons.

Web Extension
www.phschool.com

For Students
- Chapter Support with Internet Links
- Internet Activities

For Teachers
- Curriculum Support
- Professional Development
- Product Information
- Regional Information

Also available for use throughout the chapter:

- Algebra Instructional Videos: A Step by Step Guide to Key Concepts

CHAPTER 3

Skills & Concepts You Need for Chapter 3

2-3   Add.

1. $-3 + (-8)$ 2. $8 + (-3) + (-11)$ 3. $-3.1 + 6.8$

2-4   Subtract.

4. $9 - (-13)$ 5. $-7.2 - (-10.1)$ 6. $\frac{2}{3} - \frac{9}{10}$

2-5   Multiply.

7. $9 \cdot (-4)$ 8. $\frac{3}{2} \cdot \frac{-4}{7}$ 9. $-\frac{2}{3} \cdot \frac{5}{8}$

10. $-6 \cdot 8$ 11. $-11(-3)$ 12. $-7(-5)$

2-6   Divide.

13. $\frac{3}{4} \div -\frac{1}{8}$ 14. $-\frac{7}{9} \div -\frac{2}{3}$ 15. $-9.37 \div -0.1$

2-7   Factor.

16. $9y - 45$ 17. $bw + bx - by$
18. $3y + 15 - 21x$ 19. $6w - 12x + 10$

2-7   Multiply.

20. $3(x - 5)$ 21. $8(4 + w)$

2-8   Simplify.

22. $5x - (6 + 3x)$ 23. $7w - 3 - (4w - 8)$
24. $[3(5 - 2) + 18] - [12 - (3 + 4)]$
25. $[2(4x + 7) - 3] + [5(3 + x) + 2x]$

112

Skills & Concepts You Need for Chapter 3

1. -11
2. -6
3. 3.7
4. 22
5. 2.9
6. $-\frac{7}{30}$
7. -36
8. $-\frac{6}{7}$
9. $\frac{-5}{12}$
10. -48
11. 33
12. 35
13. -6
14. $\frac{7}{6}$
15. 93.7
16. $9(y - 5)$
17. $b(w + x - y)$
18. $3(y + 5 - 7x)$
19. $2(3w - 6x + 5)$
20. $3x - 15$
21. $32 + 8w$
22. $2x - 6$
23. $3w + 5$
24. 22
25. $15x + 26$

Equations

The tallest building in Los Angeles, Library Tower, rises 565 ft higher than the venerable City Hall to stand 1017 ft tall. Use the equation $h + 565 = 1017$ to find the height h of City Hall.

Photo Caption

452 ft

3-1

1. FOCUS

FIRST FIVE MINUTES

Find the missing term.
1. $2a + 4 + 3 = 2a + ?$ 7
2. $8x - 2x + 9 = ? + 9$ $6x$
3. If $x = 9$, then $x + 5 = ? + 5$ 9
4. If $x = 2$, then $x + 5 = 2 + ?$ 5
5. If $a + 7 = 2 + 7$, then $a = ?$ 2

INTRODUCING THE CONCEPT

Students should realize that there are many ways of balancing the scales. Some students will come up with obvious ones; others will be more creative. To check whether their scales balance, students should substitute. They should replace each pyramid with three balls and each cube with two balls. If they end up with the same number of balls on each side, the scale balances.

2. TEACH the Mathematics

1 Using the Addition Property of Equality

This chapter presents a formal approach to solving equations.

Note that the direction "Solve" includes checking. Students can be asked to write formal checks, to use a calculator, or to check mentally.

You may wish to introduce the concept of "undoing" an equation. Students should look at the variable and determine what has been done to it. If something has been added to it, they can "undo" the addition by adding the inverse to both sides. Emphasize that the goal is to isolate the variable on one side of the equation.

Key Questions

■ If $m + 4 = 7$, does $m = 4 + 7$? No
■ If $a = b$, then does $a + 3 = b + 3$? Yes

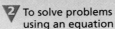

What You'll Learn

1 To use the addition property of equality in solving equations

2 To solve problems using an equation

...And Why

To use and solve algebraic models of the forms
$x + a = b$ and $x - a = b$

The Addition Property of Equality

Introducing the Concept: The Addition Property

The scales at the right are balanced. Suppose you have as many of each object as you want. What are five different ways you can add objects to both sides of the scale below so it remains balanced?

PART 1 — Using the Addition Property of Equality

Objective: Use the addition property of equality to solve equations.

In Chapter 1 you learned two ways to solve equations: using mental math and the problem-solving strategy *Try, Test, Revise.* Recall that replacements that make an equation true are called solutions and that to solve an equation means to find all of its solutions.

You also learned that you can add the same number to both sides of an equation and get an equivalent equation. We call this the **addition property of equality.**

The Addition Property of Equality

For all rational numbers a, b, and c, if $a = b$, then $a + c = b + c$.

To solve an equation like $x + 5 = -7$, we need to get the variable alone on one side of the equation. In this equation, we have to add a number to 5 to "get rid of" the 5. Since -5 is the additive inverse, or the opposite of 5, $5 + (-5) = 0$. If we add -5 to both sides of the equation, we will get the variable alone. The following examples show these steps.

EXAMPLES Solve.

1
$$x + 5 = -7$$
$$x + 5 + (-5) = -7 + (-5)$$

We must add -5, the opposite of 5.
Using the addition property to add -5 to both sides

$$x + 0 = -12$$
$$x = -12$$

Using the additive inverse property
Using the additive identity property

Check:
$$\frac{x + 5 = -7}{\begin{array}{c|c} -12 + 5 & -7 \\ \hline & -7 \end{array}} \quad \frac{}{-7} \checkmark$$

Substituting -12 for x

The solution is -12.

2
$$-6 = y - 8$$
$$-6 + 8 = y - 8 + 8$$

We must add 8, the opposite of -8.
Using the addition property to add 8 to both sides of the equation

$$2 = y$$

Check:
$$\frac{-6 = y - 8}{\begin{array}{c|c} -6 & 2 - 8 \\ \hline -6 & -6 \end{array}} \checkmark$$

Substituting 2 for y

The solution is 2.

3
$$x - 5.4 = 2.3$$
$$x - 5.4 + 5.4 = 2.3 + 5.4$$

We must add 5.4, the opposite of -5.4.
Using the addition property to add 5.4 to both sides of the equation

$$x = 7.7$$

The solution is 7.7.

Substitution will show that 7.7 checks.

Try This Solve.

a. $x + 7 = 2$ **b.** $y - 8 = -3$ **c.** $5 = -4 + a$

PART 2 Solving Problems

Objective: Solve problems using an equation.

PROBLEM-SOLVING GUIDELINES
■ UNDERSTAND the problem
▪ Develop and carry out a PLAN
■ Find the ANSWER and CHECK

Many problems can be solved by translating the situation into an equation (Lesson 2-9) and then solving the equation.

Try This
a. -5
b. 5
c. 9

3-1   *The Addition Property of Equality*   **115**

Solve each equation for x.

46. $8 - 25 = 8 + x - 21$ **47.** $16 + x - 22 = -16$

48. $x + 5 = x - (3 + x)$ **49.** $x + 3 = 3 + a - b$

50. $x + 7 = b + 10$ **51.** $1 - c = a + x$

Solve.

52. The end-of-month inventory indicated that there were 319 blank videocassettes in stock. This was after sales of 142 and a restocking of 75 during the month. How many videocassettes were in stock at the beginning of the month?

53. At the end of the week, Andrea found that she had $124.23 in her checking account. During the week, she had written checks for $12.24, $15.05, and $22.00, and she had deposited $55.12. How much was in her checking account at the beginning of the week?

54. *Critical Thinking*   Write an equation for which the solution $-\frac{7}{12}$ is found using addition.

Challenge

55. *Mathematical Reasoning*   If k is a solution of $x + a = b$, is $-k$ sometimes, always, or never a solution of $x + a = b$? Of $x - a = -b$? Explain.

56. Solve $x - 1 + 2x - 2 + 3x - 3 = 30 + 4x$.

57. If $x - 4720 = 1634$, find $x + 4720$.

58. Solve $x + x = x$.

59. *Mathematical Reasoning*   Solve each equation. Explain each result.
   a. $x + 3 = 3 + x$ **b.** $x - 3 = 3 + x$

60. *Error Analysis*   One student solved the equation $6 - x = 10$ by subtracting 6 from both sides and got 4. Explain what that student did wrong.

Mixed Review

Simplify.   **61.** $9y - (2y + 4)$ **62.** $7c - (8c + 2)$

63. $8w - 3(5w - 8)$ **64.** $6a + 2c - 3(2a + 3c)$

65. $3[5 + 4(3 - y)]$ **66.** $5t - (3 + 9t)$ *2-8*

Evaluate.   **67.** $(5a)^2$ for $a = 2$ **68.** $5a^2$ for $a = 2$ **69.** s^1 for $s = 32$ *1-3*

Multiply.   **70.** $3(-5)$ **71.** $\left(-\frac{1}{3}\right)\left(-\frac{3}{5}\right)$ **72.** $4(-2)(-1)(-3)$ *2-5*

Divide.   **73.** $-4 \div 2$ **74.** $\frac{2}{7} \div \left(-\frac{3}{8}\right)$ **75.** $-\frac{14}{15} \div \frac{5}{7}$ *2-6*

76. Mario spent half of his weekly allowance to buy a book. The book cost $5.75. Write an equation to find Mario's allowance.   *2-9*

Exercises

46. -4
47. -10
48. -8
49. $a - b$
50. $b + 3$
51. $1 - c - a$
52. 386
53. $118.40
54. Answers may vary.
55. Sometimes; when $k = 0$ and $a = b$.
    Always; If $k + a = b$, then $a - b = -k$.
    Using $-k$ for x, $x - a = -k - a = a - b - a = -b$ and $-k$ is a solution of $x - a = -b$.

56. 18
57. 11,074
58. 0
59. a. All values of x are solutions.
       Adding $-x$ to both sides
       gives $3 = 3$, which is true
       for all values of x.
    b. No solution. Adding $-x$ to
       both sides gives $-3 = 3$,
       which is not true for any
       value of x.
60. The student solved for $-x$.
    $x = -4$.

Mixed Review

61. $7y - 4$
62. $-c - 2$
63. $-7w + 24$
64. $-7c$
65. $51 - 12y$
66. $-3 - 4t$
67. 100
68. 20
69. 32
70. -15
71. $\frac{1}{5}$
72. -24
73. -2

74. $-\frac{16}{21}$
75. $-\frac{98}{75}$
76. $\frac{1}{2}a = 5.75$ or $2(5.75) = a$

The Multiplication Property of Equality

CA: Building toward 5.0

Math in Action

The California condor can be reclassified from "endangered" to "threatened" if its numbers reach about 459 (and other conditions apply). This would be 17 times as many as were alive in 1987 when all living condors were captured in an effort to save them from extinction. How many condors were there in 1987?

In this lesson you will learn how to solve equations like $17c = 459$. This equation can be used to find how many condors there were in captivity in 1987.

The number of endangered California condors grew to 161 by 1999. This is about 6.7 times the number counted in 1982. How many condors were counted in 1982?

What You'll Learn

1 To use the multiplication property of equality in solving equations

2 To solve problems using an equation

...And Why

To use and solve algebraic models of the forms $ax = b$ and $\frac{a}{b}x = c$

3-2

TIME-FOCUS METER

1. FOCUS

FIRST FIVE MINUTES

Find the number that goes in the blank.
1. $2 \cdot 3 = 3 \cdot \underline{2}$
2. $3x = \underline{3} \, x$
3. $a \cdot 5 = a \cdot \underline{5}$
4. $(x \cdot 7) \cdot \frac{1}{7} = (x \cdot 7) \cdot \underline{\frac{1}{7}}$
5. If $x = 5$, then $3 \cdot x = \underline{3} \cdot 5$
6. If $4u = 9$, then $\underline{\frac{1}{4}} \cdot 4u = \frac{1}{4} \cdot 9$

MATH IN ACTION

You may want to ask students to translate this problem to an equation. The problem will be solved in Example 1.

2. TEACH the Mathematics

1 Using the Multiplication Property of Equality

Remind students that $-\frac{2}{3} = \frac{2}{-3} = \frac{-2}{3}$. The rules for multiplying and dividing integers guarantee that these numbers are equal.

Emphasize again that the goal is to isolate the variable, and that this can be attained by "undoing" the multiplication using the multiplication property of equality.

In Example 1, you can show that "multiplying by $\frac{1}{17}$" is equivalent to "dividing by 17," as shown in Chapter 1.

Example 1 shows the solution to the Math in Action application on page 119; there were 27 condors in captivity in 1987.

Key Questions

■ If $d = e$, does $7d = 7e$? Yes
■ Which of the following are reciprocals of $-\frac{3}{4}$?

$-\frac{4}{3}$ Yes

$\frac{-4}{3}$ Yes

$\frac{3}{-4}$ No

$\frac{4}{-3}$ Yes

$-\frac{16}{9}$ Yes

Objective: Use the multiplication property to solve equations.

Equations such as $17c = 459$ can be solved using the **multiplication property of equality.**

The Multiplication Property of Equality

For all rational numbers a, b, and c, if $a = b$, then $ac = bc$.

When using the multiplication property of equality, we can say that "we multiply both sides of the equation by the same number."

To solve an equation like $17c = 459$, we need to get the variable alone on one side of the equal sign. Here we have to multiply $17c$ by some number to "get rid of" the 17. Since $\frac{1}{17}$ is the multiplicative inverse or reciprocal of 17, $\frac{1}{17} \cdot 17 = 1$. Therefore, if we multiply both sides of the equation by $\frac{1}{17}$, we will get the variable alone. The following example shows these steps.

Photo Caption
24

Chalkboard Examples

Solve and check.

1. $5x = 30$

$\frac{1}{5} \cdot 5x = \frac{1}{5} \cdot 30$

$1x = 6$

$x = 6$

2. $-6z = 42$

$\frac{1}{-6} \cdot (-6z) = \frac{1}{-6} \cdot 42$

$1z = \frac{42}{-6}$

$z = -7$

3. $\frac{3}{5}v = \frac{2}{7}$

$\frac{5}{3} \cdot \frac{3}{5}v = \frac{5}{3} \cdot \frac{2}{7}$

$1v = \frac{10}{21}$

$v = \frac{10}{21}$

Solve.

4. $\frac{z}{4} = 12$

$4 \cdot \frac{z}{4} = 4 \cdot 12$

$z = 48$

5. $\frac{w}{13} = -2$

$13 \cdot \frac{w}{13} = 13 \cdot (-2)$

$w = -26$

6. $\frac{r}{-3} = -7$

$-3 \cdot \frac{r}{-3} = -3 \cdot (-7)$

$r = 21$

▼2 Solving Problems

Chalkboard Examples

1. Kayla bought twelve identical bowling balls, which weighed a total of 90 pounds. How much did each ball weigh?

   Let b be the weight of one bowling ball.

   $12b = 90$

   $\frac{1}{12} \cdot 12b = \frac{1}{12} \cdot 90$

   $b = \frac{90}{12} = 7.5$

   Each ball weighs 7.5 lb.

2. If 16 turnips cost a total of $4, how much does one turnip cost?

   Let r be the cost of one turnip.

   $16r = 4$

   $\frac{1}{16} \cdot 16r = \frac{1}{16} \cdot 4$

   $r = \frac{4}{16} = 0.25$

   One turnip costs $0.25.

Quick Review

$$-\frac{4}{5} \cdot \frac{3}{8} = -\frac{4 \cdot 3}{5 \cdot 8}$$
$$= -\frac{3 \cdot 4}{5 \cdot 2 \cdot 4}$$
$$= -\frac{3}{5 \cdot 2} \cdot \frac{4}{4}$$
$$= -\frac{3}{10}$$

Try This

a. 5

b. $-\frac{7}{4}$

c. 14

d. -12

e. $-\frac{5}{4}$

f. -6

EXAMPLE 1 Solve.

$17c = 459$ — We must multiply by $\frac{1}{17}$, the reciprocal of 17.

$\frac{1}{17} \cdot 17c = \frac{1}{17} \cdot 459$ — Using the multiplication property to multiply both sides of the equation by $\frac{1}{17}$

$1 \cdot c = 27$ — Using the multiplicative inverse property

$c = 27$ — Using the multiplicative identity property

Check:
$$17c = 459$$

$17 \cdot 27$	459
459	459 ✔

Substituting 27 for c

The solution is 27.

EXAMPLE 2 Solve.

$-x = 9$

$-1(-x) = -1(9)$ — Using the multiplication property to multiply both sides by -1

$-(-x) = -9$ — Using the property of -1, $-1 \cdot a = -a$

$x = -9$ — The inverse of the inverse of a number is the number itself.

Check:
$$-x = 9$$

$-(-9)$	9
9	9 ✔

Substituting -9 for x

The solution is -9.

EXAMPLE 3 Solve.

$\frac{3}{8} = -\frac{5}{4}x$

$-\frac{4}{5} \cdot \frac{3}{8} = -\frac{4}{5}\left(-\frac{5}{4}x\right)$ — Using the multiplication property to multiply both sides by $-\frac{4}{5}$, the reciprocal of $-\frac{5}{4}$

$-\frac{3}{10} = x$

Check:
$$\frac{3}{8} = -\frac{5}{4}x$$

$\frac{3}{8}$	$-\frac{5}{4}\left(-\frac{3}{10}\right)$
$\frac{3}{8}$	$\frac{3}{8}$ ✔

Substituting $-\frac{3}{10}$ for x

The solution is $-\frac{3}{10}$.

Try This Solve.

a. $5x = 25$ b. $4a = -7$ c. $-3y = -42$

d. $-\frac{1}{3}y = 4$ e. $\frac{5}{6} = -\frac{2}{3}x$ f. $-x = 6$

An equation like $\frac{y}{9} = 14$ can also be solved using the multiplication property. In Chapter 2 you learned that $\frac{y}{9}$ can be written

$$\frac{y}{9} = \frac{1}{9} \cdot y$$

We know that the multiplicative inverse of $\frac{1}{9}$ is 9, since $\frac{1}{9} \cdot 9 = 1$. Example 4 shows how to use this relationship to solve the equation $\frac{y}{9} = 14$.

EXAMPLE 4 Solve.

$$\frac{y}{9} = 14 \qquad\qquad \text{Check:} \quad \frac{y}{9} = 14$$

$$9 \cdot \frac{y}{9} = 9 \cdot 14 \qquad\qquad\qquad \frac{126}{9} \;\Big|\; 14$$

$$y = 126 \qquad\qquad\qquad\qquad 14 \;\Big|\; 14 \; ✔$$

The solution is 126.

Try This Solve.

g. $\frac{x}{5} = 10$ **h.** $\frac{m}{-3} = -12$ **i.** $\frac{-t}{4} = 6$

PART 2 Solving Problems

Objective: Solve problems using an equation.

PROBLEM-SOLVING GUIDELINES
■ UNDERSTAND the problem
▨ Develop and carry out a PLAN
■ Find the ANSWER and CHECK

After translating a problem to an equation, we may need to use the multiplication property to solve the equation.

EXAMPLE 5 Solve.

In 1990, the population of Napa, California, was about 61,800. That was about one sixth the population of Sacramento, the California state capital. What was the approximate population of Sacramento?

Let s = population of Sacramento.
$\frac{1}{6}s$ = population of Napa   The population of Napa, about $\frac{1}{6}$ the size of Sacramento's, can be written as $\frac{1}{6}s$.

We can write the following equation.

$$\frac{1}{6}s = 61{,}800 \qquad \frac{1}{6}s \text{ and } 61{,}800 \text{ both represent the approximate population of Napa.}$$

$$6 \cdot \frac{1}{6}s = 6 \cdot 61{,}800 \qquad \text{Using the multiplication property}$$

$$s = 370{,}800$$

Try This
g. 50
h. 36
i. −24

LESSON QUIZ

Solve.

1. $7x = 56$

   $x = \frac{56}{7} = 8$

2. $8y = -72$

   $y = -\frac{72}{8} = -9$

3. $-5m = -8$

   $m = \frac{-8}{-5} = \frac{8}{5}$

4. $3.5n = 17.5$

   $n = \frac{17.5}{3.5} = 5$

5. $\frac{m}{6} = 13$

   $m = 6 \cdot 13 = 78$

Assignment Guide

To provide flexible scheduling, this lesson can be split into parts.

▼ Core 1–12, 13–33 odd,
   Extension 36, 42, 49–53

▼ Core 14–32 even, 34, 35, 37–41, 43
   Extension 44–48, 54, 55

Use Mixed Review to maintain skills.

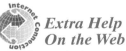

Extra Help On the Web

Look for worked-out examples at the Prentice Hall Web site.
www.phschool.com

There were about 370,800 people in Sacramento in 1990. If we estimate using 360,000 rather than 370,800, we get $\frac{1}{6} \cdot 360,000 = 60,000$, which is close to 61,800. Therefore, the number 370,800 seems reasonable.

Try This   Solve.

j. Penny bought a 12-bottle case of juice on sale for $6.72. What was the price for each bottle?

3-2 Exercises

A

Solve.

1. $6x = 36$	**2.** $3x = 39$	**3.** $5x = 45$
4. $9x = 72$	**5.** $84 = 7x$	**6.** $56 = 8x$
7. $-x = 40$	**8.** $100 = -x$	**9.** $-x = -1$
10. $-68 = -r$	**11.** $7x = -49$	**12.** $9x = -36$
13. $-12x = 72$	**14.** $-15x = 105$	**15.** $-21x = -126$
16. $-13x = -104$	**17.** $\frac{t}{7} = -9$	**18.** $\frac{y}{-8} = 11$
19. $\frac{3}{4}x = 27$	**20.** $\frac{4}{5}x = 16$	**21.** $\frac{-t}{3} = 7$
22. $\frac{-x}{6} = 9$	**23.** $-\frac{m}{3} = \frac{1}{5}$	**24.** $\frac{1}{9} = -\frac{z}{7}$
25. $-\frac{3}{5}r = -\frac{9}{10}$	**26.** $-\frac{2}{5}y = -\frac{4}{15}$	**27.** $-\frac{3}{2}r = -\frac{27}{4}$
28. $\frac{5}{7}x = -\frac{10}{14}$	**29.** $6.3x = 44.1$	**30.** $2.7y = 54$
31. $-3.1y = 21.7$	**32.** $-3.3y = 6.6$	**33.** $38.7m = 309.6$

Translate to an equation and solve.

34. Eighteen times a number is -1008. Find the number.

35. Some number multiplied by negative eight is 744. Find the number.

36. *Critical Thinking*   If a, b, and c are rational numbers such that $a = b$ and $c = 0$, does $ac = bc$? Explain.

37. Katha paid the same price for each of 8 tickets to a concert. If she paid a total of $170, what was the price of each ticket?
Let p = price of each ticket.
   a. Write an expression using p that represents the price of all 8 tickets.
   b. What did Katha pay for all 8 tickets?
   c. What are you asked to find in this problem?
   d. Write an equation using the information you know.
   e. Without solving the equation, decide whether the price of each ticket is more than or less than $30. How do you know?
   f. Solve the equation and answer the problem.

Try This

j. $12x = \$6.72$; $0.56

Exercises

1. 6
2. 13
3. 9
4. 8
5. 12
6. 7
7. -40
8. -100
9. 1
10. 68

11. -7
12. -4
13. -6
14. -7
15. 6
16. 8
17. -63
18. -88
19. 36
20. 20
21. -21
22. -54
23. $\frac{-3}{5}$
24. $\frac{-7}{9}$

25. $\frac{3}{2}$
26. $\frac{2}{3}$
27. $\frac{9}{2}$
28. -1
29. 7
30. 20
31. -7
32. -2
33. 8
34. $18x = -1008$; -56
35. $-8x = 744$; -93
36. Yes; $ac = 0$ and $bc = 0$

38. Deployment of the Chandra X-ray Observatory, named in honor of the Indian-American scientist Subrahmanyan Chandrasekhar, was the main objective of the 26th mission of the shuttle *Columbia*. When main engine cut-off occurred at about 8 min after launch, the *Columbia* was traveling about 16,700 mi/h. This is about 5.8 times its speed at about 2 min when it jettisoned its huge solid rocket boosters. What was *Columbia's* speed 2 min into flight?

Let s = speed at 2 min.

a. Write an expression, using s, that represents the speed at 8 min.

b. What was the speed at 8 min?

c. What are you asked to find in this problem?

d. Write an equation using the information you know.

e. Without solving the equation, estimate the speed at 2 min.

f. Solve the equation and answer the problem.

The 1999 *Columbia* space-shuttle mission commanded by Eileen Collins was launched just after midnight in Florida. The *Columbia* landed in Florida after averaging about 15,100 miles each hour for 1,796,000 miles. Did it land in the daylight or the dark?

39. In 1990 the population of Las Vegas, the largest city in Nevada, was 258,295. That was about 42 times the population of Winnemucca, Nevada's tenth largest city. What was the population of Winnemucca?

Let w = the population of Winnemucca, Nevada.

a. Write an expression, using w, for the population of Las Vegas in 1990.

b. What was the population of Las Vegas in 1990?

c. What are you asked to find in this problem?

d. Write an equation using the information you know.

e. Without solving the equation, estimate the population of Winnemucca, Nevada, in 1990.

f. Solve the equation and answer the problem.

40. A case of a dozen videocassette tapes costs $23.40. Find the cost of a single tape.

41. A wildlife expert estimates that in a certain year the number of male fawns born will be about $\frac{1}{3}$ the number of adult female deer. Suppose 1131 male fawns are born. About how many female deer are there?

42. *Write a Convincing Argument* Tell why it is not necessary to state a division property of equality.

37. a. 8p
   b. $170
   c. The price of one ticket
   d. 8p = 170
   e. Less; if each ticket costs $30, 8 tickets would cost $240.
   f. p = $21.25
38. a. 5.8s
   b. 16,700 mi/h
   c. the speed of Columbia 2 min into the flight
   d. 5.8s = 16,700
   e. about 3,000 mi/h
   f. s = 2,879.3 mi/h (approximately)

Photo caption: the dark
39. a. 42w
   b. 258,295
   c. the population of Winnemucca
   d. 42w = 258,295
   e. about 6000
   f. w = 6150 (approximately)

40. 12t = 23.40; $1.95
41. 1131 = $\frac{1}{3}$f; 3393
42. You can divide both sides of an equation by a nonzero number by multiplying both sides by the reciprocal of the number.

43. The 1996 population of San Diego, California, was estimated to be about 1,170,000. This was about $\frac{3}{7}$ of the estimate for Chicago. What was the approximate population of Chicago?

B

44. *Multi-Step Problem*   Joe Montana and John Elway were pro football quarterbacks. Montana completed 3409 passes in his career. This is about $\frac{7}{11}$ of the passes he threw. It is also about $\frac{3}{4}$ the number that Elway completed. Elway completed about $\frac{4}{7}$ of the passes he threw. Who threw more passes? About how many more?

Mathematical Reasoning   Use the first equation to find the missing value in the second equation. Justify your result.

45. $6a + 6b = 72$
$a + b =$??

46. $\frac{x}{3} + 2 = 12$
$x + 6 =$??

47. $\frac{2m}{5} - 2 = 12$

$2m - 10 =$??

48. $\frac{2a^2}{3} + 1 = 8$

$2a^2 + 3 =$??

Solve each equation for x.

49. $ax = 5a \ (a \neq 0)$

50. $3x = \frac{b}{a} \ (a \neq 0)$

51. $cx = a^2 + 1 \ (c \neq 0)$

52. $abx = 1 \ (ab \neq 0)$

53. *Critical Thinking*   Write two different equations that each have the solution 2 and could be solved using the multiplication property.

Challenge

54. *Mathematical Reasoning*   Solve each equation. Explain each result.
  a. $0 \cdot x = 0$ **b.** $0 \cdot x = 9$

55. Explain or give a counterexample. a and b are integers.
  a. If $a = b$, does $a^2 = b^2$?   **b.** If $a^2 = b^2$, does $a = b$?

Mixed Review

Simplify.   **56.** $8x + 4y - (4x - 5y)$ **57.** $3 - (4a + 7)$
58. $7r - (s + 2r) - 4s$ **59.** $(2a + 4b) - (2a + 4b)$ *2-8*
Multiply.   **60.** $-5 \cdot 8 \cdot 2$ **61.** $(-7) \cdot (-24) \cdot 0$ **62.** $(-2.1)(-1.2)$
63. $(-3)(-7)(-2)$ **64.** $(-4)(-2.2)(-5)$ **65.** $(-2)(-3.1)3$ *2-5*
Evaluate.   **66.** $t^4 + 1$ for $t = 2$ **67.** $8y^3$ for $y = 3$
68. $3|x|$ for $x = -8$ **69.** $y^2 + 2y$ for $y = -3$
70. $4z + |z|$ for $z = -1$ *1-3, 2-1*
Factor.   **71.** $4x + 8y - 12z$ **72.** $6a - 12b - 9c$ *2-7*

Exercises

43. 2,730,000
44. Montana threw about 5357 passes. Elway completed about 4545 passes. Elway threw about 7954 passes. Elway threw about 2597 more passes than Montana.
45. 12
46. 36
47. 60
48. 24
49. 5
50. $\frac{b}{3a}$

51. $\frac{a^2 + 1}{c}$

52. $\frac{1}{ab}$
53. Answers may vary.
54. a. All values of x are solutions. Zero times any number is zero.
  b. No solution. Zero times any number is zero.
55. a. Yes; If $a = b$, then $a^2 = ab$. Also, $ab = b^2$. Therefore, $a^2 = b^2$.
  b. No; for example, $3^2 = (-3)^2$, but $3 \neq -3$.

Mixed Review

56. $4x + 9y$
57. $-4a - 4$
58. $5r - 5s$
59. 0
60. -80
61. 0
62. 2.52
63. -42
64. -44
65. 18.6
66. 17
67. 216
68. 24
69. 3
70. -3
71. $4(x + 2y - 3z)$
72. $3(2a - 4b - 3c)$

Using the Properties Together

 3-3

 PART 1 Applying Both Properties

Objective: Solve equations using the addition and multiplication properties.

To solve some equations, you may need to use both the addition property and the multiplication property.

EXAMPLE 1 Solve.

$$3x + 4 = 13$$
$$3x + 4 + (-4) = 13 + (-4)$$ Using the addition property to add -4 to both sides
$$3x = 9$$
$$\frac{1}{3} \cdot 3x = \frac{1}{3} \cdot 9$$ Using the multiplication property to multiply both sides by $\frac{1}{3}$
$$x = 3$$

Check:
$3x + 4 = 13$
$3(3) + 4$ | 13
$9 + 4$ | 13
13 | 13 ✔

The solution is 3.

EXAMPLE 2 Solve.

$$-5x + 6 = 16$$
$$-5x + 6 + (-6) = 16 + (-6)$$ Using the addition property to add -6 to both sides
$$-5x = 10$$
$$-\frac{1}{5} \cdot (-5x) = -\frac{1}{5} \cdot 10$$ Using the multiplication property to multiply both sides by $-\frac{1}{5}$
$$x = -2$$

Check:
$-5x + 6 = 16$
$-5(-2) + 6$ | 16
$10 + 6$ | 16
16 | 16 ✔

The solution is -2.

What You'll Learn

1 To solve equations by using the addition and multiplication properties

2 To solve equations by first collecting like terms

3 To solve equations containing parentheses

. . . And Why

To use and solve algebraic models in various forms

3-3 TIME-FOCUS METER

1. FOCUS

FIRST FIVE MINUTES

Solve.
1. $x - 13 = 17$ $x = 30$
2. $-5 + z = 21$ $z = 26$
3. $8a = 7$ $a = \frac{7}{8}$
4. $\frac{3}{5}y = \frac{1}{2}$ $y = \frac{5}{6}$

2. TEACH the Mathematics

1 Applying Both Properties

Point out that when the equation is in the form $ax + b = c$, it is usually easier to use the addition property before using the multiplication property.

When students become proficient with the addition and multiplication properties, they may take shortcuts, such as subtracting instead of adding the inverse and dividing instead of multiplying by the reciprocal. They may also skip steps, going directly from $3x = 15$ to $x = 5$. You may want to allow students to skip steps as long as they demonstrate that they understand the process.

Key Question

■ Solve $ax + b = c$ for x.
$$ax + b + (-b) = c + (-b)$$
$$ax = c - b$$
$$\frac{1}{a} \cdot ax = \frac{1}{a}(c - b)$$
$$x = \frac{c - b}{a}$$

Chalkboard Examples

Solve.
1. $7x + 6 = 13$
$$7x + 6 + (-6) = 13 + (-6)$$
$$7x = 7$$
$$x = 1$$
2. $-4y + 3 = 12$
$$-4y = 9$$
$$y = -\frac{9}{4}$$
3. $34 - 3z = 14$
$$-3z = -20$$
$$z = \frac{20}{3}$$
4. $5 = 4x - 12$
$$17 = 4x$$
$$\frac{17}{4} = x$$

**Collecting Like Terms
in Equations**

Stress the need to simplify as a first step
in solving an equation.

Chalkboard Examples

Solve.

1. $7x - 3x + 4 = 6$
$$4x + 4 = 6$$
$$4x = 2$$
$$x = \frac{2}{4}$$
$$x = \frac{1}{2}$$

2. $-2a + 3 + 6a = 14$
$$4a + 3 = 14$$
$$4a = 11$$
$$a = \frac{11}{4}$$

3. $-7z + 2z - 3z - 7 = 17$
$$-8z - 7 = 17$$
$$-8z = 24$$
$$z = -3$$

 **Equations Containing
Parentheses**

Explain to students that in some places
parentheses must be used, and in some
places parentheses are optional. The
parentheses in the expression
$$2(x + 1)$$
are necessary, although the expression can
be rewritten in an equivalent form that
doesn't use parentheses. The parentheses
in the expression
$$(-3)x$$
can be removed without changing the
meaning of the expression. Parentheses
are often a matter of style.

Key Questions

Would the expression change in meaning
if the parentheses were removed?
- $3(x)$ No
- $3(x + 1)$ Yes
- $7(-x)$ Yes

Chalkboard Examples

Solve.

1. $8(3x + 2) = 30$
$$24x + 16 = 30$$
$$24x = 14$$
$$x = \frac{14}{24} \text{ or } \frac{7}{12}$$

2. $5x + 5(4x - 1) = 20$
$$5x + 20x - 5 = 20$$
$$25x \quad - 5 = 20$$
$$25x = 25$$
$$x = 1$$

Try This   Solve.

a. $9x + 6 = 51$ b. $-8y - 4 = 28$
c. $-18 - 3x = -57$ d. $4 - 8x = 12$

PART 2 Collecting Like Terms in Equations

Objective: Solve equations by first collecting like terms.

If there are like terms on one side of an equation, we collect them before
using the properties.

EXAMPLE 3   Solve.

$$6x + 2x = 15$$
$$8x = 15 \qquad \text{Collecting like terms}$$
$$\tfrac{1}{8} \cdot 8x = \tfrac{1}{8} \cdot 15 \qquad \text{Multiplying both sides by } \tfrac{1}{8}$$
$$x = \frac{15}{8}$$

Substitution will show that $\frac{15}{8}$ checks.
The solution is $\frac{15}{8}$.

Try This   Solve.

e. $4c + 3c = 21$ f. $9x - 4x = 20$

PART 3 Equations Containing Parentheses

Objective: Solve equations containing parentheses.

Equations containing parentheses can often be solved by first using the
distributive property.

EXAMPLE 4   Solve.

$$2(2y + 3) = 14$$
$$4y + 6 = 14 \qquad \text{Using the distributive property}$$
$$4y + 6 + (-6) = 14 + (-6) \qquad \text{Using the addition property}$$
$$4y = 8$$
$$\tfrac{1}{4} \cdot 4y = \tfrac{1}{4} \cdot 8 \qquad \text{Using the multiplication property}$$
$$1 \cdot y = 2$$
$$y = 2$$

Substitution will show that 2 checks.

The solution is 2.

Try This

a. 5
b. -4
c. 13
d. -1
e. 3
f. 4

Solve.

$$4(3x - 2) + 12x = 40$$
$$12x - 8 + 12x = 40 \qquad \text{Using the distributive property}$$
$$24x - 8 = 40 \qquad \text{Collecting like terms}$$
$$24x - 8 + 8 = 40 + 8 \qquad \text{Using the addition property}$$
$$24x = 48$$
$$\tfrac{1}{24} \cdot 24x = \tfrac{1}{24} \cdot 48 \qquad \text{Using the multiplication property}$$
$$1 \cdot x = 2$$
$$x = 2$$

Substitution will show that 2 checks.
The solution is 2.

Try This   Solve.

g. $9 = 3(x + 6)$ **h.** $24 - 2(2m + 1) = -6$
i. $3a + 5(a - 2) = 6$

3-3 Exercises

Extra Help On the Web
Look for worked-out examples at the Prentice Hall Web site.
www.phschool.com

A

Solve.

1. $5x + 6 = 31$
2. $3x + 6 = 30$
3. $8x + 4 = 68$
4. $7z + 9 = 72$
5. $4x - 6 = 34$
6. $6x - 3 = 15$
7. $3x - 9 = 33$
8. $5x - 7 = 48$
9. $7x + 2 = -54$
10. $5x + 4 = -41$
11. $-4x + 7 = 35$
12. $-5x - 7 = 108$
13. $-7x - 24 = -129$
14. $-6z - 18 = -132$

Solve.

15. $5x + 7x = 72$
16. $4x + 5x = 45$
17. $4x + 3x = 42$
18. $6x + 19x = 100$
19. $4y - 2y = 10$
20. $8y - 5y = 48$
21. $-6y - 3y = 27$
22. $-4y - 8y = 48$
23. $-7y - 8y = -15$
24. $-10y - 3y = -39$
25. $10.2y - 7.3y = -58$
26. $6.8y - 2.4y = -88$

27. *Critical Thinking*   Solve $4x - 8 = 32$ by using the multiplication property first. Then solve it using the addition property first. Are the results the same?

Solve.

28. $5(3x - 2) = 35$
29. $3(2y - 3) = 27$
30. $-2(4y - 3) = 6$
31. $(4 + 3x)(-3) = -9$

3-3   *Using the Properties Together*   **127**

Try This

g. -3
h. 7
i. 2

Exercises

1. 5
2. 8
3. 8
4. 9
5. 10
6. 3
7. 14
8. 11
9. -8
10. -9
11. -7
12. -23
13. 15
14. 19
15. 6
16. 5
17. 6
18. 4
19. 5
20. 16
21. -3
22. -4
23. 1
24. 3
25. -20
26. -20
27. $\quad 4x - 8 = 32$
$\quad \tfrac{1}{4}(4x - 8) = \tfrac{1}{4}(32)$
$\quad x - 2 = 8$
$\quad x = 10$

$\quad 4x - 8 = 32$
$\quad 4x = 40$
$\quad x = 10$

Yes.

28. 3
29. 6
30. 0
31. $-\tfrac{1}{3}$

Teach the Mathematics (continued)

LESSON ENRICHMENT
Have students solve the following equation by two different methods.
$$4(x - 2) = 4$$

$4x - 8 = 4$	$(x - 2) = \tfrac{4}{4}$
$4x = 12$	$x - 2 = 1$
$x = 3$	$x = 3$

3. PRACTICE/ASSESS

LESSON QUIZ

Solve.
1. $4z + 5 = 13$
$\quad 4z = 8$
$\quad z = 2$
2. $9u - 3 = -4$
$\quad 9u = -1$
$\quad u = -\tfrac{1}{9}$
3. $-2y + 7y = 6$
$\quad 5y = 6$
$\quad y = \tfrac{6}{5}$
4. $4(x + 2) + 2 = 8$
$\quad 4x + 8 + 2 = 8$
$\quad 4x + 10 = 8$
$\quad 4x = -2$
$\quad x = -\tfrac{2}{4} \text{ or } -\tfrac{1}{2}$

Assignment Guide
To provide flexible scheduling, this lesson can be split into parts.
▼ Core 1–14, 27
   Extension 56
▼ Core 15–26, 47–50, 53
   Extension 54
▼ Core 28–46, 51, 52
   Extension 55

Use Mixed Review to maintain skills.

Solve.

32. $2(3 + 4m) - 9 = 45$

33. $3(5 + 3m) - 8 = 88$

34. $12 - 3(x - 5) = 21$

35. $5 - 2(y + 1) = 21$

36. $5r - 2(2r + 8) = 16$

37. $6b - 4(2b + 8) = 16$

38. $2(2x - 4) + 3x = -1$

39. $-5a + 4(2 + 2a) = -1$

40. $\frac{1}{3}x + 2\left(\frac{1}{3}x + 5\right) = 12$

41. $3\left(\frac{1}{8}m - \frac{1}{2}\right) + \frac{3}{4}m = \frac{3}{2}$

42. When Erica learned that her company matches employee gifts to schools, she added $15 to her gift. This made the value of her gift $90. How much did Erica originally intend to give?

B

Mathematical Reasoning   Provide a reason to justify each step.

43. $6(2x - 8) = 36$

  a. $12x - 48 = 36$ _____

  b. $12x - 48 + 48 = 36 + 48$ _____

  c. $12x = 84$ _____

  d. $\frac{1}{12} \cdot 12x = \frac{1}{12} \cdot 84$ _____

  e. $x = 7$ _____

44. $6(2x - 8) = 36$

  a. $\frac{1}{6} \cdot 6(2x - 8) = \frac{1}{6} \cdot 36$ _____

  b. $2x - 8 = 6$ _____

  c. $2x - 8 + 8 = 6 + 8$ _____

  d. $2x = 14$ _____

  e. $\frac{1}{2} \cdot 2x = \frac{1}{2} \cdot 14$ _____

  f. $x = 7$ _____

45. $7y + (8 + 3y) = 38$

  a. $7y + (3y + 8) = 38$ _____

  b. $(7y + 3y) + 8 = 38$ _____

  c. $10y + 8 = 38$ _____

  d. $10y + 8 - 8 = 38 - 8$ _____

  e. $10y = 30$ _____

  f. $\frac{1}{10} \cdot 10y = \frac{1}{10} \cdot 30$ _____

  g. $y = 3$ _____

46. $9m - 2(2m + 6) = 28$

  a. $9m - 4m - 12 = 28$ _____

  b. $5m - 12 = 28$ _____

  c. $5m - 12 + 12 = 28 + 12$ _____

  d. $5m = 40$ _____

  e. $\frac{1}{5} \cdot 5m = \frac{1}{5} \cdot 40$ _____

  f. $m = 8$ _____

Practice
Multiple Choice

Choose the best answer.

1. To solve
$9x + (4 - 3x) = 34$,   (1)
rewrite it as
$9x + (-3 + 4) = 34$.   (2)
Then rewrite it as
$(9x - 3x) + 4 = 34$.   (3)

What property changes equation (2) to equation (3)?

A Distributive property

B Associative property of addition

C Inverse property of multiplication

D Associative property of multiplication

2. If you solve the above equation, what solution do you get?

F $x = 5$

G $x = 6\frac{1}{3}$

H $x = 3.4$

J A value cannot be found for x.

---

1. B; Algebra 4.0
2. F; Algebra 4.0

Exercises

32. 6

33. 9

34. 2

35. −9

36. 32

37. −24

38. 1

39. −3

40. 2

41. $\frac{8}{3}$

42. $30

43. a. Using the distributive property
  b. Using the addition property
  c. Simplifying
  d. Using the multiplication property
  e. Simplifying

44. a. Using the multiplication property
  b. Simplifying
  c. Using the addition property
  d. Simplifying
  e. Using the multiplication property
  f. Simplifying

45. a. Using the commutative property
  b. Using the associative prop.
  c. Collecting like terms
  d. Using the addition property
  e. Simplifying
  f. Using the multiplication property
  g. Simplifying

46. a. Using the distributive property
  b. Collecting like terms
  c. Using the addition property
  d. Simplifying
  e. Using the multiplication property
  f. Simplifying

Solve.

47. $(0.26 + y) + 3y = 0.98$ **48.** $0 = y - (-14) - (-3y)$

49. $12 - (-5m) + 3m + 12 = 0$ **50.** $4a + 5a - 2(2a) + 35 = 0$

51. $4(a - 2) + 3(2a + 1) = 5$ **52.** $2(3x + 5) + 3(2x + 5) = 1$

53. Rafael spent \$2011 to operate his car last year. He drove 12,500 miles. He paid \$972 for insurance and \$114 for the registration fee. Rafael's only other expense was for gas. How much did the gas cost per mile?

Challenge

Solve the first equation for x. Substitute your result into the second equation. Then solve for y. Check your work.

54. $9x - 5 = 22$

$4x + 2y = 2$

55. $9x + 2 = -1$

$4x - y = \frac{11}{3}$

56. *Error Analysis* The "Check" suggests an error was made. Explain.

Solve:

$$1.2x + 7.7 = 2.9$$
$$1.2x + 7.7 + (-7.7) = 2.9 + (-7.7)$$
$$1.2x = -4.8$$
$$\frac{1}{1.2} \cdot 1.2x = \frac{1}{1.2} \cdot -4.8$$
$$x = -4$$

Check:

$$1.2x + 7.7 = 2.9$$

$1.2x + 7.7$	2.9
$1.2(-4) + 7.7$	2.9
$-4.8 + 7.7$	2.9
$3.9 \neq 2.9$	

Mixed Review

Use $>$ or $<$ to write a true sentence. **57.** $-5.2 \square 4$ **58.** $-2.3 \square 2.2$

59. $\frac{2}{3} \square \frac{3}{5}$ **60.** $\frac{1}{5} \square -\frac{3}{5}$ **61.** $-6.7 \square -3.9$ *2-2*

Divide. **62.** $\frac{5}{12} \div \frac{3}{4}$ **63.** $-\frac{2}{5} \div -\frac{5}{6}$ **64.** $\frac{2}{9} \div -\frac{1}{2}$ *2-6*

Solve. **65.** $x + 10 = 25$ **66.** $t - 84 = 72$ **67.** $5y = 30$ *3-1, 3-2*

Factor. **68.** $4t + 4n - 12m$ **69.** $3a - 3c - 3d$ **70.** $4c - 12d$ *2-7*

Multiply. **71.** $4(3x - 4y)$ **72.** $3(2q - r - 4)$ *2-7*

◈ Connections: Geometry

Find the length of each side, given the perimeter.

1. a square with perimeter 64 ft

$3x - 2$

2. a rectangle with perimeter 36 in.

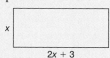

x

$2x + 3$

47. 0.18
48. $-\frac{7}{2}$
49. -3
50. -7
51. 1
52. -2
53. Let x = cost of gas per mile.
$972 + 114 + 12,500x = 2011$
$12,500x = 925$
$x = 0.074$
\$0.074/mi or 7.4¢ per mile
54. $x = 3, y = -5$
55. $x = -\frac{1}{3}, y = -5$

56. In the Check,
$-4.8 + 7.7 = 2.9$, not 3.9.

Mixed Review

57. $<$
58. $<$
59. $>$
60. $>$
61. $<$
62. $\frac{5}{9}$
63. $\frac{12}{25}$
64. $-\frac{4}{9}$

65. $x = 15$
66. $t = 156$
67. $y = 6$
68. $4(t + n - 3m)$
69. $3(a - c - d)$
70. $4(c - 3d)$
71. $12x - 16y$
72. $6q - 3r - 12$

Connections: Geometry

1. 16 ft
2. 5 in., 13 in.

1. FOCUS

FIRST FIVE MINUTES

Write an algebraic expression for each of the following.

1. twice the number n $2n$
2. half of the number n $\frac{1}{2}n$
3. 5 more than a number $n + 5$

Translate to an equation and solve.

4. Arthur is two years younger than Chan. Arthur is 21. How old is Chan?
   Let c be the age of Chan.
   The age of Arthur is $c - 2$.
   $c - 2 = 21$
   $\quad c = 21 + 2 = 23$

5. The number of salted peanuts in a nut mix is 13 times the number of cashews. There are 52 salted peanuts. How many cashews are there?
   Let c be the number of cashews.
   $13c = 52$
   $\quad c = 4$

MATH IN ACTION

Students will solve this problem in Try This **h.**

2. TEACH the Mathematics

1 Phrases to Algebraic Expressions

Remind students that "3 less than x" is equivalent to $x - 3$, not $3 - x$.

Also, stress that the same expression can represent two phrases. For example, $8 + x$ can represent "the sum of 8 and some number" and "8 more than some number."

Key Questions

Translate to a phrase.

- $6n - 9$
  9 less than the quantity 6 times a number
- $\frac{x + 3}{2}$
  half the sum of a number and 3

What You'll Learn

1 To translate phrases to algebraic expressions

2 To solve problems by writing and solving equations

...And Why

To apply algebraic models to real-life situations

Quick Review

To review how to translate simple phrases to algebraic expressions, see Lesson 1-6.

Reading Math

The phrase *the quantity* suggests a grouping of the terms that follow. A pause after reading "the quantity" will help you understand the grouping.

The words *sum, difference, product,* and *quotient* also suggest a grouping of the terms that follow.

 CA 5.0: Solve multi-step problems involving linear equations in one variable.

3-4 ▷ Expressions and Equations

Math in Action

The distance from Exit 18 to Exit 19 on the interstate highway is 18 miles. The first 3 miles have been paved. The same number of miles will be paved each day. How many miles should be paved each day to complete this section of highway in the next 10 days?

In this lesson you will learn techniques for solving problems similar to the one above.

After paving 10 ft, this paver needed 12 loads of concrete to finish a 100-ft section. How much roadway did the paver complete for each load of concrete?

PART 1   Phrases to Algebraic Expressions

Objective: Translate phrases to algebraic expressions.

In Chapters 1 and 2 you translated simple phrases like "5 less than a number" to algebraic expressions. In this lesson you will translate more difficult phrases to algebraic expressions.

EXAMPLES   Write as an algebraic expression.

1   5 times the quantity 3 less than a number

$5(n - 3)$ "The quantity 3 less than a number" translates to $(n - 3)$, and "5 times the quantity . . ." translates to $5(n - 3)$.

2 $\frac{1}{2}$ the sum of a number and 4

$\frac{1}{2}(n + 4)$ "The sum of a number and 4" translates to $(n + 4)$, and "$\frac{1}{2}$ the sum . . . " translates to $\frac{1}{2}(n + 4)$.

3   14 less than the product of 3 and a number

$3n - 14$ "The product of 3 and a number" translates to $3n$, and "14 less than . . . " translates to $3n - 14$.

Photo Caption

7.5 ft

Try This　Write as an algebraic expression.

a. 3 less than twice a number
b. $\frac{1}{2}$ the difference of a number and 1
c. 4 times the quantity 3 greater than a number
d. 2 fewer than the product of 10 and a number

EXAMPLE 4

Jason's weekly salary is \$35 less than twice David's weekly salary. Let $D =$ David's weekly salary in dollars. Write an expression, using D, for Jason's weekly salary.

David's weekly salary $= D$
Jason's weekly salary $= 2D - 35$ 　"Twice David's weekly salary" translates to $2D$, and "\$35 less than . . ." translates to $2D - 35$.

Try This

e. This year Todd sold five fewer houses than twice as many as he sold last year. Let $n =$ the number he sold last year. Write an expression for the number of houses that Todd sold this year.
f. Ellen Ikeda scored two points more than half the number scored by the whole team. Let $t =$ the number of points scored by the whole team. Write an expression for the number of points Ellen scored.

PART 2 Using Equations to Solve Problems

Objective: Solve problems by writing and solving equations.

You can use the Problem-Solving Guidelines below to help you solve problems when your plan involves writing and solving an equation.

PROBLEM-SOLVING GUIDELINES
■ **Phase 1: UNDERSTAND the problem**   What am I trying to find?   What data am I given?   Have I ever solved a similar problem?
■ **Phase 2: Develop and carry out a PLAN**   What strategies might I use to solve the problem?   How can I correctly carry out the strategies I select?
■ **Phase 3: Find the ANSWER and CHECK**   Does the proposed solution check?   What is the answer to the problem?   Does the answer seem reasonable?   Have I stated the answer clearly?

Try This
a. $2n - 3$
b. $\frac{1}{2}(n - 1)$
c. $4(n + 3)$
d. $10n - 2$
e. $2n - 5$
f. $\frac{1}{2}t + 2$

3. On a committee of 18 persons, there were four more women than men. How many men were on the committee?
Let m be the number of men.
The number of women is $m + 4$.
The total of men and women is 18, hence
$$m + (m + 4) = 18$$
$$2m + 4 = 18$$
$$2m = 14$$
$$m = 7$$
There were 7 men on the committee.

LESSON ENRICHMENT

Write a problem that can be solved using each of the following equations. Then solve the problem. Was your answer realistic? *Answers may vary.*

1. $5x + 18 = 98$ $x = 16$
2. $\frac{3m + 2}{2} = 10$ $m = 6$
3. $4(c - 6) = 26$ $c = \frac{50}{4}$
4. $3p - \frac{2p - 24}{3} = 1$ $p = -3$

EXAMPLE 5

The number of girls in the band is 6 more than twice the number of boys. There are 88 girls in the band. How many boys are in the band?

■ **UNDERSTAND the problem**

Question: How many boys are in the band?   Clarifying the question and identifying the data given in the problem

Data: The number of girls is 6 more than twice the number of boys; 88 girls are in the band.

■ **Develop and carry out a PLAN**

Let b = the number of boys in the band.   Choosing a variable
$2b + 6$ = the number of girls in the band   The number of girls is given in terms of the number of boys.

$$2b + 6 = 88$$ The number of girls is also 88.
$$2b + 6 + (-6) = 88 + (-6)$$ Using the addition property
$$2b = 82$$
$$\tfrac{1}{2} \cdot 2b = \tfrac{1}{2} \cdot 82$$ Using the multiplication property

$$1 \cdot b = 41$$
$$b = 41$$

■ **Find the ANSWER and CHECK**

There are 41 boys in the band. If there were 40 boys in the band, $2 \cdot 40 + 6 = 86$, so 41 is a reasonable answer.   Estimating to check whether the answer is reasonable

EXAMPLE 6

Kara has driven 75 miles. She averages 55 mi/h. How many more hours must Kara drive to travel a total of 350 mi?

■ **UNDERSTAND the problem**

Question: How many additional hours must Kara drive?
Data: She averages 55 mi/h; she has already traveled 75 mi; she wants to travel a total of 350 mi.

■ **Develop and carry out a PLAN**

Let h = the number of additional hours she must drive.
$55h$ = the additional distance she must travel

Drawing a diagram can often help you understand a problem.

$55h + 75 =$ the total distance for the trip

Since $55h + 75$ represents the total distance for the trip, and we know that the total distance is 350 miles, we have the equation

$$55h + 75 = 350$$

We can solve this equation.

$$55h + 75 = 350$$
$$55h + 75 + (-75) = 350 + (-75)$$
$$55h = 275$$
$$\frac{1}{55} \cdot 55h = \frac{1}{55} \cdot 275$$
$$h = 5$$

■ **Find the ANSWER and CHECK**

Kara must drive for 5 more hours.
$5 \cdot 55 = 275$ miles. This plus 75 miles gives the total of 350 miles. The answer checks.

Try This   Solve.

g. When Jill sells 2 more buckets, she will have sold 3 times as many buckets as Jack sold. Jill has sold 19 buckets. How many buckets has Jack sold?

h. An 18-mile section of highway is being paved. The first 3 miles are done. The same number of miles will be paved each day. How many miles should be paved each day to complete this section in the next 10 days?

3-4 Exercises

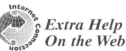

Extra Help On the Web

Look for worked-out examples at the Prentice Hall Web site.
www.phschool.com

A

Write as an algebraic expression.

1. 3 less than the product of 5 and a number

2. 5 more than twice a number

3. 18 fewer than half a number

4. 12 more than half a number

5. 3 less than the quotient of a number and 5

6. 3 more than the quotient of a number and 2

7. 4 times the quantity 1 less than a number

8. 2 times the quantity 4 greater than a number

9. $\frac{1}{2}$ the sum of a number and 6

10. $\frac{3}{4}$ the difference of a number and 3

11. 4 less than a third of a number

12. 7 greater than half a number

3. PRACTICE/ASSESS

LESSON QUIZ

Write as an algebraic expression.

1. 7 more than the quantity three times a number
   $3n + 7$

2. twice the sum of a number and 6
   $2(n + 6)$

3. 9 less than twice a number
   $2n - 9$

4. The repair bill totaled $150 for labor and parts. The labor cost was twice the parts cost. What did the parts cost?
   Let p be the parts cost.
   The labor cost is $2p$.
   The total 150 is the sum of the parts and labor costs, hence
   $p + 2p = 150$
   $3p = 150$
   $p = \frac{150}{3} = 50$
   The parts cost $50.

5. There are 3 more women than men in the Glee Club. There are 45 people in the club altogether. How many men are in the club?
   Let m be the number of men.
   The number of women is $m + 3$.
   The number of men plus the number of women equals 45, hence
   $m + (m + 3) = 45$
   $2m + 3 = 45$
   $2m = 42$
   $m = \frac{42}{2} = 21$
   There are 21 men in the club.

Assignment Guide

To provide flexible scheduling, this lesson can be split into parts.
▼ Core 1–12, 13, 15, 21
   Extension 17, 18
▼ Core 14, 16, 19, 20, 22–25
   Extension 26–29

Use Mixed Review to maintain skills.

Try This
g. 7
h. 1.5

Exercises
1. $5n - 3$
2. $2n + 5$
3. $\frac{1}{2}n - 18$
4. $\frac{1}{2}n + 12$
5. $\frac{n}{5} - 3$
6. $\frac{n}{2} + 3$
7. $4(n - 1)$
8. $2(n + 4)$
9. $\frac{1}{2}(n + 6)$
10. $\frac{3}{4}(n - 3)$
11. $\frac{1}{3}n - 4$
12. $\frac{1}{2}n + 7$

13. Today Harvey ran 2 km more than twice as far as he ran yesterday. Let y = the number of kilometers he ran yesterday. Write an expression for the number of kilometers he ran today.

14. Darrell sold 3 fewer subscriptions than 4 times the number Brenda sold. Let B = the number Brenda sold. Write an expression for the number Darrell sold.

15. Lyle still has $2 more than half of his allowance. Let a = the amount of his allowance. Write an expression for the amount he has.

16. Last year Chu found 3 more customers than Ralph found. This year Chu found 2 times as many customers as he found last year. Let r = the number of customers Ralph found last year. Write an expression for the number of customers Chu found this year.

17. *Critical Thinking*   Large drinks cost 15¢ more than small drinks.

   a. Let s = the cost of a small drink. Write an expression for the cost of the large drink.

   b. Let L = the cost of a large drink. Write an expression for the cost of a small drink.

18. *Critical Thinking*   The cost of a small television set is $25 more than half the cost of a large TV.

   a. Let C = the cost of a large television set. Write an expression for the cost of the small television.

   b. Let c = the cost of a small television set. Write an expression for the cost of the large television.

19. Elena has ridden 20 mi on her bike so far. She travels at an average rate of 10 mi/h. How many more hours will she have to ride to go a total of 55 mi?

   Let h = number of additional hours of travel needed.

   $10h$ = distance traveled in h hours

   a. Draw a diagram that shows this situation.

   b. Write an expression using h that represents 55 miles.

   c. What are you asked to find in this problem?

   d. Write an equation using the information you know.

   e. Solve the equation and answer the problem.

20. One hundred twenty-two vans were supposed to be shipped by railroad, but 2 vans could not fit on the railroad cars. There were 8 railroad cars, each holding the same number of vans. How many vans were on each car?

   Let v = the number of vans on each railroad car.

   a. What does the expression $8v$ represent?

   b. Write an expression using v that represents the 122 vans.

   c. Write an equation using the information you know.

   d. Solve the equation and answer the problem.

Exercises

13. $2y + 2$
14. $4B - 3$
15. $\frac{1}{2}a + 2$
16. $2(r + 3)$
17. **a.** $s + 15$
    b. $L - 15$
18. **a.** $\frac{1}{2}C + 25$
    b. $2(c - 25)$

19. **a.**

   b. $10h + 20$
   c. the number of additional hours that Elena must ride
   d. $10h + 20 = 55$
   e. $h = 3\frac{1}{2}$
   Elena must ride $3\frac{1}{2}$ hours more.

20. **a.** the total number of vans in the railroad cars
    b. $8v + 2$
    c. $8v + 2 = 122$
    d. $v = 15$
    There are 15 vans in each railroad car.

21. **TEST PREP** Let c = the number of cows in a herd. Then $2(c + 4)$ represents which quantity?

A. 4 more than twice the number of cows in the herd

B. twice the number of cows in a herd that has 4 more cows

C. the number of cows in a herd that has 6 more cows

D. the number of cows in a herd that has 8 more cows

B

22. The number of boys in the tennis club is 10 more than half the number of girls. There are 30 boys in the tennis club. Altogether, how many boys and girls are in the club?

23. A salesman rented a car that got 35 miles per gallon. He paid $19.50 a day for the car plus $0.26 per mile. He rented the car for 1 day and paid $39. How many miles did he travel?

24. Bowling at Sunset Lanes cost Danny and Zorina $9. This included shoe rental of $0.75 a pair. How much did each game cost if Danny bowled 3 games and Zorina bowled 2 games?

25. Popcorn costs $0.75 a box. Carl and Diane each bought 1 box of popcorn at the ball game. Carl bought 3 cans of juice and Diane bought 2 cans of juice during the game. Each can cost the same. They spent a total of $5.25. What did they pay for each can of juice?

26. *Critical Thinking* If you add 2 to a certain number, multiply the result by 3, subtract 1 from the product, and divide the difference by 2, you get 10. Find the number.

Challenge

27. Ronald can do a job alone in 3 days. His assistant can do the same job alone in 6 days. How long would it take Ronald and his assistant to do the same job together? (Hint: Determine what part of the job each can do in one day.)

28. One cashier works at a rate of 3 minutes per customer and a second cashier works at a rate of 2 customers per minute. How many customers can they serve in 1 hour?

29. Ruth has some money in a savings account. After the bank adds 5% interest to her account, she has $126. How much was in her account before the interest was added?

Mixed Review

Solve. **30.** $3x + 2x = 15$ **31.** $-\frac{1}{2}x + 3 = 1$ **32.** $3(4y - 2) = 18$ *3-3*

Write using exponential notation. **33.** $4 \cdot n \cdot n \cdot m \cdot 3 \cdot m \cdot n$

34. $y \cdot y \cdot y \cdot x$ **35.** $5 \cdot t \cdot 3 \cdot t \cdot 2 \cdot t$ **36.** $2 \cdot 6 \cdot r \cdot r$ *1-3*

Solve. **37.** $\frac{w}{-5} = -4$ **38.** $\frac{1}{2} = -\frac{1}{8}c$ **39.** $\frac{5}{7} = \frac{2}{3}x$ **40.** $\frac{4}{9}y = 2$ *3-2*

21. B
22. 70
23. 75
24. $1.50
25. $0.75
26. 5
27. 2 days
28. 140 customers
29. $120

Mixed Review

30. 3
31. 4
32. 2
33. $12n^3m^2$
34. y^3x
35. $30t^3$
36. $12r^2$
37. 20
38. -4
39. $\frac{15}{14}$
40. $\frac{9}{2}$

3-5

3-5 ▷ More on Solving Equations

1. FOCUS

FIRST FIVE MINUTES

Solve.

1. $2x + 1 = 9$
   $2x = 8$
   $x = 4$

2. $3y + 2y - 4 = 6$
   $5y = 10$
   $y = 2$

3. $4(x + 3) = 7$
   $4x + 12 = 7$
   $4x = -5$
   $x = -\frac{5}{4}$

4. $2z + 3(4z + 5) = 20$
   $2z + 12z + 15 = 20$
   $14z + 15 = 20$
   $14z = 5$
   $z = \frac{5}{14}$

2. TEACH the Mathematics

1 Variables on Both Sides

Stress that there is more than one correct way to solve each of these equations. Some students may choose to keep the variables on the left, while others may choose to move the variable with the smaller coefficient, regardless of where it is, to the other side.

Chalkboard Examples

1. $5x = 8 + x$
   $5x - x = 8 + x - x$
   $4x = 8$
   $x = 2$

2. $8a + 1 = 3a + 7$
   $8a + 1 - 1 = 3a + 7 - 1$
   $8a = 3a + 6$
   $8a - 3a = 3a - 3a + 6$
   $5a = 6$
   $a = \frac{6}{5}$

3. $8w + 4 - 2w = w + 1$
   $6w + 4 = w + 1$
   $6w + 4 - 4 = w + 1 - 4$
   $6w = w - 3$
   $6w - w = w - w - 3$
   $5w = -3$
   $w = -\frac{3}{5}$

What You'll Learn

1 To solve equations by first getting all variables on the same side of the equation

2 To solve equations that contain parentheses

... And Why

To use and solve algebraic models in various forms

Objective: Solve equations by first getting all variables on the same side of the equation.

If there are variable terms on opposite sides of an equation, we can get them on the same side by using the addition property. Then we collect like terms.

EXAMPLE 1 Solve.

$$2x - 2 = -3x + 3$$
$$2x + 3x - 2 = -3x + 3x + 3 \qquad \text{Using the addition property; adding } 3x \text{ to both sides}$$
$$5x - 2 = 3 \qquad \text{Collecting like terms and simplifying}$$
$$5x - 2 + 2 = 3 + 2 \qquad \text{Using the addition property}$$
$$5x = 5$$
$$\tfrac{1}{5} \cdot 5x = \tfrac{1}{5} \cdot 5 \qquad \text{Using the multiplication property}$$
$$x = 1$$

Substitution will show that 1 checks.
The solution is 1.

If there are like variable terms on the same side of the equation, they should be collected first.

EXAMPLE 2 Solve.

$$6m + 5 - 7m = 10 - 5m + 3$$
$$-m + 5 = 13 - 5m \qquad \text{Collecting like terms}$$
$$-m + m + 5 = 13 - 5m + m \qquad \text{Using the addition property; adding } m \text{ to both sides}$$
$$5 = 13 - 4m \qquad \text{Collecting like terms and simplifying}$$
$$-13 + 5 = -13 + 13 - 4m \qquad \text{Using the addition property}$$
$$-8 = -4m$$
$$-\tfrac{1}{4}(-8) = -\tfrac{1}{4}(-4m) \qquad \text{Using the multiplication property}$$
$$2 = m$$

Substitution will show that 2 checks.
The solution is 2.

Try This   Solve.

a. $7y + 5 = 2y + 10$

c. $7x - 17 + 2x = 2 - 8x + 15$

b. $5 - 2p = 3p - 5$

d. $3n - 15 = 5n + 3 - 4n$

PART 2 Equations Containing Parentheses

Objective: Solve equations that contain parentheses.

Some equations containing parentheses can be solved by first using the distributive property.

EXAMPLE 3   Solve.

$$
\begin{aligned}
3(n - 2) - 1 &= 2 - 5(n + 5) \\
3n - 6 - 1 &= 2 - 5n - 25 &&\text{Using the distributive property} \\
3n - 7 &= -5n - 23 &&\text{Simplifying} \\
3n + 5n - 7 &= -5n + 5n - 23 &&\text{Using the addition property} \\
8n - 7 &= -23 \\
8n - 7 + 7 &= -23 + 7 &&\text{Using the addition property} \\
8n &= -16 \\
\tfrac{1}{8} \cdot 8n &= \tfrac{1}{8} \cdot -16 &&\text{Using the multiplication property} \\
n &= -2
\end{aligned}
$$

Substitution will show that -2 checks. The solution is -2.

Try This   Solve.

e. $3(7 + 2x) = 30 + 7(x - 1)$

f. $4(3 + 5y) - 4 = 3 + 2(y - 2)$

3-5 Exercises

A
Solve.

1. $4x - 7 = 3x$

3. $8x - 1 = 23 - 4x$

5. $2x - 1 = 4 + x$

7. $6x + 3 = 2x + 11$

9. $5 - 2x = 3x - 7x + 25$

11. $4 + 3x - 6 = 3x + 2 - x$

2. $9x - 6 = 3x$

4. $5y - 2 = 28 - y$

6. $5x - 2 = 6 + x$

8. $5y + 3 = 2y + 15$

10. $10 - 3x = 2x - 8x + 40$

12. $5 + 4x - 7 = 4x + 3 - x$

13. 2 less than 3 times a number is the same as 3 more than 2 times the number. Find the number.

14. 3 less than 2 times a number is the same as 2 more than 3 times the number. Find the number.

Extra Help On the Web

Look for worked-out examples at the Prentice Hall Web site.
www.phschool.com

Solve.

15. $5r - (2r + 8) = 16$

16. $6b - (3b + 8) = 16$

17. $3g - 3 = 3(7 - g)$

18. $3d - 10 = 5(d - 4)$

19. $5(d + 4) = 7(d - 2)$

20. $9(t + 2) = 3(t - 2)$

21. $8(3t - 2) = 4(7t - 1)$

22. $7(5x - 2) = 6(6x - 1)$

23. $3(r - 6) + 2 = 4(r + 2) - 21$

24. $5(t + 3) + 9 = 3(t - 2) + 6$

25. $19 - (2x + 3) = 2(x + 3) + x$

26. $13 - (2c + 2) = 2(c + 2) + 3c$

27. $\frac{1}{4}(8y + 4) - 17 = \frac{-1}{2}(4y - 8)$

28. $\frac{1}{3}(6x + 24) - 20 = \frac{-1}{4}(12x - 72)$

29. Placing planks of equal length end to end, Jules found that 3 planks were one foot short of the porch length, while 4 planks were two feet too long. How long was each plank?

B

Solve.

30. $\frac{2x + 4}{4} = 3x - 4$

31. $\frac{3x - 14}{-2} = 3x - 2$

32. $5(x - 1) = \frac{2(x + 4)}{-2}$

33. $-4(2x + 2) = \frac{-4(x + 1)}{4}$

Solve.

34. Terry has walked 3 miles. He averages 4 miles an hour. In how many more hours will he have traveled 13 miles?

35. *Critical Thinking* An **identity** is an equation that is true for all acceptable replacements. Is each equation an identity? Explain.

    a. $2x + 4 + x = 4 + 3x$ **b.** $2(x - 3) + 5 = 3(x - 2) + 5$

Challenge

Solve for x. Assume that all variables represent positive numbers.

36. $a - b(x + c) = d$

37. $a(bx - c) = d - (x + e)$

38. How many equations having different solutions can you find by using parentheses to group the terms below? What are the solutions?

$$4 - 2x - 3 = 2 - x + 1$$

Mixed Review

Collect like terms.   **39.** $\frac{2}{5}x + \frac{1}{7}y - \frac{3}{5}x + \frac{2}{7}y$

40. $\frac{3}{8}m - \frac{7}{8}n + \frac{1}{8}m + \frac{3}{8}n$ **41.** $\frac{2}{3}a - \frac{1}{3}a + \frac{4}{9} - \frac{1}{9}$ *2-7*

Write as an algebraic expression.   *3-4*

42. 3 more than twice a number

43. 5 times the difference of a number and 2

44. 4 more than the quotient of a number and 2

Exercises

15. 8
16. 8
17. 4
18. 5
19. 17
20. -4
21. -3
22. -8
23. -3
24. -12
25. 2
26. 1
27. 5

28. 6
29. 3 ft
30. 2
31. 2
32. $\frac{1}{6}$
33. -1
34. $2\frac{1}{2}$ hours
35. a. Yes; true for all values of x.
    b. No; true only for $x = 0$.
36. $\frac{d - a + bc}{-b}$
37. $\frac{d - e + ac}{ab + 1}$
38. 4 equations; $-2, 0, 4, 6$

Mixed Review

39. $-\frac{1}{5}x + \frac{3}{7}y$
40. $\frac{1}{2}m - \frac{1}{2}n$
41. $\frac{1}{3}a + \frac{1}{3}$
42. $3 + 2n$
43. $5(n - 2)$
44. $\frac{n}{2} + 4$

Clearing an Equation of Fractions or Decimals

 3-6

Objective: Clear an equation of fractions or decimals.

In equations containing fractions, you can use the multiplication property to make the equation easier to solve. To clear the equation of fractions, multiply both sides of the equation by the least common denominator of all the fractions in the equation.

EXAMPLE 1 Solve.

$\frac{2}{3}x + \frac{1}{2}x = \frac{5}{6} + 2x$

The number 6 is the least common denominator.

$6\left(\frac{2}{3}x + \frac{1}{2}x\right) = 6\left(\frac{5}{6} + 2x\right)$ Multiplying both sides by 6

$6 \cdot \frac{2}{3}x + 6 \cdot \frac{1}{2}x = 6 \cdot \frac{5}{6} + 6 \cdot 2x$ Using the distributive property

$4x + 3x = 5 + 12x$
$7x = 5 + 12x$
$7x - 12x = 5 + 12x - 12x$
$-5x = 5$
$x = -1$

Substitution will show that -1 checks.

The solution is -1.

If you wish to clear the decimals in an equation, multiply on both sides by the appropriate power of 10.

EXAMPLE 2 Solve.

$16.3 - 7.2y = -8.18$ Multiplying by 100 will clear the decimals.

$100(16.3 - 7.2y) = 100(-8.18)$
$100(16.3) - 100(7.2y) = 100(-8.18)$ Using the distributive property
$1630 - 720y = -818$
$-720y = -818 - 1630$
$-720y = -2448$
$y = \frac{-2448}{-720}$
$y = 3.4$

Substitution will show that 3.4 checks.

The solution is 3.4.

What You'll Learn

▼ To clear an equation of fractions or decimals

... And Why

To make an equation easier to solve

Quick *Review*

The least common denominator of two fractions is the least common *multiple* of their denominators. In Example 1, the least common multiple of 2 and 3 is 6.

 3-6  TIME-FOCUS METER

1. FOCUS

FIRST FIVE MINUTES

Simplify.

1. $3 \cdot \frac{1}{3}x$
   x
2. $2(\frac{1}{2}y + \frac{3}{2})$
   $2 \cdot \frac{1}{2}y + 2 \cdot \frac{3}{2} = y + 3$
3. $10(1.2u + 0.5)$
   $12u + 5$

2. TEACH the Mathematics

When clearing an equation of decimal coefficients, have students choose the smallest power of ten that will convert all coefficients to integers. Show students that a larger power of ten will work, but will create coefficients that are more difficult to work with.

Key Questions

Can you find a multiplier that will simplify the equations?

■ $0.21x + 4.52 = -0.73 - 0.84x$ 100
■ $\frac{3}{4}x - 7 = 8 + \frac{2}{3}x$ 12

Chalkboard Examples

Solve.

1. $\frac{1}{3}p + \frac{1}{6} = \frac{3}{2}$

   The least common denominator is 6.
   $6(\frac{1}{3}p + \frac{1}{6}) = 6 \cdot \frac{3}{2}$
   $6 \cdot \frac{1}{3}p + 6 \cdot \frac{1}{6} = 9$
   $2p + 1 = 9$
   $2p = 8$
   $p = 4$

2. $0.5r + 1.5 = 3.0$

   Multiply by 10 to clear the decimals.
   $10(0.5r + 1.5) = 10 \cdot 3.0$
   $10 \cdot 0.5r + 10 \cdot 1.5 = 30$
   $5r + 15 = 30$
   $5r = 15$
   $r = 3$

3. PRACTICE/ASSESS

LESSON QUIZ

Solve. Clear fractions first, if necessary.

1. $\frac{2}{3}x - \frac{1}{3} = \frac{5}{3}x + \frac{7}{3}$

   Multiply by 3 to clear the fractions.

   $x = -\frac{8}{3}$

2. $\frac{1}{5}z + \frac{1}{10} = \frac{4}{5}z + \frac{2}{10}$

   Multiply by 10 to clear the fractions.

   $z = -\frac{1}{6}$

3. $0.8a + 0.2 = 0.4a + 0.7$

   Multiply by 10 to clear the decimals.

   $a = \frac{5}{4}$

Assignment Guide

▼ Core 1–30
   Extension 31–33

Use Mixed Review to maintain skills.

Quick Review

Step 1: This lesson
Step 2: Lesson 3-3
Step 3: Lessons 3-5, 3-1
Step 4: Lesson 3-3
Step 5: Lesson 3-2

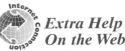

***Extra Help
On the Web***

Look for worked-out examples at the Prentice Hall Web site.
www.phschool.com

Try This Solve.

a. $\frac{7}{8}x + \frac{3}{4} = \frac{1}{2}x + \frac{3}{2}$

b. $\frac{5}{6}x + \frac{1}{2} = \frac{2}{3}x + 4$

c. $26.45 = 4.2x + 1.25$

d. $41.68 = 4.7 - 8.6y$

The following summarizes the steps for solving an equation.

Solving Equations

1. Multiply both sides to clear fractions or decimals, if necessary.
2. Collect like terms on each side, if necessary.
3. Use the addition property to move the variable to one side and all other terms to the other side of the equation.
4. Collect like terms again, if necessary.
5. Use the multiplication property to solve for the variable.

3-6 Exercises

A

Mental Math By what number would you multiply to clear the fractions?

1. $\frac{1}{4}x + 2 = \frac{3}{4}x$

2. $5d - \frac{2}{3} = \frac{1}{3}d$

3. $\frac{3}{4}k + 1 = \frac{3}{8} - 2k$

4. $2 - \frac{4}{5}w = \frac{7}{15}w + \frac{1}{5}$

5. $\frac{1}{38}g + \frac{1}{2} = \frac{5}{6}g$

6. $\frac{3}{4} - \frac{1}{6}m = \frac{2}{3}m$

Solve. Clear the fractions first, if necessary.

7. $\frac{7}{2}x + \frac{1}{2}x = 3x + \frac{3}{2} + \frac{5}{2}x$

8. $\frac{1}{2} + 4m = 3m - \frac{5}{2}$

9. $\frac{5}{3} + \frac{2}{3}x = \frac{25}{12} + \frac{5}{4}x + \frac{3}{4}$

10. $1 - \frac{2}{3}y = \frac{9}{5} - \frac{y}{5} + \frac{3}{5}$

11. $\frac{4}{5}x - \frac{3}{4}x = \frac{3}{10}x - 1$

12. $\frac{8}{5}y - \frac{2}{3}y = 23 - \frac{1}{15}y$

13. $\frac{7}{8}x - \frac{1}{4} + \frac{3}{4}x = \frac{1}{16} + x$

14. $\frac{2}{3} + \frac{1}{4}t = \frac{1}{3}$

15. $-\frac{3}{2} + x = -\frac{5}{6} - \frac{4}{3}$

16. $\frac{2}{3} + 3y = 5y - \frac{2}{15}$

17. $\frac{2}{7}x + \frac{1}{2}x = \frac{3}{4}x + 1$

18. $\frac{5}{16}y + \frac{3}{8}y = 2 + \frac{1}{4}y$

19. $2.1x + 45.2 = 3.2 - 8.4x$

20. $0.96y - 0.79 = 0.21y + 0.46$

21. $1.03 - 0.62x = 0.71 - 0.22x$

22. $0.42 - 0.03y = 3.33 - y$

23. $1.7t + 8 - 1.62t = 0.4t - 0.32 + 8$

24. $0.7n - 15 + n = 2n - 8 - 0.4n$

Try This

a. 2
b. 21
c. 6
d. −4.3

Exercises

1. 4
2. 3
3. 8
4. 15
5. 6
6. 12
7. −1
8. −3
9. −2
10. −3
11. 4
12. 23
13. $\frac{1}{2}$

14. $-\frac{4}{3}$
15. $-\frac{2}{3}$
16. $\frac{2}{5}$
17. 28
18. $\frac{32}{7}$
19. −4
20. $\frac{5}{3}$
21. 0.8
22. 3
23. 1
24. 70

B

Solve.

25. $7\frac{1}{2}x - \frac{1}{2}x = 3\frac{3}{4}x + 39$

26. $\frac{1}{5}t - 0.4 + \frac{2}{5}t = 0.6 - \frac{1}{10}t$

27. $\frac{1}{4}(8y + 4) - 17 = -\frac{1}{2}(4y - 8)$

28. $\frac{1}{3}(6x + 24) - 20 = -\frac{1}{4}(12x - 72)$

29. $30,000 + 20,000x = 55,000$

30. $25,000(4 + 3x) = 125,000$

31. *Critical Thinking*   After the death (about 290 A.D.) of Diophantus, a famous Greek mathematician, someone described his life as a puzzle.

He was a boy for $\frac{1}{6}$ of his life.

After $\frac{1}{12}$ more, he acquired a beard.

After another $\frac{1}{7}$, he married.

In the fifth year after his marriage his son was born.

The son lived half as many years as his father.

Diophantus died 4 years after his son.

How old was Diophantus when he died?

Challenge

32. Apples are collected in a basket for six people. One third, one fourth, one eighth, and one fifth of the apples are given to four people, respectively. The fifth person gets ten apples with one apple remaining for the sixth person. Find the original number of apples in the basket.

33. Carol shared a package of graph paper with 3 of her friends. She gave $\frac{1}{4}$ of the pack to Willy. Sara got $\frac{1}{3}$ of what was left. Then Marcy took $\frac{1}{6}$ of what was left in the package. Carol kept the remaining 30 sheets. How many sheets were in the package to start?

Mixed Review

Write a true sentence using $<$ or $>$.   **34.** $7.301 \square 7.310$

35. $5.4 \square |-5|$ **36.** $-0.783 \square -0.781$ **37.** $|6| \square |-7|$ *2-1, 2-2*

Write as an algebraic expression.   **38.** 7 more than half a number

39. 5 less than twice a number   **40.** twice the sum of a number and 3   *3-4*

Solve.   **41.** $-4(2t + 7) = -4$ **42.** $3a + 2(2a + 5) = 3$

43. $x + \frac{1}{3}x = 8$ **44.** $x + \frac{1}{4}x = 10$ **45.** $\frac{3}{8}y + \frac{3}{4}y = 3$ *3-2, 3-5*

Evaluate each expression for $x = -2$.   **46.** $9x^2 - 4$ **47.** $\frac{1}{2}x^3 + 32$ *1-3*

25. 12
26. $\frac{10}{7}$
27. 5
28. 6
29. $\frac{5}{4}$
30. $\frac{1}{3}$
31. 84 yr
32. 120
33. 72

Mixed Review

34. $<$
35. $>$
36. $<$
37. $<$
38. $\frac{n}{2} + 7$
39. $2n - 5$
40. $2(n + 3)$
41. -3
42. -1
43. 6
44. 8

45. $\frac{8}{3}$
46. 32
47. 28

3-7

1. FOCUS

FIRST FIVE MINUTES

Solve.

1. $7 = 2t$
$\frac{7}{2} = t$

2. $8 = \frac{5h}{2}$
$16 = 5h$
$\frac{16}{5} = h$

3. $14 = w \cdot 7$
$\frac{14}{7} = w$
$w = 2$

2. TEACH the Mathematics

Formulas allow us to process large amounts of data quickly. By programming a formula like the one in Example 3 into a computer, a sportswriter can enter values for the variables *R* and *I* for every pitcher in a league and quickly find each one's earned-run average.

Remind students that solving equations for a given variable means getting that variable by itself on one side of the equation, and that solving a formula is the same as solving an equation.

Chalkboard Examples

1. Solve for *h* where $A = \frac{bh}{2}$.

$2A = bh$
$\frac{2A}{b} = h$

2. Solve for *L* where $P = 2L + 2W$.
$P - 2W = 2L$
$\frac{1}{2}(P - 2W) = L$

3. Solve for *E* where $I = \frac{E}{R}$.
$IR = E$

3-7 ▷ Formulas

Objective: Solve for a given variable in a formula.

What You'll Learn

1 To solve for a given variable in a formula

... And Why

To find formulas equivalent to the given formula

Math in Action

Computers are used by air traffic controllers to quickly determine the flight times of thousands of airplanes. The computer program must include a formula that will compute the time given the rate and distance for each flight. The formula that is needed is based on the formula for distance, $d = rt$, where *d* is the distance, *r* is the rate, and *t* is the time.

We can solve the formula $d = rt$ for the variable *t* using the same rules as for solving equations.

EXAMPLES

1 Solve $d = rt$ for *t*.

$$d = rt$$
$$\frac{1}{r} \cdot d = \frac{1}{r} \cdot rt$$ Using the multiplication property to multiply both sides by the multiplicative inverse of r, $\frac{1}{r}$
$$\frac{d}{r} = t$$

2 A formula for the average *A* of three numbers, *a*, *b*, and *c* is

$$A = \frac{a + b + c}{3}$$

Solve for *a*. Justify each step.

$$A = \frac{a + b + c}{3}$$

$$3A = a + b + c \qquad \textit{Multiplication property of equality}$$

$$3A - b - c = a \qquad \textit{Addition property of equality}$$

Try This

  a. Solve $C = 2\pi r$ for *r*.

  b. Solve $P = 2l + 35$ for *l*. Justify each step.

  c. A formula for the average *A* of four numbers *a*, *b*, *c*, and *d* is

$$A = \frac{a + b + c + d}{4}$$

  Solve for *c*.

Reading Math

Formulas and other equations that use more than one letter are often called *literal equations*.

Try This

a. $r = \frac{C}{2\pi}$

b. $l = \frac{P - 35}{2}$

c. $c = 4A - a - b - d$

EXAMPLE 3

A formula for computing the earned-run average A of a pitcher who has given up R earned runs in I innings of pitching is

$$A = \frac{9R}{I}$$

Solve for I.

$$A = \frac{9R}{I}$$
$$AI = 9R \qquad \text{Multiplying both sides by } I$$
$$I = \frac{9R}{A} \qquad \text{Multiplying both sides by } \frac{1}{A}$$

Try This

d. A formula for a football player's rushing average r with a total of y yards rushed in n carries of the ball is $r = \frac{y}{n}$. Solve for n.

In 1999, Pedro Martinez gave up 49 earned runs for an earned-run average of 2.067. How many innings did he pitch that year?

3-7 Exercises

A

Solve.

1. $A = bh$, for b (an area formula)
2. $A = bh$, for h
3. $d = rt$, for r (a distance formula)
4. $d = rt$, for t
5. $I = Prt$, for P (an interest formula)
6. $I = Prt$, for t
7. $F = ma$, for a (a physics formula)
8. $F = ma$, for m
9. $P = 2l + 2w$, for w (a perimeter formula)
10. $P = 2l + 2w$, for l
11. $A = \pi r^2$, for r^2 (an area formula)
12. $A = \pi r^2$, for π
13. $A = \frac{1}{2}bh$, for b (an area formula)
14. $A = \frac{1}{2}bh$, for h
15. $E = mc^2$, for m (a relativity formula)
16. $E = mc^2$, for c^2
17. $A = \frac{a + b + c}{3}$, for b
18. $A = \frac{a + b + c}{3}$, for c
19. $v = \frac{3k}{t}$, for t
20. $P = \frac{ab}{c}$, for c

Internet Connection

Extra Help On the Web

Look for worked-out examples at the Prentice Hall Web site.
www.phschool.com

Writing Math

Mathematicians may solve Exercise 17 in much the same way that you do. Then, however, they will quickly give the answer to Exercise 18, writing "by symmetry" to justify it. Can you solve Exercise 18 by using the "symmetry" of Exercises 17 and 18?

A formula for the area of a sector of a circle is $A = \frac{\pi r^2 S}{360}$ where r is the radius and S is the central angle measure of the sector.

21. Solve for S.

22. Solve for r^2.

A formula to find the horsepower H of an N-cylinder engine is

$$H = \frac{D^2 N}{2.5}$$

23. Solve for D^2.

24. Solve for N.

B

In Exercises 25–33, solve. Justify each step.

25. $A = \frac{1}{R}$, for R

26. $g = 40n + 20k$, for k

27. $r = 2h - \frac{1}{4}f$, for f

28. $\frac{s}{t} = \frac{t}{v}$, for s

29. $a^2 = b^2 + 2xc$, for x

30. $m = ax^2 + bx + c$, for b

31. $\frac{a}{b} = \frac{c}{d}$, for a

32. $d = \frac{1}{e + f}$, for f

33. $l = a + (n - 1)d$, for n

34. If $a^2 = b^2$, does $a = b$?

35. The formula $R = -0.00625t + 3.85$ can be used to estimate the world record in the 1500 m run t years after 1930. Solve for t.

36. *Critical Thinking*   In Exercise 23, you solved for D^2. How might you solve for D?

Challenge

Solve.

37. $y = a - ab$, for a

38. $ax + b = cb$, for b

39. $x = a + b - 2ab$, for a

40. $x - a = a(y - b)$, for a

41. *Mathematical Reasoning*   Solve $2p - q = 2r - s$ for $4p + 2s$.

42. **TEST PREP**   If $\frac{a}{b - c} = d$, then $b = $?

A. $\frac{a + c}{d}$ **B.** $\frac{a + cd}{d}$ **C.** $\frac{a}{d - c}$ **D.** $\frac{d + c}{a}$

Factor.   **43.** $4x + 12$ **44.** $3c + 12d - 9$ *2-7*

Collect like terms.   **45.** $2x + 3y - 4x$ **46.** $8a - 3c + 4 - 2a$ *1-5*

Solve.   **47.** $16 - 2c = 4c - 2$ **48.** $1.7m + 16.8 = 25.8 - 0.55m$

49. $\frac{1}{2}(8m + 4) + 2 = \frac{1}{3}(18m - 18)$ **50.** $\frac{2}{5} + 3y = 10y - 1$

51. $15.4 - 9.1t = 2.4t - 19.1$ **52.** $27 - 3(t + 4) = 9(t - 2) - 15$ *3-5, 3-6*

144   Chapter 3   *Equations*

Exercises

21. $\frac{360A}{\pi r^2}$

22. $\frac{360A}{\pi S}$

23. $\frac{2.5H}{N}$

24. $\frac{2.5H}{D^2}$

25. $\frac{1}{A}$

26. $\frac{g - 40n}{20}$

27. $8h - 4r$

28. $\frac{t^2}{v}$

29. $\frac{a^2 - b^2}{2c}$

30. $\frac{m - ax^2 - c}{x}$

31. $\frac{b}{d}$

32. $\frac{1}{d} - e$

33. $\frac{d - a + l}{d}$

34. No, a may be $-b$.

35. $t = \frac{R - 3.85}{-0.00625}$ or $-160R + 616$

36. by taking the square root of D^2;
$$D = \sqrt{\frac{2.5H}{N}}$$

37. $\frac{y}{1 - b}$

38. $\frac{ax}{c - 1}$

39. $\frac{x - b}{1 - 2b}$

40. $\frac{x}{y - b + 1}$

41. $4r + 2q$

42. B

Mixed Review

43. $4(x + 3)$

44. $3(c + 4d - 3)$

45. $3y - 2x$

46. $6a - 3c + 4$

47. 3

48. 4

49. 5

50. $\frac{1}{5}$

51. 3

52. 4

Solving Equations Involving Absolute Value

Objective: Solve equations involving absolute value.

In Chapter 2 you learned that the absolute value of a number is its distance from zero on a number line. You also learned that the absolute value of a number is always positive or zero. In this lesson you will solve equations involving absolute values.

EXAMPLES Solve.

1 $|x| = 6$
$x = 6$ or $x = -6$ 6 and -6 are both 6 units from 0 on the number line.

Check:

$|x| = 6$		$|x| = 6$	
$|6|$	6	$|-6|$	6
6	6 ✔	6	6 ✔

The solutions are 6 and -6.

2
$$|x| + 2 = 12$$
$$|x| + 2 + (-2) = 12 + (-2) \quad \text{Using the addition property}$$
$$|x| = 10$$
$$x = 10 \text{ or } x = -10$$

Check:

$|x| + 2 = 12$		$|x| + 2 = 12$	
$|10| + 2$	12	$|-10| + 2$	12
$10 + 2$	12	$10 + 2$	12
12	12 ✔	12	12 ✔

The solutions are 10 and -10.

3
$$3|b| - 4 = 2$$
$$3|b| - 4 + 4 = 2 + 4 \quad \text{Using the addition property}$$
$$3|b| = 6$$
$$\tfrac{1}{3} \cdot 3|b| = \tfrac{1}{3} \cdot 6 \quad \text{Using the multiplication property}$$
$$|b| = 2$$
$$b = 2 \text{ or } b = -2$$

Substitution will show that the numbers 2 and -2 check.
The solutions are 2 and -2.

Try This Solve.

a. $|y| = 17$ **b.** $|y| - 5 = 1$ **c.** $2|x| + 1 = 15$

3-8 *Solving Equations Involving Absolute Value* **145**

Try This
a. 17, −17
b. 6, −6
c. 7, −7

CA: 3.0, 25.2, 25.3

What You'll Learn
1 To solve equations involving absolute value

. . . And Why
To learn what to do with the simple form $|x|$ when it appears in an equation

1. FOCUS

FIRST FIVE MINUTES
Evaluate.
1. $|3|$
   3
2. $|-5|$
   5
3. $|3 - 5|$
   $|-2| = 2$
4. $|-4| + |4|$
   $4 + 4 = 8$
5. $|x - 7|$ when $x = 3$
   $|3 - 7| = |-4| = 4$

2. TEACH the Mathematics

Emphasize that there are two numbers that have a distance of 6 from 0: 6 and -6.

Key Questions
- How many numbers are there whose absolute value is 3?
  Two: 3, -3
- How many numbers are there whose absolute value is 0?
  One: 0
- How many numbers are there whose absolute value is -3?
  None

Chalkboard Examples
Solve.
1. $|y| = 3$
   $y = 3$ or $y = -3$
2. $|x| + 5 = 12$
   $|x| = 12 - 5$
   $|x| = 7$
   $x = 7$ or $x = -7$
3. $5|a| + 3 = 10$
   $5|a| = 10 - 3$
   $5|a| = 7$
   $|a| = \tfrac{7}{5}$
   $a = \tfrac{7}{5}$ or $a = -\tfrac{7}{5}$

LESSON QUIZ

Solve.

1. $|x| = 2$
   $x = 2$ or $x = -2$

2. $|a| = |-4|$
   $|a| = 4$
   $a = 4$ or $a = -4$

3. $|y| + 5 = 9$
   $|y| = 9 - 5$
   $|y| = 4$
   $y = 4$ or $y = -4$

4. $3|x| + 7 = 13$
   $3|x| = 13 - 7$
   $3|x| = 6$
   $|x| = \frac{6}{3} = 2$
   $x = 2$ or $x = -2$

5. $\frac{2}{5}|b| + |-2| = 5$
   $\frac{2}{5}|b| + 2 = 5$
   $\frac{2}{5}|b| = 5 - 2$
   $\frac{2}{5}|b| = 3$
   $\frac{5}{2} \cdot \frac{2}{5}|b| = \frac{5}{2} \cdot 3$
   $|b| = \frac{15}{2}$
   $b = \frac{15}{2}$ or $b = -\frac{15}{2}$

Assignment Guide

▼ Core 1–33, 40–53, 67–70
   Extension 34–39, 54–66

Use Mixed Review to maintain skills.

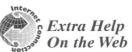

**Extra Help
On the Web**

Look for worked-out
examples at the Prentice
Hall Web site.
www.phschool.com

3-8 Exercises

A

Mental Math   Solve.

1. $|x| = 19$
2. $|y| = 9$
3. $4 = |m|$
4. $|n| = 7$
5. $|h| = 0$
6. $3 = |a|$
7. $|b| = 12$
8. $|x| = 15$
9. $|a| = |-2|$
10. $|-20| = |-x|$
11. $|y| = 12 - 5$
12. $|y| + 5 = 16$
13. $|a| - 7 = 21$
14. $4 + |m| = 9$
15. $-2 + |n| = 0$
16. $|x| + 3 + 9 = 15$
17. $5 + |x| - 9 = 2$
18. $|x| - 23 = 34$
19. $|-4| + |-6| + |m| = 10$
20. $|-8| + |x| = |-8| + |-3|$
21. $5|x| = 35$
22. $3|y| = 27$

Solve.

23. $2|x| + 6 = 12$
24. $4|r| - 2 = 18$
25. $\frac{|m|}{4} = 5$
26. $\frac{|t|}{-2} = -9$
27. $-4|x| = -5$
28. $4|x| + |-4| = |-6|$
29. $-3|a| - 5 = -17$
30. $-2|b| + 4 = 2$
31. $\frac{|x|}{5} + 7 = 42$
32. $\frac{1}{4} + \frac{1}{2}|x| = \frac{5}{8}$

33. *Write a Convincing Argument* $|x| = -5$ has no solutions. Why?

Mathematical Reasoning   Show that the statement is sometimes true.
Then give a counterexample to show that the statement is not always true.

34. $|x| = x$
35. $|x| = -x$
36. $|-x| = x$
37. $|-x| = -x$
38. $|x + y| = |x| + |y|$
39. $|x + y| < |x| + |y|$

B

Solve.

40. $-|x| = -4$
41. $-12 = -|y|$
42. $-2|a| + 5 = 1$
43. $2|x| + 3|x| + 4 = 24$
44. $-3|m| + 5|m| - 3 = 1$
45. $|n| - 3 + 5|n| = 15$
46. $|x| + 12 = 5|x| - 4$
47. $6 - 3|a| = 2|a| + 1$
48. $-\frac{2}{3}|m| - \frac{4}{5} = -4$
49. $-\frac{1}{3}|y| + \frac{5}{6} = \frac{1}{6}$
50. $|3m| = 6$
51. $|2a| = 8$
52. $|-m| = 5$
53. $|-x| = 7$

Exercises

1. $19, -19$
2. $9, -9$
3. $4, -4$
4. $7, -7$
5. 0
6. $3, -3$
7. $12, -12$
8. $15, -15$
9. $2, -2$
10. $20, -20$
11. $7, -7$
12. $11, -11$
13. $28, -28$
14. $5, -5$

15. $2, -2$
16. $3, -3$
17. $6, -6$
18. $57, -57$
19. 0
20. $3, -3$
21. $7, -7$
22. $9, -9$
23. $3, -3$
24. $5, -5$
25. $20, -20$
26. $18, -18$
27. $\frac{5}{4}, -\frac{5}{4}$
28. $\frac{1}{2}, -\frac{1}{2}$

29. $4, -4$
30. $1, -1$
31. $175, -175$
32. $\frac{3}{4}, -\frac{3}{4}$
33. The absolute value of a
    number cannot be negative.
34. true for $x = 2$; false for $x = -2$
35. true for $x = -2$; false for $x = 2$
36. true for $x = 2$; false for $x = -2$
37. true for $x = -2$; false for $x = 2$
38. true for $x = 2$, $y = 3$; false for
    $x = -2$, $y = 3$
39. true for $x = -2$, $y = 3$; false
    for $x = 2$, $y = 3$

40. $4, -4$
41. $12, -12$
42. $2, -2$
43. $4, -4$
44. $2, -2$
45. $3, -3$
46. $4, -4$
47. $1, -1$
48. $\frac{24}{5}, -\frac{24}{5}$
49. $2, -2$
50. $m = 2, -2$
51. $a = 4, -4$
52. $m = 5, -5$
53. $x = 7, -7$

Critical Thinking Complete.

54. If $x > 0, |x| = ?$ **55.** If $x < 0, |x| = ?$ **56.** If $x = 0, |x| = ?$

Challenge

Solve.

57. $|x + 2| = 7$ **58.** $|m - 4| = 1$ **59.** $|2a + 1| = 5$

Mathematical Reasoning   Is the statement sometimes true, always true, or never true? Explain.

60. $|x| > x$ **61.** $|x| = |-x|$ **62.** $|x^2| = x^2$

63. $|x| + |y| > 0$ **64.** $|xy| = |x||y|$ **65.** $|x - y| = |x| - |y|$

66. If $|x| > |y|$, what is the most you know about x and y?

Error Analysis   The solution of each equation has an error commonly made by algebra students. Find and correct the error.

67. $4 - 3x = 5$

$3x = 9$

$x = 3$

68. Solve $ax - b = c$ for b.

$ax = b + c$

$x = \dfrac{b + c}{a}$

69. $4|c| - 3 = 1$

$4|c| - 3 = 1$ or $4|c| - 3 = -1$

$4|c| = 4$ or $4|c| = 2$

$|c| = 1$ or $|c| = \frac{1}{2}$

$c = 1$ or $c = -1$ $c = \frac{1}{2}$ or $c = -\frac{1}{2}$

70. $|x| = -3$

$x = 3$ or $x = -3$

Mixed Review

Solve.   **71.** $-12t - 4 = 32$ **72.** $3m + 2m + 15 = 35$

73. $x + 0.75x = 21$ **74.** $\frac{1}{2}n + \frac{2}{5}n = -\frac{9}{10}$ **75.** $\frac{2}{5}(m - 4) = 4$ *3-3*

Collect like terms.   **76.** $2x - \frac{1}{2}x + \frac{3}{4}x - 4x$

77. $3a - \frac{2}{5}b - \frac{1}{2}a - 6b$ **78.** $5x + \frac{2}{3}y - \frac{1}{4}x + y$ *2-7*

Translate to an equation and solve.

79. The sum of two consecutive even integers is 94. What are the integers?

80. The sum of three consecutive odd integers is 123. What are the integers?

81. One angle of a triangle is 3 times as large as another. The third angle is 60° less than the sum of the other two angles. Find the measure of each angle.

82. The length of a rectangle is twice the width. The perimeter is 24 m. Find the length and the width.   *3-4*

---

54. x
55. $-x$
56. 0
57. 5, -9
58. 5, 3
59. 2, -3
60. Sometimes; true for $x = -2$; false for $x = 2$.
61. Always; a number and its opposite are the same distance from 0.
62. Always; $x^2 \geq 0$, so $|x^2| = x^2$.
63. Sometimes; false only for $x = y = 0$.
64. Always; the factors on the right are the same as the factors inside the absolute value symbol on the left, except possibly for a factor of -1 inside the absolute value symbol. The absolute value symbol eliminates the factor of -1.
65. Sometimes; true for $x = 3$, $y = 2$; false for $x = 3$, $y = -2$.
66. $x \neq y, x \neq 0$
67. The correct solution is $x = -\frac{1}{3}$.
68. The correct solution is $b = ax - c$.
69. The correct solution is $c = 1$ or $c = -1$.
70. There is no solution.

Mixed Review
71. -3
72. 4
73. 12
74. -1
75. 14
76. $-\frac{7}{4}x$
77. $\frac{5}{2}a - \frac{32}{5}b$
78. $\frac{19}{4}x + \frac{5}{3}y$
79. 46, 48
80. 39, 41, 43
81. 30°, 60°, 90°
82. 8 m, 4 m

3-9

TIME-FOCUS METER

1. FOCUS

FIRST FIVE MINUTES

Simplify.

1. $\frac{14}{21}$ $\frac{2}{3}$

2. $\frac{15}{25}$ $\frac{3}{5}$

3. $\frac{16}{8}$ 2

4. $\frac{4a}{2b}$ $\frac{2a}{b}$

5. $\frac{x \cdot 3}{x}$ 3

2. TEACH the Mathematics

▼ Solving Proportions

You may want to introduce cross multiplication as a way of checking proportions. In Example 1 the solution is 14. Substituting 14 for x,

$$\frac{14}{63} = \frac{2}{9}$$
$$14 \cdot 9 = 2 \cdot 63$$
$$126 = 126$$

The solution, 14, checks.

Key Questions

- If one ratio in a proportion is less than 1, must the other ratio also be less than 1? Yes

- Is $\frac{8}{13}$ a proportion? No

Chalkboard Examples

Solve.

1. $\frac{x}{21} = \frac{3}{7}$

$$21 \cdot \frac{x}{21} = 21 \cdot \frac{3}{7}$$
$$x = 9$$

2. $\frac{4}{7} = \frac{24}{x}$

Multiply by $7x$ to clear the fractions.

$$7x \cdot \frac{4}{7} = 7x \cdot \frac{24}{x}$$
$$x \cdot 4 = 168$$
$$x = \frac{168}{4}$$
$$x = 42$$

What You'll Learn

❶ To solve proportions

❷ To solve problems involving proportions

... And Why

To develop and solve proportional relationships

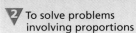

CA 5.0: Solve multi-step problems involving linear equations in one variable.

3-9 ▷ Proportions

Objective: Solve proportions.

A **ratio** of two quantities is a comparison, often expressed as a fraction. For example, the ratio of the age of a 34-year-old parent to that of a 10-year-old child is 34 to 10 or $\frac{34}{10}$. The ratio of 34 to 10 can be expressed in several ways.

$$34:10 \qquad 34 \div 10 \qquad \frac{34}{10} \qquad 3.4$$

An equation that states that two ratios are equal is called a **proportion.** These are proportions.

$$\frac{2}{3} = \frac{6}{9} \qquad \frac{5}{7} = \frac{25}{35} \qquad \frac{x}{24} = \frac{2}{3} \qquad \frac{9}{y} = \frac{32}{81}$$

Since proportions are equations, we can use equation-solving properties to solve them.

EXAMPLE 1   Solve.

$$\frac{x}{63} = \frac{2}{9}$$
$$63 \cdot \frac{x}{63} = 63 \cdot \frac{2}{9} \qquad \text{Using the multiplication property}$$
$$x = 14$$

EXAMPLE 2   Solve.

$$\frac{65}{10} = \frac{13}{x}$$
$$10x \cdot \frac{65}{10} = 10x \cdot \frac{13}{x} \qquad \text{Using the multiplication property; multiplying by } 10x \text{ to clear fractions}$$
$$65x = 130$$
$$\frac{1}{65} \cdot 65x = \frac{1}{65} \cdot 130 \qquad \text{Using the multiplication property}$$
$$x = 2$$

Try This   Solve.

a. $\frac{3}{5} = \frac{12}{y}$ **b.** $\frac{1}{2} = \frac{x}{5}$ **c.** $\frac{m}{4} = \frac{7}{6}$

148   Chapter 3   *Equations*

Try This

a. 20

b. $\frac{5}{2}$

c. $\frac{14}{3}$

Objective: Solve problems involving proportions.

PROBLEM-SOLVING GUIDELINES
■ UNDERSTAND the problem
Develop and carry out a PLAN
■ Find the ANSWER and CHECK

Some problems can be solved by writing and solving a proportion. Use the Problem-Solving Guidelines to help you solve the following problems.

EXAMPLE 3

The property tax on a house is $8 per $1000 assessed valuation. What is the tax on a house assessed at $165,000?

$$\frac{8}{1000} = \frac{x}{165,000}$$

Think: $8 is to $1000 as x dollars is to $165,000.

$$\frac{8}{1000} \cdot 165,000 = \frac{x}{165,000} \cdot 165,000$$

$$1320 = x$$

The tax is $1320.

EXAMPLE 4

A certain car can travel 180 miles on 8 gallons of gasoline. How far can this car travel on 19 gallons of gasoline?

Solve: $\frac{180}{8} = \frac{x}{19}$

Think: 180 miles is to 8 gallons as x miles is to 19 gallons.

$$\frac{180}{8} \cdot 19 = \frac{x}{19} \cdot 19$$

$$\frac{180 \cdot 19}{8} = x$$

$$427.5 = x$$

The car can travel 427.5 miles on 19 gallons.

Try This   Solve.

d. The scale on a map says that 0.5 cm represents 25 km. On the map the measurement between two cities is 5 cm. What is the actual distance between these two cities?

e. According to the scale on a road map, 3 inches represent 40 miles. If two cities measure 10 inches apart on the map, how many miles apart are they?

Try This

d. 250 km

e. $133\frac{1}{3}$ miles

---

2 Solving Problems

For Example 3, explain to students that "assessed valuation" simply refers to the rated value of a house.

Math Point

The study of proportions is one of the oldest and most useful areas of mathematics. Around 550 B.C., the philosopher Pythagoras discovered that if one string on a musical instrument was twice the length of another, their sounds would go well together. Today we call this musical interval an octave. Pythagoras was deeply impressed that the *ratios* were important rather than the actual lengths of each string. He and his followers believed that by studying ratios one could understand the nature of the world. In fact, the word "rational" comes from the word ratio. It was believed that a rational person is one who has a sense of proportion.

Chalkboard Example

1. If a car moving at constant speed travels 55 miles in 2 hours, how many miles will it travel in 7 hours?

   Let x be the distance traveled in 7 hours. Since the rate is constant, the rate can be computed either as $\frac{55}{2}$ or as $\frac{x}{7}$, hence

   $$\frac{55}{2} = \frac{x}{7}$$
   $$7 \cdot \frac{55}{2} = 7 \cdot \frac{x}{7}$$
   $$192.5 = x$$

   The car will travel 192.5 miles.

LESSON ENRICHMENT

Make up a problem whose answer can be found by writing and solving the proportion $\frac{x}{400} = \frac{4}{500}$. Then solve the problem. $x = 3.2$

3. PRACTICE/ASSESS

LESSON QUIZ

Solve these proportions.

1. $\frac{a}{3} = \frac{5}{6}$

$a = \frac{5}{2}$

2. $\frac{4}{x} = \frac{8}{3}$

$x = \frac{3}{2}$

3. $\frac{6}{7} = \frac{2}{z}$

$z = \frac{14}{6} = \frac{7}{3}$

4. On a certain map, 2 inches represent 5 miles. 9 inches represent how many miles?

Let m be the number of miles. Since the scale proportion remains constant, the scale is equal to $\frac{2}{5}$ and to $\frac{9}{x}$, hence $\frac{2}{5} = \frac{9}{x}$

Multiply by 5x.

$5x \cdot \frac{2}{5} = 5x \cdot \frac{9}{x}$

$x \cdot 2 = 45$

$x = \frac{45}{2}$

9 inches represent $22\frac{1}{2}$ miles.

Assignment Guide

To provide flexible scheduling, this lesson can be split into parts.

▼ Core 1–24
  Extension 39
▼ Core 25–37, 43
  Extension 38, 40–42

Use Mixed Review to maintain skills.

 **Practice Multiple Choice**

Choose the best answer.

1. Solve.

$8 + |y| - 11 = 3$

A $y = -6$ or $y = 6$
B $y = 6$
C $y = 22$
D $y = 22$ or $y = -22$

2. Norman received $60 for working 8 hours. At this rate, how much would he receive for working 35 hours?

F $262.50
G $7.50
H $2100
J $480

1. A; Algebra 3.0
2. F; Algebra 5.0

 **3-9 Exercises**

A

Solve these proportions.

1. $\frac{y}{3} = \frac{9}{27}$ 2. $\frac{7}{8} = \frac{m}{4}$ 3. $\frac{9}{x} = \frac{2}{3}$ 4. $\frac{25}{75} = \frac{1}{x}$

5. $\frac{2}{y} = \frac{5}{9}$ 6. $\frac{16}{m} = \frac{1}{4}$ 7. $\frac{8}{5} = \frac{40}{y}$ 8. $\frac{12}{15} = \frac{t}{5}$

9. $\frac{y}{4} = \frac{5}{8}$ 10. $\frac{3}{8} = \frac{12}{x}$ 11. $\frac{5}{x} = \frac{9}{11}$ 12. $\frac{2}{7} = \frac{5}{y}$

13. $\frac{x}{40} = \frac{3}{5}$ 14. $\frac{n}{20} = \frac{3}{4}$ 15. $\frac{18}{c} = \frac{2}{7}$ 16. $\frac{24}{x} = \frac{4}{3}$

17. $\frac{15}{y} = \frac{10}{8}$ 18. $\frac{63}{144} = \frac{u}{16}$ 19. $\frac{12}{30} = \frac{10}{k}$ 20. $\frac{5}{3} = \frac{y}{42}$

21. $\frac{7}{b} = \frac{4}{9}$ 22. $\frac{100}{a} = \frac{90}{45}$ 23. $\frac{4}{5} = \frac{28}{h}$ 24. $\frac{y}{18} = \frac{150}{126}$

Solve.

25. A car travels 150 km on 12 L of gasoline. How many liters of gasoline are needed to travel 500 km?

26. A baseball pitcher strikes out an average of 3.6 batters per 9 innings. At this rate, how many batters would the pitcher strike out in 315 innings?

27. A watch loses 2 minutes every 15 hours. How much time will it lose in 2 hours?

28. A school has a policy that 2 adults must accompany every group of 15 students on school trips. How many adults are needed to take 180 students on a trip?

29. Four shovels of sand are used for every 5 shovels of gravel in making concrete. How much gravel is needed for 64 shovels of sand?

30. The ratio of international students to U.S. students at a college is 2 to 35. How many international students are there if there are 1575 U.S. students?

31. A loading crew estimates that it can load 8 boxes in 20 minutes. At this rate, how many boxes could it load in 1 hour?

32. On a map, 1 cm represents 3.27 km. It is 24.5 cm between two cities on this map. What is the actual distance between the two cities?

33. A television station found that 145 out of the 350 people surveyed watched a special program on education on Monday night. If this survey is representative of the total viewing population (12,250 people), about how many people watched the television special?

34. A survey of 250 people in a city found that Channel 5 is the favorite station of 52 people. If this survey is representative of the city's population of 35,000, about how many people in this city favor Channel 5?

Exercises

1. 1
2. $\frac{7}{2}$
3. $\frac{27}{2}$
4. 3
5. $\frac{18}{5}$
6. 64
7. 25
8. 4
9. $\frac{5}{2}$
10. 32
11. $\frac{55}{9}$
12. $\frac{35}{2}$
13. 24
14. 15
15. 63
16. 18
17. 12
18. 7
19. 25
20. 70
21. $\frac{63}{4}$
22. 50
23. 35
24. $\frac{150}{7}$
25. 40
26. 126
27. $\frac{4}{15}$ minute
28. 24
29. 80
30. 90
31. 24
32. 80.115 km
33. 5075
34. 7280

35. If two out of five people wear red to support the Ohio State football team, then how many in a full Ohio Stadium (capacity 89,841) are wearing red?

B

Solve.

36. An automobile engine crankshaft revolves 3000 times per minute. How long does it take to revolve 50 times?

37. A refrigerator goes on a defrost cycle for 1 hour out of every 14 hours. How many hours is this each week?

38. The ratio of full seats to empty seats in an auditorium is 5 to 2. If there are 120 empty seats, what is the seating capacity of this auditorium?

39. *Critical Thinking* $9m = 5n$. Find the ratio $m:n$.

Challenge

40. *Mathematical Reasoning*   The boy : girl ratio in a school is 4 : 5.

  a. If there are 225 girls, how many students are in the school?

  b. If there are 225 students, how many girls are in the school?

41. *Mathematical Reasoning*   Alena wants to guess the number of marbles in an 8-gal jar in order to win a moped. She knows there are 128 oz in a gallon, and she finds that 46 marbles fill an 8-oz jar. What should be her guess?

42. *Critical Thinking*   It takes 12 minutes to cut a log into 4 pieces. How long would it take to cut a log into 8 pieces?

43. A scale model of an experimental airplane measures 2.5 m from wingtip to wingtip. The actual plane will measure 60 m from wingtip to wingtip. If the highest point on the model will just fit under a $\frac{1}{2}$ m workbench, how tall does the airplane hangar doorway have to be?

In this sample, about 67 of 200 people are wearing red. If there were 85,000 people at this Ohio State game, estimate how many wore red.

Mixed Review

Divide.   **44.** $\frac{-32}{-8}$ **45.** $-\frac{7}{8} \div \frac{1}{4}$ **46.** $\frac{1}{6} \div -\frac{2}{3}$ *2-6*

Solve.   **47.** $9a - 6 = 30 - 3a$ **48.** $17 - 5c = 2c + 3$

49. $-11w = -132$ **50.** $|x| = 15$ **51.** $|c| + 9 = 12$

52. $6|m| = 24$ **53.** $|n| = 0$ **54.** $4(3x - 12) = 12$

55. $\frac{x}{3} + 5 = \frac{3x}{5} - \frac{7}{3}$ **56.** $0.3r - 2.8 = 3.2 - 0.2r$ *3-2, 3-5, 3-6, 3-8*

Solve for the given variable.   **57.** $y = mx + b$ for m

58. $PV = nRT$ for T **59.** $I = Prt$ for r *3-7*

Simplify.   **60.** $2w - (3w - 1)$ **61.** $2[3x - 2(3x + 4)]$ *2-8*

---

35. 35,936
Photo caption: 28,475
36. 1 second
37. 12
38. 420
39. 5:9
40. a. 405
    b. 125
41. 5888 marbles
42. 28 minutes
43. 12 meters

Mixed Review
44. 4
45. $-\frac{7}{2}$ or $-3\frac{1}{2}$
46. $-\frac{1}{4}$
47. 3
48. 2
49. 12
50. ±15
51. ±3
52. ±4
53. 0
54. 5
55. $x = \frac{55}{2}$

56. $r = 12$
57. $m = \frac{y - b}{x} = \frac{y}{x} - \frac{b}{x}$
58. $T = \frac{PV}{nR}$
59. $r = \frac{I}{Pt}$
60. $-w + 1$
61. $-6x - 16$

3-10

1. FOCUS

FIRST FIVE MINUTES

Write as a decimal.

1. $\frac{23}{100}$ 0.23   2. $\frac{475}{100}$ 4.75

3. $\frac{2}{100}$ 0.02   4. $\frac{0.5}{100}$ 0.005

Write as a fraction with 100 in the denominator.

5. 0.67 $\frac{67}{100}$ 6. 1.98 $\frac{198}{100}$

7. 0.01 $\frac{1}{100}$ 8. 0.001 $\frac{0.1}{100}$

2. TEACH the Mathematics

1 Percent

Emphasize that each of the three ways to write a percent,

$$5\% = 0.05 = \frac{5}{100}$$

is useful in different situations. We can remember numbers like 5%. We can add and compare sizes with the decimal form 0.05. We can multiply and divide easily with the fractional form $\frac{5}{100}$.

Avoiding Common Errors

Too often, .11 becomes 11 and .54 becomes 54. Remind students that when writing decimals, like 0.54, they are to write the leading 0 before the decimal point. The leading 0 makes the decimal point more visible.

Key Questions

- What is 10% of 10? 1
- What is 10% of 50? 5
- What is 50% of 10? 5
- What is 100% of 315? 315

Chalkboard Examples

Write as a decimal.
1. 41% 0.41
2. 2% 0.02
3. 150% 1.50
4. 0.5% 0.005

3-10 ▷ Using Percent

What You'll Learn

1 To express decimals and fractions as percents and vice versa

2 To solve equations involving percent

3 To solve percent problems

...And Why

To become proficient with percent

Math History

The idea of percent was used as early as the Roman Empire. The Roman Emperor Augustus levied a tax at a rate of $\frac{1}{100}$ of the selling price on all goods. In the 15th century, Italian manuscripts used expressions such as "20 p 100" and "xx p cento" to indicate 20 percent. Near the end of that century, phrases such as "viii in x percento" (8 percent) were used to express percent. The percent symbol (%) probably came from the symbol "⌒ᵒ" introduced in Italy at the end of the 15th century. By 1650, the symbol "per ÷" was used for percent. Later the "per" was dropped, leaving a symbol that closely resembles the one used today.

PART 1 Percent

Objective: Express decimals and fractions as percents and vice versa.

The ratio of a number to 100 is called **percent.** The word "percent" means *per one hundred*, and is represented by the symbol %. We can write a percent as a fraction or as a decimal.

$$78.5\% = 78.5 \times \frac{1}{100} = \frac{78.5}{100} = 0.785$$

$$4\% = 4 \times \frac{1}{100} = \frac{4}{100} = 0.04$$

To solve problems involving percent, we can first change the percent to a decimal.

EXAMPLES   Write as a decimal.

1   35% = 0.35   The hundredths place is the second place to the right of the decimal point.

2   5% = 0.05

3   138% = 1.38

4   0.8% = 0.008

Try This   Write as a decimal.

a. 48%   b. 3%   c. 145%   d. 0.5%

Try This
a. 0.48
b. 0.03
c. 1.45
d. 0.005

Some problems require that we change a fraction to a percent. The easiest way to do this usually is to change the fraction to a decimal first.

EXAMPLES Express as a percent. Round to the nearest tenth of a percent if necessary.

5 $\frac{2}{3} = 0.666\overline{6}$ $2 \div 3 = 0.666\overline{6}$ The bar shows that the digit 6 repeats.

≈ 0.667 Rounding to the nearest thousandth

$= \frac{66.7}{100}$ Writing in fraction form with a denominator of 100

$= 66.7\%$

6 $\frac{5}{4} = 1.25$ $5 \div 4 = 1.25$

$= \frac{125}{100}$

$= 125\%$

Try This Express as a percent. Round to the nearest tenth of a percent if necessary.

e. $\frac{3}{4}$ f. $\frac{3}{8}$ g. $\frac{24.5}{5}$

h. $\frac{12.4}{25}$ i. $\frac{0.02}{500}$ j. $\frac{3}{40}$

PART 2 Using Equations with Percent

Objective: Solve percent problems.

We can solve problems involving percent by using a proportion or by translating to an equation and solving. When fractional percents are used, translating to an equation is usually the better method.

EXAMPLE 7 Solve.

15.5% of 60 is what number?

$$\begin{array}{ccccc} 15.5\% & \text{of} & 60 & \text{is} & \text{what number?} \\ \downarrow & \downarrow & \downarrow & \downarrow & \downarrow \\ 0.155 & \cdot & 60 & = & n \end{array}$$ Translating to an equation

$15.5\% = \frac{15.5}{100} = 0.155$

$9.3 = n$

15.5% of 60 is 9.3.

Try This
e. 75%
f. 37.5%
g. 490%
h. 49.6%
i. 0.004%
j. 7.5%

Express as a percent.

5. $0.62 = \frac{62}{100} = 62\%$

6. $\frac{1}{4} = 0.25 = \frac{25}{100} = 25\%$

7. $\frac{6}{5} = 1.20 = \frac{120}{100} = 120\%$

8. $1 = \frac{100}{100} = 100\%$

2 Using Equations with Percent

You may want to show students how to solve problems involving percent using a proportion.

Example 7
15.5% of 60 is what number?

$\frac{n}{60} = \frac{15.5}{100}$

$n = (60)(\frac{15.5}{100})$

$n = 9.3$

Example 8
24 is what percent of 120?

$\frac{24}{120} = \frac{p}{100}$

$100(\frac{24}{120}) = p$

$20\% = p$

You may wish to show the 3 basic types of percent problems with the same phrase. For example, in Example 9, we have

25% of 60 is 15

This leads to the following.
1) 25% of 60 is what number?
2) What percent of 60 is 15?
3) 25% of what number is 15?

You can also illustrate that many sentences have the same translation. For example,
1) What percent of 150 is 30?
2) 30 is what percent of 150?
Both translate to $30 = p \cdot 150$.

Chalkboard Examples
Solve.
1. What is 20% of 90?
   20% of 90 =
   $0.20 \cdot 90 = 18$
2. 12% of 40 is what number?
   $0.12 \cdot 40 = 4.8$
3. What percent of 60 equals 12?
   Let p be the percent, expressed as a decimal.
   $p \cdot 60 = 12$
   $p = \frac{12}{60} = 0.20 = 20\%$
4. 35% of what number equals 1.4?
   $0.35 \cdot x = 1.40$
   $x = \frac{1.40}{0.35} = \frac{140}{35} = 4$

Use Teaching Transparency T13 for more examples of percent problems.

3 Percent Problems

Chalkboard Examples

Solve.

1. The population decreased to 90% of last year's population. The population is now 270. What was it last year?
   Let p be last year's population.
   $0.90p = 270$
   $p = \frac{270}{0.90} = 300$

2. The stock market index is now at 15,600, which is 130% of last year's value. What was the value last year?
   Let s be the stock market index for last year.
   $1.30s = 15,600$
   $s = \frac{15,600}{1.30} = 12,000$

EXAMPLE 8   Solve.

24 is what percent of 120?

24	is	what percent	of	120?	Translating to an equation
↓	↓	↓	↓	↓	
24	=	p	·	120	Let p represent the percent expressed as a decimal.

$\frac{24}{120} = p$

$0.2 = p$

$p = 0.2$ or 20%   Express the decimal as a percent.

24 is 20% of 120.

EXAMPLE 9   Solve.

25% of what number is 15?

25%	of	what number	is	15?	Translating to an equation
↓	↓	↓	↓	↓	
0.25	·	n	=	15	Let n be the number you are trying to find. $25\% = \frac{25}{100} = 0.25$

$n = \frac{15}{0.25}$

$n = 60$

25% of 60 is 15.

Try This   Solve.

k. What percent of 40 is 15?   **l.** 3 is 16% of what number?

m. 7.5% of 80 is what number?   **n.** What number is 12.5% of 40?

◇ Connections: Estimating

Estimating with percents is easy if you remember some key fraction-percent relationships. Here are approximate percents for the thirds.

$\frac{1}{3} \approx 33\%$ $\frac{2}{3} \approx 67\%$

1. In your journal, on an index card, or on some other form of ready reference, make a chart showing fraction-percent relationships for halves, thirds, fourths, fifths, sixths, eighths, and tenths.

2. Show how you could estimate each of the following.
   a. 25% of 445   **b.** $\frac{33}{40} = ??\%$ **c.** the number that 9 is 12% of

Try This

k. 37.5%

l. 18.75

m. 6

n. 5

Connections: Estimating

1. $\frac{1}{2} = 50\%$

$\frac{1}{3} = 33\frac{1}{3}\%$ $\frac{2}{3} = 66\frac{2}{3}\%$

$\frac{1}{4} = 25\%$ $\frac{2}{4} = 50\%$ $\frac{3}{4} = 75\%$

$\frac{1}{5} = 20\%$ $\frac{2}{5} = 40\%$ $\frac{3}{5} = 60\%$ $\frac{4}{5} = 80\%$

$\frac{1}{6} = 16\frac{2}{3}\%$ $\frac{2}{6} = 33\frac{1}{3}\%$ $\frac{3}{6} = 50\%$ $\frac{4}{6} = 66\frac{2}{3}\%$ $\frac{5}{6} = 83\frac{1}{3}\%$

$\frac{1}{8} = 12\frac{1}{2}\%$ $\frac{2}{8} = 25\%$ $\frac{3}{8} = 37\frac{1}{2}\%$ $\frac{4}{8} = 50\%$ $\frac{5}{8} = 62\frac{1}{2}\%$ $\frac{6}{8} = 75\%$ $\frac{7}{8} = 87\frac{1}{2}\%$

$\frac{1}{10} = 10\%$ $\frac{2}{10} = 20\%$ $\frac{3}{10} = 30\%$ $\frac{4}{10} = 40\%$ $\frac{5}{10} = 50\%$ $\frac{6}{10} = 60\%$ $\frac{7}{10} = 70\%$ $\frac{8}{10} = 80\%$ $\frac{9}{10} = 90\%$

2. a. 25% of 445 is about $\frac{1}{4}$ of 444, or 111.

   b. $\frac{33}{40}$ is about $\frac{3}{4}$, or 75%.

   c. 12% is about $\frac{1}{8}$, and 9 is $\frac{1}{8}$ of 72.

PART 3 Percent Problems

Objective: Solve problems involving applications of percent.

PROBLEM-SOLVING GUIDELINES
■ UNDERSTAND the problem
Develop and carry out a PLAN
■ Find the ANSWER and CHECK

You can use the Problem-Solving Guidelines to help you solve problems involving percent.

EXAMPLE 10

The tax on an automobile was 6% of its price. What was the price of this car if the tax was $633?

■ **UNDERSTAND the problem**

Question: What was the price of the car?
Data: The tax was 6% of the price.

Clarifying the question and identifying the given data

■ **Develop and carry out a PLAN**

Let $p =$ the price of the car.

Using a variable to represent the price of the car.

$(0.6)p = 633$

6% of the price is the tax, $633.

$p = \frac{633}{0.06}$

$p = 10{,}550$

■ **Find the ANSWER and CHECK**

The price of the car was $10,550. If we find 6% of $10,550, we get $633. The answer checks.

Since 6% of 10,000 is 600, the answer is reasonable.

Try This   Solve.

o. Ms. Pelligrini received a $750 bonus with her monthly paycheck. Her regular monthly pay is $2500. What percent of her regular monthly pay was her bonus?

p. Truong's junior college expenses were $5000 last term. She spent $1500 on tuition, $2250 on room and board, and $1250 on miscellaneous expenses. What percent of her college expenses went toward tuition?

Try This
o. 30%
p. 30%

Write as a decimal.
1. 54% 0.54
2. 4% 0.04
3. 104% 1.04
4. 0.3% 0.003

Express as a percent.
5. $\frac{7}{5}$

$$\frac{7}{5} = 1.4 = \frac{140}{100} = 140\%$$

Solve.
6. What number is 40% of 120?
   $0.40 \cdot 120 = 48$
7. 18 is what percent of 20?
   $18 = \frac{p}{100} \cdot 20$
   $p = 90; 90\%$

Assignment Guide

To provide flexible scheduling, this lesson can be split into parts.

▼ Core 1–20
   Extension Connections 1, 2 (p.154)

▼ Core 21–36
   Extension 44, 51

▼ Core 37–43, 45–50
   Extension 52–54

Use Mixed Review to maintain skills.

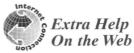

***Extra Help
On the Web***

Look for worked-out examples at the Prentice Hall Web site.
www.phschool.com

3-10 Exercises

A

Write as a decimal.
1. 41%   2. 60%   3. 7%   4. 1%   5. 125%
6. 180%   7. 0.8%   8. 0.6%   9. 1.5%   10. 2.8%

Express as a percent. Round to the nearest tenth of a percent if necessary.

11. $\frac{3}{4}$ 12. $\frac{1}{25}$ 13. $\frac{24}{25}$ 14. $\frac{3}{8}$ 15. $\frac{1}{3}$

16. $\frac{3}{25}$ 17. $\frac{5}{8}$ 18. $\frac{5}{6}$ 19. $\frac{3}{16}$ 20. $\frac{1}{20}$

Solve.
21. What percent of 68 is 17?
22. What percent of 75 is 36?
23. What percent of 125 is 30?
24. What percent of 300 is 57?
25. 45 is 30% of what number?
26. 20.4 is 24% of what number?
27. 0.3 is 12% of what number?
28. 7 is 175% of what number?
29. What percent of 80 is 100?
30. What percent of 10 is 205?
31. What is 2% of 40?
32. What is 40% of 2?
33. 2 is what percent of 40?
34. 40 is 2% of what number?
35. 2 is 40% of what number?
36. 40 is what percent of 2?
37. On a test of 88 items, a student got 76 correct. What percent were correct?
38. A softball player had 13 hits in 25 times at bat. What percent of her times at bat resulted in hits?
39. A family spent $408 one month for food. This was 26% of its income. What was its monthly income?
40. The sales-tax rate in New York City is $8\frac{1}{4}\%$. How much city sales tax would be charged on a purchase of $428.86? What will be the total cost of the purchase?
41. Water volume increases 9% when it freezes. If 400 cm³ of water are frozen, how much will the volume increase? What will be the volume of the ice?
42. Sales tax in Freeberg is 5%. What would be the sales tax on a motorbike that costs $775? What would be the total cost for the motorbike, including tax?
43. A salesperson's quota was set at $7500 for one month. During this month the salesperson sold $10,000. What percent of the quota is this?
44. ***Write a Convincing Argument***   Which is greater,
    a. 50% of 40 or 40% of 50?
    b. 20% of 90 or 90% of 20?
    c. *a*% of *b* or *b*% of *a*?

Exercises
1. 0.41
2. 0.6
3. 0.07
4. 0.01
5. 1.25
6. 1.8
7. 0.008
8. 0.006
9. 0.015
10. 0.028
11. 75%
12. 4%
13. 96%
14. 37.5%
15. 33.3%
16. 12%
17. 62.5%
18. 83.3%
19. 18.8%
20. 5%
21. 25%
22. 48%
23. 24%
24. 19%
25. 150
26. 85
27. 2.5
28. 4
29. 125%
30. 2050%
31. 0.8
32. 0.8
33. 5%
34. 2000
35. 5
36. 2000%
37. 86.4%
38. 52%
39. $1569.23
40. $35.38; $464.24
41. 36 cm³; 436 cm³
42. $38.75; $813.75
43. 133.3%
44. a. They are equal.
    $$\frac{50}{100} \cdot 40 = \frac{40}{100} \cdot 50$$
    b. They are equal.
    $$\frac{20}{100} \cdot 90 = \frac{90}{100} \cdot 20$$
    c. They are equal.
    $$\frac{a}{100} \cdot b = \frac{b}{100} \cdot a$$

B

45. A meal came to $16.41 without tax. Calculate a 6% sales tax, and then calculate a 15% tip based on the sum of the meal and the tax. What is the total cost of the meal?

46. Debby's Discs charges $12.99 for a CD. DISCount, Inc., charges $14.95, but you have a $2.00 DISCount coupon. A sales tax of 7% is charged on the *regular* prices. How much does the CD cost at each store?

To find the **percent of increase** (or **decrease**), divide the amount of increase (or decrease) by the original amount.

47. Wendi worked for $6 an hour for the first month she was on the job. She was then given a raise to $6.24 an hour. What was the percent of her wage increase?

48. A car stereo that originally cost $175 was on sale for $150. What was the percent of decrease for the car stereo?

49. The dimensions of a rectangular design are 7.5 cm by 12.5 cm. Each is $37\frac{1}{2}\%$ of the original design. What were the original dimensions?

50. The new price of a car is 25% higher than the old price of $8800. The old price is less than the new price by what percent?

51. *Critical Thinking*   If x is 160% of y, y is what percent of x?

Challenge

52. A store has a 30% discount on every item in stock. By how much is the 5% sales tax reduced on an item that regularly sells for $10?

53. A bank offered two plans for a two-year investment. One was 5% the first year and 10% the second year. The other was 10% the first year and 5% the second year. Which investment plan was better?

54. *Write a Convincing Argument*   Here are seven different discount plans. List them in order from best to worst. Justify your listing.

successive discounts   of 10%, 10%, 10%, 10%;   of 10%, 10%, 20%
                         of 20%, 10%, 10%;   of 10%, 30%;
                         of 30%, 10%;   of 20%, 20%;
                         of 40% (one discount only)

Mixed Review

Give the additive inverse.   **55.** 4.1   **56.** −9   **57.** 16   *2-3*

Simplify.   **58.** $-4 - (-2x) + 6x + x + 9$ **59.** $8c + 8 - (-2c)$

60. $-6 + 5x - (-2x) - 4x$ **61.** $2t - (-13) - 3t - (-6t) - 19$ *2-8*

Calculate.   **62.** $-6(3.4)(-1)$ **63.** $-3.2(0)$ **64.** $-2(-8)(-2)$

65. $99 \div (-3)$ **66.** $-72 \div 3$ **67.** $45 \div (-15)$ *2-5, 2-6*

---

45. $20
46. $13.90, $14.00
47. 4%
48. 14.3%
49. 20 cm by 33.3 cm
50. 20%
51. 62.5%
52. $0.15
53. Equal. Both earn $15.50 interest on $100 over two years.

54.

Plan	Of original price
40%;	pay 60%
30%, 10%;	pay 63%
10%, 30%;	pay 63%
20%, 20%;	pay 64%
20%, 10%, 10%;	pay 64.8%
10%, 10%, 20%;	pay 64.8%
10%, 10%, 10%, 10%;	pay 65.6%

Mixed Review
55. −4.1
56. 9
57. −16
58. $9x + 5$
59. $10c + 8$
60. $3x - 6$
61. $5t - 6$
62. 20.4
63. 0
64. −32
65. −33
66. −24
67. −3

3-11

TIME-FOCUS METER

CA 5.0: Solve multi-step problems involving linear equations in one variable.

3-11 ▷ **More Expressions and Equations**

1. FOCUS

FIRST FIVE MINUTES
Write as an algebraic expression.
1. the sum of x and the quantity three times x
   $x + 3x$
2. the difference between c and one third of c
   $c - \frac{1}{3}c$
3. the integer one greater than the integer n
   $n + 1$
4. the product of s and the quantity s plus 5
   $s(s + 5)$
5. three times the number n
   $3n$

2. TEACH the Mathematics

1 Compound Phrases to Algebraic Expressions

Stress that there may be more than one way to translate a phrase to an algebraic expression. It may vary depending on which quantity we let the variable represent.

You may wish to have students give answers in simplified form. Answers in this lesson will be given in both simplified and unsimplified forms.

Key Questions
■ Simplify the answer to Example 1.
   $4b$
■ Simplify the answer to Example 2.
   $4x + 3$
■ Suppose we let $m =$ the cost of the main-floor seat in Example 1. What would be the expression for the total cost of one of each type of seat?
   $\frac{1}{3}m + m$ or $\frac{4}{3}m$

Chalkboard Examples
1. Write an expression for the sum of two consecutive integers.
   Let n represent the first integer.
   The next integer is $n + 1$.
   The sum is $n + (n + 1)$ or $2n + 1$.

What You'll Learn
① To translate compound phrases into algebraic expressions
② To solve problems by writing and solving equations

. . . And Why
To use mathematical models to solve problems

Quick *Review*
An even integer has 2 as a factor. An odd integer does not have 2 as a factor.

Some problems contain two or more unknowns. To solve such problems, you must first decide which unknown quantity the variable will represent and then express the other unknown quantities in terms of that variable.

Objective: Translate compound phrases into algebraic expressions.

EXAMPLE 1
The cost of a main-floor seat is three times as much as the cost of a balcony seat. Write an expression showing the total cost for one of each type of seat.

Let $b =$ cost of a balcony seat.
$3b =$ cost of a main floor seat

The cost of a main floor seat is expressed in terms of the cost of a balcony seat. Therefore, let the variable b represent the cost of a balcony seat, and express the cost of a main floor seat in terms of b.

$b + 3b =$ total cost

To find the total cost, add the cost of each seat.

Try This
a. There are half as many boys in a certain club as there are girls. Write an expression for the total number of boys and girls in the club.

The integers 22, 23, and 24 are *consecutive integers*. These numbers follow each other when we count by ones. The integers 6, 8, and 10 are *consecutive even integers*. These numbers follow each other when we count by twos, beginning with 6. The integers 7, 9, and 11 are *consecutive odd integers* because they follow each other when we count by twos, beginning with 7.

EXAMPLE 2
Write an expression for the sum of an integer and three times the next larger integer.

Let $x =$ an integer
$(x + 1) =$ the next larger integer
$x + 3(x + 1) =$ the sum of an integer and three times the next integer

Try This
a. $\frac{1}{2}g + g$ or $b + 2b$

Try This

b. Write an expression for the sum of three consecutive odd integers.

PART 2 Using Equations to Solve Problems

Objective: Solve problems by writing and solving equations.

You can use the Problem-Solving Guidelines on page 155 to help you solve problems when your plan involves writing and solving an equation.

EXAMPLE 3

Manuel scored 35 points fewer in his second bowling game than in his first game. His total score for two games was 395. How many points did he score in each game?

■ **UNDERSTAND the problem**

Question: How many points did Manuel score in each game?
Data: The total for the 2 games was 395. In the second game, he scored
      35 points fewer than in the first.

We can show this in a diagram.

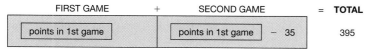

FIRST GAME	+	SECOND GAME	=	TOTAL
points in 1st game		points in 1st game − 35		395

■ **Develop and carry out a PLAN**

Let f = points in the first game.
$f - 35$ = points in the second game

The points for the second game are expressed in terms of points for the first game. Therefore, let the variable represent the points in the first game.

$$f + (f - 35) = 395$$
$$2f - 35 = 395$$
$$2f - 35 + 35 = 395 + 35$$
$$2f = 430$$
$$\tfrac{1}{2} \cdot 2f = \tfrac{1}{2} \cdot 430$$
$$f = 215$$

Second game = $f - 35 = 215 - 35 = 180$

■ **Find the ANSWER and CHECK**

Manuel scored 215 points in the first game and 180 points in the second game.

If we estimate by rounding we get $200 + 200 = 400$. The answer seems reasonable.

Teach the Mathematics (continued)

2. Write an expression for the sum of an even integer and the next even integer.
   Assume x is an even integer. Then $x + 2$ is the next even integer and the sum is $x + (x + 2)$ or $2x + 2$.

2 Using Equations to Solve Problems

Remind students to estimate whether their answers are reasonable and to see that they are labeled correctly.
   Before working Try This Exercise **c**, students may need to review the formula for finding the perimeter of a rectangle.

Key Question

■ Ask students to estimate answers and give units, if any, for Try This Exercises **c**, **d**, and **e**.

Chalkboard Example

1. The local bank pays 8% yearly interest on deposits. The interest is added into the account at the end of the year. How much money should be invested now, in order to have $972 at the end of the year?
   Let p be the amount of dollars to be invested. At the end of one year there will be
   $$p + 0.08p$$
   in the account, hence
   $$p + 0.08p = 972$$
   $$1.08p = 972$$
   $$p = \tfrac{972}{1.08} = 900$$
   $900 should be invested now.

Try This

b. $x + x + 2 + x + 4 = 3x + 6$

LESSON QUIZ

1. The height of a table is 1.5 times the height of the seat of a chair. Write an expression for the difference between the height of the table and the height of the chair.

   Let c be the height of the chair.

   $1.5c - c$ or $0.5c$

2. Write an expression for the sum of an integer plus twice the next integer.

   Let n be the integer.

   $n + 2(n + 1)$ or $3n + 2$

3. If you add one fifth of a number to that number you get 42. What is the number?

   Let n be the number.

   $\frac{1}{5}n + n = 42$

   $\frac{6}{5}n = 42$

   $n = \frac{5}{6} \cdot 42 = 35$

Assignment Guide

To provide flexible scheduling, this lesson can be split into parts.

▼ Core 1–11
   Extension 12–14
▼ Core 15–20, 22–37, 40
   Extension 21, 38, 39, 41, 42

Use Mixed Review to maintain skills.

Try This   Solve.

c. The perimeter of a rectangle is 150 cm. The length is 15 cm greater than the width. Find the dimensions.

d. The sum of an integer and twice the next consecutive integer is 29. What are the integers?

e. Mrs. Lee deposited a sum of money in a savings account that pays 4% interest per year. At the end of one year, Mrs. Lee had a total of $9620 in the account. How much did she invest originally?

 ***Extra Help On the Web***

Look for worked-out examples at the Prentice Hall Web site.
www.phschool.com

3-11 Exercises

A

1. A CD costs $3.50 more than a tape. Write an expression for the total cost of 1 CD and 1 tape.

2. The second math test was worth half as many points as the first test. Write an expression for the total number of points on the 2 tests.

3. There are 9 fewer math books than English books. Write an expression for the total number of books.

4. There are 12 more history books than science books. Write an expression for the total number of books.

5. A hardback book cost $7 more than a paperback book. Write an expression for the total cost of 1 paperback book and 3 hardback books.

6. A large drink costs 50¢ more than a small drink. Write an expression for the total cost of 3 small drinks and 2 large drinks.

Write an expression for each of the following.

7. the sum of an even integer and the next even integer

8. the sum of an odd integer and the next odd integer

9. the sum of an even integer and two times the next even integer

10. the sum of an integer and three times the next integer

11. the sum of an even integer and the next two even integers

12. the sum of $\frac{1}{4}$ of an integer, $\frac{1}{5}$ of the next integer, and $\frac{1}{2}$ of the following integer

13. the sum of an even integer, $\frac{1}{2}$ of the next even integer, and $\frac{1}{4}$ of the following even integer

14. the sum of an odd integer, $\frac{3}{4}$ of the next odd integer, and two times the following odd integer

Solve.

15. The sum of a number and $\frac{2}{5}$ of itself is 56. What is the number?

16. If you add one third of a number to the number itself, you get 48. What is the number?

Try This

c. Width is 30 cm; length is 45 cm
d. 9, 10
e. $9250

Exercises

Answers may vary depending on which quantity the variable represents.

1. Let c = cost of one CD.
   $c + (c - 3.50)$ or $2c - 3.50$
   Let t = cost of one tape.
   $t + (t + 3.50)$ or $2t + 3.50$

2. Let t = points on first test.
   $t + \frac{1}{2}t$ or $\frac{3}{2}t$
   Let s = points on second test.
   $s + 2s$ or $3s$

3. Let e = number of English books.
   $e + (e - 9)$ or $2e - 9$
   Let m = number of math books.
   $m + (m + 9)$ or $2m + 9$

4. Let s = number of science books.
   $s + (s + 12)$ or $2s + 12$
   Let h = number of history books.
   $h + (h - 12)$ or $2h - 12$

5. Let p = cost of paperback book.
   $p + 3(p + 7)$ or $4p + 21$
   Let h = cost of hardback book.
   $3h + (h - 7)$ or $4h - 7$

6. Let s = cost of small drink.
   $3s + 2(s + 50)$ or $5s + 100$
   Let l = cost of large drink.
   $2l + 3(l - 50)$ or $5l - 150$

7. $x + (x + 2) = 2x + 2$
8. $x + (x + 2) = 2x + 2$

17. The sum of two consecutive odd integers is 76. What are the integers?

18. The sum of two consecutive even integers is 106. What are the integers?

19. The sum of three consecutive integers is 126. What are the integers?

20. The sum of three consecutive odd integers is 189. What are the integers?

21. *Critical Thinking*   Redo Exercise 19. Let x be the second of the three consecutive integers. Then redo Exercise 20 using a similar procedure.

22. The perimeter of a rectangle is 310 m. The length is 25 m greater than the width. What are the length and the width of this rectangle?

23. One angle of a triangle is 4 times as large as another. The third angle is equal to the sum of the other two angles. What is the measure of the smallest angle? (Hint: The sum of the measures of the angles of a triangle is 180°.)

24. *Critical Thinking*   Abraham Lincoln's 1863 Gettysburg Address refers to the year 1776 as "four score and seven years ago." Write an equation and solve for a score.

25. The combined lengths of the Nile and Amazon rivers is 13,108 km. If the Amazon were 234 km longer, it would be as long as the Nile. What is the length of each river?

26. In 1999, tennis-playing sisters Venus and Serena Williams earned a total of $4,921,107. If Venus had earned $289,097 more, she would have earned the same as Serena. How much did each earn?

27. A 48-ft wire is cut into three pieces. The second piece is three times as long as the first piece. The third piece is four times as long as the second piece. How long is each piece?

28. Mrs. Gutierrez borrowed some money. At the end of the year, she repaid the loan plus 10.5% of the original amount for interest. She paid back a total of $8287.50. How much money did she borrow originally?

29. Mr. Horvath put some money into a savings account and deposited no more into this account for one year. At the end of the year, there was $6272 in the account, including 6% of the original amount for interest. How much did he deposit originally?

30. After a 20% discount, an item was sold for $9600. What was the original price of the item?

31. The population of the United States in 1998 was estimated to be 270 million. This was a 79% increase over the population in 1950. What was the population in 1950, to the nearest million?

32. The number of students, ages 5 to 17 years, enrolled in school in 1970 was 45.6 million. The number enrolled in 1995 was 3.3% less than in 1970.

  a. How many students were enrolled in 1995?

  b. Can you tell which year had the greater percentage of students in this age group in school? Explain.

FOUR SCORE AND SEVEN YEARS AGO OUR FATHERS BROUGHT FORTH ON THIS CONTINENT A NEW NATION CONCEIVED IN LIBERTY AND DEDICATED TO THE PROPOSITION THAT ALL MEN ARE CREATED EQUAL · NOW WE ARE ENGAGED IN A GREAT CIVIL WAR TESTING WHETHER THAT NATION OR ANY NATION SO CONCEIVED AND SO DEDICATED CAN LONG ENDURE · WE ARE MET ON A GREAT BATTLEFIELD OF THAT WAR · WE HAVE COME TO DEDICATE A PORTION OF THAT FIELD A FINAL RESTING PLACE FOR THOSE WHO HERE GAVE THEIR LIVES THAT NATION MIGHT LIVE

How many score years ago did Lincoln give his Gettysburg Address? (See Exercise 24.)

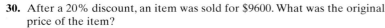

9. $x + 2(x + 2) = 3x + 4$

10. $x + 3(x + 1) = 4x + 3$

11. $x + (x + 2) + (x + 4) = 3x + 6$

12. $\frac{1}{4}x + \frac{1}{5}(x + 1) + \frac{1}{2}(x + 2) = \frac{19}{20}x + \frac{6}{5}$

13. $x + \frac{1}{2}(x + 2) + \frac{1}{4}(x + 4) = \frac{7}{4}x + 2$

14. $x + \frac{3}{4}(x + 2) + 2(x + 4) = \frac{15}{4}x + \frac{19}{2}$

15. 40

16. 36

17. 37, 39

18. 52, 54

19. 41, 42, 43

20. 61, 63, 65

21. 41, 42, 43; 61, 63, 65

22. 65 m, 90 m

23. 18°

24. $4s + 7 = 1863 - 1776$; $s = 20$

Photo caption: 7 score years in 2003

25. Amazon 6437 km, Nile 6671 km

26. Venus $2,316,005; Serena $2,605,102

27. 3 ft, 9 ft, 36 ft

28. $7500

29. $5916.98

30. $12,000

31. 151 million

32. a. 44.1 million

  b. No; you need to know the total number of students in this age group.

B

33. One number is 25% of another. The larger number is 12 more than the smaller. Both numbers are positive. What are the numbers?

34. If the daily rental for a car is $38.90, and a person must drive 190 miles and stay within a $100.00 budget, what is the highest price per mile the person can afford?

35. Jane scored 78 on a test that had 4 seven-point fill-ins and 24 three-point multiple-choice questions. She had one fill-in wrong. How many multiple-choice answers did she get right?

36. The width of a rectangle is $\frac{3}{4}$ the length. The perimeter of the rectangle becomes 50 cm when the length and width are each increased by 2 cm. Find the length and width.

37. Phone charges are $13.72 per month plus 13¢ per call and 8¢ per minute. How much did it cost one month for 35 calls totaling 172 minutes?

Challenge

38. In a basketball league, the Falcons won 15 of their first 20 games. If they win only half the time from now on, how many more games will they have to play in order to win 60% of the total games?

39. *Error Analysis*   In one city, a city sales tax of 9% was added to the gasoline price registered on the pump. What, if anything, is wrong with each scenario?

   a. At one station, a driver asked for $10 worth. The attendant filled the tank until the pump read $9.10 and charged the driver $10.00.

   b. On Tuesdays, this gas station gives 9% off the total cost to the customer. On one Tuesday, the attendant simply collected the amount that registered on the pump.

40. The buyer of a piano priced at $2000 is given the choice of paying cash at the time of purchase or $2150 at the end of one year. What rate of interest is being charged if payment is made at the end of one year?

41. If you receive 7% interest on savings, but 20% tax is charged on the interest, how much do you have left from an initial $1000 deposit?

42. A storekeeper goes to the bank to get $10 worth of change. He requests twice as many quarters as half dollars, twice as many dimes as quarters, three times as many nickels as dimes, and no pennies or dollars. How many of each coin did the storekeeper get?

Mixed Review

Solve. **43.** $7x = 10$ **44.** $7a - 9a = 6$ **45.** $-8w + 13w = 45$

46. $8c + 6 = 6c + 10$ **47.** $15 - (5m - 6) = 1$ **48.** $\frac{3}{4}b = 9$ *3-2, 3-5*

Solve. **49.** $\frac{3}{4}a - 6 = 3 + \frac{1}{2}a$ **50.** $\frac{3}{5}y + 2 = \frac{1}{2}y$ *3-5, 3-6*

Exercises

33. 4, 16
34. 32¢
35. 19
36. 12 cm, 9 cm
37. $32.03
38. 30
39. a. The driver owed only
      $9.10 + (0.09)(9.10) \approx \$9.92$.
    b. If the pump registered $10,
      the driver owed
      $10 + (0.09)10 = \$10.90$,
      less the 9% discount, or
      $10.90 - (0.09)(10.90)$
      $= \$9.92$.

40. 7.5%
41. $1056
42. 5 half dollars, 10 quarters, 20 dimes, 60 nickels

Mixed Review

43. $\frac{10}{7}$
44. -3
45. 9
46. 2
47. 4
48. 12
49. 36
50. -20

CA 24.0: Use and know simple aspects of a logical argument.

Reasoning Strategies

 **3-12**

 PART 1 Make an Organized List

Objective: Solve problems using the strategy
Make an Organized List **and other strategies.**

PROBLEM-SOLVING GUIDELINES
■ UNDERSTAND the problem
▨ Develop and carry out a PLAN
■ Find the ANSWER and CHECK

Some problems can be solved by listing information in a systematic or organized way. This strategy for solving problems is called *Make an Organized List.*

EXAMPLE   Use the strategy *Make an Organized List* to solve this problem. The team that wins 3 games in a "best-3-of-5" basketball playoff wins the playoff. In how many ways can a team win 3 games?

We can solve this problem by first listing all of the ways to win if there are no losses. Next we will list the ways if there is 1 loss and then the ways with 2 losses. Listing the possibilities according to the number of losses keeps the list organized. After the list is organized, we can tell when we have listed all possibilities.

WWW	1 way to win 3 games with 0 losses
LWWW WLWW WWLW	3 ways to win 3 games with 1 loss
LLWWW LWLWW LWWLW WLLWW WLWLW WWLLW	6 ways to win 3 games with 2 losses
1 + 3 + 6 = 10	There are 10 ways to win 3 games in the playoff.

Reasoning Strategies

Draw a Diagram	Try, Test, Revise	Write an Equation
Make an Organized List	Use Logical Reasoning	Make a Table
Look for a Pattern	Simplify the Problem	Work Backward

What You'll Learn

▼ To solve problems using the strategy *Make an Organized List* and other strategies

...And Why

To increase efficiency in solving problems by applying reasoning skills

 CA: 24.0

 **3-12** TIME-FOCUS METER

1. FOCUS

FIRST FIVE MINUTES

1. Jody drives 10 miles north, 20 miles east, 10 miles south, and 5 miles west. How far is she from where she started? 15 miles

2. TEACH the Mathematics

▼ **Make an Organized List**

Stress that the key to a successful list is organization. It may be necessary for students to try several different ways of organizing data before they find a way that leads to a solution. Use the example in the text to show an organized approach to making a list.

Key Questions

■ How many games must a team win to win the playoff? 3
■ What is the greatest number of games a team could lose and still win the playoff? 2
■ What is the least number of games a team could play in order to win?
3, if it wins all 3

Chalkboard Example

1. In Mr. Dismond's math class there are 4 tests and a final exam. To get an A in the class, a student must get an A on the final exam and on at least 2 tests, and a B or better on the remaining tests. How many ways are there to get an A?
First, list the ways to get an A if the student gets no Bs. Then list the ways if the student gets one B, then the ways if the student gets 2 Bs. The student must get an A on the final exam, so the italicized grade is always an A.
AAAA*A*
BAAA*A* ABAA*A* AABA*A* AAAB*A*
AABB*A* ABAB*A* BAAB*A* ABBA*A* BABA*A*
BBAA*A*
There are 11 ways to get an A in the class.

3. PRACTICE/ASSESS

Hints for Problems

1. Make an organized list of all the teams each team would play. How many times does each team play the other team?
2. Try a number of cartons with 2 rackets in each. Test and revise your guess.
3. Draw diagrams to represent different arrangements.
4. Make an organized list of different combinations.
5. Try two factors of 120 as dimensions, test perimeter, and revise. Compare the perimeters.
6. Try five items, test cost, revise your guess. Can you find more than one solution?
7. Draw a calendar. Circle each day off that Charles has. Mark each day off that Eva has.
8. Try a number for large calculators, then find the number of small calculators and the total cost. Revise your guess.

Assignment Guide
▼ Core 1–5, 7, 8
  Extension 6

Use Mixed Review to maintain skills.

Problems

1. There will be 72 games played when each team has played each other team twice.
2. Fourteen cartons of 2 rackets each and 24 cartons of 3 rackets each were used to pack 100 rackets.

3. a. 1
   b. 3
   c. 5
   d. 12

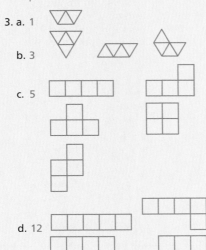

164 Chapter 3 *Equations*

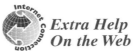

Extra Help On the Web

Look for worked-out examples at the Prentice Hall Web site.
www.phschool.com

Practice Multiple Choice

Choose the best answer.

1. A family spent $420 for food in one month. This was 27% of their income. What was their income?

A $113.40
B $1134.00
C $1555.56
D $1680.00

2. A 63-ft wire was cut into three pieces. The second piece is 5 times as long as the first piece. The third piece is 3 times as long as the second piece. How long is the first piece?

F 7 ft
G 51 ft
H 3 ft
J $7\frac{7}{8}$ ft

1. C; Algebra 5.0
2. H; Algebra 5.0

▶ 3-12 Problems

Solve using one or more problem-solving strategies.

1. There are 9 teams that play in a soccer league. During the season each team will play each other team in the league twice. How many games will be played?

2. Tennis rackets can be packaged in cartons holding 2 rackets each or in cartons holding 3 rackets each. Yesterday's packing slip showed that 38 cartons were used to pack a total of 100 rackets. How many cartons of each size were used yesterday?

3. In how many *different* ways can you arrange the shapes in each set so that at least one side of each shape is completely touching one side of another shape, and all shapes are adjacent? Sketch each arrangement. (Arrangements you can turn or flip to match each other count as one arrangement.)

   a. 3 equilateral triangles   **b.** 4 equilateral triangles
   c. 4 squares   **d.** 5 squares

4. A vending machine had to be programmed to accept any combination of nickels, dimes, and quarters that totals 40¢. How many different combinations are possible?

5. A garden plot has an area of 120 square meters. The measures of the length and width are whole numbers. The length and width of the garden were selected so that the least amount of fencing would be required to enclose the garden. What are the dimensions of this garden?

6. A sporting goods store was having a sale. One customer bought 5 different items and paid $120, not including tax. He could have chosen any of the items listed in the chart below. What combination of 5 items could he have bought?

■ soccer shoes $25	■ jogging suits $35	■ sweat shirts $15
■ basketballs $20	■ swimsuits $10	■ softball bats $15
■ leg weights $45	■ racquetball racket $40	■ tennis outfit $50

7. Charles and Eva want to have a party for their friends. Both work at night. Charles has every ninth night off from work, and Eva has every fifth night off. Today is Sunday and Charles is off work. Eva has tomorrow night off. When is the first night they would both be available to have the party?

8. ***Write a Convincing Argument***   Solve the problem below. Then write an argument that would convince a classmate that your solution is correct.

   A school club sold calculators to raise money for a field trip. The members sold small calculators for $5 each and large desk-top calculators for twice as much as the small calculators. At the end of the sale, they sold three times as many small calculators as large calculators for a total of $600. How many of each size calculator did they sell?

4. There are 7 different combinations possible.
5. The garden's measurements were 10 m by 12 m.
6. Some possible solutions:
   a. soccer shoes ($25) + leg weights ($45) + sweat shirt ($15) + softball bat ($15) + basketball ($20) = $120
   b. tennis outfit ($50) + basketball ($20) + swimsuit ($10) + sweat shirt ($15) + soccer shoes ($25) = $120
   c. tennis outfit ($50) + basketball ($20) + swimsuit ($10) + softball bat ($15) + soccer shoes ($25) = $120
   d. racquetball racket ($40) + basketball ($20) + jogging suit ($35) + swimsuit ($10) + softball bat ($15) = $120
   e. racquetball racket ($40) + basketball ($20) + jogging suit ($35) + swimsuit ($10) + sweat shirt ($15) = $120
7. Charles and Eva will both be off on a Monday 5 weeks later.
8. 24 large, 72 small

3 ▷ Chapter Wrap Up

3-1

To solve an equation using the **addition property of equality,** you add the same number to both sides of the equation.

Solve.

1. $x + 12 = -8$

2. $-7 = y - 11$

3. $x - 11 = 14$

4. $w + \frac{3}{7} = -\frac{5}{7}$

Translate to an equation and solve.

5. A color TV sold for $629 in May. This was $38 more than the price in January. Find the January price.

6. In La Ciudad Fría the average daily high temperature in the winter is $-65°F$. This is $150°$ less than the average daily high temperature in Ciudad Caliente. What is the average daily high temperature in Ciudad Caliente in the winter?

3-2

To solve an equation using the **multiplication property of equality,** you multiply both sides of the equation by the same nonzero number.

Solve.

7. $6x = 24$

8. $-\frac{x}{4} = 48$

9. $\frac{3}{5} = \frac{-2}{5}x$

10. $-11x = 121$

Translate to an equation and solve.

11. Rosita gets a $4 commission for each small appliance that she sells. One week she got $108 in commissions. How many small appliances did she sell?

3-3

To solve an equation, you may need to use both the addition and multiplication properties of equality. Collect like terms on each side of the equation before using the properties. You may need to use the distributive property to remove parentheses before collecting like terms.

Solve and check.

12. $2x + 5 = 13$

13. $-8x + 3 = 27$

14. $50 - 4x = 14$

15. $7x + 8x = 45$

16. $4(3y + 2) = 44$

17. $6(3a - 2) + 5a = 57$

Chapter 3 Wrap Up

1. -20
2. 4
3. 25
4. $-\frac{8}{7}$
5. 591
6. $85°$
7. 4
8. -192
9. $-\frac{3}{2}$
10. -11
11. 27
12. 4
13. -3
14. 9
15. 3
16. 3
17. 3

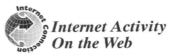

**Internet Activity
On the Web**

Look for extension problems
for this chapter at the
Prentice Hall Web site.
www.phschool.com

3-4

Use the Problem-Solving Guidelines to help you understand a problem, write
an equation, and check your solution.

Write as an algebraic expression.

18. 6 more than twice a number

19. 18 less than the product of 5 and a number

20. 6 less than $\frac{1}{3}$ of the number

21. $\frac{1}{2}$ of the sum of a number and 10

22. Betsy swims every day. She swam 3 fewer laps today than twice the
number of laps she swam yesterday. Write an expression for the number
of laps she swam today.

23. After 8 weeks at the exercise club, Nadia could lift 10 pounds more than
twice what she could lift before joining the club. Write an expression for
the weight Nadia could lift after 8 weeks at the club.

24. The number of girls in the swim club is 5 less than twice the number of
boys. There are 75 girls in the club. How many boys are in the club?

25. Chris has ridden her bike 10 miles. She averages 12 mi/h. How many more
minutes must she ride before she has traveled 60 miles?

26. If the Menlo High football team scored 4 more points in Friday night's
game, they would have tripled the score of Woodside High. Woodside
scored 14 points. How many points did Menlo score?

3-5

To solve an equation, you must get all variable terms on the same side of the
equation. If the equation contains parentheses, you may need to use the
distributive property first. An **identity** is an equation that is true for all
acceptable replacements of the variables.

Solve.

27. $6x - 5 = -2x + 11$

28. $3y - 6 - 7y = 12 - 2y + 6$

29. $4(x + 3) = 36$

30. $8(x - 2) = 5(x + 4)$

31. $x + 7 - 2 = 5 + x$

32. $2(x + 3) - 3x = 5 - x + 1$

3-6

To clear an equation of fractions, multiply both sides of the equation by the
least common denominator. To clear an equation of decimals, multiply both
sides of the equation by a power of 10.

Solve.

33. $\frac{3}{4}x + \frac{1}{2}x + \frac{1}{4} = 1 + 2x$

34. $12.21 - 4.3a = 24.25$

35. $\frac{4}{9}y - \frac{4}{3} = \frac{1}{6}y + \frac{11}{18}$

36. $0.83w + 0.29 = 0.5w - 0.7$

166   Chapter 3   *Equations*

Chapter 3 Wrap Up

18. $2n + 6$
19. $5n - 18$
20. $\frac{1}{3}n - 6$
21. $\frac{1}{2}(n + 10)$
22. $2n - 3$
23. $2x + 10$
24. 40
25. 4 h 10 min or 250 min
26. 38
27. 2
28. -12
29. 6

30. 12
31. true for all values of x; an
    identity
32. true for all values of x; an
    identity
33. -1
34. -2.8
35. 7
36. -3

3-7

To solve a formula for a given variable, use the same rules you use to solve equations.

Solve.

37. $V = Bh$ for h

38. $b = \frac{3A}{r}$ for A

39. $P = 2x + 2w$ for x

40. $V = \frac{1}{3}Ar$ for A

3-8

To solve an equation involving absolute value, remember that the absolute value of a number is its distance from 0 on a number line. If $|a| = 3$, then $a = 3$ or -3.

Solve.

41. $|x| = 5$

42. $|x| - 4 = 6$

43. $-9 + 3|y| = 24$

3-9

An equation that states two **ratios** are equal is called a **proportion.** Some problems can be solved by writing and solving a proportion.

Solve.

44. $\frac{b}{42} = \frac{6}{7}$

45. $\frac{45}{15} = \frac{30}{x}$

Translate to a proportion and solve.

46. The winner of an election for class president won by a vote of 3 to 2, having received 324 votes. How many votes did the other candidates get?

47. A student traveled 234 km in 14 days. At this rate, how far would the student travel in 42 days?

3-10

The ratio of a number to 100 is called **percent.** When solving problems involving percent, the percent should be expressed as a fraction or a decimal. To find the **percent of increase** (or **decrease**), divide the amount of increase (or decrease) by the original amount.

Write as a decimal.

48. 48%

49. 7%

50. 150%

Express as a percent. Round to the nearest tenth if necessary.

51. $\frac{1}{3}$

52. $\frac{7}{8}$

53. 0.012

Solve.

54. 60 is what percent of 150?

55. 75% of what number is 187.5?

56. Sales tax in a certain city is 6.5% of the cost. What would the sales tax be on a motorcycle that costs $850?

57. A Shea CD player cost $80 last year and $112 this year. What was the percent of increase in its price?

37. $h = \frac{V}{B}$

38. $A = \frac{br}{3}$

39. $x = \frac{P - 2w}{2}$

40. $A = \frac{3V}{r}$

41. 5, −5

42. 10, −10

43. 11, −11

44. 36

45. 10

46. 216

47. 702 km

48. 0.48

49. 0.07

50. 1.5

51. 33.3%

52. 87.5%

53. 1.2%

54. 40%

55. 250

56. $55.25

57. 40%

3-11

To solve a problem with more than one unknown quantity, you may be able to represent all of the unknown quantities in terms of one variable. First decide which unknown quantity the variable will represent.

58. An adult's ticket to the movie theater costs twice as much as a child's ticket. Write an expression for the cost of admission for one child and one adult.

59. Write an expression for the sum of two consecutive even integers.

Translate to an equation and solve.

60. The sum of two consecutive odd integers is 116. Find the integers.

61. The perimeter of a rectangle is 56 cm. The width is 6 cm less than the length. Find the width and the length.

3 ▷ Chapter Assessment

Solve.

1. $x + 7 = 15$ **2.** $t - 9 = 17$

3. $3x = -18$ **4.** $-7x = -28$

5. $-\frac{x}{8} = 5$ **6.** $-\frac{2}{3}y = -\frac{4}{15}$

7. $8a + 11 = 35$ **8.** $-4y + 7 = -21$

9. $3(x + 2) = 27$ **10.** $45 - 3x = 30$

11. $3t + 7 = 2t - 5$ **12.** $-3x + 6(x + 4) = 9$

13. $0.51m + 0.03 = 0.4m - 0.74$ **14.** $\frac{1}{2}x - \frac{3}{5} = \frac{1}{10} + \frac{3}{10}$

15. $|x| + 3 = 8$ **16.** $2|y| - 4 = 8$

Write as an algebraic expression.

17. the number of days in x weeks

18. fifteen decreased by four times a number

19. the sum of two consecutive integers

20. two less than one fifth of a number

Solve the formulas for the given variable.

21. $A = 2\pi rh$ for r **22.** $b = \frac{2A}{h}$ for A

23. $P = 2x + 2w$ for x **24.** $V = \frac{1}{3}Ar$ for r

Chapter 3 Wrap Up

58. $2x + x = 3x$
59. $x + x + 2 = 2x + 2$
60. 57, 59
61. 11 cm, 17 cm

Chapter 3 Assessment

1. 8
2. 26
3. −6
4. 4
5. −40
6. $\frac{2}{5}$
7. 3
8. 7
9. 7
10. 5
11. −12
12. −5
13. −7
14. 2
15. 5, −5
16. 6, −6
17. $7x$
18. $15 - 4n$
19. $2x + 1$
20. $\frac{1}{5}x - 2$
21. $r = \frac{A}{2\pi h}$
22. $A = \frac{bh}{2}$
23. $x = \frac{P - 2w}{2}$
24. $r = \frac{3V}{A}$

Solve.

25. $\frac{16}{3} = \frac{c}{12}$ **26.** $\frac{21}{x} = \frac{105}{5}$

Translate to a proportion and solve.

27. A sample of 184 light bulbs contained 6 defective bulbs. At this rate, how many defective bulbs would you expect to find in a sample of 1288 light bulbs?

28. In traveling 350 miles, Raul used 21 gallons of gas. How many gallons of gas would Raul use on a trip of 525 miles if his car consumed gas at the same rate?

Write as a decimal.

29. 89% **30.** 3% **31.** 200%

Express as a percent. Round off to the nearest tenth of a percent if necessary.

32. $\frac{2}{5}$ **33.** $\frac{2}{3}$

Solve.

34. 96 is what percent of 150?

35. 90% of what number is 45?

36. 87.5% of 200 is what number?

37. A family spends $660 a month for rent. This is 30% of the family's monthly income. What is their monthly income?

Translate to an equation and solve.

38. Jim scored 22 points in a basketball game. That was six points more than Frank scored. How many points did Frank score?

39. A carpenter worked on a job for 5 days and earned $440. How much did he earn per day?

40. Marisa and Lisa earned a total of $65 babysitting during the month of November. Marisa earned $5 more than $\frac{1}{2}$ of what Lisa earned. How much did they each earn?

41. The perimeter of a rectangle is 36 cm. The length is 4 cm greater than the width. Find the width and length.

42. Money is invested in a "guaranteed fund" at 12% simple interest. After one year, there is $840 in the account. How much was originally invested?

25. 64
26. 1
27. 42 defective bulbs
28. 31.5 gallons
29. 0.89
30. 0.03
31. 2.00 or 2
32. 40%
33. 66.7%
34. 64%
35. 50
36. 175
37. $2200
38. 16
39. $88
40. Lisa $40, Marisa $25
41. 7 cm, 11 cm
42. $750

CHAPTER 4 ▷ Inequalities

CHAPTER AT A GLANCE

4-1	Inequalities and Their Graphs	pp. 172–174

CA 1
- ▼ Solutions of Inequalities
- ▼ Graphing Inequalities

4-2	The Addition Property of Inequalities	pp. 175–179

CA 5
- ▼ Using the Addition Property

4-3	The Multiplication Property of Inequalities	pp. 180–182

CA 5
- ▼ Using the Multiplication Property

California Practice

4-4	Using the Properties Together	pp. 183–186

CA 5
- ▼ Solving Two-Step Inequalities

4-5	Using Inequalities	pp. 187–191

CA 5,24, 24.1, 24.2, 24.3
- Translating Phrases to Inequalities
- ▼ Solving Problems

4-6	Reasoning Strategies: Use Logical Reasoning	pp. 194–195

CA 24
- ▼ Use Logical Reasoning

California Practice

PACING OPTIONS

This chart suggests pacing only for the lessons and their parts. It is provided as a possible guide.
It will help you determine how much time you have in your schedule to cover other features, such as the Chapter Wrap Up and Assessment.

	Day 1	Day 2	Day 3	Day 4	Day 5	Day 6	Day 7	Day 8	Day 9	Day 10	Day 11	
Traditional (40–45 min. class periods)	4-1 ▼	4-1 ▼²	4-2 ▼	4-3 ▼	4-4 ▼	4-5 ▼	4-5 ▼²	4-6 ▼				
Algebra 1 Over 2 Years (40–45 min. class periods)	4-1 ▼	4-1 ▼	4-1 ▼²	4-1 ▼²	4-2 ▼	4-2 ▼	4-3 ▼	4-3 ▼	4-4 ▼	4-4 ▼	4-4 ▼	
Block Scheduling (90 min. class periods)	4-1 ▼ / 4-1 ▼²	4-2 ▼ / 4-3 ▼	4-4 ▼ / 4-5 ▼	4-5 ▼² / 4-6 ▼								

170A

SKILLS TRACE

SKILL	FOUNDATION	DEVELOPED IN LESSONS	REVIEWED/REINFORCED/EXTENDED
Determining if a number is a solution of an inequality	1-1	**4-1**	9-5
Graphing inequalities on the number line	2-1	**4-1**	9-1, 9-5
Using addition and multiplication properties of inequalities	3-1 through 3-3	**4-2 through 4-4**	Used throughout the text
Solving problems using inequalities	1-8, 1-10, 2-9	**4-5**	9-6
Using strategies in solving problems	3-10 through 3-12	**4-6**	Used throughout the text, at least once per chapter

CORRELATION TO STANDARDIZED TESTS

 YOUR LOCAL TEST*

Lesson		CAT5	CTBS/5 TerraNova™	ITED	MAT7	SAT9		CA Algebra
4-1	Inequalities and Their Graphs	■						1.0
4-2	The Addition Property of Inequalities	■						5.0
4-3	The Multiplication Property of Inequalities					■		5.0
4-4	Using the Properties Together					■		5.0
4-5	Using Inequalities	■			■			5.0, 24.0, 24.1, 24.2, 24.3
4-6	Reasoning Strategies: Use Logical Reasoning	■	■					24.0

CAT5 California Achievement Test, 5th Edition
CTBS/5 Comprehensive Test of Basic Skills, 5th Edition
ITED Iowa Test of Educational Development
    Level 15, Complete Battery, Form M

MAT7 Metropolitan Achievement Test, 7th Edition
SAT 9 Stanford Achievement Test/Task 1

For other standardized test correlations, follow the link to your state at **www.phschool.com**.

*See pp. T34–T39 for the California Standards.

Day 12	Day 13	Day 14	Day 15	Day 16	Day 17	Day 18	Day 19	Day 20	Day 21	Day 22	Day 23	Day 24
5 ▽	4–5 ▽	4–5 ▽²	4–5 ▽²	4–6 ▽¹	4–6 ▽¹	4–6 ▽¹						

Math Background

Chapter Overview

The multiplication and addition properties of inequalities are introduced, and inequalities in one variable are solved. Since most inequalities have an infinite number of solutions, all solutions cannot be checked; however, a simple test is introduced to find computational errors. Conditional statements and logical reasoning are discussed. Bar and picture graphs are reviewed.

The translation and solution skills used to solve equations are adapted to the solution of inequalities. The strategy *Logical Reasoning* is added to the students' reasoning repertoire.

4-1 Inequalities and Their Graphs

Mathematical sentences containing $<$ (is less than) and $>$ (is greater than) are sometimes referred to as *strict inequalities* to distinguish them from sentences containing $\leq$ (is less than or equal to) and $\geq$ (is greater than or equal to). Students with experience in set theory may wonder if the *or* in these phrases is like the logical *or* representing set union. It is; $x \leq 3.65$ represents the union of the set of numbers less than 3.65 with the set whose only element is 3.65. The solutions to Exercises 33–35 use the logical *and* representing set intersection. Logical disjunctions and conjunctions (*or* and *and*) are treated in Chapter 9.

For an inequality such as $x \leq 3.65$, the endpoint 3.65 (called a boundary point in Lesson 4-2) belongs to the solution set and its graph is represented by a solid dot. For a strict inequality such as $x < 3.65$, the endpoint 3.65 does not belong to the solution set and its graph is represented by a hollow dot.

4-2 The Addition Property of Inequalities

The second statement of the addition property of inequalities can be obtained from the first by knowing that $a < b$ is equivalent to $b > a$. However, writing both forms reassures students that all possibilities have been considered.

Every inequality has a related equation, obtained by replacing the inequality symbol with an equal sign. The solution to this equation is the end or boundary point of the solution set of the inequality. Therefore, substituting into this equation the boundary point found in *solving the inequality* checks the accuracy of the boundary point.

It is impossible to check every value in an infinite solution set. However, once the boundary point has been verified, it is sufficient to check a representative or sample number from the supposed solution set. If the sample number checks, all numbers in that interval will satisfy the inequality and the inequality is solved correctly. The solution set includes the boundary point unless the inequality is a strict inequality. Solution sets composed of multiple intervals will be considered in Chapter 9.

Some students may ask about clearing an inequality of fractions. They may do this as long as they multiply by a positive number. Suggest that they wait until Lesson 4-3.

4-3 The Multiplication Property of Inequalities

Again, two of the statements in the multiplication property of inequalities can be obtained from the other two by knowing that $a < b$ is equivalent to $b > a$. However, it can help students to see all four statements.

If students have not discovered by now that 0 is the easiest sample number to use to check a solution set, point this out to them after Example 2. Zero can be used as a sample number either when it is in the solution set (the inequality will check) or when it is not in the solution set (the inequality will not check). Similarly, 1 is an easy sample number to use if 0 is not appropriate. For example, 0 may be a boundary point or may not be in the domain of the inequality.

4-4 Using the Properties Together

While it is not necessary, students may make fewer errors if they keep the coefficient of the variable positive when there are variable terms on both sides of an inequality. This is done in Example 2 but not in Example 3. In Example 3, adding $5y$ to both sides of the inequality would result in positive coefficient of y. This technique is also used in Exercise 53.

This lesson provides an opportunity to discuss clearing an inequality of fractions as is done in Exercise 55. For example, an inequality such as $\frac{x}{4} + \frac{1}{6} < \frac{1}{3}$ can be simplified by multiplying both sides by 12.

$$\frac{x}{4} + \frac{1}{6} < \frac{1}{3}$$
$$12 \cdot \frac{x}{4} + 12 \cdot \frac{1}{6} < 12 \cdot \frac{1}{3}$$
$$3x + 2 < 4$$

For an inequality such as $\frac{3}{5} - \frac{x}{4} > \frac{7}{20}$, it may be helpful to multiply both sides by a negative number to avoid getting a negative coefficient for x. Remind students to reverse the inequality when multiplying by a negative number.

$$\frac{3}{5} - \frac{x}{4} > \frac{7}{20}$$
$$-20 \cdot \frac{3}{5} - (-20) \cdot \frac{x}{4} < -20 \cdot \frac{7}{20}.$$
$$-12 + 5x < -7$$

This is one of the few occasions when the multiplication property of inequalities is applied before the addition property of inequalities. Most of Exercises 32–51 can be done in several ways. Encourage students to simplify inequalities as well as equations by clearing of fractions and decimals.

▶ 4-5 Using Inequalities

Students may find that money examples help them to determine the meanings of phrases such as *is at least*, *is no more than*, and so on. They can make a table showing the appropriate inequality symbol for each phrase.

exceeds	>
falls below	<
is at least	≥
is at most	≤
is no less than	≥
is no more than	≤

Students interested in logic may notice that *x is less than a* ($x < a$) and *x is no less than a* ($x \geq a$) are logical negations of each other, and describe the separation of the number line into two disjoint sets.

Connections: Deductive Reasoning

Deductive reasoning is the process of reasoning logically from given facts to a conclusion. Watch for opportunities to identify the hypothesis (the given facts) and the conclusions in conditional statements. In particular, you may wish to point out how the deductive reasoning model has been used in solving inequalities and equations, such as $3x - 2 = 10$. (If $3x - 2 = 10$, then $x = 4$.)

Connections: Inductive Reasoning

Inductive reasoning leads to conjectures based on patterns that are observed. Observation and conjectures are key elements in many mathematical situations and should regularly be encouraged. Students should be equally encouraged to look for counterexamples that prove conjectures false. Failure to find any counterexample provides support, but not proof, that the conjecture is indeed true. Interested students should be encouraged to look for proofs of the conjectures, or at least convincing arguments that provide further support.

Reasoning Strategies:
▶ 4-6 Use Logical Reasoning

The Example assumes that office holders are unique. This is an unstated, though not unreasonable, assumption. It is possible to design an exercise requiring the use of the strategy *Use Logical Reasoning* where the same person could be vice-president and secretary, or secretary and treasurer, and so on. Chalkboard Example 1 has no hidden assumptions.

Ask students to look for hidden assumptions in Problems 1–7. Here are some.

Each team has only one coach and each person coaches only one team.

3. The addresses include all the integers from 1 to 225.

7. The phrase *live in* implies one person lives in each town, though some may insist this is a hidden assumption. Without it, Scott can live anyplace but Springstown, and Nellie and Jeff could live in Springstown.

Also, as a review, ask if any earlier strategies would be useful in these problems. Here are some suggestions.

2, 3. *Make an Organized List.* (pretty daunting)

4. *Write an Equation.*

5. *Draw a Diagram.*

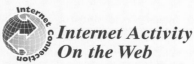

Internet Activity On the Web

For professional development tips visit our Web site.
www.phschool.com

Monitoring Progress

UNIVERSAL ACCESS

▶ Preventing a Student from Falling Behind

These resources are particularly helpful in preventing a student from falling behind his or her appropriate math level. For a complete list of resources for this chapter, see page 170F.

Before Lessons

Skills You Need for Chapter 4 (p. 170)

- Graphing on a number line
- Writing algebraic expressions
- Solving simple equations

Preteaching Math Vocabulary

- List of Key Terms (p. 170 and p. 196)
- Writing Math (p. 187)

Skills Intervention Kit With CD-ROM

With Lesson	Use this Unit
4-3	Operations with Fractions
4-1, 4-2, 4-3, 4-5	Pre-Algebra Basics

During Lessons

Try This Exercises (Student Edition)

Additional Examples (Teacher's Edition)

Help at Home

- Lessons 4-1 to 4-3
- Lessons 4-4 to 4-6
- Available in English and Spanish

Skills Intervention Kit

Innovative resource package for diagnosing students' gaps in basic skills, prescribing an individualized course of study, and monitoring progress. Eight intervention units cover core skills students need to succeed.

After Lessons

Lesson Quiz (Teacher's Edition)

Reteaching Worksheets (Teaching Resources Box)

Daily Cumulative Review Masters

There is a Daily Cumulative Review worksheet for every lesson in this chapter.

ASSESSMENT OPTIONS

Lesson	4-1	4-2	4-3	4-4	4-5	4-6	End
Try This Exercises	■	■	■	■	■		
Mixed Reviews	■	■	■	■	■		
Quizzes		■		■			
Chapter Assessment							■
Cumulative Review	A Cumulative Review for Chapters 1–4 is found on pp. 198–201.						
Standardized Test Prep		■		■	■		
Computer Item Generator CD-ROM	Can be used to create custom-made practice pages or assessment pages at any time.						
Student Tutorial CD-ROM	Students can self-assess and access tutorial help at any time.						

Test-Taking Tips on Transparencies

Test-Taking Tip: Choose "Answer Not Here"

Several strategies can help you determine that the correct answer is not given.

Example The wholesale price for a sweater is $19. The retail markup is 175%. On a 25%-off sale, how much profit is made on each sweater?

A. $52.25 B. $39.19 C. $33.25 D. $10.00 E. Not here

Compute the markup: $19 \times 1.75 = \$33.25$

Choice C is $33.25, but this is the full-price profit.

Work backward. Choices A and B are more than $33.25, so they are wrong.

Use mental math. The full price is $19 + 33.25 = \$52.25$.

Estimate the sale markdown: $52 \times 0.25 = \$13$.

The sale price should be about $52 − $13 = $39, so the sale profit is about $39 − 19 = $20.

The answer is not A, B, C, or D, so choose E.

Explain why the correct answer is not given.

1. Pam walks 300 yd north and 400 yd east to school. What is the shortest distance from school to home?

   A. 300 yd B. 400 yd C. 700 yd D. 350 yd E. Not Here

2. Juan drove 150 miles in 2.5 hours. At this rate, how long will it take Juan to drive 360 miles?

   A. 1 h B. 4.5 h C. 7.5 h D. 10 h E. Not Here

For use with Lesson 4-6

Resources for Chapter 4

TEACHING RESOURCES BOX

	First Five Minutes	Practice	Reteach	Enrichment	Problem Solving	Assessment	Cumulative Review	Lesson Planner		Success-Building	Teaching Transparencies	Help at Home	SE Answers on Transparencies
4-1	■	■	■	■			■	■		■ ■			■
4-2	■	■ ■	■			■	■	■		■ ■	■ ■		■
4-3	■	■	■				■	■			■	■	■
4-4	■	■	■	■		■	■	■					■
4-5	■	■ ■	■	■	■		■	■		■			■
4-6	■		■				■	■				■	■
End				■	■	5 Forms							■

Also available for use throughout the chapter:

Solution Key
Mathematics Standardized Test Prep
   Student Edition and Teacher's Edition

Overhead Manipulatives Kit
Practice Workbook

Student Manipulatives Kit
Test-Taking Tips on Transparencies

California Assessment Success Kit
Graphing Calculator Handbook

TECHNOLOGY

Computer Item Generator
CD-ROM with an unlimited supply of questions with varying degrees of difficulty for customized practice sheets, quizzes, and tests.

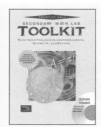

Secondary Math Toolkit™ with Integrated Math Labs
Integrated software package with linkable math tools for exploring key concepts.

Student Tutorial
Test preparation software for students on CD-ROM with management system for teachers; includes Secondary Math Lab Toolkit.

Resource Pro® with Planning Express®
CD-ROM with complete classroom planning tool and teaching resources for customizing and planning lessons.

Web Extension
www.phschool.com

For Students
- Chapter Support with Internet Links
- Internet Activities

For Teachers
- Curriculum Support
- Professional Development
- Product Information
- Regional Information

Also available for use throughout the chapter:
- Algebra Instructional Videos: A Step by Step Guide to Key Concepts

CHAPTER 4

What You'll Learn in Chapter 4

- How to graph inequalities

- How to solve inequalities in one variable

- How to write inequalities to solve problems

- How to use logical reasoning to solve problems

Skills & Concepts You Need for Chapter 4

2-2 Graph each number on the number line.

1. $\frac{5}{3}$ **2.** $\frac{2}{5}$ **3.** $-\frac{3}{4}$

Use the proper symbol $>$ or $<$.

4. $-\frac{3}{4} \ \square \ -\frac{2}{5}$ **5.** $-1.5 \ \square \ 0.65$ **6.** $\frac{3}{4} \ \square \ -2$

3-3 Solve.

7. $3x - 2 = 7$ **8.** $-6x + 4 = 28$
9. $40 - 2x = 26$ **10.** $5x + 3x = 64$
11. $2(5y + 3) = 56$ **12.** $8(3a + 5) + a = 65$

3-4 Write as an algebraic expression.

13. the sum of three consecutive even integers
14. one half of the number plus 12
15. thirty-two less than twice the number
16. two greater than 3 times a number

3-5 Solve.

17. $2x + 20 + 33x = 80 + 15x$ **18.** $3(2x - 1) + 4 = x + 25$
19. $14p - 10 = 8 + 2p$ **20.** $4(2x + 1) = 3(x + 13)$

Solve.

21. $\frac{b}{3} - 2 = 6$ **22.** $\frac{2}{9}b + \frac{1}{3}b = \frac{4}{9} - \frac{1}{3}b$

23. $0.9x - 0.5x = 6$ **24.** $0.32y = 0.3y + 32$

170

Skills & Concepts You Need for Chapter 4

1.

2.

3.

4. $<$
5. $<$
6. $>$
7. 3
8. -4
9. 7
10. 8
11. 5
12. 1
13. $n + n + 2 + n + 4$
14. $\frac{1}{2}n + 12$
15. $2n - 32$
16. $3n + 2$

17. 3
18. $\frac{24}{5}$
19. $\frac{3}{2}$
20. 7
21. 24
22. $\frac{1}{2}$
23. 15
24. 1600

Inequalities

Suppose peanuts cost $2.50/lb, almonds cost $5.60/lb, and cashews cost $7.60/lb. A 1-lb mixture has 8 oz of peanuts, 4 oz of almonds, and 4 oz of cashews. How much should the 1-lb mixture cost?

Photo Caption

$4.55

4-1

1. FOCUS

FIRST FIVE MINUTES

Fill in each blank with $<$, $>$, or $=$ to make each statement true.

1. 2 ___ 3 $2 < 3$
2. 5 ___ 4 $5 > 4$
3. 3 ___ -1 $3 > -1$
4. 5 ___ $\frac{10}{2}$ $5 = \frac{10}{2}$
5. -7 ___ -4 $-7 < -4$
6. -2 ___ -5 $-2 > -5$
7. $\frac{4}{7}$ ___ $\frac{11}{21}$ $\frac{4}{7} > \frac{11}{21}$

2. TEACH the Mathematics

1 Solutions of Inequalities

Point out that there can be infinitely many solutions for an inequality.

Key Questions

■ Is the statement $0 \leq 0$ true? Yes
■ Is the statement $0 \geq 0$ true? Yes
■ Is the statement $-1 \geq 1$ true? No
■ Is the statement $1 > 1$ true? No

Chalkboard Examples

1. Determine whether each number is a solution of $x \leq 7$.
   a. 3 Yes, because $3 \leq 7$ is true.
   b. -2 Yes, because $-2 \leq 7$ is true.
   c. 9 No, because $9 \leq 7$ is false.
   d. 7 Yes, because $7 \leq 7$ is true.

2 Graphing Inequalities

Chalkboard Examples

1. Graph $x > 5$ on the number line.

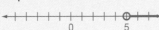

The solution is all points to the right of 5. Note that 5 is not included.

2. Graph $x \leq -1$ on the number line.

The solution is all points to the left of -1. Note that -1 is included.

What You'll Learn

▽ 1 To determine whether a number is a solution of an inequality

▽ 2 To graph inequalities on the number line

... And Why

To understand statements of inequality

CA 1.0: Use arithmetic properties of integers.

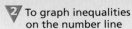

4-1 ▷ Inequalities and Their Graphs

Math in Action

The phrases italicized below are statements of inequality. An inequality tells the relationship between two numbers or expressions.

■ Motorized vehicles must be able to maintain a speed *greater than or equal to* 35 miles per hour to travel on most freeways.
■ Most elevators can carry a load *less than or equal to* 2000 pounds.

PART 1 Solutions of Inequalities

Objective: Determine whether a given number is a solution of an inequality.

In Chapter Two you learned the meaning of the symbols $<$ (is less than) and $>$ (is greater than). We now include the symbols $\leq$ and $\geq$.

> We read $\leq$ as "is less than or equal to."
> We read $\geq$ as "is greater than or equal to."

Mathematical sentences containing $<$, $>$, $\leq$, or $\geq$ are called **inequalities.**

A solution of an inequality is any number that makes the inequality true.

EXAMPLE 1   Determine whether each number is a solution of $x \geq 5$.

   5   Yes, 5 is a solution because $5 \geq 5$ is true.
   12   Yes, 12 is a solution because $12 \geq 5$ is true.
   -7 No, -7 is not a solution because $-7 \geq 5$ is not true.

Try This   Determine whether the given number is a solution of the inequality.

a. $x < 3$ (1) 2   (2) 0   (3) -5 (4) 15   (5) 3
b. $x \geq 6$ (1) 6   (2) 0   (3) -4 (4) 25   (5) -6

PART 2 Graphing Inequalities

Objective: Graph inequalities on the number line.

A **graph** of an inequality in one variable is a picture of its solution set on a number line.

Try This

a. (1) Yes
   (2) Yes
   (3) Yes
   (4) No
   (5) No
b. (1) Yes
   (2) No
   (3) No
   (4) Yes
   (5) No

c.

d.

Exercises

1. a. No   b. No
   c. No   d. Yes
2. a. Yes   b. No
   c. Yes   d. Yes
3. a. No   b. No
   c. Yes   d. Yes
4. a. Yes   b. Yes
   c. Yes   d. No

5. a. No   b. No
   c. Yes   d. No
6. a. Yes   b. No
   c. Yes   d. Yes
7. a. Yes   b. Yes
   c. Yes   d. No
8. a. Yes   b. Yes
   c. No   d. Yes

EXAMPLE 2 Graph $x < 2$ on a number line.

The solutions of $x < 2$ are all numbers less than 2. They are shown by shading all points to the left of 2 on a number line.

Note that 2 is not a solution. We indicate this by an open circle at 2. The red arrow indicates that all points to the left of 2 are solutions of the inequality.

EXAMPLE 3 Graph $x \geq -3$ on a number line.

The solutions of $x \geq -3$ are -3 and all points to the right of -3.

Note that -3 is a solution. We indicate this by a closed circle at -3. The red arrow indicates that all points to the right are also solutions of the inequality.

Try This Graph on a number line.

c. $x < 8$ **d.** $y \geq -5$

4-1 Exercises

A

Mental Math Determine whether the given number is a solution of the inequality.

1. $x > 4$ **a.** 4 **b.** 0 **c.** -4 **d.** 6
2. $y < 5$ **a.** 0 **b.** 5 **c.** -1 **d.** -5
3. $x \geq 6$ **a.** -6 **b.** 0 **c.** 6 **d.** 8
4. $x \leq 10$ **a.** 4 **b.** -10 **c.** 0 **d.** 11
5. $x < -8$ **a.** 0 **b.** -8 **c.** -9 **d.** -7
6. $x \geq 0$ **a.** 2 **b.** -3 **c.** 0 **d.** 3
7. $y \geq -5$ **a.** 0 **b.** -4 **c.** -5 **d.** -6
8. $y \leq -\frac{1}{2}$ **a.** -1 **b.** $-\frac{2}{3}$ **c.** 0 **d.** -0.5

Graph on a number line.

9. $x < 5$ 10. $y < 0$ 11. $t < -3$ 12. $h < -5$
13. $y > 6$ 14. $m > 4$ 15. $k \geq -4$ 16. $n \geq -2$
17. $x \leq 5$ 18. $g \leq 8$ 19. $b \leq -3$ 20. $c \leq -1$

Internet Connection
Extra Help On the Web
Look for worked-out examples at the Prentice Hall Web site.
www.phschool.com

Teach the Mathematics (continued)

Use Teaching Transparencies T14 and T1 to illustrate graphs of inequalities.

LESSON ENRICHMENT
True or false. Assume that x, y, and z are rational numbers.
  a. $x < x$ False
  b. If $x < y$ then $x \leq y$. True
  c. If $x < y$, then there is some z such that $x < z$ and $z < y$.
    True. This says there is some z between x and y.
  d. For any x, there is a y such that $y > x$.
    True. This says that there is always a bigger number y.

3. PRACTICE/ASSESS

LESSON QUIZ
Determine whether each given number is a solution of the inequality.
  1. $y \leq 4$ a. 4 b. 0 c. 8
    Yes, yes, no
  2. $a > -1$ a. 5 b. 0 c. -1
    Yes, yes, no
Graph on a number line.
  3. $x < 3$

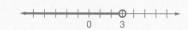

  4. $z \geq -2$

Assignment Guide
To provide flexible scheduling, this lesson can be split into parts.
▼ Core 1–8, 21–24
  Extension 32
▼ Core 9–20, 25–31
  Extension 33–36

Use Mixed Review to maintain skills.

Exercises

9.

10.

11.

12.

13.

14.

15.

16.

17.

18.

19.

20.

See Exercise 25.

B

Classify each statement as true or false.

21. $3 \leq 3$ **22.** $\left| -\frac{1}{4} \right| \geq 0$ **23.** $|-10| \leq 4$ **24.** $|-.08| \leq 0.4$

25. Write an inequality for the sign at the left.

Write the inequality shown by each graph.

26.

27.

28.

29.

30.

31.

32. *Critical Thinking* The solutions to $|x| = 5$ are the same distance from 0. What can you say about the solutions to $|x - 2| = 5$?

Challenge

Graph on a number line.

33. all values of x such that $x < 3$ and $x > -1$
34. all values of x such that $x \geq 4$ and $x \leq 1$
35. all values of x such that $x > 2$ and $x < 5$
36. all values of x such that $|x| \geq 4$

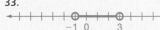

Solve. **37.** $\frac{1}{3} + 8m = 3m - \frac{1}{2}$ **38.** $5x - (2x + 7) = 2$

39. $7.5y - 0.5y = 3.75y + 39$ **40.** $16 - 2w = 10w - 2 - 6w$

41. $|y| + 6 = 21$ **42.** $|a| = |-9|$ **43.** $|x| = -6$ *3-5, 3-6, 3-8*

Write an equation to solve.

44. The perimeter of a rectangle is 30 in. The length is 5 in. greater than the width. Find the dimensions.

45. Maury bought concert tickets at the Ticket Outlet. He paid $12 for each ticket, plus a $5 service charge for the whole set of tickets. The total cost was $77. How many tickets did he buy? *3-11*

Exercises
21. T
22. T
23. F
24. T
25. $s \leq 25$
26. $x \geq 2$
27. $x \leq -2$
28. $x < 4$
29. $x < 0$
30. $x \geq 3$
31. $x \leq 7$

32. The solutions to $|x - 2| = 5$ are symmetrically located about 2.
33.

34. No points meet requirements.
35.

36.

Mixed Review
37. $-\frac{1}{6}$
38. 3
39. 12
40. 3
41. ± 15
42. ± 9
43. No solution
44. 5 in., 10 in.
45. 6 tickets

Building toward CA 5.0: Solve multi-step linear inequalities in one variable.

The Addition Property of Inequalities

Objective: Solve inequalities using the addition property.

We can use a scale to think about inequalities. We know that the inequality $3 < 7$ is true. If we add the same number to both sides of the inequality, we get another true inequality in the same direction.

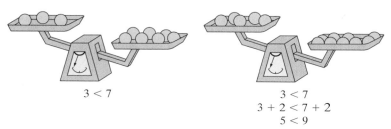

$$3 < 7$$

$$3 < 7$$
$$3 + 2 < 7 + 2$$
$$5 < 9$$

We can state this observation as a property.

The Addition Property of Inequalities

For all rational numbers a, b, and c,

if $a < b$, then $a + c < b + c$

if $a > b$, then $a + c > b + c$

Similar statements hold for $\leq$ and $\geq$.

We use the addition property of inequalities when solving inequalities just as we use the addition property of equality when solving equations.

EXAMPLE 1 Solve the inequality and graph the solution.

$$x + 3 > 4$$
$$x + 3 + (-3) > 4 + (-3) \qquad \text{Using the addition property}$$
$$x > 1$$

Since there are an infinite number of solutions to an inequality, it is not possible to "check" the solution. It is possible, however, to check whether the computations used in solving the inequality were done correctly.

 **4-2**

  CA: 2.0

What You'll Learn

1 To solve inequalities using the addition property

...And Why

To prepare for solving more complicated inequalities

1. FOCUS

FIRST FIVE MINUTES

For which numbers is the inequality true?
1. $x > -1$ a. 3   b. 0   c. 1
   Yes, yes, yes
2. $a \leq 3$ a. 3   b. 4   c. 1
   Yes, no, yes
3. $b \geq -3$ a. 3   b. -4 c. -1
   Yes, no, yes
4. Graph the inequality $x \geq -1$.

   -1 0

2. TEACH the Mathematics

Use Teaching Transparency T8 for a balance scale.

Just as a balanced scale can represent an equation, an unbalanced scale can represent an inequality. Add the same amount to both sides and the scale remains unbalanced in the same direction.

Key Questions
- If $x < y$, is $x + 50 < y + 50$?
  Yes
- If $z > 15$, is $z - 5 > 15 - 5$?
  Yes
- If $m > 9$, can $m = 9$?
  No
- If $x \leq -5$, can $x = -5$?
  Yes

Teach the Mathematics (continued)

Chalkboard Examples

Solve and graph the solution set.

1. $x + 7 \leq 9$

$x + 7 + (-7) \leq 9 + (-7)$

$x \leq 2$

(number line with solid dot at 2, labeled 0 and 2)

To check the answer, try $x = 2$ in the original inequality.

$(2) + 7 \leq 9$

$9 \leq 9$

2. $8z + 6 - 7z \geq 16$

$z + 6 \geq 16$

$z \geq 10$

(number line with solid dot at 10, labeled 0 and 10)

3. $y - \frac{1}{4} \leq \frac{1}{2}$

$y \leq \frac{1}{4} + \frac{1}{2}$

$y \leq \frac{3}{4}$

(number line with solid dot at $\frac{3}{4}$, labeled 0 and $\frac{3}{4}$)

4. $5x + 2 \leq 4x + 7$

$5x + 2 - 2 \leq 4x + 7 - 2$

$5x \leq 4x + 5$

$5x - 4x \leq 4x - 4x + 5$

$x \leq 5$

(number line with solid dot at 5, labeled 0 and 5)

Use Teaching Transparency T15 to present Chalkboard Examples 1–4.

Write the equation $x + 3 = 4$ for the inequality $x + 3 > 4$. Then substitute 1, the boundary point of the solution, into the equation. If the computations were done correctly, the equation will check.

Check the computation.

Use $x = 1$ to check the computation.

$x + 3 = 4$

$1 + 3 = 4$ Substituting 1 for x

$4 = 4$ ✔

We can also check whether the inequality symbol in the solution is correct. Choose any number greater than 1. Substitute this number into the original inequality. An easy number to use is 3.

Check the inequality symbol.

$x + 3 > 4$

$3 + 3 > 4$ Substituting 3 for x

$6 > 4$ ✔

Any number greater than 1 is a solution.

Try This   Solve each inequality and graph the solution.

a. $x + 3 > 5$

b. $x - 5 \leq 8$

c. $x - 2 \geq 7$

d. $x + 1 < 3$

EXAMPLE 2   Solve the inequality and graph the solution.

$$x + \frac{1}{3} \geq \frac{3}{4}$$

$$x + \frac{1}{3} + \left(-\frac{1}{3}\right) \geq \frac{3}{4} + \left(-\frac{1}{3}\right) \quad \text{Using the addition property}$$

$$x \geq \frac{3}{4} - \frac{1}{3}$$

$$x \geq \frac{9}{12} - \frac{4}{12}$$

$$x \geq \frac{5}{12}$$

We can check the computation and the inequality symbol to ensure that the answer is correct.

176   Chapter 4   *Inequalities*

Try This

a. $x > 2$

b. $x \leq 13$

c. $x \geq 9$

d. $x < 2$

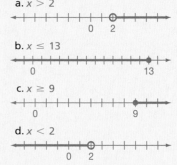

Check the computation.
Use $\frac{5}{12}$, the boundary point.

$$x + \frac{1}{3} = \frac{3}{4}$$

$$\frac{5}{12} + \frac{4}{12} = \frac{3}{4}$$

$$\frac{9}{12} = \frac{3}{4}$$

$$\frac{3}{4} = \frac{3}{4} \; ✔$$

Check the inequality symbol.
Use any number greater than $\frac{5}{12}$, say 1.

$$x + \frac{1}{3} \geq \frac{3}{4}$$

$$1 + \frac{1}{3} \geq \frac{3}{4}$$

$$1\frac{1}{3} \geq \frac{3}{4} \; ✔$$

Any number greater than or equal to $\frac{5}{12}$ is a solution.

Try This Solve each inequality and graph the solution.

e. $y + \frac{1}{8} < -\frac{3}{8}$

f. $\frac{3}{10} \leq -\frac{1}{5} + y$

As in solving equations, you should collect like terms on the same side of the inequality symbol first. Then solve the inequality.

EXAMPLE 3 Solve the inequality and graph the solution.

$$3y + 1 - 2y < -3$$
$$y + 1 < -3 \qquad\qquad \text{Collecting like terms}$$
$$y + 1 + (-1) < -3 + (-1) \qquad \text{Using the addition property}$$
$$y < -4$$

Check the computation.
Use -4, the boundary point.

$$3y + 1 - 2y = -3$$
$$3(-4) + 1 - 2(-4) = -3$$
$$-12 + 1 + 8 = -3$$
$$-3 = -3 \; ✔$$

Check the inequality symbol.
Choose any number less than -4, say -6.

$$3y + 1 - 2y < -3$$
$$3(-6) + 1 - 2(-6) < -3$$
$$-18 + 1 + 12 < -3$$
$$-5 < -3 \; ✔$$

Any number less than -4 is a solution.

Try This Solve each inequality and graph the solution.

g. $5y + 2 - 4y \leq -1$ **h.** $-4x + 5x + 1 < -2$

Try This

e. $y < -\frac{1}{2}$

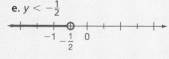

f. $y \geq \frac{1}{2}$

g. $y \leq -3$

h. $x < -3$

4-2 Exercises

A

Solve each inequality and graph the solution.

1. $x + 7 > 2$　　　　　　　　**2.** $x + 6 > 3$

3. $y + 5 > 8$　　　　　　　　**4.** $y + 7 > 9$

5. $x + 8 \le -10$　　　　　　**6.** $x + 9 \le -12$

7. $a + 12 < 6$　　　　　　　　**8.** $a + 20 < 8$

9. $x - 7 \le 9$　　　　　　　**10.** $x - 3 \le 14$

11. $x - 6 > 2$　　　　　　　**12.** $x - 9 > 4$

13. $y - 7 > -12$　　　　　**14.** $y - 10 > -16$

15. $4m - 3m < 2$　　　　　**16.** $2x + 3 - x > 5$

Solve.

17. $3x - 2x + 9 \le 6$　　　　**18.** $-2y + 3y + 10 \le 8$

19. $5n - 6 - 4n < -2$　　　**20.** $-5x + 6x - 8 < -9$

21. $3y + 4 - 2y \le -7$　　　**22.** $4a - 3a + 5 \ge -8$

23. $m + \frac{1}{4} \le \frac{1}{2}$　　　　　**24.** $y + \frac{1}{3} \ge \frac{5}{6}$

25. $x - \frac{1}{3} > \frac{1}{4}$　　　　　**26.** $b - \frac{1}{8} > \frac{1}{2}$

27. $c + \frac{4}{5} \le \frac{3}{10}$　　　　**28.** $\frac{2}{3} + a \ge \frac{5}{6}$

29. **TEST PREP** Which number is *not* a solution of $t - 5 \le 1$?

A. -5　　　**B.** 1　　　**C.** 6　　　**D.** 10

B

Solve.

30. $3(r + 2) - 2r < 4$　　　**31.** $4(r + 5) - 3r \ge 7$

32. $3a + 6 - 2a \ge -19$　　**33.** $-5 \le 3m - 10 - 2m$

34. $4(x + 3) - 3x > 4$　　　**35.** $5(y - 2) - 4(y - 1) < 0$

36. $-6(a + 2) + 7a \le -12$　**37.** $-2(a - 3) + 3(a + 2) < 4$

Use the first inequality to find the unknown number or expression in the second inequality.

38. $y + 2 + 3y > 9$　　　　　**39.** $a^2 + 4 - b \le -2$
　　　$y + 3y > ??$　　　　　　　$a^2 - b \le ??$

40. $m + n - 4 \le n$　　　　　**41.** $p + q + z \ge -2$
　　　$m - 4 \le ??$　　　　　　　$p + z \ge ??$

42. $a + b < 2a - 4$　　　　　**43.** $x - y > 7 + y$
　　　$b < ??$　　　　　　　　　$x > ??$

178 Chapter 4 *Inequalities*

Exercises

1. $x > -5$

2. $x > -3$

3. $y > 3$

4. $y > 2$

5. $x \le -18$

6. $x \le -21$

7. $a < -6$

8. $a < -12$

9. $x \le 16$

10. $x \le 17$

11. $x > 8$

12. $x > 13$

13. $y > -5$

14. $y > -6$

15. $m < 2$

16. $x > 2$

17. $x \le -3$

18. $y \le -2$

19. $n < 4$

20. $x < -1$

21. $y \le -11$

22. $a \ge -13$

23. $m \le \frac{1}{4}$

24. $y \ge \frac{1}{2}$

25. $x > \frac{7}{12}$

26. $b > \frac{5}{8}$

27. $c \le -\frac{1}{2}$

28. $a \ge \frac{1}{6}$

29. D

30. $r < -2$

31. $r \ge -13$

32. $a \ge -25$

33. $m \ge 5$

34. $x > -8$

35. $y < 6$

36. $a \le 0$

37. $a < -8$

38. 7

39. -6

40. 0

41. $-2 - q$

42. $a - 4$

43. $7 + 2y$

Mathematical Reasoning Give a reason that justifies each step in the solution.

52. $8 + 3x - 7x \geq 32$

   a. $8 - 4x \geq 32$ _____

   b. $-8 + 8 - 4x \geq 32 - 8$ _____

   c. $-4x \geq 24$ _____

   d. $-\frac{1}{4}(-4x) \leq -\frac{1}{4} \cdot 24$ _____

   e. $x \leq -6$ _____

53. $11 - 6y < -34 + 9y$

   a. $11 - 6y + 6y < -34 + 9y + 6y$ _____

   b. $11 < -34 + 15y$ _____

   c. $34 + 11 < 34 - 34 + 15y$ _____

   d. $45 < 15y$ _____

   e. $\frac{1}{15} \cdot 45 < \frac{1}{15} \cdot 15y$ _____

   f. $3 < y$ _____

54. $3(m - 8) \geq 4(m + 4)$

   a. $3m - 24 \geq 4m + 16$ _____

   b. $3m - 24 + 24 \geq 4m + 16 + 24$ _____

   c. $3m \geq 4m + 40$ _____

   d. $-4m + 3m \geq -4m + 4m + 40$ _____

   e. $-m \geq 40$ _____

   f. $-1(-m) \leq -1 \cdot 40$ _____

   g. $m \leq -40$ _____

55. $\frac{x}{4} - \frac{1}{6} \leq \frac{2}{3}$

   a. $12\left(\frac{x}{4} - \frac{1}{6}\right) \leq 12\left(\frac{2}{3}\right)$ _____

   b. $12\left(\frac{x}{4}\right) - 12\left(\frac{1}{6}\right) \leq 12\left(\frac{2}{3}\right)$ _____

   c. $3x - 2 \leq 8$ _____

   d. $3x - 2 + 2 \leq 8 + 2$ _____

   e. $3x \leq 10$ _____

   f. $\frac{1}{3}(3x) \leq \frac{1}{3}(10)$ _____

   g. $x \leq \frac{10}{3}$ _____

49. $d < \frac{3}{22}$

50. $x < 2$

51. $w > 1.5$

52. a. Simplifying
   b. Using the addition property
   c. Simplifying
   d. Using the multiplication property
   e. Simplifying

53. a. Using the addition property
   b. Simplifying
   c. Using the addition property

   d. Simplifying
   e. Using the multiplication property
   f. Simplifying

54. a. Using the distributive property
   b. Using the addition property
   c. Simplifying
   d. Using the addition property
   e. Simplifying
   f. Using the multiplication property

   g. Simplifying

55. a. Using the multiplication property
   b. Using the distributive property
   c. Simplifying
   d. Using the addition property
   e. Simplifying
   f. Using the multiplication property
   g. Simplifying

Determine whether each inequality is sometimes, always, or never true for any value of the variable.

56. $w + 3 \leq w - 4$ **57.** $2t < 5t$ **58.** $x^2 > x$

59. *Error Analysis*   A student solved the inequality $4x + 9 < 7x - 1$ as shown below.

$$4x + 9 < 7x - 1$$
$$8 < 3x$$
$$\tfrac{8}{3} < x$$

What error did the student make?

60. *Critical Thinking*   Solve $\tfrac{1}{2}(5x + 5) < \tfrac{1}{3}(5x - 30)$ and describe its positive solutions.

Challenge

Solve for x.

61. $-(x + 5) \geq 4a - 5$ **62.** $\tfrac{1}{2}(2x + 2b) > \tfrac{1}{3}(21 + 3b)$

63. $-6(x + 3) \leq -9(y + 2)$ **64.** $y < ax + b$

65. $6x + 3 > 7x - c$ **66.** $8 - 0.5x < w + 6.7$

67. *Mathematical Reasoning*   If $x \geq y$ and $-x \geq -y$, what can we conclude about x and y?

68. If $0 < x < 1$, then which of the following is true, $x^2 < x$ or $x < x^2$?

69. If $-1 < x < 0$, then which of the following is true, $x^2 < |x|$ or $|x| < x^2$?

Mixed Review

Evaluate for $m = 6$.   **70.** $m(m + 2)$ **71.** $0.5(m)$

72. $(m + 3)(m - 4)$ **73.** $m^2 - m - 12$ *1-1*

Solve.   **74.** $9y = 3y - 45$ **75.** $3z + 45 < 36$

76. $-2.05n = -9.02$ **77.** $2x = 3x - 4$ *3-3, 3-5, 3-6*

Write each as a percent.   **78.** $\tfrac{6}{8}$ **79.** $\tfrac{27}{15}$ **80.** $\tfrac{60}{12}$ **81.** $\tfrac{45}{75}$ **82.** $\tfrac{18}{4}$ *3-10*

83. Let M be Michele's age. Nicole is 2 years younger than Michele. Write an expression for Nicole's age.

84. Let s be the total amount Heidi spent for scarves. Each of the 4 scarves that she bought cost the same. Write an expression for the cost of each scarf.

85. Let L be the amount Lewis earns. Harry earns three times as much as Lewis. Write an expression for the amount Harry earns.   *1-6*

---

60. $x < -15$. There are no positive solutions.
61. $x \leq -4a$
62. $x > 7$
63. $x \geq \tfrac{3y}{2}$
64. $x > \tfrac{y - b}{a}$ if $a > 0$

     $x < \tfrac{y - b}{a}$ if $a < 0$

65. $x < c + 3$
66. $x > -2w + 2.6$
67. $x \geq y$ and $x \leq y$, so $x = y$
68. $x^2 < x$

69. $x^2 < |x|$

Mixed Review

70. 48
71. 3
72. 18
73. 18
74. -7.5
75. $z < -3$
76. 4.4
77. 4

78. 75%

79. 180%

80. 500%

81. 60%

82. 450%

83. $M - 2$

84. $\tfrac{s}{4}$

85. $3L$

Exercises

56. Never
57. Sometimes
58. Sometimes
59. In the second line the student added 1 to the right side, but subtracted 1 from the left side.

CA 5.0: Solve multi-step problems, including word problems, involving linear inequalities in one variable.

Using Inequalities

PART 1 Translating Phrases to Inequalities

Objective: Translate phrases to mathematical inequalities.

You have learned how to translate a problem to an equation and solve the equation to answer the problem. Some problems can be solved by translating to an inequality and solving the inequality to answer the problem.

EXAMPLES   Translate to an inequality.

1   A number y is greater than 4.
$y > 4$

2   A number x is less than or equal to $2\frac{1}{2}$.
$x \le 2\frac{1}{2}$

3   A number m is at least 3.
$m \ge 3$ "At least 3" means the number could be 3 or greater.

4   A number p is at most $\frac{1}{3}$.

$p \le \frac{1}{3}$ "At most $\frac{1}{3}$" means the number could be $\frac{1}{3}$ or less.

5   3 is greater than or equal to some number n.
$3 \ge n$ We can also write this as $n \le 3$.

6   12 more than twice a number is less than 20.
$2x + 12 < 20$ "12 more than twice a number" translates to $2x + 12$.
"Is less than 20" translates to < 20.

Try This   Translate to an inequality.

a. A number x is greater than or equal to 8.
b. A number t is less than 12.
c. A number x is at most $4\frac{1}{2}$.
d. A number n is at least 0.
e. 3 less than a number is greater than 4.

What You'll Learn

1 To translate phrases to mathematical inequalities

2 To solve problems by translating and solving inequalities

...And Why

To use inequalities to solve problems

Writing Math

You can translate words for inequalities into symbols.

less than	$<$
greater than	$>$
less than or equal to	$\le$
greater than or equal to	$\ge$
at least	$\ge$
at most	$\le$

Try This
a. $x \ge 8$
b. $t < 12$
c. $x \le 4\frac{1}{2}$
d. $n \ge 0$
e. $n - 3 > 4$

4-5

TIME-FOCUS METER

1. FOCUS

FIRST FIVE MINUTES
Solve.
1. $9u + 1 < 19$
   $9u < 18$
   $u < \frac{18}{9}$
   $u < 2$
2. $5b + 2 - b > 8$
   $4b > 6$
   $b > \frac{6}{4}$
   $b > \frac{3}{2}$
3. $-7c \ge -14$
   $c \le \frac{-14}{-7}$
   $c \le 2$
4. $4x - 7x + 2 < x + 5$
   $-3x < x + 3$
   $-4x < 3$
   $x > \frac{3}{-4}$
   $x > -\frac{3}{4}$

2. TEACH the Mathematics

1 Translating Phrases to Inequalities

You may wish to illustrate certain phrases with arithmetic examples to make sure students understand them. For instance,
   "5 is at least 5" is true.
   "5 is more than 5" is false.
   "5 is as great as 5" is true.

Key Questions
■ If a quantity is "at least 8," can it be greater than 8 or less than 8?
   Greater than 8
■ If a quantity is "at most 10," can it be greater than 10 or less than 10?
   Less than 10

Chalkboard Examples
Translate to an inequality.
1. A number y is less than 4.
   $y < 4$
2. A number x is greater than $\frac{4}{3}$.
   $x > \frac{4}{3}$
3. 8 less than 3 times a number is more than 13.
   $3x - 8 > 13$

Solving Problems

Although the three main phases of problem solving remain unchanged, you may want to present the following guidelines for solving inequalities in the second phase of the problem-solving process.

Develop and carry out a PLAN
Can I use a variable to represent an unknown number?
Can I represent other conditions in terms of the variable?
Can I find any relationships?
Can I write and solve an inequality?

Key Questions

- In Example 7, what word indicates that a greater than or equal sign is to be used?
exceeds
- In Example 8, what words indicate that a less than or equal sign is to be used?
at most

Avoiding Common Errors

Students often see the words "more than" or "less than" and assume that they indicate inequalities. Remind students that "3 more than 10" is a specific number, 10 + 3 or 13. Point out that an inequality is implied if the question "Can there be more?" or "Can there be less?" can be answered as yes.

Chalkboard Examples

1. Thornton needs at least 500 milligrams of vitamin C each day. He gets his vitamin C by munching brussel sprouts. Each sprout furnishes 10 milligrams of vitamin C. Find the number of sprouts he must eat each day.
Let s be the number of sprouts Thornton must eat each day. The amount of vitamin C is $10s$. This must be at least 500.
$$10s \geq 500$$
$$s \geq \frac{500}{10}$$
$$s \geq 50$$
He must eat at least 50 sprouts.

2. Your test grades are 85, 74, and 91. What is the lowest grade you can get on the next test and have an average of at least 80?
Let s be your next test score. The average of the four tests must be greater than or equal to 80.
$$\frac{(85 + 74 + 91 + s)}{4} \geq 80$$
$$85 + 74 + 91 + s \geq 320$$
$$s \geq 70$$
You must score at least 70.

Objective: Solve problems by translating and solving inequalities.

PROBLEM-SOLVING GUIDELINES
■ UNDERSTAND the problem
Develop and carry out a PLAN
■ Find the ANSWER and CHECK

You can use the Problem-Solving Guidelines at the left to help you solve problems when your plan involves writing and solving an inequality.

EXAMPLE 7

Calves weigh about 75 lb at birth and gain about 2 lb per day for a few weeks.

Ruth Anne wants to enter her newborn calf in the 4-H competition at the county fair. In order to qualify for the competition, her calf must weigh at least 200 pounds. Calves weigh approximately 75 pounds at birth and gain around 2 pounds per day for the first few weeks. How many days will it take before the calf's weight exceeds 200 pounds?

■ **UNDERSTAND the problem**

Question: How many days until the calf exceeds 200 pounds?
Data: Calf weighs 75 lb at birth; gains 2 lbs per day.

■ **Develop and carry out a PLAN**

Let $d =$ the number of days until the calf exceeds 200 pounds.
$2d =$ the amount of weight gained in d days

$$75 + 2d > 200$$
$$2d > 125$$
$$d > 62.5$$

$75 + 2d$ is the total weight after d days. This amount must be greater than ($>$) 200.

■ **Find the ANSWER and CHECK**

On average, a calf should reach 200 pounds in about 63 days, or about 9 weeks. At 2 lb per day plus the birth weight, this answer seems reasonable.

EXAMPLE 8

The medium-size box of dog food weighs 1 lb more than the small size. The large size weighs 2 lb more than the small size. If the total weight of the three boxes is at most 30 lb, what is the most a small box could weigh?

■ **UNDERSTAND the problem**

Question: What is the most the small box could weigh?
Data: Medium box weighs 1 lb more than the small;
large box weighs 2 lb more than the small;
total weight of the three boxes is at most 30 lb.

■ **Develop and carry out a PLAN**

Let $s =$ the maximum weight of the small box.
$s + 1 =$ the maximum weight of the medium box.
$s + 2 =$ the maximum weight of the large box.

$s + (s + 1) + (s + 2) \leq 30$	The total weight of the 3 boxes is 30 lb or less.
$3s + 3 \leq 30$	Simplifying
$3s \leq 27$	Adding -3 to both sides
$s \leq 9$	Multiplying both sides by $\frac{1}{3}$

■ **Find the ANSWER and CHECK**

The small box can weigh at most 9 lb. We know that $3 \times 10 = 30$, so we can estimate that each box should weigh about 10 lb. The answer is reasonable.

Try This

f. Each student agreed to sell at least 50 seed packages for a school project. Yesterday one student sold 22 packages, and today this student sold 18. How many more packages does the student need to sell to reach the goal of 50 packages?

g. In an algebra course you must get a total of at least 360 points on four tests for a grade of A. You get 85, 89, and 92 on the first three tests. What score on the last test will give you an A?

h. The sum of two consecutive integers is less than 35. What is the greatest possible pair?

 4-5 Exercises

A
Translate to an inequality.

1. 3 is less than a number y.

2. $5\frac{1}{2}$ is greater than a number k.

3. A number h is at least $4\frac{5}{6}$.

4. A number j is at most 2.

Extra Help On the Web
Look for worked-out examples at the Prentice Hall Web site.
www.phschool.com

4-5   *Using Inequalities*   **189**

Try This
f. $p \geq 10$; at least 10 packages
g. $s \geq 94$; at least 94 points
h. 16, 17

Exercises
1. $y > 3$
2. $k < 5\frac{1}{2}$
3. $h \geq 4\frac{5}{6}$
4. $j \leq 2$

5. A number is greater than or equal to 0.

6. 7 less than a number is less than 5.

7. 2 more than a number is greater than 9.

8. Twice a number is greater than 12.

9. Half a number is less than or equal to 6.

10. 3 more than one third of a number is less than 9.

11. 18 is greater than or equal to 4 less than twice a number.

12. 4 more than twice a number is less than the opposite of the number.

13. 2 more than the quantity 3 times a number is at most 11.

14. 5 less than a third of a number is at most 15.

Solve.

15. Your quiz grades are 73, 75, 89, and 91. What is the lowest grade you can obtain on the last quiz and still achieve an average of at least 85?

16. The sum of three consecutive odd integers is less than 100. What are the greatest possible values of these integers?

17. Find the greatest possible pair of integers such that one integer is twice the other and their sum is less than 30.

18. The sum of two integers is greater than 12. One integer is ten less than twice the other. What are the least values of the integers?

19. Find all sets of four consecutive even whole numbers whose sum is less than 35.

20. Find the length of the base of a triangle when one side is 2 cm shorter than the base and the other side is 3 cm longer than the base. The perimeter is greater than 19 cm.

21. Armando and Drew do volunteer work at an animal shelter. Drew worked 3 more hours than Armando, and together they worked more than 27 hours. What is the least number of hours each worked?

22. Mrs. Hays has promised her two teenagers that they may go to a concert if together they save more than $25.00 of their spending money. The older teenager agrees to save twice as much as the younger. How much must each save?

B

Solve.

23. The length of a rectangle is 26 cm. What width will make the perimeter greater than 80 cm?

24. The width of a rectangle is 8 cm. What length will make the area at least 150 cm^2?

25. The height of a triangle is 20 cm. What length base will make the area greater than 40 cm^2?

Exercises

5. $x \geq 0$

6. $x - 7 < 5$

7. $x + 2 > 9$

8. $2x > 12$

9. $\frac{x}{2} \leq 6$

10. $\frac{x}{3} + 3 < 9$

11. $2x - 4 \leq 18$

12. $2x + 4 < -x$

13. $3x + 2 \leq 11$

14. $\frac{x}{3} - 5 \leq 15$

15. 97

16. 31, 33, 35

17. 9, 18

18. 8, 6

19. 0, 2, 4, 6; 2, 4, 6, 8; 4, 6, 8, 10

20. $b > 6$ cm; the base is longer than 6 cm.

21. $A > 12$, $D > 15$; Armando worked more than 12 hours, and Drew worked more than 15 hours.

22. $16.68; $8.34

23. $w > 14$ cm

24. $l \geq 18.75$ cm

25. $b > 4$ cm

Translate to an inequality and solve.

26. Half of a number is at least -8.

27. 7 less than a third of a number is less than 12.

28. *Critical Thinking*   A painter can be paid in two ways.

    Plan A: $500 plus $19 per hour
    Plan B: $24 per hour

    Suppose the job takes n hours. For what values of n is Plan A better for the painter than Plan B?

Challenge

29. You have 5 sections of chain and each section has 3 links. The cost to have a link cut is 10¢. The cost to have a link welded is 20¢. How can you join the sections together for less than $1?

30. The Wilsons are remodeling their bathroom. A new vanity and sink will cost $151, the mirror and lights will cost $179.75, and a new tub with the vinyl behind it will cost $191. The plumber will install everything and will charge a certain percent of the total cost of the material for his labor. What is the greatest percent the Wilsons can afford to pay to keep the total for material and labor less than $1000?

Mixed Review

Evaluate for $n = \frac{2}{3}$.   **31.** $n - \frac{3}{2}$ **32.** $\left(\frac{4}{5}\right)n$ **33.** $\frac{3}{5} - n$ *1-1, 2-4, 2-5*

Solve.   **34.** $4(c + 3) = 14c - 3$ **35.** $9y + 16 = 3 - 4y$

36. $9 - 2x < -11$ **37.** $14a + 3 \le 15a + 7$ *3-5, 4-4*

TEST PREP   Compare the boxed quantity in column A with the boxed quantity in column B. Choose the best answer.   *2-4, 3-2*

    A. The quantity in column A is greater.
    B. The quantity in column B is greater.
    C. The two quantities are equal.
    D. The relationship cannot be determined with the information supplied.

	column A	column B			column A	column B
38.	$3x - 2$	$3x + 7$	**39.**		$-2x + 1$	$7x + 1$
40.	the solution of $4x = 25$	the solution of $-3z = -18$	**41.**		the solution of $\frac{m}{3} = \frac{5}{12}$	the solution of $\frac{c}{8} = \frac{4}{15}$

Exercises

26. $x \ge -16$

27. $x < 57$

28. $n < 100$

29. Cut all three links of one section (30¢). Use each link to join the remaining 4 sections, requiring 3 welds (60¢). The total cost will be 90¢.

30. 91.66%

Mixed Review

31. $-\frac{5}{6}$

32. $\frac{8}{15}$

33. $-\frac{1}{15}$

34. $\frac{3}{2}$

35. -1

36. $x > 10$

37. $a \ge -4$

38. B

39. D

40. A

41. B

California Topic

CA 24.0: Use and know simple aspects of a logical argument.
CA 24.2: Identify the hypothesis and conclusion in logical deduction.

 Connections: Deductive Reasoning

If–Then Statements

Deductive reasoning is a process of reasoning logically from given facts to a conclusion. One of the most common statements used in deductive reasoning is a statement of the form *if A, then B.* Here are some examples:

> If an animal is a cat, then it has four legs.
> If a figure is a square, then it has four sides.
> If $x = 1$, then $x + 1 = 2$.
> If $x < 5$, then $x < 10$.

A statement of this form is called a **conditional statement.** In the statement *if A, then B*, A is the antecedent, or **hypothesis,** and B is the consequent, or **conclusion.**

The **converse** of a conditional statement can be found by interchanging the hypothesis and the conclusion. The converse of a true conditional statement may or may not be true.

EXAMPLE 1

Conditional: If the product of two numbers is 0, then at least one of the numbers must be 0.
Converse: If at least one of the numbers is 0, then the product of the two numbers is 0.

The converse is also a true statement.

EXAMPLE 2

Conditional: If a figure is a square, then it has four sides.
Converse: If it has four sides, then the figure is a square.

The converse is not necessarily true. A rectangle has four sides, but it is not a square. To show that a converse is not true, you need to give a counterexample. A rectangle is a counterexample for the statement above.

Exercises

Give the converse for each of the conditional statements below. Decide whether the converse is true. If not, give a counterexample.
1. If it's raining, then we can't play soccer.
2. If a number is divisible by 2, then it is an even number.
3. If a number is divisible by 4, then it is an even number.
4. If $5x + 4 = 24$, then $x = 4$.
5. If $x < 5$, then $x < 10$.

Exercises

1. If we can't play soccer, then it's raining. False
   Counterexample: It is a sunny day but we can't play soccer because no one can find the ball.
2. If a number is even, then it is divisible by 2. True
3. If a number is even, then it is divisible by 4. False
   Counterexample: 10 is even and is not divisible by 4.
4. If $x = 4$, then $5x + 4 = 24$. True
5. If $x < 10$, then $x < 5$. False
   Counterexample: 7 is less than 10 and is not less than 5.

Connections: Inductive Reasoning

California Topic

CA 24.1: Explain the difference between inductive and deductive reasoning and identify and provide examples of each.

CA 24.3: Use counterexamples to show that an assertion is false and recognize that a single counterexample is sufficient to refute an assertion.

In everyday life we most commonly reach conclusions using inductive reasoning. With inductive reasoning, you make conclusions based on what you observe has happened before. A conclusion reached by inductive reasoning is sometimes called a conjecture.

EXAMPLE 1

The first five streets that cross First Avenue are Adams Street, Bedford Street, Carlisle Street, Desmond Street, and Everett Street. What is a reasonable conjecture to make about the names of the next five streets?

Since the names of the first five streets are in alphabetical order, a reasonable conjecture is that the names of the next five streets continue in alphabetical order.

A conjecture may or may not be true. One counterexample is enough to prove that a conjecture is false. In Example 1, if the tenth street is named Orange Street, then the conjecture that the street names continue in alphabetical order is false.

Try This

a. Consider this conjecture: "The square of any number is always greater than or equal to the number." Find several examples that support this conjecture. If possible, find a counterexample.

Exercises

Look at each pattern of the sums. Based on the pattern, predict the last sum shown. Verify your prediction.

1.
1	= 1	= 1^2
1 + 3	= 4	= 2^2
1 + 3 + 5	= 9	= 3^2
1 + 3 + 5 + 7	= 16	= 4^2

sum of the first 25 positive odd integers = ??

2.
1	= 1	= $\frac{1(2)}{2}$
1 + 2	= 3	= $\frac{2(3)}{2}$
1 + 2 + 3	= 6	= $\frac{3(4)}{2}$
1 + 2 + 3 + 4	= 10	= $\frac{4(5)}{2}$

sum of the first 30 positive integers = ??

Give a counterexample to show that each conjecture is FALSE.

3. The product of two positive rational numbers is always greater than or equal to both numbers.

4. The difference of two rational numbers is always less than at least one of the numbers.

5. Explain the difference between inductive and deductive reasoning. Give an example of each.

Connections: Inductive Reasoning **193**

Try This

a. The conjecture is true for all numbers ≥ 1 or ≤ 0. The conjecture is false for all numbers between 0 and 1. Check students' work for examples and counterexamples.

Exercises

1. 625
2. 465

Counterexamples may vary. Examples:

3. $\frac{1}{2} \cdot \frac{1}{3} = \frac{1}{6}$, and $\frac{1}{6} < \frac{1}{2}, \frac{1}{6} < \frac{1}{3}$

4. $2 - (-4) = 6$, and $6 > 2$, $6 > -4$

5. Answers may vary. Deductive reasoning uses logic to show that the truth of certain statements follows from the truth of other statements. Inductive reasoning uses observation to reach conclusions that seem reasonable based on earlier experience. Check student's work for examples.

4-6

TIME-FOCUS METER

1. FOCUS

FIRST FIVE MINUTES

1. What integer added to its reciprocal gives 5.2?
   5 (Try, Test, Revise)

2. How many different ways are there to label the corners of a computer screen with the letters A, B, C, D?
   24 (Make an Organized List)

2. TEACH the Mathematics

▼1 Logical Reasoning

Note that one must reason logically to solve any problem. The strategy called *Use Logical Reasoning* refers to a specific logical approach in which some information is given and "if–then" reasoning is used to make further conclusions, building up enough information to solve the problem.

Setting up information in a chart, as shown in the example, helps show the process of deductive logic. The given information is recorded and conclusions are drawn until all the possibilities except the solution are ruled out.

Key Questions

- In the example, what does the first headline tell you? Neither Murata nor Holden is the new vice-president.
- What does the second headline tell you? Wells is the president.
- What does the third headline tell you? Holden is not the treasurer.

Chalkboard Example

1. To celebrate getting their drivers' licenses, Liz, Ann, and Phil borrowed their parents' cars: a white sedan, a red sports car, and a red compact.
   (1) Phil's parents own only red cars.
   (2) Liz borrowed a red car, but her parents wouldn't let her drive their sports car. Who was driving which car?
   Make a chart like the one in the example. The number in the chart corresponds to the clue that ruled out that combination.

 CA 24.0: Use and know simple aspects of a logical argument.

4-6 ▷ Reasoning Strategies

What You'll Learn

▼1 To solve problems using the strategy *Use Logical Reasoning* and other strategies

...And Why

To increase efficiency in solving problems by applying reasoning skills

Objective: Solve problems using the strategy *Use Logical Reasoning* and other strategies.

Some problems are solved by understanding the given relationships among the facts and using known facts and relationships to draw conclusions. This problem-solving strategy is called *Use Logical Reasoning*.

You can use the Problem-Solving Guidelines at the right to help you solve problems when your plan involves the strategy *Use Logical Reasoning*.

PROBLEM-SOLVING GUIDELINES
■ UNDERSTAND the problem
□ Develop and carry out a PLAN
■ Find the ANSWER and CHECK

EXAMPLE

A newspaper gave information about an election, but did not tell who was elected to which office. The offices were president, vice-president, secretary, and treasurer. Those elected, but not necessarily in the order of the offices above, were Mr. Berry, Ms. Wells, Mr. Murata, and Ms. Holden. Use these headlines from the paper to decide who was elected to which office.

(1) Murata and Holden Congratulate New Vice-President
(2) Wells—First Woman President
(3) Former Treasurer Holden Happy in New Office

You can solve this problem by recording the given information in a chart and making conclusions based on it. The charts below show the reasoning you might go through to solve this problem.

	B	W	M	H
P				
VP			no	no
S				
T				

Murata and Holden were not elected vice-president.

	B	W	M	H
P	no	yes	no	no
VP	yes	no	no	no
S	no	no		
T	no	no		

If Wells is president, no one else is president. Berry must be vice-president.

	B	W	M	H
P	no	yes	no	no
VP	yes	no	no	no
S	no	no	no	yes
T	no	no	yes	no

Since Holden was not treasurer, she has to be secretary. Murata must be treasurer.

Those elected were: president, Wells; vice-president, Berry; secretary, Holden; and treasurer, Murata.

	Sports	Sedan	Compact
Liz	2	2	✔
Ann	✗	✔	✗
Phil	✔	1	✗

Clue 2 means Liz was driving the compact. Clue 1 means Phil was driving the sports car, so Ann was driving the sedan.

Problem-Solving Strategies

Draw a Diagram	Try, Test, Revise	Write an Equation
Make an Organized List	Use Logical Reasoning	Make a Table
Look for a Pattern	Simplify the Problem	Work Backward

Extra Help On the Web

Look for worked-out examples at the Prentice Hall Web site.
www.phschool.com

4-6 Problems

Solve using one or more strategies.

1. William, Carrie, Lester, and Rosa were hired as coaches at a high school. The coaching positions were for basketball, tennis, racquetball, and volleyball. William's sister was among those hired, and she was to be the tennis coach. Neither William nor Lester ever played basketball or knew how to coach it. Rosa had never learned to play tennis. Lester disliked all sports involving a racket. Who was hired to coach which sport?

2. A certain town can use the digits 0, 1, 2, 3, 7, and 9 for its telephone prefixes. How many 3-digit telephone prefixes are possible for this town if each digit can be used only once in a prefix and the first digit cannot be a 1 or a 0?

3. A student was hired by a city's maintenance department to paint house numbers on the curbs in a particular neighborhood. Each digit had to be painted separately, and the student was paid 50¢ per digit. He painted house numbers from 1 to 225. How much did he earn?

4. Two consultants were hired by a company. The total consultant fees were $18,500. If one consultant had earned $500 less, each consultant would have been paid the same. How much was each consultant paid?

5. Five tiles, each 1 foot square, were used to cover a spot on a floor. The tiles had to be placed so that the sides of any two tiles matched evenly. The perimeter of the spot that was covered was 10 feet. What are the possible shapes for the spot?

6. Five cars in a race all finished within 8 seconds of each other. Car 1 finished 1 second ahead of car 4, and car 4 was not last. Car 2 finished 6 seconds before car 5. Car 5 finished 3 seconds behind car 1. Car 1 finished 5 seconds behind car 3. In what order did the cars finish?

7. *Write a Convincing Argument* Solve the problem below. Then write an argument that would convince a classmate that your solution is correct.

Meg, Scott, Nellie, and Jeff live in the towns Jackson, Springstown, Newton, and Mowetown. None lives in a town that has the same first letter as his or her name. Neither Jeff nor Nellie has ever been to Mowetown. Meg has spent all of her life in Springstown. Which person lives in which town?

Practice Multiple Choice

Choose the best answer.

1. Solve
   $28 - 3b < 5b + 4$.

   A $b < 3$
   B $b > 4$
   C $b > 3$
   D $b < 4$

2. Seven plus one half of a number is greater than one third of the number, minus 5. (Use *n* for the variable.) What values of the variable would make this statement true?

   F $n > -72$
   G $n > -12$
   H $n < -72$
   J $n > -14.4$

1. C; Algebra 4.0
2. F; Algebra 5.0

4-6 *Reasoning Strategies* **195**

3. PRACTICE/ASSESS

Hints for Problems

1. Record the given information in a chart, and make conclusions to solve the problem.
2. Make an organized list of possible prefixes.
3. Make an organized list to find the number of digits painted. Find the number of houses with just one-digit house numbers.
4. Guess an amount for one consultant, find the fee for the other consultant, and check the total. Revise your guess.
5. Draw a diagram of possible placements of the 5 tiles.
6. Draw a diagram to show the order in which the cars finished.
7. Make a table similar to the one in the example.

Assignment Guide

▼ Core 1–6
   Extension 7

Problems

1. William coaches racquetball. Carrie coaches tennis. Lester coaches volleyball. Rosa coaches basketball.
2. There are 80 possible 3-digit telephone prefixes.
3. The student earned $283.50 for painting the house numbers.
4. Consultant A earned $9000, and consultant B earned $9500.

5. There are two ways the five tiles could be arranged.

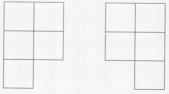

6. Car 3 finished first, followed by cars 2, 1, 4, and 5.

7. Nellie lives in Jackson; Meg lives in Springstown; Scott lives in Mowetown; and Jeff lives in Newton.

Chapter Wrap Up

4 ▷ **Chapter Wrap Up**

Key Terms

addition property of inequalities (p. 175)
conclusion (p. 192)
conditional statement (p. 192)
converse (p. 192)
graph (p. 172)
hypothesis (p. 192)
inequality (p. 172)
multiplication property of inequalities (p. 180)

4-1

A sentence containing $<$, $>$, $\leq$, or $\geq$ is an inequality. A solution of an **inequality** is any number that makes the inequality true when that number is substituted for the variable.

Determine whether the given number is a solution of the inequality.

1. $y \leq 4$ **a.** 3   **b.** 0   **c.** -2 **d.** 8

2. $x > -12$ **a.** 6   **b.** -18 **c.** 0   **d.** 18

A **graph** of an inequality is a diagram of all its solutions on a number line. A closed circle indicates that the end point is part of the solution, and an open circle indicates that the end point is not part of the solution.

Graph on a number line.

3. $x > -1$ **4.** $x \leq 5$ **5.** $x < -5$

4-2

The **addition property of inequalities** states that if we add the same number to both sides of an inequality, we get another inequality with the same solutions.

Solve and graph the solution.

6. $y + 5 > 3$ **7.** $b - \frac{1}{4} \geq 2$ **8.** $4a + 6 - 3a < 12$

Solve.

9. $4x + 6 - 3x > 2$ **10.** $a + \frac{2}{3} \leq \frac{5}{6}$ **11.** $-4y + 5y - 8 \leq 12$

4-3

The **multiplication property of inequalities** states that if we multiply both sides of an inequality by a positive number, we get another inequality with the same solutions. If, however, we multiply both sides of an inequality by a negative number, we must reverse the inequality symbol.

Solve and graph the solution.

12. $5x < 25$ **13.** $-3b \geq 21$ **14.** $-2y > 3$

4-4

The addition and multiplication properties are often used together in solving inequalities. The addition property is usually used first.

Solve.

15. $3y + 4 < 25$ **16.** $4a + 9 \leq 2a - 4$ **17.** $14 - 8x < 6x + 36$

18. $7 - 6y > 3y - 20$ **19.** $6 - 5y > 3 - 4y$ **20.** $15a + 3 - 12a \leq 14$

Chapter 4 Wrap Up

1. a. Yes
   b. Yes
   c. Yes
   d. No
2. a. Yes
   b. No
   c. Yes
   d. Yes

3.

4.

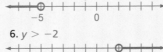

5.

6. $y > -2$

7. $b \geq \frac{9}{4}$

8. $a < 6$

9. $x > -4$

10. $a \leq \frac{1}{6}$

11. $y \leq 20$

12. $x < 5$

13. $b \leq -7$

14. $y < -\frac{3}{2}$

15. $y < 7$

16. $a \leq -\frac{13}{2}$

17. $x > -\frac{11}{7}$

18. $y < 3$

19. $y < 3$

20. $a \leq \frac{11}{3}$

Some problems can be solved by translating to an inequality and solving the inequality. Use the Problem-Solving Guidelines to help you.

Solve.

21. Alicia weighs 60 lb less than her father. Their combined weights total 300 lb at most. What is the most Alicia could weigh?

22. Heather received grades of 80, 75, and 86 on three algebra tests. What must her grade be on the next test if her average for the four tests is to be at least 82?

23. The sum of three consecutive even integers is less than or equal to 42. Find the largest set of these numbers.

24. Find all sets of four consecutive odd whole numbers whose sum is less than 38.

Internet Activity
On the Web

Look for extension problems for this chapter at the Prentice Hall Web site.
www.phschool.com

Assessment Item Analysis

Item	Lesson
1–5	4-1
6	4-2
7	4-4
8	4-2
9, 10	4-3
11–17	4-4
18, 19	4-5

4 ▷ Chapter Assessment

1. Determine whether each number is a solution of $b \geq -3$.
   a. 0   b. -3 c. -5 d. 6

2. Determine whether each number is a solution of $x < 5$.
   a. 3   b. -3 c. -8 d. 0

Graph on a number line.

3. $a \geq -5$ 4. $c < -4$ 5. $y \leq 6$

Solve.

6. $x - 2 > 5$

7. $9x + 2 - 4x > 17$

8. $x + \frac{1}{3} \geq -5$

9. $7y > -42$

10. $-6x \leq -24$

11. $5x \geq 8x - \frac{3}{2}$

12. $5a - 6 \geq 3a$

13. $2x - 15 > 5x$

14. $-5y - 34 \geq -19$

15. $7 - 6x < 2x + 87$

16. $5 - 8y \geq 23$

17. $9a - 16 < -52$

18. Kim is 3 years older than Bridget. The sum of their ages is less than 16. What is the oldest Bridget could be?

19. The sum of two consecutive even integers is less than or equal to 90. What is the greatest possible pair?

Chapter 4 Wrap Up

21. 120 lbs
22. $T \geq 87$
23. 12, 14, 16
24. 1, 3, 5, 7; 3, 5, 7, 9; 5, 7, 9, 11

Chapter 4 Assessment

1. a. Yes
   b. Yes
   c. No
   d. Yes
2. a. Yes
   b. Yes
   c. Yes
   d. Yes

3.

4.

5.

6. $x > 7$
7. $x > 3$

8. $x \geq -\frac{16}{3}$

9. $y > -6$

10. $x \geq 4$

11. $x \leq \frac{1}{2}$

12. $a \geq 3$

13. $x < -5$

14. $y \leq -3$

15. $x > -10$

16. $y \leq -\frac{9}{4}$

17. $a < -4$

18. $x < 6.5$; 6 years old

19. 44, 46

1-1

Evaluate.

1. $\frac{y - x}{4}$ for $y = 12$ and $x = 6$ **2.** $\frac{3x}{y}$ for $x = 5$ and $y = 4$

Simplify.

3. $16 \div (4 \cdot 2) + 9 - 3$ **4.** $(48 - 8) \div 5 + 3$

1-2

Write an equivalent expression using a commutative property or an identity property. Use $\frac{4}{4}$ for 1.

5. $12 + y$ **6.** $\frac{5}{6}$

Simplify.

7. $\frac{9xy}{12yz}$ **8.** $\frac{108}{72y}$

1-3

Evaluate each expression.

9. y^4 for $y = 2$ **10.** $x^3 + 5$ for $x = 3$

11. $(2a)^4$ for $a = 5$ **12.** $3a^2$ for $a = 2$

1-4

Calculate.

13. $(3 + 7)^3$ **14.** $5 + 4^4$

Use an associative property to write an equivalent expression.

15. $(3 \cdot y) \cdot z$ **16.** $x + (y + 21)$

1-5

Use the distributive property to write an equivalent expression.

17. $5(3x + 5y + 2z)$ **18.** $8(2w + 4x + 3y)$

Factor.

19. $54y + 6$ **20.** $42x + 36y + 12$

Collect like terms.

21. $9b + 18y + 6b + 4y$ **22.** $3y + 4z + 6z + 6y$

Chapters 1–4
Cumulative Review

1. $\frac{3}{2}$

2. $\frac{15}{4}$

3. 8

4. 11

5. $y + 12$

6. $\frac{20}{24}$

7. $\frac{3x}{4z}$

8. $\frac{3}{2y}$

9. 16
10. 32
11. 10,000
12. 12
13. 1000
14. 261
15. $3 \cdot (y \cdot z)$
16. $(x + y) + 21$
17. $15x + 25y + 10z$
18. $16w + 32x + 24y$
19. $6(9y + 1)$
20. $6(7x + 6y + 2)$
21. $15b + 22y$
22. $9y + 10z$

1-6

Write as an algebraic expression.

23. four less than twice w

24. three times the sum of x and y

1-7

Solve for the given replacement set.

25. $6y = 54$ $\{7, 8, 9\}$

26. $x^2 - x = 3$ $\{1, 3, 9\}$

27. $2.5y = 15$ $\{0.6, 6, 60\}$

28. $m - 18 = 56$ $\{38, 64, 74\}$

Each pair of equations is equivalent. What was done to the first equation to get the second one?

29. $\frac{4y}{7} = 3$

$4y = 21$

30. $5x = 30$

$5x - 4 = 26$

1-9

Evaluate.

31. Find the perimeter (p) of a rectangle with a length (l) of 12 m and a width (w) of 8.4 m using the formula $p = 2l + 2w$.

32. Find the area (A) of a rectangle with a length (l) of 12 m and a width (w) of 8.4 m using the formula $A = l \cdot w$.

2-1

Use $>$ or $<$ to write a true sentence.

33. $-4 \ \square \ -6$

34. $-2 \ \square \ 2$

Find the absolute values.

35. $|-14|$

36. $|65|$

2-2

Use $>$ or $<$ to write a true sentence.

37. $-2.5 \ \square \ -4.25$

38. $-\frac{3}{4} \ \square \ -\frac{3}{8}$

Graph each rational number on a number line.

39. -3.5

40. $\frac{5}{4}$

2-3

Add.

41. $5 + (-9) + 7$

42. $-3.5 + 7.2$

**Chapters 1–4
Cumulative Review**

23. $2w - 4$
24. $3(x + y)$
25. $\{9\}$
26. No solution
27. $\{6\}$
28. $\{74\}$
29. Both sides were multiplied by 7.
30. 4 was subtracted from both sides.
31. $p = 40.8$ m
32. $A = 100.8$ m^2
33. $>$

34. $<$
35. 14
36. 65
37. $>$
38. $<$
39. -3.5

40. $\frac{5}{4}$

41. 3
42. 3.7

2-4

Subtract.

43. $-7 - (-8)$

44. $-\frac{3}{4} - \frac{2}{3}$

Simplify.

45. $-2 - 4x - 6x + 5$

46. $7 - 2x - (-5x) - 8$

2-5

Multiply.

47. $5(-7)(3)(-4)$

48. $-\frac{5}{8}\left(-\frac{4}{3}\right)$

49. $(-7)(5)(-6)(-0.5)$

2-6

Divide.

50. $\frac{-10.8}{36}$

51. $\frac{-4}{5} \div \frac{25}{8}$

52. $\frac{81}{-90}$

2-7

Multiply.

53. $4(-3x - 2)$

54. $-6(2y - 4x)$

55. $-5(-x - 1)$

Factor.

56. $16y - 56$

57. $-2x - 8$

58. $5a - 15b + 25$

Collect like terms.

59. $-4d - 6a + 3a - 5d + 1$

60. $3.2x + 2.9y - 5.8x - 8.1y$

2-8

Remove parentheses and simplify.

61. $-3x - (-x + y)$

62. $-3(x - 2) - 4x$

63. $10 - 2(5 - 4x)$

2-10

Which properties of equality justify each statement?

64. $2a + 3b = 2a + 3b$

65. $60 = 45t$ and $60 = 35(t - 1)$. Therefore, $45t = 35(t - 1)$.

3-1 to 3-6

Solve.

66. $-2.6 + x = 8.3$

67. $4\frac{1}{2} + y = 8\frac{1}{3}$

68. $\frac{-3}{4}x = 36$

69. $-2.2y = -26.4$

70. $-4x + 3 = 15$

71. $-3x + 5 = -8x - 7$

200 Chapter 4 *Inequalities*

Chapters 1–4
Cumulative Review

43. 1

44. $-\frac{17}{12}$

45. $3 - 10x$

46. $-1 + 3x$

47. 420

48. $\frac{5}{6}$

49. -105

50. -0.3

51. $-\frac{32}{125}$

52. $-\frac{9}{10}$

53. $-12x - 8$

54. $-12y + 24x$

55. $5x + 5$

56. $8(2y - 7)$

57. $-2(x + 4)$

58. $5(a - 3b + 5)$

59. $-9d - 3a + 1$

60. $-2.6x - 5.2y$

61. $-2x - y$

62. $-7x + 6$

63. $8x$

64. Reflexive property

65. Transitive property

66. 10.9

67. $3\frac{5}{6}$

68. -48

69. 12

70. -3

71. $-\frac{12}{5}$

72. $4y - 4 + y = 6y + 20 - 4y$ **73.** $-3(x - 2) = -15$

74. $\frac{1}{3}x - \frac{5}{6} = \frac{1}{2} + 2x$ **75.** $-3.7x + 6.2 = -7.3x - 5.8$

3-7

Solve.

76. $c = 10d + 5n$ for n **77.** $L = 2rh$ for r

3-8

Solve.

78. $|y| = 7$ **79.** $|x| + 2 = 11$ **80.** $3|a| = 27$

3-9

Solve.

81. $\frac{x}{12} = \frac{16}{18}$ **82.** $\frac{16}{6} = \frac{x}{24}$

83. A car uses 32 L of gas to travel 450 km. How many liters would be required to drive 800 km (to the nearest tenth)?

3-10

Translate to an equation and solve.

84. What percent of 60 is 18?   **85.** Two is four percent of what number?

86. What is 16.5% of 80?

3-11

87. Money is invested in a savings account at 12% simple interest. After one year there is $1680 in the account. How much was originally invested?

88. The sum of three consecutive integers is 114. Find the integers.

4-1

Determine whether each number is a solution of $a \geq -4$.

89. -6 **90.** 2   **91.** 0   **92.** -4

4-2 to 4-5

Solve and graph on a number line.

93. $x - \frac{1}{6} \geq \frac{2}{3}$ **94.** $-4x \geq 24$

95. $-3x < 30 + 2x$ **96.** $x + 3 \geq 6(x - 4) + 7$

97. Find the length and width of a rectangle when the width is 4 ft shorter than the length. The perimeter of the rectangle is greater than 72 ft.

Chapters 1–4 Cumulative Review

72. 8

73. 7

74. $-\frac{4}{5}$

75. $-3\frac{1}{3}$ or $-3.3\overline{3}$

76. $n = \frac{c - 10d}{5}$

77. $r = \frac{L}{2h}$

78. $7, -7$

79. $9, -9$

80. $9, -9$

81. $\frac{32}{3}$

82. 64

83. 56.9 L

84. 30%

85. 50

86. 13.2

87. $1500

88. 37, 38, 39

89. No

90. Yes

91. Yes

92. Yes

93. $x \geq \frac{5}{6}$

94. $x \leq -6$

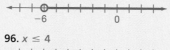

95. $x > -6$

96. $x \leq 4$

97. $l > 20$ ft, $w > 16$ ft

CHAPTER

5 ▷ Exponents and Polynomials

CHAPTER AT A GLANCE

PACING OPTIONS

This chart suggests pacing only for the lessons and their parts. It is provided as a possible guide.
It will help you determine how much time you have in your schedule to cover other features, such as the Chapter Wrap Up and Assessment.

	Day 1	Day 2	Day 3	Day 4	Day 5	Day 6	Day 7	Day 8	Day 9	Day 10	Day 11
Traditional (40–45 min. class periods)	5-1 ▼¹▼²	5-2 ▼¹▼²	5-3 ▼¹▼²	5-4 ▼	5-5 ▼¹▼²	5-5 ▼³ 5-6 ▼¹	5-6 ▼²	5-7 ▼¹▼²	5-8 ▼	5-9 ▼¹	5-9 ▼²
Algebra 1 Over 2 Years (40–45 min. class periods)	5-1 ▼¹	5-1 ▼²	5-2 ▼¹	5-2 ▼²	5-3 ▼¹	5-3 ▼²	5-4 ▼	5-4 ▼	5-5 ▼¹▼²	5-5 ▼²▼³	5-6 ▼¹
Block Scheduling (90 min. class periods)	5-1 ▼¹▼² 5-2 ▼¹▼²	5-3 ▼¹▼² 5-4 ▼	5-5 ▼¹▼²▼³ 5-6 ▼¹	5-6 ▼² 5-7 ▼¹▼²	5-8 ▼ 5-9 ▼¹	5-9 ▼² 5-10 ▼¹▼²	5-11 ▼ 5-12 ▼				

SKILLS TRACE

SKILL	FOUNDATION	DEVELOPED IN LESSONS	REVIEWED/REINFORCED/EXTENDED
Multiplying and dividing using exponents	1-3	**5-1**	10-1
Raising a power to a power	5-1	**5-2**	11-5
Finding the power of a product or a quotient	5-1	**5-2**	13-2
Multiplying and dividing monomials	5-1	**5-3**	10-2, 10-3
Identifying and simplifying polynomials	1-1, 1-3, 1-5	**5-5**	12-4
Adding and subtracting polynomials	1-5, 5-5	**5-7, 5-8**	6-8
Multiplying monomials, special binomials, and polynomials	2-8	**5-9 through 5-11**	6-1 through 6-7

CORRELATION TO STANDARDIZED TESTS

 YOUR LOCAL TEST*

Lesson		CAT5	CTBS/5 TerraNova™	ITED	MAT7	SAT9		CA Algebra
5-1	Exponents	■		■				2.0
5-2	More with Exponents							2.0
5-3	Multiplying and Dividing Monomials							10.0
5-4	Scientific Notation	■	■					2.0
5-5	Polynomials				■			10.0
5-6	More on Polynomials		■		■			10.0
5-7	Addition of Polynomials							10.0
5-8	Subtraction of Polynomials							10.0
5-9	Multiplication of Monomials and Binomials							10.0
5-10	Multiplying Binomials: Special Products							10.0
5-11	Multiplying Polynomials							10.0
5-12	Reasoning Strategies: Make a Table, Look for a Pattern	■	■	■	■	■		24.0

CAT5 California Achievement Test, 5th Edition
CTBS/5 Comprehensive Test of Basic Skills, 5th Edition
ITED Iowa Test of Educational Development
    Level 15, Complete Battery, Form M

MAT7 Metropolitan Achievement Test, 7th Edition
SAT 9 Stanford Achievement Test/Task 1

For other standardized test correlations, follow the link to your state at **www.phschool.com**.

*See pp. T34–T39 for the California Standards.

Day 12	Day 13	Day 14	Day 15	Day 16	Day 17	Day 18	Day 19	Day 20	Day 21	Day 22	Day 23	Day 24
10 ▽▽	5-11 ▽	5-12 ▽										
6 ▽	5-7 ▽	5-7 ▽	5-8 ▽	5-8 ▽	5-9 ▽	5-9 ▽	5-10 ▽	5-10 ▽	5-11 ▽	5-11 ▽	5-12 ▽	5-12 ▽

Math Background

Chapter Overview

Earlier work with exponents and like terms is expanded. Students manipulate exponential expressions; use scientific notation; and simplify sums, differences, and products of monomials and polynomials, as well as quotients of monomials. The degree of a polynomial is defined, as is arrangement in ascending or descending order.

In preparation for factoring, patterns for the product of the sum and the difference of two terms and for the square of a binomial are exhibited.

The reasoning strategies *Make a Table* and *Look for a Pattern* are introduced to develop systematic methods to find solutions. Both strategies are often used with the strategy *Write an Equation*.

5-1 Exponents

Students who make the error of multiplying the base by the exponent should be encouraged to consider numerical examples such as 2^3 and 3^2.

$$2^3 = 2 \cdot 2 \cdot 2 = 8 \neq 2 \cdot 3$$

$$3^2 = 3 \cdot 3 = 9 \neq 2 \cdot 3$$

Students might begin to keep a list of such helpful numerical examples.

Point out to students that the patterns used to suggest which values should be assigned to powers with zero and negative exponents are just suggestions that will maintain a consistent system. For example, 5^0 could be defined to be -5, 23, or any other number; but defining it to be 1 is the only definition that fits with earlier definitions of exponents.

Students may want to discuss why 0^0 is not defined. It could be defined to be 1 since any other rational number to the zero power is one, or it could be defined to be 0 since zero to any other power is 0. Since either definition creates some inconsistencies, we leave it undefined and 0^0 has no meaning. (There are areas in higher level mathematics where $0^0 = 1$ is a useful definition, but that does not concern algebra students.)

5-2 More with Exponents

Students who do not have a clear understanding of the meaning of base of an exponent will have difficulty with this section. Point out to them that the exponent is always "next to" its base—whether the base is an expression in parentheses, a variable, or a number. Discuss the differences among these expressions.

$$(-7x)^2 \quad -(7x^2) \quad -(7x)^2 \quad -7x^2$$

In each case, what is the base of the exponent 2? (Answers: $-7x$, x, $7x$, and x.)

Which expressions are positive for any nonzero value of x? (Only the first expression.)

Will any of the expressions always have the same value? (The second and fourth expressions are equivalent.)

Some students may make errors such as the following.

$$(x^2)^3 = x^5 \quad x^2 x^3 = x^6$$

Here again they should keep numerical examples in mind.

$$(2^2)^3 = 4^3 = 64 = 2^6 \neq 2^5$$

$$2^2 \cdot 2^3 = 4 \cdot 8 = 32 = 2^5 \neq 2^6.$$

Multiplying and Dividing

5-3 Monomials

Monomial is derived from *mono-* (one) and *-nomial* (name). So a monomial is an expression with a single term. Use the word frequently in teaching the lesson so that the students are familiar with it; they will see it frequently later.

It may help some students to be told that the exercises in this lesson generally require them to combine the applications of the laws of exponents presented in the first two lessons of the chapter. Most errors occur when the base of an exponent is not correctly identified.

Many students can skip lines two, three, and four in the following example. Other students should be encouraged to write down each step until their work is generally error-free.

$$(2a^3 d^2)^2 (2^2 a^{-2} d^{-3})^3 = (2^2 a^6 d^4)(2^6)(a^{-6} d^{-9})$$

$$= 2^2 (2^6)(a^6 a^{-6})(d^4 d^{-9})$$

$$= 2^{2+6} a^{6-6} d^{4-9}$$

$$= 2^8 a^0 d^{-5}$$

$$= 256 d^{-5}$$

5-4 Scientific Notation

Scientific notation is a practical application of exponents that is easily accessible to students. Those fascinated with large numbers might like to research the different uses of the words *billion* and *trillion* (also *billionth* and *trillionth*) in the United States and France, versus England and other European countries. (One trillion is 10^{12} in the United States and France. It is 10^{18} in the United Kingdom, Germany, and Spain and some other Spanish-speaking countries. Students could research usage in other countries as well.)

5-5 Polynomials

Students may know words such as *monaural, monorail, monotone, monocle, monologue, bilingual, biped, bicycle, bilateral, tricycle, triangle, triplet, polygraph, polygamy,* and *polygon,* which can help them remember the meanings of the prefixes for *one, two, three,* and *many.* They could use a dictionary to find many more. Again, use the words *monomial, binomial, trinomial,* and *polynomial* frequently, as the students will need to be very comfortable using them.

A polynomial with more than three terms—say 7 terms—is simply called a 7-term polynomial. Point out that there are now two distinct ways to classify polynomials—by degree and by the number of terms.

Some students may ask why, in Exercise 54, the third expression is not a polynomial since x appears to be raised to the first power. Without discussing fractional exponents, point out that square roots of variables do not fit the definition of monomial in Lesson 5-3. (Even the square root of the square of a variable is the absolute value of the variable, and not a monomial.)

5-6 More on Polynomials

Remind students that in a term involving only variables, such as x^5m^2, "1" is understood to be the coefficient. So $x^6 - x^5m^2 + 2x^5m^2 = x^6 + (-1)x^5m^2 + 2x^5m^2 = x^6 + (-1 + 2)x^5m^2 = x^6 + x^5m^2$. Students should be encouraged to write out this use of the distributive property if they have difficulty remembering this.

5-7, 5-8 Addition of Polynomials, Subtraction of Polynomials

Even students who have mastered the skills needed for these lessons may gain new insights from the area models of second degree polynomials and their sums and differences. However, students who do not easily deal with spatial representations do not need to master this illustration if they already possess the algebraic skills needed. (They might be challenged to do so, however!)

It is important to stress two things when beginning to use columns to subtract one polynomial from another. First, the sign of the coefficient must be recorded carefully, and second, a method must be chosen to reliably record the change in sign of each subtrahend term in order to add the inverse. The technique shown in the text—rewriting the problem to add the inverse—is time consuming though necessary to begin with. Later, students may just write new signs near each term. It is generally a bad idea to add a vertical bar to convert a subtraction symbol into an addition symbol, because it then becomes impossible to check what was changed.

5-9 Multiplication of Monomials and Binomials

Many students have probably used the FOIL technique before; some may use *outer* and *inner* instead of *outside* and *inside* but this should cause no problem.

5-10 Multiplying Binomials: Special Products

Students should memorize these formulas for special products, and it is important that they recognize that A and B can represent any algebraic expressions.

Point out to students that, just as they have used the distributive property to justify factoring a common monomial from a polynomial, learning these properties will later enable them to factor some kinds of polynomials. This is also a good opportunity to begin making students aware of fractional perfect squares, such as $\frac{9}{16}$ or $\frac{25y^2}{49}$. Again, point out that this information will be helpful later when they factor certain polynomials.

5-11 Multiplying Polynomials

Students should be required to identify which of the exercises can be done using one of the three special product formulas. Some students may need more experience satisfying themselves that FOIL supplies the same answer as the special formulas, but they must learn to use the formulas well—they will need to be facile with them later.

5-12 Reasoning Strategies: Make a Table, Look for a Pattern

Most students will recognize that the strategy *Look for a Pattern* can frequently be used in conjunction with *Make an Organized List,* as well as *Make a Table.*

Internet Activity On the Web

For professional development tips visit our Web site.
www.phschool.com

Monitoring Progress

UNIVERSAL ACCESS

▶ Preventing a Student from Falling Behind

These resources are particularly helpful in preventing a student from falling behind his or her appropriate math level. For a complete list of resources for this chapter, see page 202F.

Before Lessons

Skills You Need for Chapter 5 (p. 202)
- Using exponents
- Evaluating expressions
- Collecting like terms
- Simplifying expressions

Preteaching Math Vocabulary
- List of Key Terms (p. 202 and p. 256)
- Reading Math (p. 211)
- Writing Math (pp. 223, 235)

Skills Intervention Kit With CD-ROM

With Lesson	Use this Unit
5-2, 5-7, 5-9	Measurement
5-1, 5-2, 5-4	Pre-Algebra Basics

During Lessons

Try This Exercises (Student Edition)

Additional Examples (Teacher's Edition)

Help at Home
- Lessons 5-1 to 5-5
- Lessons 5-6 to 5-11
- Available in English and Spanish

Skills Intervention Kit

Innovative resource package for diagnosing students' gaps in basic skills, prescribing an individualized course of study, and monitoring progress. Eight intervention units cover core skills students need to succeed.

After Lessons

Lesson Quiz (Teacher's Edition)

Reteaching Worksheets (Teaching Resources Box)

Daily Cumulative Review Masters

There is a Daily Cumulative Review worksheet for every lesson in this chapter.

ASSESSMENT OPTIONS

Lesson	5-1	5-2	5-3	5-4	5-5	5-6	5-7	5-8	5-9	5-10	5-11	5-12	End
Try This Exercises	■	■	■	■	■	■	■	■	■	■	■		
Mixed Reviews	■	■	■	■	■	■	■	■	■	■	■		
Quizzes				■					■				
Chapter Assessment													■
Cumulative Review	A Cumulative Review for Chapters 1–7 is found on pp. 351–355.												
Standardized Test Prep	■	■		■					■				
	Sample College Entrance Exams are found in Problem Solving Practice Masters.												
Computer Item Generator CD-ROM	Can be used to create custom-made practice pages or assessment pages at any time.												
Student Tutorial CD-ROM	Students can self-assess and access tutorial help at any time.												

Test-Taking Tips on Transparencies

Test-Taking Tip: Use Mental Math

Sometimes, it is easiest to compute mentally.

Example Find the 7th term in the pattern.

1, 2, 4, 8, . . .

A. 16   B. 32   C. 64   D. 128   E. Not Here

To find the pattern, mentally compute how the terms relate to their position in the list.

1, 2, 4, 8
×2 ×2 ×2

The terms can be rewritten as $2^0, 2^1, 2^2, 2^3, ...$ So the 7th term must be 2^6.

The answer is 64, or choice C.

Use mental math to find the answer. Explain your reasoning.

1. Complete the table below, using the rule $y = 2x - 1$.

x	−1	0	1	2	3
y	−3	−1	1		

A. 4, 6   B. 2, 4   C. 3, 5   D. 3, 7   E. Not Here

2. Which pattern has the rule that the nth term is $3 - 2n$?
F. 1, −1, −3, −5, . . .   G. −1, 1, 3, 5, . . .
H. 1, 2, 3, 4, . . .   J. −2, −4, −6, −8, . . .
K. 1, −1, 3, −15, . . .

For use with Lesson 5-12

Resources for Chapter 5

TEACHING RESOURCES BOX

	First Five Minutes	Practice	Reteach	Enrichment	Problem Solving	Assessment	Cumulative Review	Lesson Planner	Success-Building	Teaching Transparencies	Help at Home	SE Answers on Transparencies
5-1	■	■	■	■			■	■	■	■		■
5-2	■	■	■				■	■				■
5-3	■	■	■				■	■	■			■
5-4	■	■■	■			■	■	■	■	■		■
5-5	■	■	■				■	■	■■		■	■
5-6	■	■	■				■	■				■
5-7	■	■	■				■	■				■
5-8	■	■	■				■	■				■
5-9	■	■■	■	■		■	■	■	■■	■		■
5-10	■	■	■				■	■	■			■
5-11	■	■	■	■			■	■	■■		■	■
5-12	■	■					■	■	■■■			■
End				■	■	5 Forms						■

Also available for use throughout the chapter:

Solution Key
Mathematics Standardized Test Prep
   Student Edition and Teacher's Edition

Overhead Manipulatives Kit
Practice Workbook

Student Manipulatives Kit
Test-Taking Tips on Transparencies

California Assessment Success Kit
Graphing Calculator Handbook

TECHNOLOGY

Computer Item Generator

CD-ROM with an unlimited supply of questions with varying degrees of difficulty for customized practice sheets, quizzes, and tests.

Secondary Math Toolkit™ with Integrated Math Labs

Integrated software package with linkable math tools for exploring key concepts.

Student Tutorial

Test preparation software for students on CD-ROM with management system for teachers; includes Secondary Math Lab Toolkit.

Resource Pro® with Planning Express®

CD-ROM with complete classroom planning tool and teaching resources for customizing and planning lessons.

Web Extension
www.phschool.com

For Students
- Chapter Support with Internet Links
- Internet Activities

For Teachers
- Curriculum Support
- Professional Development
- Product Information
- Regional Information

Also available for use throughout the chapter:

- Algebra Instructional Videos: A Step by Step Guide to Key Concepts

You may wish to preteach some of the key terms used in this chapter. Particularly for English Language Learners (ELL), presenting the vocabulary before the chapter or lesson begins gives students a head start into understanding the new material. Writing new words on poster paper, pointing to the words as you say them, then displaying the poster for a period of time is a useful technique.

additive inverses (p. 236)
ascending order (p. 226)
binomial (p. 222)
coefficient (p. 222)
constant (p. 214)
degree of a polynomial (p. 223)
degree of a term (p. 223)
descending order (p. 226)
evaluating a polynomial (p. 227)
exponential notation (p. 204)
FOIL (p. 241)
leading coefficient (p. 223)
leading term (p. 223)
monomial (p. 214)
polynomial (p. 221)
scientific notation (p. 217)
standard notation (p. 217)
trinomial (p. 222)

CHAPTER 5

What You'll Learn in Chapter 5

- How to multiply, divide, and raise a power to a power using exponents

- How to use scientific notation

- How to add and subtract polynomials

- How to multiply monomials and polynomials

Skills & Concepts You Need for Chapter 5

1-3 Write using exponential notation.

1. $8 \cdot 8 \cdot 8 \cdot 8$ 　　　　　　　　　**2.** $12 \cdot b \cdot b \cdot b$

1-3 Evaluate each expression.

3. $m^4 - 5$ for $m = 2$ 　　　　　　　**4.** $3b^2$ for $b = 4$

1-5, 2-7 Multiply.

5. $3(s + t + w)$ 　　　　　　　　　　**6.** $-7(x + 4)$

1-5 Collect like terms.

7. $2x + 8y + 7x + 5y$ 　　　　　　　**8.** $7b^2 + 9b + 2b^2 + 8$

2-5 Multiply.

9. $(-6)(-5)$ 　　　　　　　　　　　**10.** $-\frac{1}{2} \cdot \frac{5}{8}$

2-6 Divide.

11. $-\frac{16}{-2}$ 　　　　　　　　　　　　**12.** $-\frac{24}{16}$

2-8 Rename each additive inverse without parentheses.

13. $-(4x - 7y + 2)$ 　　　　　　　**14.** $-(12r + 7p - 9s)$

2-8 Simplify.

15. $5y - 8 - (9y - 6)$ 　　　　　　**16.** $5b - 4(6b - 2)$

202

Skills & Concepts You Need for Chapter 5

1. 8^4
2. $12b^3$
3. 11
4. 48
5. $3s + 3t + 3w$
6. $-7x - 28$
7. $9x + 13y$
8. $9b^2 + 9b + 8$
9. 30
10. $-\frac{5}{16}$
11. 8

12. $-\frac{3}{2}$
13. $-4x + 7y - 2$
14. $-12r - 7p + 9s$
15. $-4y - 2$
16. $-19b + 8$

Exponents and Polynomials

The thickness of a soap bubble is about 0.0000001 m. You can express this measurement with scientific notation as 1.0×10^{-7} m.

5-1 ▷ Exponents

1. FOCUS

FIRST FIVE MINUTES

1. $2 \cdot 2 \cdot 2 =$
   8
2. $3^2 =$
   9
3. $(2 \cdot 2 \cdot 2) \cdot (2 \cdot 2) =$
   32
4. $100 \cdot 1000 =$
   100,000

Rewrite without exponents.

5. x^3
   $x \cdot x \cdot x$

6. $\frac{1000}{100} =$
   10

7. $\frac{a^3}{a} =$
   a^2

2. TEACH the Mathematics

1 Multiplying Using Exponents

Point out that we are not multiplying bases, but counting how many times the base is used as a factor.

Note that a^0 is discussed in the next subsection.

Key Questions

- Does $a^2 \cdot a^4 = a^3 \cdot a^3$?
  Yes
- Does $1^2 = 1^3$?
  Yes
- Does $a^3 \cdot a^2 = a^6$?
  No, $a^3 \cdot a^2 = a^5$.
- Does $a^2 \cdot b^2 = ab^4$?
  No, the bases are *not* the same.

Chalkboard Examples

Simplify. Express using exponents.
1. $2^3 \cdot 2^6$
   $2^{3+6} = 2^9$
   $(2 \cdot 2 \cdot 2)(2 \cdot 2 \cdot 2 \cdot 2 \cdot 2 \cdot 2) = 2^9$
2. $a^2 \cdot a^4$
   $a^{2+4} = a^6$
   $(a \cdot a)(a \cdot a \cdot a \cdot a) = a^6$
3. $z \cdot z^5 \cdot z^3$
   $z^{1+5+3} = z^9$

What You'll Learn

1 To multiply numbers in exponential form

2 To divide numbers in exponential form

. . . And Why

To simplify expressions containing exponents

Recall that an exponent tells how many times we use a base as a factor. For example, $a^3 = a \cdot a \cdot a$. An expression written with exponents is written using **exponential notation.**

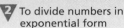

PART 1 Multiplying Using Exponents

Objective: Multiply numbers in exponential form.

We can use the meaning of an exponent to develop a rule for multiplying powers with like bases.

$$8^3 \cdot 8^2 \text{ means } (8 \cdot 8 \cdot 8)(8 \cdot 8) = 8^5$$
$$5^2 \cdot 5^4 \text{ means } (5 \cdot 5)(5 \cdot 5 \cdot 5 \cdot 5) = 5^6$$
$$a^5 \cdot a \text{ means } (a \cdot a \cdot a \cdot a \cdot a)(a) = a^6$$

Notice we could add the exponents to find the exponent of the product.

$$8^3 \cdot 8^2 = 8^{3+2} = 8^5$$
$$5^2 \cdot 5^4 = 5^{2+4} = 5^6$$
$$a^5 \cdot a = a^{5+1} = a^6 \qquad a = a^1$$

Multiplying Powers with Like Bases

For any rational number a, and for all whole numbers m and n,
$$a^m \cdot a^n = a^{m+n}$$

EXAMPLES Simplify. Express using exponents.

1 $8^4 \cdot 8^3 = 8^{4+3}$ $\qquad\qquad (8 \cdot 8 \cdot 8 \cdot 8)(8 \cdot 8 \cdot 8) = 8^7$
$\qquad\quad = 8^7$

2 $y \cdot y^2 \cdot y^5 = y^{1+2+5}$ $\qquad (y)(y \cdot y)(y \cdot y \cdot y \cdot y \cdot y) = y^8$
$\qquad\qquad\quad = y^8$

3 $(a^3b^2)(a^3b^5) = (a^3a^3)(b^2b^5)$
$\qquad\qquad\qquad = a^{3+3}b^{2+5}$
$\qquad\qquad\qquad = a^6b^7$

Try This Simplify. Express using exponents.

a. $5^2 \cdot 5^4$ **b.** $a^5 \cdot a^3$ **c.** $y^3 \cdot y^2 \cdot y^5$ **d.** $(mn^2)(m^4n^6)$

204 Chapter 5 *Exponents and Polynomials*

Try This

a. 5^6
b. a^8
c. y^{10}
d. m^5n^8

Objective: Divide numbers in exponential form.

The following suggests a rule for simplifying expressions in the form $\frac{a^m}{a^n}$.

$$\frac{3^5}{3^2} = \frac{3 \cdot 3 \cdot 3 \cdot 3 \cdot 3}{3 \cdot 3} = 3 \cdot 3 \cdot 3 = 3^3$$

Notice that we can subtract the exponents to find the exponent of the quotient.

Dividing Powers with Like Bases

For any rational number a except 0, and for all whole numbers m and n,

$$\frac{a^m}{a^n} = a^{m-n}$$

EXAMPLES Simplify. Express using exponents.

4 $\frac{4^5}{4^2} = 4^{5-2} = 4^3$ $\qquad\frac{4 \cdot 4 \cdot 4 \cdot 4 \cdot 4}{4 \cdot 4} = 4^3$

5 $\frac{x^6}{x^2} = x^{6-2} = x^4$ $\qquad\frac{x \cdot x \cdot x \cdot x \cdot x \cdot x}{x \cdot x} = x^4$

6 $\frac{p^5 \cdot q^7}{p^2 \cdot q^5} = p^{5-2}q^{7-5}$ $\qquad Think\ \frac{p^5}{p^2} \cdot \frac{q^7}{q^5}.$
$\qquad\qquad = p^3 q^2$

Try This Simplify. Express using exponents.

e. $\frac{7^6}{7^2}$ $\qquad$**f.** $\frac{a^7}{a^2}$ $\qquad$**g.** $\frac{m^4}{m^2}$ $\qquad$**h.** $\frac{x^4 y^3}{x^2 y^2}$

You can use the meaning of an exponent to simplify $\frac{5^2}{5^5}$.

$$\frac{5^2}{5^5} = \frac{5 \cdot 5}{5 \cdot 5 \cdot 5 \cdot 5 \cdot 5} = \frac{1}{5^3}$$

You can also use the rule above to simplify the expression $\frac{5^2}{5^5}$.

$$\frac{5^2}{5^5} = 5^{2-5} = 5^{-3}$$

This suggests that $5^{-3} = \frac{1}{5^3}$.

Try This
e. 7^4
f. a^5
g. m^2
h. $x^2 y$

---

4. $(x^2 y^3)(x^4 y^5)$
  $(x^2 x^4)(y^3 y^5) = x^{2+4}y^{3+5} = x^6 y^8$

2 Dividing Using Exponents

Use Teaching Transparency T17.
Note that the rule for dividing powers with like bases is given with the only restriction of $a \neq 0$. The definition of a negative exponent follows immediately. In the B-level exercises these two rules are combined.

To help students understand negative exponents, show them this pattern.
$$5^2 = 5 \cdot 5$$
$$5^1 = 5$$
To continue the pattern for 0 and negative exponents, continue to divide by 5.
$$5^0 = 1$$
$$5^{-1} = \frac{1}{5}$$
$$5^{-2} = \frac{1}{5 \cdot 5}$$
You may wish to point out to students that 0^0 is undefined.

Avoiding Common Errors

Many students will mistakenly replace x^0 with 0 rather than 1. Remind students that *any number* (other than 0) to the zero power is 1.

Key Questions
- What is $54,321^0$? 1
- What is 1^{-1}? 1

Chalkboard Examples
Simplify. Express using exponents.

1. $\frac{7^5}{7^3}$
  $7^{5-3} = 7^2$

2. $\frac{y^8}{y^5}$
  $y^{8-5} = y^3$

3. $\frac{r^3 s^4}{r^2 s^2}$
  $r^{3-2}s^{4-2} = rs^2$

Simplify.
4. 6^{-1}
  $\frac{1}{6}$

5. 5^{-2}
  $\frac{1}{5^2}$

6. x^{-4}
  $\frac{1}{x^4}$

In general, we can state the following.

Definition

For any rational number a except 0, and for all whole numbers m,
$$a^{-m} = \frac{1}{a^m}$$

EXAMPLES Express using positive exponents.

7 $4^{-2} = \frac{1}{4^2}$

8 $m^{-3} = \frac{1}{m^3}$

9 $ab^{-1} = a \cdot \frac{1}{b} = \frac{a}{b}$ The exponent affects only b.

Try This Express using positive exponents.

i. 2^{-2} **j.** y^{-4} **k.** $3c^{-2}$

You know that any nonzero number divided by itself equals 1. For example, $\frac{a^2}{a^2} = 1$. Using the rule given above, we also find that $\frac{a^2}{a^2} = a^{2-2} = a^0$. We can state the following about zero as an exponent.

Definition

$a^0 = 1$ for any rational number a except 0.

EXAMPLES Simplify.

10 $3^{-2} = \frac{1}{3^2} = \frac{1}{9}$

11 $1^{-4} = \frac{1}{1^4} = 1$

12 $p^0 = 1$ Any nonzero number to the 0 power $= 1$.

Try This Simplify.

l. 4^{-2} **m.** 1^{-10} **n.** 3^0

Try This

i. $\frac{1}{2^2}$

j. $\frac{1}{y^4}$

k. $\frac{3}{c^2}$

l. $\frac{1}{16}$

m. 1

n. 1

Exercises

1. 2^7
2. 3^7
3. 8^{14}
4. n^{23}
5. x^7
6. y^{16}
7. n^4
8. z^{14}
9. x^4
10. a^{14}
11. m^7
12. p^3

13. x^7
14. y^9
15. a^9
16. b^{10}
17. $a^8 b^7$
18. $x^7 y^3$
19. $p^3 q^4 r^5$
20. $x^9 y^9 z^{12}$
21. $5^2 s^4 t^4$
22. $2^2 x^3 y^4$
23. 7^3
24. 4^4
25. 8^6

26. 9^{13}
27. 1
28. 1
29. y^4
30. x
31. 1
32. h^3
33. 1
34. x^2
35. $a^2 b^3$
36. x
37. $4x^2$
38. $6^2 a^3$

39. $\frac{1}{3^2}$
40. $\frac{1}{6^3}$
41. $\frac{1}{x^4}$
42. $\frac{1}{n^6}$
43. $\frac{3}{a}$
44. $\frac{1}{3x}$
45. $\frac{1}{2y}$
46. $\frac{4}{x^3}$

5-1 Exercises

**Extra Help
On the Web**

Look for worked-out examples at the Prentice Hall Web site.
www.phschool.com

A

Simplify. Express using exponents.

1. $2^4 \cdot 2^3$ **2.** $3^5 \cdot 3^2$ **3.** $8^5 \cdot 8^9$ **4.** $n^3 \cdot n^{20}$

5. $x^4 \cdot x^3$ **6.** $y^7 \cdot y^9$ **7.** $n^3 \cdot n$ **8.** $z^7 \cdot z^7$

9. $x^3 \cdot x^1$ **10.** $a^6 \cdot a^8$ **11.** $m^7 \cdot m^0$ **12.** $p \cdot p \cdot p$

13. $x^4 \cdot x^2 \cdot x$ **14.** $y^2 \cdot y^4 \cdot y^3$ **15.** $a^3 \cdot a^4 \cdot a \cdot a$ **16.** $b \cdot b^5 \cdot b^2 \cdot b^2$

17. $(a^3b^6)(a^5b)$ **18.** $(x^2y)(x^5y^2)$ **19.** $(p^2q^3r^2)(pqr^3)$

20. $(x^7y^4z^4)(x^2y^5z^8)$ **21.** $(5s^2t^3)(5s^2t)$ **22.** $(2xy^2)(2x^2y^2)$

23. $\dfrac{7^5}{7^2}$ **24.** $\dfrac{4^7}{4^3}$ **25.** $\dfrac{8^{12}}{8^6}$ **26.** $\dfrac{9^{15}}{9^2}$

27. $\dfrac{6^4}{6^4}$ **28.** $\dfrac{2^7}{2^7}$ **29.** $\dfrac{y^9}{y^5}$ **30.** $\dfrac{x^{12}}{x^{11}}$

31. $\dfrac{g^5}{g^5}$ **32.** $\dfrac{h^4}{h}$ **33.** $\dfrac{m^8}{m^8}$ **34.** $\dfrac{x^7}{x^5}$

35. $\dfrac{a^3b^4}{ab}$ **36.** $\dfrac{x^8y}{x^7y}$ **37.** $\dfrac{4^3x^3}{4^2x}$ **38.** $\dfrac{6^4a^5b}{6^2a^2b}$

Express using positive exponents.

39. 3^{-2} **40.** 6^{-3} **41.** x^{-4} **42.** n^{-6}

43. $3a^{-1}$ **44.** $(3x)^{-1}$ **45.** $(2y)^{-1}$ **46.** $4x^{-3}$

47. $5c^{-4}$ **48.** $8m^{-1}$ **49.** $(3a)^{-1}$ **50.** cd^{-2}

Mental Math Simplify. Express without using exponents.

51. 4^{-2} **52.** 8^{-1} **53.** 5^{-3} **54.** 1^{-4}

55. 5^0 **56.** 2^{-4} **57.** 10^0 **58.** x^0

B

Simplify.

59. $(-2)^4(-2)^2$ **60.** $(-5)^2(-5)$ **61.** $\dfrac{(-3)^6}{(-3)^4}$ **62.** $\dfrac{(-10)^7}{(-10)^6}$

63. $\dfrac{4^3}{4^5}$ **64.** $\dfrac{3^4}{3^6}$ **65.** $\dfrac{(-2)^2}{(-2)^5}$ **66.** $\dfrac{(-5)^3}{(-5)^4}$

Simplify. Express using (a) negative exponents; (b) positive exponents.

67. $\dfrac{x^3}{x^7}$ **68.** $\dfrac{y}{y^4}$ **69.** $\dfrac{a^2}{a^6}$ **70.** $\dfrac{m^5}{m^{10}}$

Evaluate each expression.

71. $x^5 \cdot x^3$ for $x = 2$ **72.** $10^m \cdot 10^n$ for $m = 2$ and $n = 4$

73. $a^3 \cdot a^2 \cdot a$ for $a = -2$ **74.** $2^a \cdot 2^b \cdot 2^c$ for $a = 3, b = 2, c = 2$

3. PRACTICE/ASSESS

LESSON QUIZ

Simplify.

1. $5^6 \cdot 5^4$
   5^{10}

2. $m^4 \cdot m^5$
   m^9

3. $(a^2b^6)(a^4b^3)$
   a^6b^9

Express using positive exponents.

4. 7^{-1}
   $\dfrac{1}{7}$

5. 8^{-2}
   $\dfrac{1}{8^2}$

6. x^{-5}
   $\dfrac{1}{x^5}$

Assignment Guide

To provide flexible scheduling, this lesson can be split into parts.
▼ Core 1–22, 59, 60, 71–74
   Extension 76–78, 87–93
▼ Core 23–58, 61–70, 75
   Extension 79–86, 94, 95

Use Mixed Review to maintain skills.

47. $\dfrac{5}{c^4}$ **56.** $\dfrac{1}{16}$ **67.** (a) x^{-4}

48. $\dfrac{8}{m}$ **57.** 1 (b) $\dfrac{1}{x^4}$

58. 1

49. $\dfrac{1}{3a}$ **59.** 64 **68.** (a) y^{-3}

50. $\dfrac{c}{d^2}$ **60.** -125

61. 9 (b) $\dfrac{1}{y^3}$

51. $\dfrac{1}{16}$ **62.** -10

52. $\dfrac{1}{8}$ **69.** (a) a^{-4}

63. $\dfrac{1}{16}$

53. $\dfrac{1}{125}$ **64.** $\dfrac{1}{9}$ (b) $\dfrac{1}{a^4}$

54. 1 **65.** $-\dfrac{1}{8}$

55. 1 **70.** (a) m^{-5}

66. $-\dfrac{1}{5}$ (b) $\dfrac{1}{m^5}$

71. 256
72. 1,000,000
73. 64
74. 128

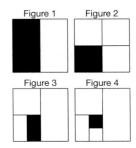

Figure 1   Figure 2

Figure 3   Figure 4

75. *Multi-Step Problem*   Use the figures at the left.
  a. What fraction of each figure is shaded?
  b. Rewrite each fraction in part (a) as a power of 2.
  c. *Mathematical Reasoning*   What pattern occurs in your answers to part (b)?
  d. If the pattern were to continue to Figure 10, what portion of the square would be shaded?

Error Analysis   Find and correct each error in Exercises 76 and 77.

76. $(3x^2)(2x^5) = 6x^{2 \cdot 5} = 6x^{10}$ **77.** $x^5 \cdot x \cdot x^2 = x^{5+2} = x^7$

78. **TEST PREP**   If $5^{x+1} = 125$, what is the value of x?

A. 2   **B.** 3   **C.** 4   **D.** 5

Simplify.

79. $\dfrac{4^2 \cdot 4^5}{4^3}$ **80.** $\dfrac{2^5 \cdot 3^4}{2^2 \cdot 3^2}$ **81.** $\dfrac{a^2 \cdot b^3}{a^2 \cdot b^5}$ **82.** $\dfrac{m^5 \cdot n^6}{m^2 \cdot m^2}$

83. $4^{-1} \cdot 4^5$ **84.** $\dfrac{(-3)}{(-3)^{-4}}$ **85.** $\dfrac{x^6 \cdot x^{-2}}{x^2}$ **86.** $\dfrac{a^{-2} \cdot b^{-3}}{a^4 \cdot b^{-1}}$

87. *Critical Thinking*   Is $(a + b)^m = a^m + b^m$ true for all numbers? If yes, justify your answer. If no, give a counterexample.

Challenge

Write each of the following as a power of 2.

88. 16   **89.** 4^3 **90.** 8^2 **91.** $4^3 \cdot 8 \cdot 16$

92. Write $2^8 \cdot 16^3 \cdot 64$ as a power of 4.

93. Write $9 \cdot 27 \cdot 3 \cdot 81$ as a power of 3.

Simplify.

94. $\dfrac{\left(\frac{1}{c}\right)^4}{\left(\frac{1}{c}\right)^5}$ **95.** $\dfrac{\left(\frac{a}{b}\right)^3}{\left(\frac{a}{b}\right)^6}$

Mixed Review

Simplify.   **96.** $3[8 - 2(t + 3)]$ **97.** $(5m + 6n) - (6m + 9n)$

98. $6a - 9a(4a + 3)$ **99.** $7a(a + 2) + 3a^2 + 2a^2$ *2-8*

Write as an algebraic expression.   **100.** the difference of w and 4

101. 8 less than the product of a and c **102.** twice the sum of m and n *1-6*

Solve.   **103.** $m - 422 = -53$ **104.** $21t = -693$

105. $6(m + 3) = 10m - 2$ **106.** $\frac{3}{4}c + 4 = \frac{1}{4}c - 2$ *3-1, 3-2, 3-5*

107. Frank needs a new shirt and sweater and wants to spend at most \$45. If he finds a shirt for \$18, how much can he spend on a sweater?   *4-5*

Exercises

75. a. $\frac{1}{2}, \frac{1}{4}, \frac{1}{8}, \frac{1}{16}$
  b. $2^{-1}, 2^{-2}, 2^{-3}, 2^{-4}$
  c. 2 raised to the opposite of the figure number
  d. 2^{-10}
76. The exponents were multiplied when they should have been added.
  $(3x^2)(2x^5) = 6x^{2+5} = 6x^7$

77. When the exponents were added, the exponent of the x term, which is 1, was not included.
  $x^5 \cdot x \cdot x^2 = x^{5+1+2} = x^8$

78. A
79. 256
80. 72
81. b^{-2} or $\frac{1}{b^2}$
82. mn^6
83. 256
84. -243
85. x^2
86. $\frac{1}{a^6 b^2}$
87. No; let
  $a = 1, b = 2, m = 3, 27 \neq 9$
88. 2^4

89. 2^6
90. 2^6
91. 2^{13}
92. 4^{13}
93. 3^{10}
94. c

95. $\frac{b^3}{a^3}$

Mixed Review
96. $6 - 6t$
97. $-m - 3n$

98. $-21a - 36a^2$
99. $12a^2 + 14a$
100. $w - 4$
101. $ac - 8$
102. $2(m + n)$
103. 369
104. -33
105. 5
106. -12
107. \$27 or less

More with Exponents

5-2

5-2

TIME-FOCUS METER

Objective: Find a power to a power.

We can use the meaning of an exponent to simplify an expression like $(3^2)^4$.

$$(3^2)^4 = (3^2)(3^2)(3^2)(3^2)$$
$$= 3^{2+2+2+2}$$ Using the rule for multiplying powers with like
$$= 3^8$$ bases

Notice that we get the same result if we multiply the exponents.

$$(3^2)^4 = 3^{2 \cdot 4} = 3^8$$

In general, we can state the following rule for raising a power to a power.

Raising a Power to a Power

For any rational number a, and any whole numbers m and n,
$$(a^m)^n = a^{mn}$$

EXAMPLES   Simplify.

1 $(3^5)^4 = 3^{5 \cdot 4} = 3^{20}$ $(3^5)(3^5)(3^5)(3^5) = 3^{5+5+5+5} = 3^{5 \cdot 4}$

2 $((-2)^3)^2 = (-2)^{3 \cdot 2} = (-2)^6$

3 $(y^5)^3 = y^{5 \cdot 3} = y^{15}$ $(y^5)(y^5)(y^5) = y^{5+5+5} = y^{5 \cdot 3}$

4 $(m^2)^2 = m^{2 \cdot 2} = m^4$

Try This   Simplify.

a. $(5^4)^3$ **b.** $(2^2)^5$ **c.** $(a^6)^3$ **d.** $(n^4)^4$

Evaluating Expressions

We can evaluate numbers expressed in exponential notation using a calculator. For example, evaluate $(3^2)^4$.

   3   y^x 2   = y^x 4   =   → 6561

Try This
a. 5^{12}
b. 2^{10}
c. a^{18}
d. n^{16}

What You'll Learn

1 To find a power of a power

2 To find a power of a product or quotient

...And Why

To use the rules of exponents to get an answer quickly

---

1. FOCUS

FIRST FIVE MINUTES
Write without exponents.
1. 2^3
   $2 \cdot 2 \cdot 2 = 8$
2. 2^{-1}
   $\frac{1}{2}$
3. 5^{-2}
   $\frac{1}{5^2} = \frac{1}{25}$

Simplify. Express using exponents.
4. $7^3 \cdot 7^4 \cdot 7^2$
   $7^{3+4+2} = 7^9$
5. $5^4 \cdot 5^4 \cdot 5^4$
   $5^{4+4+4} = 5^{12}$
6. $3^2 \cdot 3^2 \cdot 3^2 \cdot 3^2 \cdot 3^2 \cdot 3^2$
   $3^{2 \cdot 6} = 3^{12}$

2. TEACH the Mathematics

1 **Raising a Power to a Power**

Emphasize that $(a^2)^3$ is short for $a^2 \cdot a^2 \cdot a^2 = a^{2+2+2} = a^6$. Since multiplication is short for repeated addition, we can multiply the powers to get the answer quickly.

Note that if $a = 0$ and either n or $m = 0$, then both sides of the equation $(a^m)^n = a^{mn}$ are undefined.

Avoiding Common Errors

Students often confuse the rule for multiplying with exponents with the rule for taking a power to a power. They may incorrectly write $(a^3)^2 = a^5$.
   Point out that $(a^3)^2$ is short for $(a^3)(a^3) = a^6$. Using the rule for raising a power to a power, $(a^3)^2 = a^{3 \cdot 2} = a^6$.

Key Questions
- What does $(2^3)^2$ equal?
   $2^6 = 64$
- Does $(2^3)^2 = (2^2)^3$?
   Yes
- Does $(2^2)^3 = 2^2 2^3$?
   No

Chalkboard Examples
Simplify.
1. $(5^2)^3$
   $5^{2 \cdot 3} = 5^6$

2. $(4^5)^6$
   $4^{5 \cdot 6} = 4^{30}$

3. $(x^4)^7$
   $x^{4 \cdot 7} = x^{28}$

4. $(t^2)^5$
   $t^{2 \cdot 5} = t^{10}$

▽2 Raising a Product or a Quotient to a Power

You may wish to show that -1 raised to an even power is 1, while -1 raised to an odd power is -1.

Note that if $n = 0$ and either a or $b = 0$, then both sides of the equation $(ab)^n = a^n \cdot b^n$ are undefined. This is also true of $\left(\frac{a}{b}\right)^n = \frac{a^n}{b^n}$.

Key Questions

■ Does $(2x)^3 = 2x^3$?
  No, $(2x)^3 = (2x)(2x)(2x) = 8x^3$.
■ Does $(2a)^3 = 2^3 \cdot a^3$?
  Yes
■ Does $\frac{2^3}{x} = \left(\frac{2}{x}\right)^3$?
  No

Chalkboard Examples

Simplify.

1. $(5x)^3$
   $(5x)(5x)(5x) = 5 \cdot 5 \cdot 5 \cdot x \cdot x \cdot x$
   $= 5^3 x^3 = 125x^3$

2. $(3z)^2$
   $(3z)(3z) = 3^2 z^2 = 9z^2$

3. $(2y)^4$
   $(2y)(2y)(2y)(2y)$
   $= 2^4 y^4 = 16y^4$

4. $(2a^3)^2$
   $2^2(a^3)^2 = 4a^6$

5. $(4x^5y^2)^3$
   $4^3(x^5)^3(y^2)^3$
   $= 64x^{15}y^6$

6. $(-2x^5y^2)^7$
   $(-2)^7(x^5)^7(y^2)^7$
   $-128x^{35}y^{14}$

7. $[(-1)^3]^{11}$
   $(-1)^{3 \cdot 11} = (-1)^{33} = -1$
   The product of an odd number of (-1) factors equals -1.

8. $\left(\frac{b^3}{5}\right)^2$
   $\frac{(b^3)^2}{5^2} = \frac{b^6}{25}$

9. $\left(\frac{x^5}{y^3}\right)^4$
   $\frac{(x^5)^4}{(y^3)^4} = \frac{x^{20}}{y^{12}}$

Try This

e. $9y^2$
f. $1296m^4$
g. $8a^9$
h. $16x^6$

Objective: Find the power of a product or a quotient.

Recall from Chapter 1 that when an expression inside parentheses is raised to a power, everything inside the parentheses is the base. Compare $2n^3$ and $(2n)^3$.

$2n^3$ means $2 \cdot n \cdot n \cdot n$ (n is the base.)
$(2n)^3$ means $(2n)(2n)(2n)$ ($2n$ is the base.)

We can use the meaning of an exponent to write expressions like $(2n)^3$ without parentheses.

EXAMPLES   Simplify.

5 $(2n)^3$ means $(2n)(2n)(2n) = 2 \cdot 2 \cdot 2 \cdot n \cdot n \cdot n$ Using the associative and commutative properties
$$= 2^3 n^3$$
$$= 8n^3$$

6 $(4x)^2$ means $(4x)(4x) = 4 \cdot 4 \cdot x \cdot x$
$$= 4^2 x^2$$
$$= 16x^2$$

7 $(3a^2)^3$ means $(3a^2)(3a^2)(3a^2) = 3 \cdot 3 \cdot 3 \cdot a^2 \cdot a^2 \cdot a^2$
$$= 3^3 \cdot a^{2+2+2}$$
$$= 3^3 a^{2 \cdot 3}$$
$$= 27a^6$$

Try This   Simplify.

e. $(3y)^2$ **f.** $(6m)^4$ **g.** $(2a^3)^3$ **h.** $(4x^3)^2$

Note the following relationship in Example 7.

$$(3a^2)^3 = (3^1 a^2)^3$$
$$= 3^{1 \cdot 3} a^{2 \cdot 3}$$
$$= 3^3 \cdot a^6$$

Each factor inside parentheses is raised to the third power. We can use the following rule for raising a product to a power.

Raising a Product to a Power

For any rational numbers a and b, and for any whole number n,
$$(ab)^n = a^n \cdot b^n$$

EXAMPLES Simplify.

8 $(3x^2)^3 = 3^3(x^2)^3$
$= 3^3x^6$
$= 27x^6$

9 $(5x^3y^5z^2)^4 = 5^4(x^3)^4(y^5)^4(z^2)^4$
$= 625x^{12}y^{20}z^8$

10 $(-5x^4y^3)^3 = (-5)^3(x^4)^3(y^3)^3$
$= -125x^{12}y^9$

11 $[(-x)^{25}]^2 = (-x)^{50}$
$= (-1 \cdot x)^{50}$ Using the property of -1
$= (-1)^{50}x^{50}$
$= 1 \cdot x^{50}$ An even number of negative factors
$= x^{50}$ gives a positive product.

Try This Simplify.

i. $(4y^3)^4$ **j.** $(3x^4y^7z^6)^5$ **k.** $(-7x^9y^6)^2$ **l.** $[(-y)^{15}]^3$

The rule for raising a quotient to a power is similar to the rule for raising a product to a power.

Raising a Quotient to a Power

For any rational numbers a and b except $b = 0$, and for any whole number n,

$$\left(\frac{a}{b}\right)^n = \frac{a^n}{b^n}$$

EXAMPLES Simplify.

12 $\left(\frac{x^2}{4}\right)^3 = \frac{(x^2)^3}{(4)^3} = \frac{x^6}{64}$

13 $\left(\frac{a^4}{b^3}\right)^2 = \frac{a^8}{b^6}$

Try This Simplify.

m. $\left(\frac{y^3}{2}\right)^2$ **n.** $\left(\frac{a^5}{3}\right)^3$ **o.** $\left(\frac{x^2}{y^3}\right)^2$

Reading Math

The expression $\left(\frac{2}{3}\right)^n$ is read "Two-thirds to the nth power." The expression $\left(\frac{2^n}{3^n}\right)$ is read "Two to the nth power divided by 3 to the nth power."

Try This

i. $256y^{12}$
j. $243x^{20}y^{35}z^{30}$
k. $49x^{18}y^{12}$
l. $-y^{45}$
m. $\frac{y^6}{4}$
n. $\frac{a^{15}}{27}$
o. $\frac{x^4}{y^6}$

LESSON QUIZ

Simplify.

1. $(7^6)^3$
   7^{18}

2. $(w^4)^9$
   w^{36}

3. $(6x)^3$
   $6^3x^3 = 216x^3$

4. $(3y^3)^4$
   $3^4y^{12} = 81y^{12}$

5. $(2a^2b^4)^5$
   $2^5a^{10}b^{20} = 32a^{10}b^{20}$

6. $\left(\frac{x^3}{4}\right)^3$
   $\frac{(x^3)^3}{4^3} = \frac{x^9}{4^3} = \frac{x^9}{64}$

Assignment Guide

To provide flexible scheduling, this lesson can be split into parts.

▼ Core 1–12
   Extension 68–73, 78–81,

▼ Connections
   Core 13–67
   Extension 74–77

Use Mixed Review to maintain skills.

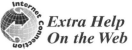
Internet Connection

Extra Help On the Web

Look for worked-out examples at the Prentice Hall Web site.
www.phschool.com

5-2 Exercises

A

Simplify.

1. $(2^5)^2$
2. $(3^4)^3$
3. $(5^2)^3$
4. $(6^8)^9$
5. $(y^5)^9$
6. $(x^3)^5$
7. $(m^8)^4$
8. $(n^5)^{12}$
9. $(a^6)^5$
10. $(y^7)^7$
11. $(p^{10})^{10}$
12. $(w^{12})^7$
13. $(3y)^4$
14. $(2t)^5$
15. $(7y)^3$
16. $(8x)^4$
17. $(5m)^2$
18. $(4y)^5$
19. $(7x)^4$
20. $(12a)^3$
21. $(2m^2)^2$
22. $(4n^3)^2$
23. $(5y^4)^3$
24. $(3x^5)^4$
25. $(-6t^2)^3$
26. $(-10b^6)^2$
27. $(8k^4)^3$
28. $(7x^5)^3$
29. $(2x^8y^3)^2$
30. $(3mn^4)^3$
31. $(-2x^2y^4)^3$
32. $(-3m^4n^2)^2$
33. $(4x^2y^3z)^4$
34. $(2m^5n^4p^3)^3$
35. $\left(\frac{3}{a^2}\right)^3$
36. $\left(\frac{7}{x^7}\right)^2$
37. $\left(\frac{x^2}{4}\right)^4$
38. $\left(\frac{y^5}{3}\right)^2$
39. $\left(\frac{m^4}{n^2}\right)^3$
40. $\left(\frac{a^8}{b^4}\right)^3$

B

Simplify.

41. $\left(\frac{3 \cdot 2^2}{5}\right)^3$
42. $\left(\frac{5 \cdot 2^4}{3}\right)^2$
43. $\left(\frac{xy^2}{z}\right)^3$
44. $\left(\frac{ab^4}{c}\right)^3$
45. $\left(\frac{-2x^2y^6}{5}\right)^2$
46. $\left(\frac{3x^3y^3}{2}\right)^4$
47. $\left(\frac{-4m^2n^5}{3}\right)^3$
48. $\left(\frac{-5p^4q^3}{2}\right)^3$
49. $[(-x^5)]^6$
50. $[(-y)^{18}]^2$
51. $\left(\frac{-x}{3y}\right)^3$
52. $\left(\frac{2c}{-y}\right)^4$
53. $\left(\frac{x^2y}{z}\right)^3$
54. $\left(\frac{m}{n^4p}\right)^3$
55. $\left(\frac{-3a^2b^4}{4c^3}\right)^2$
56. $\left(\frac{2m^5n^5}{p^4}\right)^3$
57. $(2n)^4\left(\frac{3}{2}n\right)^3$
58. $(4x^3)^2 + (2x^2)^3$
59. $(7a)(4a) - (3a)^2$
60. $(-2y^2)^3 + 4y(2y^5)$
61. $(-3z^4)^2 - (z^2)^4$
62. $(6cd^2)^2 + 3cd(cd^3)$
63. $3z^3(2z^4) - (-5z^3)^2$
64. $b^2(a^3b)^2 + a^2(a^2b^2)^2$
65. $(3c^4)^2(2c)$
66. $(-2x^2y^3)^4(xy)^3$
67. $(-3a^2b^4)^3(4a^3b)^2$

68. ***Critical Thinking*** Does $(a^m)^n = (a^n)^m$ for all rational numbers a and all natural numbers m and n? If yes, explain why. If no, provide a counterexample.

69. **TEST PREP** If $y = 2^x$, which of the following equals $4y$?
    A. 2^{2x} B. 2^{2+x} C. 2^{x^2} D. 4^x

Exercises

1. 2^{10}
2. 3^{12}
3. 5^6
4. 6^{72}
5. y^{45}
6. x^{15}
7. m^{32}
8. n^{60}
9. a^{30}
10. y^{49}
11. p^{100}
12. w^{84}
13. $81y^4$
14. $32t^5$
15. $343y^3$
16. $4096x^4$
17. $25m^2$
18. $1024y^5$
19. $2401x^4$
20. $1728a^3$
21. $4m^4$
22. $16n^6$
23. $125y^{12}$
24. $81x^{20}$
25. $-216t^6$
26. $100b^{12}$
27. $512k^{12}$
28. $343x^{15}$
29. $4x^{16}y^6$
30. $27m^3n^{12}$
31. $-8x^6y^{12}$
32. $9m^8n^4$
33. $256x^8y^{12}z^4$
34. $8m^{15}n^{12}p^9$
35. $\frac{27}{a^6}$
36. $\frac{49}{x^{14}}$
37. $\frac{x^8}{256}$
38. $\frac{y^{10}}{9}$
39. $\frac{m^{12}}{n^6}$
40. $\frac{a^{24}}{b^{12}}$
41. $\frac{1728}{125}$
42. $\frac{6400}{9}$
43. $\frac{x^3y^6}{z^3}$
44. $\frac{a^3b^{12}}{c^3}$
45. $\frac{4x^4y^{12}}{25}$
46. $\frac{81x^{12}y^{12}}{16}$
47. $-\frac{64m^6n^{15}}{27}$
48. $-\frac{125p^{12}q^9}{8}$
49. x^{30}
50. y^{36}
51. $-\frac{x^3}{27y^3}$

Challenge

Simplify.

70. $x^{2a}x^4$

71. $x^{3a}x^{2b}$

72. $x^{a+4}x^3$

73. x^5x^{2a-4}

74. $(a^{n+1}b^{m+2})^3$

75. $(x^a y^{a-3})^3$

76. $(c^3 d)^a (cd^7)^a$

77. $x^2(x^{a+2}y^3)$

Solve for a.

78. $x^{a+4} = x^4 x^8$

79. $x^{a-3} = x^5 x^3$

80. $x^{2a} = \dfrac{x^{12}}{x^9}$

81. $x^{3a} = x^4 x^6$

Mixed Review

Simplify. **82.** $6c + (-9m) - 5c + m$ **83.** $21 - 8x - 9 - (-7x)$ *2-8*

Give the reciprocal. **84.** $\dfrac{x}{y}$ **85.** $\dfrac{5c}{8}$ **86.** $\dfrac{-5}{2a}$ **87.** $\dfrac{m}{2}$ **88.** $\dfrac{7}{t}$ *2-6*

Solve. **89.** $m + 4 = -3m$ **90.** $4x + 2x = 9x - 6$ *3-5*

◇◇ Connections: Geometry

1. Find the volume of a cube with sides of length $2x$.

2. Suppose the cube has sides of length $4x$. What would its volume be?

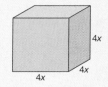

3. Suppose the cube has sides of length $8x$. What would its volume be?

4. How do the volumes of each of the cubes above change as the dimension doubles?

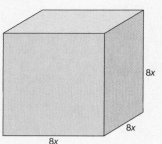

---

52. $\dfrac{16c^4}{y^4}$

53. $\dfrac{x^6 y^3}{z^3}$

54. $\dfrac{m^3}{n^{12}p^3}$

55. $\dfrac{9a^4 b^8}{16c^6}$

56. $\dfrac{8m^{15}n^{15}}{p^{12}}$

57. $54n^7$

58. $24x^6$

59. $19a^2$

60. 0

61. $8z^8$

62. $39c^2 d^4$

63. $6z^7 - 25z^6$

64. $2a^6 b^4$

65. $18c^9$

66. $16x^{11}y^{15}$

67. $-432a^{12}b^{14}$

68. Yes. We know $(a^m)^n = a^{mn}$. By the commutative property $mn = nm$, so $a^{mn} = a^{nm}$. Since $a^{nm} = (a^n)^m$, $(a^m)^n = (a^n)^m$.

69. B

70. x^{2a+4}

71. x^{3a+2b}

72. x^{a+7}

73. x^{2a+1}

74. $a^{3n+3}b^{3m+6}$

75. $x^{3a}y^{3a-9}$

76. $c^{4a}d^{8a}$

77. $x^{a+4}y^3$

78. $a = 8$

79. $a = 11$

80. $a = \dfrac{3}{2}$

81. $a = \dfrac{10}{3}$

Mixed Review

82. $c - 8m$

83. $12 - x$

84. $\dfrac{y}{x}$

85. $\dfrac{8}{5c}$

86. $-\dfrac{2a}{5}$

87. $\dfrac{2}{m}$

88. $\dfrac{t}{7}$

89. $m = -1$

90. $x = 2$

Connections: Geometry

1. $(2x)^3$ or $8x^3$

2. $(4x)^3$ or $64x^3$

3. $(8x)^3$ or $512x^3$

4. As the dimension doubles, the volume increases 8 times.

5-3

TIME-FOCUS METER

1. FOCUS

FIRST FIVE MINUTES

Simplify.

1. $3x + 2 + 4x$
   $7x + 2$

2. $x^5 \cdot x^9$
   x^{14}

3. $5a + 3b + 8a + 8b$
   $13a + 11b$

4. $a^4 \cdot a^{-7} \cdot a^2$
   a^{-1}

5. $3\left(-\frac{1}{6}\right)x^2$
   $-\frac{1}{2}x^2$

6. $(2x^3)^4$
   $16x^{12}$

2. TEACH the Mathematics

1 Multiplying Monomials

Many students will start doing part of their solutions in their heads, rather than on paper. Point out that shortcuts often lead to errors, and that steps should be written out until the student is very comfortable with the material.

Key Questions

- Is $2xy$ a monomial?
  Yes

- Is $2x + y$ a monomial?
  No

- Is the product of two monomials always a monomial?
  Yes

Chalkboard Examples

Multiply.

1. $(7y)(2y)$
   $14y^2$

2. $(5a^3)(3a^2)$
   $(5 \cdot 3)(a^3a^2) = 15a^5$

3. $(-3x^3)(4xy^5)$
   $(-3 \cdot 4)(x^3x)y^5 = -12x^4y^5$

4. $(7r^3)(-2r^4)(3r^5)$
   $7 \cdot (-2) \cdot 3 \cdot (r^3r^4r^5) = -42r^{12}$

What You'll Learn

1 To multiply monomials

2 To divide monomials

...And Why

To prepare for multiplication and division of polynomials

Try This

a. $-15x$

b. $-m^2$

c. y^2

d. x^5

e. $12p^7q^5$

f. $-8x^{11}y^9$

g. $14y^8$

h. $-21a^{13}$

 CA 10.0: Multiply and divide monomials.

5-3 ▷ Multiplying and Dividing Monomials

 PART 1 Multiplying Monomials

Objective: Multiply monomials.

A **monomial** is an expression that is either a numeral, a variable, or a product of numerals and variables with whole number exponents. If the monomial is a numeral, we call it a **constant.**

These expressions are monomials.

$$4x^3 \qquad -7ab \qquad x \qquad \tfrac{1}{2}y^5 \qquad -8 \qquad 2x^2y$$

These expressions are not monomials.

$$\frac{1}{y} \qquad x^{\frac{1}{2}} \qquad x^2 + 4 \qquad y^2 + 2y - 4$$

We can multiply two monomials using the properties of rational numbers and the properties of exponents.

EXAMPLES Multiply.

1 $(3x)(4x) = (3 \cdot 4)(x \cdot x)$ Using the associative and commutative properties

$\qquad\qquad\quad = 12x^2$ Multiplying

2 $(3x^2)(-x) = (3x^2)(-1x)$
$\qquad\qquad\quad = (3 \cdot -1)(x^2 \cdot x)$
$\qquad\qquad\quad = -3x^3$ Multiplying $(x^2 \cdot x = x^{2+1})$

3 $(-7x^2y^5)(4xy^3) = (-7 \cdot 4)(x^2 \cdot x)(y^5 \cdot y^3)$
$\qquad\qquad\qquad\quad = -28x^3y^8$ Multiplying $(x^2 \cdot x = x^{2+1}, y^5 \cdot y^3 = y^{5+3})$

4 $(4m^2)(2m^3)(-m) = (4 \cdot 2 \cdot -1)(m^2 \cdot m^3 \cdot m)$
$\qquad\qquad\qquad\quad = -8m^6$ Multiplying $(m^2 \cdot m^3 \cdot m = m^{2+3+1})$

5 $(-3a)(4a^2)(-a^4) = (-3 \cdot 4 \cdot -1)(a \cdot a^2 \cdot a^4)$
$\qquad\qquad\qquad\quad = 12a^7$

Try This Multiply.

a. $(3x)(-5)$ b. $(-m)m$ c. $(-y)(-y)$

d. $(-x)^2x^3$ e. $(3p^5q^2)(4p^2q^3)$ f. $(4x^5y^5)(-2x^6y^4)$

g. $(-7y^4)(-y)(2y^3)$ h. $(7a^5)(3a^3)(-a^5)$

214 Chapter 5 *Exponents and Polynomials*

Objective: Divide monomials.

We can also divide monomials using the properties of rational numbers and the properties of exponents.

EXAMPLES Divide.

6 $\dfrac{x^5}{x^2} = x^{5-2} = x^3$

7 $\dfrac{4x^2}{5x^7} = \dfrac{4}{5} \cdot x^{2-7} = \dfrac{4}{5}x^{-5} = \dfrac{4}{5x^5}$

8 $\dfrac{8x^5y^{12}}{-2x^3y^{10}} = \dfrac{8}{-2} \cdot x^{5-3}y^{12-10} = -4x^2y^2$

Try This Divide.

i. $\dfrac{x^8}{x^5}$ j. $\dfrac{12m^5}{8m^8}$ k. $\dfrac{-5x^3y^4}{-5x^2y}$ l. $\dfrac{-32x^{15}y^7}{8x^{14}y^6}$

5-3 Exercises

Extra Help On the Web

Look for worked-out examples at the Prentice Hall Web site. www.phschool.com

A

Multiply.

1. $(6x^2)(7)$ **2.** $(5y^3)(-2)$ **3.** $(-x^3)(-x)$

4. $(-y^4)(y^2)$ **5.** $(-x^5)(x^3)$ **6.** $(-m^6)(-m^2)$

7. $(3a^4)(2a^2)$ **8.** $(5x^3)(4x^5)$ **9.** $(7t^5)(4t^3)$

10. $(-3b^3)(5b^5)$ **11.** $(3g^4)(-6g^3)$ **12.** $(h^5)(-7h^3)$

13. $(-6x^3)(x^8)$ **14.** $(-8m^7)(-4m^3)$ **15.** $(-5n^4)(-5n^4)$

16. $(-x^7)(5x^{12})$ **17.** $(x^3y^4)(x^4y^2)$ **18.** $(2m^3n^2)(-3m^6n^5)$

19. $(4a^4b^8)(2a^4b^2)$ **20.** $(-2x^3y)(-6x^9y^8)$ **21.** $(y^5)(2y)(3y^2)$

22. $(3x^4)(x^4)(5x^2)$ **23.** $(-4m^2)(5m^4)(-2m^3)$ **24.** $(9b^2)(2b^5)(-3b^7)$

Divide.

25. $\dfrac{x^6}{x^2}$ **26.** $\dfrac{a^7}{a}$ **27.** $\dfrac{4x^5}{2x^2}$ **28.** $\dfrac{-6a^3}{6a}$

29. $\dfrac{12m^4}{4m^4}$ **30.** $\dfrac{-4x^6}{-2x^6}$ **31.** $\dfrac{5a^3}{a^7}$ **32.** $\dfrac{15y^8}{3}$

33. $\dfrac{-h^5}{2h^4}$ **34.** $\dfrac{k^3}{3k^8}$ **35.** $\dfrac{2x^{10}}{8x^5}$ **36.** $\dfrac{3m^5}{6m^7}$

Try This

i. x^3

j. $\dfrac{3}{2m^3}$

k. xy^3

l. $-4xy$

Exercises

1. $42x^2$
2. $-10y^3$
3. x^4
4. $-y^6$
5. $-x^8$
6. m^8
7. $6a^6$
8. $20x^8$
9. $28t^8$
10. $-15b^8$
11. $-18g^7$
12. $-7h^8$
13. $-6x^{11}$
14. $32m^{10}$
15. $25n^8$
16. $-5x^{19}$
17. x^7y^6
18. $-6m^9n^7$
19. $8a^8b^{10}$
20. $12x^{12}y^9$
21. $6y^8$
22. $15x^{10}$
23. $40m^9$
24. $-54b^{14}$
25. x^4
26. a^6
27. $2x^3$
28. $-a^2$
29. 3
30. 2
31. $\dfrac{5}{a^4}$
32. $5y^8$
33. $-\dfrac{1}{2}h$
34. $\dfrac{1}{3k^5}$
35. $\dfrac{1}{4}x^5$
36. $\dfrac{1}{2m^2}$

---

2 Dividing Monomials

You may want to illustrate the algebraic concept with an arithmetic example. For instance,

$\dfrac{4^3}{4^2} = \dfrac{4 \cdot 4 \cdot 4}{4 \cdot 4} = \dfrac{64}{16} = 4$

or

$\dfrac{4^3}{4^2} = 4^{3-2} = 4^1 = 4$

Key Question

- Is the quotient of two monomials always a monomial?

  No, the quotient may not have whole-number exponents. For example $x \div y = \dfrac{x}{y}$ or xy^{-1}. This is not a monomial.

Chalkboard Examples

Divide.

1. $\dfrac{y^7}{y^4}$

   $y^{7-4} = y^3$

2. $\dfrac{6a^9}{8a^4}$

   $\dfrac{6}{8}(a^{9-4}) = \dfrac{3}{4}a^5$

3. $\dfrac{9a^3b^5}{3a^2b^3}$

   $\dfrac{9}{3}a^{3-2}b^{5-3} = 3ab^2$

3. PRACTICE/ASSESS

LESSON QUIZ

Multiply.

1. $(4x)(-5)$
   $-20x$
2. $(-3a^5)(4a^7)$
   $-12a^{12}$
3. $(x^3)(-6x^2)(4x^5)$
   $-24x^{10}$

Divide.

4. $\dfrac{y^9}{y^2}$
   y^7
5. $\dfrac{4x^7}{2x^3}$
   $2x^4$

Assignment Guide

To provide flexible scheduling, this lesson can be split into parts.
▼ Core 1–24, 49–60
    Extension 70, 71, 74–77
▼ Core 25–48, 61–68
    Extension 69, 72, 73

Use Mixed Review to maintain skills.

37. $\frac{16x^2}{-4x^2}$ 38. $\frac{-25a^7}{-25}$ 39. $\frac{45x^3}{15x^2}$ 40. $\frac{6m^6}{2m^2}$

41. $\frac{10x^5y^4}{2x^3y}$ 42. $\frac{-12m^7n^8}{4m^2n^5}$ 43. $\frac{24a^6b^9}{-6a^6b^3}$ 44. $\frac{48x^6y^7}{12xy^5}$

45. $\frac{-12p^8r^3}{4p^6r^4}$ 46. $\frac{2x^{12}y^5}{3x^4y^2}$ 47. $\frac{5a^{11}b^7}{-7a^5b^9}$ 48. $\frac{6x^{13}y^4}{24x^5y^7}$

B

Simplify.

49. $x^3(x^4)^2$ 50. $p(p^4)^3$ 51. $(a^3)^2(a^4)^3$

52. $(m^2)^4(m^3)^2$ 53. $(2x^2)(3x^3)^2$ 54. $(3y^4)(5y^4)^2$

55. $(3x^4)^2(2x^5)^2$ 56. $(4y)^3(-2y^2)^2$ 57. $(2x^2y)(3x^4y^5)$

58. $(-3mn^4)(4mn^2)$ 59. $(ab^2)^3(a^3b^4)^2$ 60. $(m^3n)^2(mn^5)^3$

61. $\frac{(-2x^2)^2}{x^3}$ 62. $\frac{(3a^3)^2}{18a^2}$ 63. $\frac{(4y^3)^2}{(4y^2)^2}$ 64. $\frac{(-5m)^4}{(-25m^2)^2}$

65. $\frac{a^4b^5}{3a^2b^6}$ 66. $\frac{2x^6y^4}{8x^4y^7}$ 67. $\frac{-2m^3}{-4m^4n^6}$ 68. $\frac{-4ab^3}{-8a^2b^4}$

69. *Critical Thinking*   When a monomial is multiplied or divided by a certain monomial, you get the same result. What must be true of the certain monomial?

Challenge

Simplify.

70. $(5x^{-2})(2x^{-4})$ 71. $(8m^{-3})(-4m^4)(m^{-4})$

72. $\frac{25b^{16}}{5b^{-12}}$ 73. $\frac{12m^{-10}}{-4m^5}$

74. $(3a^{-2}b^4)(-4a^6b^{-7})$ 75. $(5x^6y^7)(3x^{-6}y^{-7})$

76. $(5x^{-4}y^{-6}z^5)(-4x^5y^5z^{-3})(-4x^2yz^{-1})$ 77. $(qrs)(-qrs^3)(-5q^{-3}r^4s^{-5})$

Mixed Review

Each problem below involves the sum or difference of monomials. Simplify each expression by collecting like terms.

78. $3x + 2y + 4x$ 79. $7x + 3y^2 + y^2$ 80. $8pt + 4t + 2pt + t$ *1-5*

81. $5m - 7m$ 82. $m - 3n - 2n$ 83. $14a + b - 5a - 3b$ *2-7*

Write each as a decimal. 84. 15% 85. 0.04% 86. 125% *3-10*

Solve.   87. $8x + 4 - 6x < -10$ 88. $6x \le -36$ 89. $3 - 6x < 9$ *4-4*

90. There were 407 books in the school library. The ninth grade returned 23 books and checked out 17; the tenth grade returned 15 books and checked out 29; the twelfth grade checked out 26 books and returned 30. How many books were left in the library? *2-3, 2-4*

Exercises

37. -4
38. a^7
39. $3x$
40. $3m^4$
41. $5x^2y^3$
42. $-3m^5n^3$
43. $-4b^6$
44. $4x^5y^2$
45. $\frac{-3p^2}{r}$
46. $\frac{2x^8y^3}{3}$
47. $\frac{-5a^6}{7b^2}$

48. $\frac{x^8}{4y^3}$
49. x^{11}
50. p^{13}
51. a^{18}
52. m^{14}
53. $18x^8$
54. $75y^{12}$
55. $36x^{18}$
56. $256y^7$
57. $6x^6y^6$
58. $-12m^2n^6$

59. a^9b^{14}
60. m^9n^{17}
61. $4x$
62. $\frac{a^4}{2}$
63. y^2
64. 1
65. $\frac{a^2}{3b}$
66. $\frac{x^2}{4y^3}$
67. $\frac{1}{2mn^6}$
68. $\frac{1}{2ab}$

69. It must be equal to one.
70. $\frac{10}{x^6}$
71. $\frac{-32}{m^3}$
72. $5b^{28}$
73. $-\frac{3}{m^{15}}$
74. $-\frac{12a^4}{b^3}$
75. 15
76. $80x^3z$
77. $\frac{5r^6}{qs}$

Mixed Review
78. $7x + 2y$
79. $4y^2 + 7x$
80. $10pt + 5t$
81. $-2m$
82. $m - 5n$
83. $9a - 2b$
84. 0.15
85. 0.0004
86. 1.25
87. $x < -7$
88. $x \le -6$
89. $x > -1$
90. 403

Scientific Notation

Objective: Write numbers using scientific notation.

Math in Action

The distance from Earth to the North Star is about 10,000,000,000,000,000,000 meters. The thickness of a soap bubble is about 0.0000001 meter. It is easy to make errors when working with numbers involving many zeros. If an extra zero is included, the resulting number is ten times larger or ten times smaller.

To prevent this type of error and to make it easier to work with very large and very small numbers, we can write these numbers in a form called **scientific notation.** Using scientific notation we can write a number as the product of a power of 10 and a number greater than or equal to 1, but less than 10. In scientific notation, the distance to the North Star is 1.0×10^{19} meters and the thickness of a soap bubble is about 1.0×10^{-7} meters. The numbers 10,000,000,000,000,000,000 and 0.0000001 are expressed using **standard notation.**

The thickness of a soap bubble is 0.0000001 m. How many times thicker than a soap bubble is a layer of plastic that is 0.00001 m thick?

EXAMPLES

1 Write 4.58×10^4 using standard notation.
$4.58 \times 10^4 = 45,800$ Multiplying 4.58 by 10^4, or 10,000, moves the decimal point 4 places to the right.

2 Write 3.4×10^{-2} using standard notation.
$3.4 \times 10^{-2} = 3.4 \times \frac{1}{10^2}$ Multiplying by 10^{-2} is the same as dividing by 10^2, or 100, and moves the decimal point 2 places to the left.

$= \frac{3.4}{100}$

$= 0.034$

Photo Caption
100 times

5-4 TIME-FOCUS METER

1. FOCUS

FIRST FIVE MINUTES
Calculate as a decimal number.
1. 10^6
   1,000,000
2. $321 \times 1,000,000$
   321,000,000
3. 0.0002×3000
   0.6
Simplify. Express using exponents.
4. $10^5 \cdot 10^2$
   10^7
5. $10^7 \cdot 10^{-4} \cdot 10^2$
   10^5
6. 1,000,000,000,000
   10^{12}
7. 0.1
   10^{-1}

MATH IN ACTION

The North Star is also known as the *Pole Star* (or *Polaris*) because it is almost directly over the North Pole. Navigators have used it for thousands of years. Because of slight changes in the rotation of Earth, it will be over the pole for only a few hundred more years. Then, after about 26,000 years, it will once again be the Pole Star.

2. TEACH the Mathematics

Use Teaching Transparency T18.
A number is in standard notation if it is expressed as a single factor, such as 34.765. A number such as 12.3×10^2 is in neither standard notation nor scientific notation.

> **Math Point**
> The number 10^{100} is called a *googol.* It was named by a young nephew of the American mathematician Edward Kasner. The number 10 to the googol power is called a *googolplex* and can be written $10^{10^{100}}$.

Key Questions

- Is 12.34×10^2 in scientific notation?
  No. 12.34 is not between 1 and 10.
- Is 0.237×10^3 in scientific notation?
  No. 0.237 is not between 1 and 10.
- Is 3.18×3^{10} in scientific notation?
  No. 3^{10} is not a power of ten.

Chalkboard Examples

Write using standard notation.

1. 1.76×10^1
   17.6
2. 1.76×10^2
   176
3. 1.76×10^4
   17,600

Write using scientific notation.

4. 32,100,000
   Move the decimal left 7 places.
   Multiply by 10^7 to bring it back.
   3.21×10^7

Multiply or divide. Express the result using scientific notation.

5. $(5.2 \times 10^9)(3.0 \times 10^{-3})$
   $= (5.2 \times 3.0)(10^9 \times 10^{-3})$
   $= 15.6 \times 10^6$
   $= 1.56 \times 10^7$

6. $\dfrac{2.7 \times 10^{16}}{9 \times 10^{-8}}$
   $= \dfrac{2.7}{9} \times \dfrac{10^{16}}{10^{-8}}$
   $= 0.3 \times 10^{24}$
   $= 3.0 \times 10^{23}$

Try This   Write using standard notation.

a. 1.25×10^3 **b.** 7×10^5 **c.** 4.8×10^{-3} **d.** 1.8×10^{-4}

EXAMPLES   Write using scientific notation.

3 $12,450 = 1.2450 \times ?$ Moving the decimal 4 places to the left, which is the same as dividing 12,450 by 10,000 or 10^4

   $= 1.245 \times 10^4$ Multiplying by 10^4 to balance this division

4 $0.2362 = 2.362 \times ?$ Moving the decimal 1 place to the right, which is the same as multiplying 0.2362×10

   $= 2.362 \times 10^{-1}$ Multiplying by 10^{-1} to balance this multiplication

5 $0.00236 = 0\,002.36 \times ?$ Moving the decimal 3 places to the right, which is the same as multiplying 0.00236 by 1000 or 10^3

   $= 2.36 \times 10^{-3}$ Multiplying by 10^{-3} to balance this multiplication

Try This   Write using scientific notation.

e. 3,200   **f.** 139,000   **g.** 0.0307   **h.** 0.2004

We can use the properties of exponents to multiply and divide numbers that are expressed in scientific notation.

EXAMPLES   Multiply or divide. Express the result using scientific notation.

6 $(3.0 \times 10^5)(4.1 \times 10^{-3}) = (3.0 \times 4.1)(10^5 \times 10^{-3})$ Applying the commutative and associative properties

   $= 12.3 \times 10^2$ Adding exponents to multiply
   $= 1.23 \times 10^3$ Converting to scientific notation

7 $\dfrac{2.5 \times 10^{-7}}{5.0 \times 10^6} = \dfrac{2.5}{5.0} \times \dfrac{10^{-7}}{10^6}$ Factoring

   $= 0.5 \times 10^{-13}$ Subtracting exponents to divide
   $= 5.0 \times 10^{-14}$ Converting to scientific notation

Try This   Multiply or divide. Express the result using scientific notation.

i. $(1.1 \times 10^{-8})(5 \times 10^{-7})$ **j.** $\dfrac{4.2 \times 10^5}{2.1 \times 10^2}$

Try This

a. 1250
b. 700,000
c. 0.0048
d. 0.00018
e. 3.2×10^3
f. 1.39×10^5
g. 3.07×10^{-2}
h. 2.004×10^{-1}
i. 5.5×10^{-15}
j. 2.0×10^3

Calculating with Scientific Notation

Some calculators allow you to enter numbers in scientific notation. Using a scientific calculator, follow the example below. The EXP key tells the calculator that you are entering a power of ten. If the exponent is negative, enter the negative sign after you enter the exponent.

Problem in standard notation
$(42{,}000{,}000)(250{,}000{,}000) = 10{,}500{,}000{,}000{,}000{,}000$

Problem using scientific notation
$$(4.2 \times 10^7)(2.5 \times 10^8) = (4.2)(2.5) \times (10^7)(10^8)$$
$$= 10.5 \times 10^{15} = 1.05 \times 10^{16}$$

Using a calculator
4.2 **EXP** 7 **X** 2.5 **EXP** 8 **=** 1.05 16
Notice that the calculator display shows only the 16 rather than 10^{16}.

5-4 Exercises

A

Write using standard notation.

1. 5.543×10^3 **2.** 3.29×10^2 **3.** 2.35×10^{-3}

4. 1.743×10^{-4} **5.** 5.7×10^4 **6.** 4.89×10^5

7. 3.4×10^{-5} **8.** 4×10^3 **9.** 6×10^{-4}

10. 1.206×10^2 **11.** 3.007×10^{-3} **12.** 8.04×10^{-5}

Write using scientific notation.

13. 425   **14.** 0.478   **15.** 12,400   **16.** 32,060

17. 0.045   **18.** 0.00003   **19.** 125,000   **20.** 12

21. 5,200,000   **22.** 12,400,000   **23.** 0.0000056   **24.** 0.000000032

Multiply or divide. Express your answer in scientific notation.

25. $(7 \times 10^4)(2 \times 10^2)$ **26.** $(2.2 \times 10^{-3})(3.0 \times 10^5)$

27. $(4.0 \times 10^7)(8.0 \times 10^3)$ **28.** $(6.1 \times 10^9)(2.5 \times 10^{-4})$

29. $(2.5 \times 10^{-3})(4.0 \times 10^{-8})$ **30.** $(5.4 \times 10^{-6})(5.1 \times 10^{-8})$

31. $\dfrac{(6.0 \times 10^7)}{(3.0 \times 10^2)}$ **32.** $\dfrac{(9.0 \times 10^8)}{(3.0 \times 10^2)}$ **33.** $\dfrac{(8.4 \times 10^6)}{(2.0 \times 10^8)}$

34. $\dfrac{(6.9 \times 10^4)}{(3.0 \times 10^8)}$ **35.** $\dfrac{(1.5 \times 10^{-2})}{(3 \times 10^{-4})}$ **36.** $\dfrac{(2.7 \times 10^{12})}{(9.0 \times 10^{12})}$

Extra Help On the Web

Look for worked-out examples at the Prentice Hall Web site.
www.phschool.com

Problems involving large numbers can also be done on calculators that do not have exponential notation. Students can write the numbers in scientific notation, perform the calculations on the decimal part, and use the laws of exponents to determine the magnitude of the answer.

3. PRACTICE/ASSESS

LESSON QUIZ

Write using standard notation.
1. 6.420×10^2
   642
2. 1.357×10^5
   135,700

Write using scientific notation.
3. 987654321
   9.87654321×10^8

Multiply or divide. Express the result in scientific notation.
4. $(4.4 \times 10^{-5})(7.0 \times 10^{-5})$
   3.08×10^{-9}

5. $\dfrac{8.1 \times 10^{-6}}{1.8 \times 10^9}$
   4.5×10^{-15}

Assignment Guide

▼ Core 1–44, 46, 47
  Extension 45, 48–51

Use Mixed Review to maintain skills.

Exercises

1. 5543	14. 4.78×10^{-1}	28. 1.525×10^6
2. 329	15. 1.24×10^4	29. 1.0×10^{-10}
3. 0.00235	16. 3.206×10^4	30. 2.754×10^{-13}
4. 0.0001743	17. 4.5×10^{-2}	31. 2.0×10^5
5. 57,000	18. 3×10^{-5}	32. 3.0×10^6
6. 489,000	19. 1.25×10^5	33. 4.2×10^{-2}
7. 0.000034	20. 1.2×10	34. 2.3×10^{-4}
8. 4000	21. 5.2×10^6	35. 5.0×10^1
9. 0.0006	22. 1.24×10^7	36. 3.0×10^{-1}
10. 120.6	23. 5.6×10^{-6}	
11. 0.003007	24. 3.2×10^{-8}	
12. 0.0000804	25. 1.4×10^7	
13. 4.25×10^2	26. 6.6×10^2	
	27. 3.2×10^{11}	

Practice Multiple Choice

Choose the best answer.

1. Simplify.

$(5x^3y^4z)^3$

A $15x^9y^4z$

B $15x^9y^4z^3$

C $125\,x^6y^7z^4$

D $125x^9y^{12}z^3$

2. Simplify.

$\left(\dfrac{-10m^3n}{2rt^2}\right)^2$

F $\dfrac{25m^6n^2}{r^2t^4}$

G $\dfrac{-50m^5n}{r^2t^4}$

H $\dfrac{-5m^5n^3}{r^3t^4}$

J $\dfrac{-8m^5n^3}{r^3t^4}$

1. D; Algebra 2.0
2. F; Algebra 2.0

B

Divide. Express the result using scientific and standard notation.

37. $\dfrac{(3.4 \times 10^6)(6 \times 10^3)}{(5 \times 10^5)}$

38. $\dfrac{(4.55 \times 10^3)(2.6 \times 10^5)}{(2 \times 10^{-2})}$

39. $\dfrac{(5.2 \times 10^{-4})(4 \times 10^5)}{(2.5 \times 10^9)}$

40. $\dfrac{(5 \times 10^{-3})(3.26 \times 10^{-4})}{(4 \times 10^2)}$

41. Light traveling from the sun at about 3.0×10^5 km per second takes about 5.0×10^2 seconds to reach Earth. Approximately what is the distance, expressed in scientific notation, from the sun to Earth?

42. *Estimation* Approximately how many seconds are there in 2000 years? Assume 365 days per year.

43. *Estimation* About how many seconds have you been alive?

44. A certain molecule has a mass of 3.01×10^{-23} g. There are 1.3×10^{21} of these molecules in a drop. What is the approximate mass of these molecules?

45. **TEST PREP** Compare the quantities in Column A and Column B.

Column A	Column B
three times (3.6×10^{-3})	half of (2.16×10^{-2})

   A. The quantity in Column A is greater.

   B. The quantity in Column B is greater.

   C. The quantities are equal.

   D. The relationship cannot be determined from the information given.

46. Light travels 1.86×10^5 miles in 1 second. How far does light travel in one year (light year)?

47. Neptune is approximately 2,790,000,000 mi from the sun. About how many seconds does it take light from the sun to reach Neptune?

48. *Critical Thinking* Use the digits 1, 2, 3, and 4 and one negative sign to write a number in scientific notation that is close to 0.001.

Challenge

Solve for y.

49. $(8 \times 10^4)y = 6.4 \times 10^7$

50. $(3.1 \times 10^5)y = 9.3 \times 10^3$

51. Simplify $\dfrac{(3.6 \times 10^6)(4 \times 10^{-3})}{(4.8 \times 10^{-2})(1.2 \times 10^6)}$

Mixed Review

Factor.   **52.** $21 - 15t$ **53.** $9a + 6$ **54.** $30 + 15k$

55. $12m - 4n$ **56.** $3a^2 + 6a + 9$ *2-7, 1-5*

Simplify.   **57.** $5x + (2x - 6)$ **58.** $(11y + 9) - 6y$

59. $4a - (3a + 15)$ **60.** $(4x - 7) - (3x - 7)$ *2-8*

Exercises

37. $4.08 \times 10^4 = 40{,}800$

38. $5.915 \times 10^{10} = 59{,}150{,}000{,}000$

39. $8.32 \times 10^{-8} = 0.0000000832$

40. $4.075 \times 10^{-9} = 0.000000004075$

Since all data are approximations, answers to Exercises 41–47 will be approximate. Students' answers may vary if they use a calculator.

41. 1.5×10^8 km $= 150{,}000{,}000$ km

42. 6.3072×10^{10} s $= 63{,}072{,}000{,}000$ s

43. Answers may vary.

44. 3.913×10^{-2} g $= 0.03913$ g

45. C

46. 5.8657×10^{12} mi
     $= 5{,}865{,}700{,}000{,}000$ mi

47. $1.5 \times 10^4 = 15{,}000$ s

48. $1.24 \times 10^{-3} = 0.00124$

49. 8×10^2

50. 3×10^{-2}

51. 2.5×10^{-1}

Mixed Review

52. $3(7 - 5t)$

53. $3(3a + 2)$

54. $15(2 + k)$

55. $4(3m - n)$

56. $3(a^2 + 2a + 3)$

57. $7x - 6$

58. $5y + 9$

59. $a - 15$

60. x

Polynomials

CA: 10.0

5-5

Math in Action

Mathematicians use expressions to model real-world situations. The expression

$$-0.346y + 914.31$$

is a mathematical model of the record time (in seconds) for the mile race in any given year (y) after 1875.

The expression

$$-16t^2 + 96t$$

is a mathematical model of the height (in feet) after t seconds for a projectile with an initial vertical velocity of 96 feet per second.

Both expressions above are called polynomials. Polynomials are used in many areas of mathematics including mathematical applications.

In 1954, Roger Bannister was the first person on record to run a mile in under four minutes. Substitute 1954 for y in the expression at the left above. Is the resulting value less than four minutes? Explain.

What You'll Learn

1 To identify terms and coefficients and factors of a term

2 To simplify a polynomial by collecting like terms

3 To identify the degree of a polynomial

...And Why

To prepare for operations with polynomials

PART 1

Identifying Terms, Factors, and Coefficients

Objective: Identify terms and their coefficients and the factors of a term.

You have learned what a monomial is and how to simplify expressions by multiplying and dividing monomials. You will now be working with expressions like these.

$$5y + 3 \qquad 3x^2 + 2x - 5 \qquad -5a^3b^2 + \tfrac{1}{2}ab$$

Each of these expressions is a sum of monomials.

Definition

A **polynomial** is a monomial or a sum of monomials.

Photo Caption

Yes; the result is 238.226 s, which equals 3 min 58.226 s.

5-5

TIME-FOCUS METER

1. FOCUS

FIRST FIVE MINUTES

Simplify.
1. $5x + 2 + 7x - 1$
   $12x + 1$
2. $3a + 2b - a - 2b$
   $2a$

Multiply.
3. $5(x + 4)$
   $5x + 20$
4. $3x(2x + 7)$
   $6x^2 + 21x$

MATH IN ACTION

Have students use the model to predict the record for the mile race for several years. Their answers will be in seconds. For 1875, the model gives an answer of 265.6 seconds or 4:25.6. The actual record in 1875 was 4:24.5 or 264.5 seconds. The model gives a record of 229.2 seconds or 3:49.2 for 1980. The actual record in 1980 was 228.8 seconds or 3:48.8.

2. TEACH the Mathematics

1 Identifying Terms, Factors, and Coefficients

Point out that monomials, trinomials and binomials are all polynomials.

> **Math Point**
> The prefix *poly* is a Greek word and means "many." The prefix *mono,* also Greek, means "one." The prefixes *bi* and *tri* are Latin words, and mean "two" and "three" respectively.

Key Questions

- Is 3 a trinomial?
  No
- Is 3 a polynomial?
  Yes
- Is 3 a monomial?
  Yes

Chalkboard Examples

Tell whether each expression is a polynomial. If it is a polynomial, identify it as a monomial, binomial, or trinomial.

1. $4x^2 + 9x + 4$

   The expression is the sum of three monomials, $4x^2$, $9x$, and 4. It is a trinomial because it has three terms.

2. $\frac{1}{2}xy^3 + a^5b^5$

   The expression is the sum of two monomials, $\frac{1}{2}xy^3$ and a^5b^5. It is a binomial because it has two terms.

3. $\frac{y}{x^2} - x^2$

   The expression is not a polynomial because $\frac{y}{x^2}$ is not a monomial.

Identify the terms. Give the coefficient of each term.

4. $4x^3y^2 - 3y^4z^2 + 5$

   The term $4x^3y^2$ has coefficient 4. The term $-3y^4z^2$ has coefficient -3. The term 5 has coefficient 5.

Collecting Like Terms

Students may be able to collect like terms mentally without showing the use of the distributive property. It is important, however, that they understand that it is the distributive property that allows us to collect like terms.

Avoiding Common Errors

Students may try to combine terms such as xy and x^2y^2 and get x^3y^3 or $2x^2y^2$. When these types of errors occur, require students to show the use of the distributive property to collect like terms as shown in Examples 6–8.

Chalkboard Examples

Collect like terms.

1. $3ab + 7ab + 2ab$

   $(3 + 7 + 2)ab = 12ab$

2. $7xy + 3x^2y^3 + 4xy - x^2y^3$

   $11xy + 2x^2y^3$

▼ Degrees and Coefficients

Emphasize that terminology is an important part of algebra, and that understanding the language will lead to an understanding of the concepts.

Key Questions

- What is the degree of 2?

  0

- What is the degree of x?

  1

In a polynomial, each monomial can be called a term. Polynomials with exactly two terms are called **binomials.** Polynomials with exactly three terms are called **trinomials.**

EXAMPLES Tell whether each expression is a polynomial. If so, identify it as a monomial, binomial, or trinomial.

1 $y^2 + y$

$y^2 + y$ is a polynomial because it is the sum of the two monomials y^2 and y. It is a binomial since it has two terms.

2 $\frac{1}{x} + 2x^2 + \frac{1}{3}x^3$

$\frac{1}{x} + 2x^2 + \frac{1}{3}x^3$ is not a polynomial because $\frac{1}{x}$ is not a monomial.

3 $5x^4 - 3x^2 + 9$

$5x^4 - 3x^2 + 9$ can be rewritten as $5x^4 + (-3x^2) + 9$. Therefore, $5x^4 - 3x^2 + 9$ is a polynomial because it is the sum of the three monomials $5x^4$, $-3x^2$, and 9. It is a trinomial since it has three terms.

Try This Tell whether each expression is a polynomial. If so, identify it as a monomial, binomial, or trinomial.

a. $\frac{7}{n^2} + 4n + 3$ **b.** $8xy^2 - 4$

Be careful not to confuse *terms* and *factors*. In a polynomial, terms are added and factors are multiplied. In the polynomial $2x^3 + 5x^4y^2$, the terms are $2x^3$ and $5x^4y^2$. In the term $2x^3$, 2 and x^3 are factors. In the term $5x^4y^2$, 5, x^4, and y^2 are factors.

The numeric factor of a term is called the **coefficient.** In the term $5x^4y^2$, 5 is the coefficient.

EXAMPLES Identify the terms. Give the coefficient of each term.

4 $4x^2 + 3x - 5$

The terms are $4x^2$, $3x$, and -5.
The coefficient of $4x^2$ is 4; the coefficient of $3x$ is 3; the coefficient of -5 is -5.

5 $2a^4b^3 - 3a^2b^3 - ab + 3$

The terms are $2a^4b^3$, $-3a^2b^3$, $-ab$, and 3.
The coefficient of $2a^4b^3$ is 2; the coefficient of $-3a^2b^3$ is -3; the coefficient of $-ab$ is -1; the coefficient of 3 is 3.

Try This Identify the terms. Give the coefficient of each term.

c. $5y^3 + 6y - 3$ **d.** $m^4 - 3m - 6$ **e.** $-3m^4n^2 - m^2n + 2n$

Try This

a. No
b. Yes; binomial
c. Terms: $5y^3$, $6y$, -3
   Coefficients: 5, 6, -3
d. Terms: m^4, $-3m$, -6
   Coefficients: 1, -3, -6
e. Terms: $-3m^4n^2$, $-m^2n$, $2n$
   Coefficients: -3, -1, 2

PART 2 Collecting Like Terms

Objective: Simplify a polynomial by collecting like terms.

We can often simplify polynomials by collecting like terms. Recall that terms like $3x^2y^3$ and $4x^2y^3$ whose variable factors are exactly the same are called like terms. The distributive property can be used as before to factor out the variable factors. The coefficients of the like terms can then be added to simplify the polynomial.

Quick Review

You can review collecting like terms in Lessons 1-5 and 2-7.

EXAMPLES   Collect like terms.

6 $2m^3 - 6m^3 = (2 - 6)m^3$ Using the distributive property
$$= -4m^3$$

7 $3x^5y^4 - 6y^5 - x^5y^4 + 2y^5 = (3 - 1)x^5y^4 + (-6 + 2)y^5$
$$= 2x^5y^4 + -4y^5$$
$$= 2x^5y^4 - 4y^5$$

Recall that the coefficient of a term like x^3y is 1 and the coefficient of a term like $-x^3$ is -1.

8 $7x^3y + 3x^3 - x^3 + x^3y = (7 + 1)x^3y + (3 - 1)x^3$
$$= 8x^3y + 2x^3$$

Writing Math

When you simplify a polynomial by collecting like terms, you are adding or subtracting monomials.

Try This   Collect like terms.

f. $2x - 4x^3 - 24 - 6x^3$ **g.** $7m^2 - m - m^2 - 7$

h. $8x^2y^2 - y^2 + y^3 - 1 - 4x^2y^2$ **i.** $4b^5 - 2ab^3 - 3b^5 + 7ab^3$

PART 3 Degrees and Coefficients

Objective: Identify the degree of a polynomial.

The **degree of a term** is the sum of the exponents of the variables. The **degree of a polynomial** is the highest degree of its terms.

EXAMPLE 9

Identify the degree of each term of $8a^4b^2 + 3ab + 7$. Give the degree of the polynomial.

The degree of $8a^4b^2$ is $4 + 2 = 6$.
The degree of $3ab$ is $1 + 1 = 2$.
The degree of 7 is 0.   Think of 7 as $7x^0$.
The degree of the polynomial $8a^4b^2 + 3ab + 7$ is 6.

The term with the highest degree is called the **leading term.** The coefficient of the leading term is called the **leading coefficient.**

Teach the Mathematics (continued)

Chalkboard Example

1. Identify the degree of each term of $5x^4y^3 - 2x^2y^4 + 3$. Give the degree of the polynomial.
   The degree of $5x^4y^3$ is 7.
   The degree of $-2x^2y^4$ is 6.
   The degree of 3 is 0.
   The degree of the polynomial is 7.

Try This
  f. $2x - 10x^3 - 24$
  g. $6m^2 - m - 7$
  h. $4x^2y^2 - y^2 + y^3 - 1$
  i. $b^5 + 5ab^3$

LESSON QUIZ

Determine whether each of the following is a polynomial.

1. $x^2 - y^2 + xy^2$ Yes

2. $a^2 - \frac{a^2}{5} + b^2$ Yes

3. Identify the terms. Give the coefficient of each term.

$5x^2y^3 - 4y^2 - 3$

The term $5x^2y^3$ has coefficient 5.
The term $-4y^2$ has coefficient -4.
The term -3 has coefficient -3.

Collect like terms.

4. $3 - 5x^4 + 7 + 8x^4 + x$

$10 + x + 3x^4$

5. $4a^3b^6 + 2ab + 3a^3b^6 + 5ab$

$7a^3b^6 + 7ab$

6. Identify the degree of each term and the degree of the polynomial.

$3x^5 + 4x^3 + 1$

$3x^5$ is of degree 5.
$4x^3$ is of degree 3.
1 is of degree 0.
The degree of the polynomial is 5.

Assignment Guide

To provide flexible scheduling, this lesson can be split into parts.

▼ Core 1–24
    Extension 54, 55
▼ Core 25–39 odd, 49–53
    Extension 41
▼ Core 26–40 even, 42–47,
    Extension 48, 56

Use Mixed Review to maintain skills.

Try This   Identify the degree of each term. Give the degree of the polynomial.

j. $-6x^4 + 8x^2 - 2x + 9$ **k.** $9x^6y^5 - 7x^4y^3 + 3x^3y^4 + 17x$

Extra Help
On the Web
Look for worked-out examples at the Prentice Hall Web site.
www.phschool.com

5-5 Exercises

A

Tell whether each expression is a polynomial. If it is a polynomial, identify it as a monomial, binomial, or trinomial.

1. $\frac{1}{x}$ 2. $5x^3 - 6x - 3$

3. $7 + 6x^2$ 4. $15p^2qr^5$

5. $-4m^5 + \frac{6}{m} - 1$ 6. $a^2 + ab + b^3$

7. $-12ab^7 - 12$ 8. $4 + y$

9. -43 10. $y^3 - 3y^2 - 5$

11. $-h^2 - 3h + 8$ 12. $5x^5y^3 + 5x^3y^2 + 6$

13. $\frac{r^2}{7}$ 14. $\frac{7}{r^2}$

Identify the terms. Give the coefficient of each term.

15. $-4m^9 + 6m - 1$ 16. $a^5 + 4a^3 - 3a^2 + a$

17. $2x^2y + 5xy^2 - 6y^4$ 18. $m^4n^3 - 3m^3n^2 + 6m^2n^4$

19. $8p^3 + 2pq - 4$ 20. $a^4b^6 - 2a^6b^4$

21. $-3n^6 + 3n - 3$ 22. $x^6 - 2x^5 + 3x^2 - 2x - 4$

23. $x^8y^6 - 2x^6y^6 + 8x^4y^7 - 4xy^8$

24. $12m^{12} - 8m^{11}n^{10} + 5m^5n^{11} - m^4n^{12} + n^{14}$

Collect like terms.

25. $2x - 5x$ 26. $x - 9x$

27. $2x^2 + 8x^2$ 28. $3x^2 - 4x^2$

29. $x^3 - 5x - 2x^3$ 30. $5x^3 + 6x^3 + 4$

31. $6x^4 - 3x^4 + 7$ 32. $6x^4 - 2x^4 + 5$

33. $5x^3 - 3 - 2x^3$ 34. $-3x^4 - 6x^4 + 5$

35. $3a^4 - 2a + 2a + a^4$ 36. $2x^2 - 6x + 3x + 4x^2$

37. $4xy^2 + 2x^2y - xy^2 + 3x^2y$ 38. $-7m^2n^2 + 2mn - 2m^2n^2 - 4mn$

39. $2ab^2 + 3ab - 5a^2b + 4ab^2$ 40. $6x^2 + 5xy^2 + 2x^2 - 3xy^2$

41. *Error Analysis*   A student simplified $7x^3 - x^3$ and got 7 as a result. Write an explanation of the student's error using the words *coefficient* and *like terms*.

Try This

j. 4, 2, 1, 0; 4
k. 11, 7, 7, 1; 11

Exercises

1. No
2. Yes; trinomial
3. Yes; binomial
4. Yes; monomial
5. No
6. Yes; trinomial
7. Yes; binomial
8. Yes; binomial
9. Yes; monomial
10. Yes; trinomial

11. Yes; trinomial
12. Yes; trinomial
13. Yes; monomial
14. No
15. Terms: $-4m^9$, $6m$, -1
    Coefficients: -4, 6, -1
16. Terms: a^5, $4a^3$, $-3a^2$, a
    Coefficients: 1, 4, -3, 1
17. Terms: $2x^2y$, $5xy^2$, $-6y^4$
    Coefficients: 2, 5, -6
18. Terms: m^4n^3, $-3m^3n^2$, $6m^2n^4$
    Coefficients: 1, -3, 6
19. Terms: $8p^3$, $2pq$, -4
    Coefficients: 8, 2, -4

20. Terms: a^4b^6, $-2a^6b^4$
    Coefficients: 1, -2
21. Terms: $-3n^6$, $3n$, -3
    Coefficients: -3, 3, -3
22. Terms: x^6, $-2x^5$, $3x^2$, $-2x$, -4
    Coefficients: 1, -2, 3, -2, -4
23. Terms:
    x^8y^6, $-2x^6y^6$, $8x^4y^7$, $-4xy^8$
    Coefficients: 1, -2, 8, -4
24. Terms:
    $12m^{12}$, $-8m^{11}n^{10}$, $5m^5n^{11}$,
    $-m^4n^{12}$, n^{14}
    Coefficients: 12, -8, 5, -1, 1

25. $-3x$
26. $-8x$
27. $10x^2$
28. $-x^2$
29. $-x^3 - 5x$
30. $11x^3 + 4$
31. $3x^4 + 7$
32. $4x^4 + 5$
33. $3x^3 - 3$
34. $-9x^4 + 5$
35. $4a^4$
36. $6x^2 - 3x$

Identify the degree of each term and the degree of the polynomial.

42. $2x - 4$

43. $3x^2 - 5x + 2$

44. $-7x^3 + 6x^2 + 3x + 7$

45. $x^2 - 3x + x^6 - 9x^4$

46. $-7x^3y^3 + 6x^2y^2 + 3xy + 7$

47. $-5x^4y^5 + 6x^3y^6 - 3x^2y^2$

48. *Mathematical Reasoning* Is the sum of the degrees of the terms of a binomial *sometimes, always,* or *never* equal to the degree of the binomial? Justify your answer.

B

Collect like terms.

49. $\frac{1}{4}x^5 - 5 + \frac{1}{2}x^5 - 2x$

50. $\frac{1}{3}x^3 + 2x - \frac{1}{6}x^3 + 4$

51. $\frac{1}{2}a^4 - 4a^2 + \frac{2}{3}a^4 - 3$

52. $\frac{2}{5}r^5 - \frac{1}{2}r^3 + \frac{7}{2}r^3$

53. Write a polynomial for the perimeter of these figures. Simplify the polynomial by collecting like terms.

 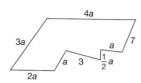

54. *Critical Thinking* Tell why the following algebraic expressions are not polynomials.

$$\frac{1}{x} \qquad 7 + \frac{5}{y} \qquad x^2 - 5x + \sqrt{x} \qquad (y^2 + 3) \div y$$

Challenge

55. The sum of a number and 2 is multiplied by the number, and then 3 is subtracted from the result. Express the final result as a polynomial.

56. The polynomial in x has degree 3. The coefficient of x^2 is 3 less than the coefficient of x^3. The coefficient of x is 3 times the coefficient of x^2. The remaining coefficient is 2 more than the coefficient of x^3. The sum of the coefficients is -4. Find the polynomial.

Mixed Review

Simplify. **57.** $c^2 \cdot c^5 \cdot c^3$ **58.** $(3m^2)^3$ **59.** $(x^3y^2)(x^4y^9)$

60. $(-2ab)^3$ **61.** $(3c^{-2})^2$ **62.** $(3c)^{-2}$ *5-1, 5-2*

Evaluate for $y = -\frac{1}{2}$. **63.** $y\left(y + \frac{2}{3}\right)$ **64.** y^4 **65.** $1 - \frac{3}{4}y$ *1-1, 2-5*

Solve. **66.** $-6x \leq 12$ **67.** $2 + 9a \geq 29$ **68.** $9 - 6c = 3c + 54$ *3-5, 4-3, 4-4*

37. $3xy^2 + 5x^2y$
38. $-9m^2n^2 - 2mn$
39. $6ab^2 + 3ab - 5a^2b$
40. $8x^2 + 2xy^2$
41. The student should have subtracted the coefficients of the like terms.
$7x^3 - x^3 = 7x^3 - 1x^3 = (7 - 1)x^3 = 6x^3$
42. 1, 0; 1
43. 2, 1, 0; 2
44. 3, 2, 1, 0; 3
45. 2, 1, 6, 4; 6
46. 6, 4, 2, 0; 6

47. 9, 9, 4; 9
48. Sometimes. For example, the degree of $4x + 1$ equals the sum of the degrees of the terms. The degree of $x^2 + x$ is less than the sum of the degrees of the terms.
49. $\frac{3}{4}x^5 - 2x - 5$
50. $\frac{1}{6}x^3 + 2x + 4$
51. $\frac{7}{6}a^4 - 4a^2 - 3$
52. $3r^3 + \frac{2}{5}r^5$
53. $19y + 12$ $\qquad 11\frac{1}{2}a + 10$

54. $\frac{1}{x}$ not a monomial; $\frac{5}{y}$ not a monomial; $\sqrt{x}$ not a monomial; $\frac{y^2 + 3}{y} = y + \frac{3}{y}, \frac{3}{y}$ not a monomial.
55. $n(n + 2) - 3 = n^2 + 2n - 3$
56. $x^3 - 2x^2 - 6x + 3$ is the polynomial.

Mixed Review

57. c^{10}
58. $27m^6$

59. x^7y^{11}
60. $-8a^3b^3$
61. $9c^{-4}$ or $\frac{9}{c^4}$
62. $\frac{1}{9c^2}$
63. $-\frac{1}{12}$
64. $\frac{1}{16}$
65. $\frac{11}{8}$
66. $x \geq -2$
67. $a \geq 3$
68. -5

 CA: 10.0

5-6

TIME-FOCUS METER

1. FOCUS

FIRST FIVE MINUTES

Multiply.
1. $x^2(x^3 + y)$
   $x^5 + x^2y$
2. $3y^2(2x^3 + 6x + 2)$
   $6x^3y^2 + 18xy^2 + 6y^2$
3. Simplify. $5x^3 + 4x + 3x^3 + 2x$
   $8x^3 + 6x$
4. Find the degree of $15x^5 + 3x^7 + 18$.
   The degree is 7.

2. TEACH the Mathematics

1 **Ascending and Descending Order**

Point out that polynomials are more often arranged in descending order than in ascending order.
  Also, remind students that $x^0 = 1$ and that a nonzero constant has degree 0.

Key Questions

■ Is $x + y$ in descending order with respect to y?
  No
■ Is $y + x$ in ascending order with respect to x?
  Yes

Chalkboard Examples

Arrange each polynomial in descending order for the variable x.
1. $3x + 3 + 4x^7 - 4x^6$
   $4x^7 - 4x^6 + 3x + 3$
2. $7xy^2 + 5x^3y^3 - 3x^2y$
   $5x^3y^3 - 3x^2y + 7xy^2$
Collect like terms and arrange in descending order for the variable x.
3. $4xy^3 - 3x^5y^4 + 2xy^3 + 4$
   $-3x^5y^4 + 6xy^3 + 4$

What You'll Learn

1 To write polynomials in ascending and descending order

2 To evaluate polynomials

...And Why

To write polynomials in a form that facilitates addition and subtraction

Try This

a. $6x^7 + 3x^5 - 2x^4 +$
   $4x^3 + 5x^2 + x$
b. $7x^5 - 5x^4 + 2x^3 + 4x^2 - 3$
c. $-14x^7 - 10x^3y^2 +$
   $7x^2y^3 - 14y$
d. $-2m^2 - 3m + 2$
e. $3m^3y - 6m^2y$

  CA 10.0: Solve multi-step problems using polynomials.

5-6 ▷ More on Polynomials

PART 1 Ascending and Descending Order

Objective: Write polynomials in ascending and descending order.

The polynomial $8x^4y^3 - 2x^3y^4 + 5x^2 - x + 3$ is written in **descending order** for the variable x. The term with the greatest exponent for x is first, the term with the next greatest exponent for x is second, and so on. The constant 3 can be written as $3x^0$. Thus the degree of the constant is 0.

The polynomial $5 - 3xy^3 + 4x^3y^4 - 3x^5y^3$ is written in **ascending order** for the variable x. The term with the least exponent for x is first, the term with the next larger exponent for x is second, and so on.

EXAMPLES   Arrange each polynomial in descending order for the variable x.

1 $4x^4 + 4x^7 + x^2 + 2x^3 = 4x^7 + 4x^4 + 2x^3 + x^2$

2 $3y + 4x^5y^2 - 4x^2 + 5xy^4 + 3x^3 = 4x^5y^2 + 3x^3 - 4x^2 + 5xy^4 + 3y$

Try This   Arrange each polynomial in descending order for the variable x.

a. $x + 3x^5 + 4x^3 + 5x^2 + 6x^7 - 2x^4$
b. $4x^2 - 3 + 7x^5 + 2x^3 - 5x^4$
c. $-14y + 7x^2y^3 - 10x^3y^2 - 14x^7$

Sometimes we may need to collect like terms before arranging a polynomial.

EXAMPLE 3   Collect like terms and arrange in descending order for the variable x.

$2x^2y^3 - 4x^3 + 3 - x^2y^3 - 2x^3 = x^2y^3 - 6x^3 + 3$ Simplifying
$ = -6x^3 + x^2y^3 + 3$ Writing in descending order

Try This   Collect like terms and arrange in descending order for the variable m.

d. $3m^2 - 2m + 3 - 5m^2 - 1 - m$
e. $-4m^2y + my - 2m^2y - my + 3m^3y$

226   Chapter 5   *Exponents and Polynomials*

Evaluating Polynomials

Objective: Evaluate polynomials.

When we replace the variable in a polynomial by a number and calculate, the result is a number. This process is called **evaluating the polynomial.**

EXAMPLES Evaluate each polynomial for the given value.

4 $3x + 5$ for $x = 6$

$3x + 5 = 3 \cdot 6 + 5$ Substituting

$\qquad = 18 + 5$

$\qquad = 23$

5 $2x^2 + 7x + 3$ for $x = 2$

$2x^2 + 7x + 3 = 2 \cdot 2^2 + 7 \cdot 2 + 3$

$\qquad\qquad = 2 \cdot 4 + 14 + 3$

$\qquad\qquad = 8 + 14 + 3$

$\qquad\qquad = 25$

Try This Evaluate each polynomial for the given value.

f. $-4x - 7$ for $x = 3$

g. $-5x^2 + 7x + 10$ for $x = 3$

h. $2x^2y + 5xy - 4$ for $x = -4$ and $y = 5$

EXAMPLE 6

The height reached by a fireworks packet is given by the polynomial

$$-16t^2 + 140t$$

(height in ft, time (t) in sec).

If the fuse is set to detonate a packet of spider design fireworks five seconds after launch, at what height will the fireworks explode?

Evaluate the polynomial for $t = 5$ to find the height for the explosion of the fireworks.

$$-16t^2 + 140t = -16(5)^2 + 140(5)$$
$$= -16(25) + 700$$
$$= -400 + 700$$
$$= 300$$

The fireworks will explode at 300 feet.

In Example 6, you use the expression $-16t^2 + 140t$ to find the height of a fireworks explosion. The term $140t$ reflects the upward speed with which the fireworks packet is launched. What force do you think is represented by the term $-16t^2$?

Teach the Mathematics (continued)

Evaluating Polynomials

Point out that evaluating a polynomial is no different from evaluating any other expression.

Chalkboard Examples

1. Evaluate $x^2 + x + 1$ for $x = 3$.
   $3^2 + 3 + 1 = 9 + 3 + 1 = 13$

2. Evaluate $3x^3 + 2x^2 + 5$ for $x = 2$.
   $3 \cdot 2^3 + 2 \cdot 2^2 + 5$
   $= 24 + 8 + 5 = 37$

3. If a rock is thrown upward at a speed of 80 ft per second, the height it reaches in t seconds is $80t - 16t^2$. Find the height of the rock after

a. 1 second
   $80(1) - 16(1^2)$
   $= 80 - 16(1)$
   $= 80 - 16$
   $= 64$ ft

b. 2 seconds
   $80(2) - 16(2^2)$
   $= 160 - 16(4)$
   $= 160 - 64$
   $= 96$ ft

c. 4 seconds
   $80(4) - 16(4^2)$
   $= 320 - 16(16)$
   $= 320 - 256$
   $= 64$ ft
   (It is on its way down.)

Try This

f. -19

g. -14

h. 56

Photo Caption

gravity

Some calculators use M and
 MR instead of STO and
 RCL , and some use x^y
instead of y^x .

3. PRACTICE/ASSESS

LESSON QUIZ

1. Arrange in descending order.
   $7 + 5x^2 + 3x^4 - 2x$
   $3x^4 + 5x^2 - 2x + 7$
2. Collect like terms and arrange in descending order.
   $4x^3 + 3x^2 + 5x^3 - 2x^2$
   $9x^3 + x^2$
3. Evaluate $3x^3 + x^2 + 1$
   a. for $x = 0$
      1
   b. for $x = 1$
      5
   c. for $x = 2$
      29
4. Evaluate $2xy + x^2y^2$ for $x = 2$, $y = 3$.
   $2 \cdot 2 \cdot 3 + 2^2 \cdot 3^2 = 48$

Assignment Guide
To provide flexible scheduling, this lesson can be split into parts.
▼ Core 1–14
   Extension 37, 38
▼ Core 15–36
   Extension 39, 40–43

Use Mixed Review to maintain skills.

EXAMPLE 7

For certain speeds, the cost of operating an automobile at speed *s* is approximated by the polynomial

$$0.005s^2 - 0.35s + 37$$

(cost in cents per mile, speed (*s*) in mi/h).

Evaluate the polynomial for $s = 50$ to find the cost of operating an automobile at 50 mi/h.

$$\begin{aligned}
0.005s^2 - 0.35s + 37 &= 0.005 \cdot 50^2 - 0.35 \cdot 50 + 37 \\
&= 0.005 \cdot 2500 - 17.5 + 37 \\
&= 12.5 - 17.5 + 37 \\
&= 32
\end{aligned}$$

The cost is approximately 32¢ per mile.

Try This

i. Evaluate the polynomial in Example 6 for $t = 7$ to find the height the fireworks will explode if set to detonate 7 seconds after launch.

j. Evaluate the polynomial in Example 7 for $s = 55$ to find the cost of operating an automobile at 55 mi/h.

k. The lung capacity in liters for a woman can be estimated by the polynomial

$$0.041h - 0.018A - 2.69$$

(height (*h*) in centimeters, age (*A*) in years).

Find the lung capacity for a 25-year-old woman who is 170 cm tall.

Evaluating Polynomials

We can evaluate polynomials using a calculator. We can use the memory key STO and the memory recall key RCL to save steps.

Evaluate $2x^3 + 4x^2 - 5$ for $x = 12$.

12 STO   Storing the variable in the memory

2 × RCL y^x 3 + 4 × RCL y^x 2

 − 5 = → 4027

Try This
i. 196 ft
j. ≈ 32.9¢ per mile
k. 3.83 L

5-6 Exercises

Internet Connection

Extra Help On the Web

Look for worked-out examples at the Prentice Hall Web site. www.phschool.com

A

Arrange each polynomial in descending order.

1. $x^5 + x + 6x^3 + 1 + 2x^2$

2. $3 + 2x^2 - 5x^6 - 2x^3 + 3x$

3. $5x^3 + 15x^9 + x - x^2 + 7x^8$

4. $9x - 5 + 6x^3 - 5x^4 + x^5$

5. $8y^3 - 7y^2 + 9y^6 - 5y^8 - y^7$

6. $p^8 - 4 + p + p^2 - 7p^4$

Collect like terms and then arrange in descending order for the variable m.

7. $3m^4 - 5m^6 - 2m^4 + 6m^6$

8. $-1 + 5m^3 - 3 - 7m^3 + m^4 + 5$

9. $-2m + 4m^3 - 7m + 9m^3 + 8$

10. $-6m^2 + m - 5m + 7m^2 + 1$

11. $3mp + 3mp + 3mp + m^2 - 4m^2$

12. $-2m - 2mp - 2m - m^3p^4 - 5m^3p^4$

13. $-m + \frac{3}{4} + 15m^4 - m - \frac{1}{2} - 3m^4$

14. $2m - \frac{5}{6} + 4m^3 + m + \frac{1}{3} - 2m$

Evaluate each polynomial for the given value.

15. $x^3 - 27$ for $x = 5$

16. $x^5 + x$ for $x = -2$

17. $x^4 - x$ for $x = 3$

18. $5x^4 - 7x + 2$ for $x = -2$

19. $2x^3 - 5x^2 + x - 3$ for $x = 3$

20. $2x - 5 + 4x^3 + x + x^2 - 2x$ for $x = -4$

21. $-4x^3 + 2x^2 + x - 3$ for $x = 5$

22. $x^5 - x^4 + x^3 - x^2 + x - 1$ for $x = -1$

Evaluate each polynomial for $x = 4$.

23. $-5x + 2$

24. $-3x + 1$

25. $2x^2 - 5x + 7$

26. $3x^2 + x - 7$

27. $x^3 - 5x^2 + x$

28. $7 - x + 3x^2$

Evaluate each polynomial for $a = -1$ and $b = 2$.

29. $3a + 5ab$

30. $6 - 2ab$

31. $a^2 - 2a + b$

32. $5a - 6 + a^2b$

33. $-3a^3 + 7a^2 - 3b - 2$

34. $-2a^3 - 5a^2 + 4a + 3b$

The daily number of automobile accidents involving drivers of age x ($x > 15$) is approximated by the polynomial $0.4x^2 - 40x + 1039$.

35. Evaluate the polynomial for $x = 18$ to find the number of daily accidents involving 18-year-old drivers.

36. Evaluate the polynomial for $x = 20$ to find the number of daily accidents involving 20-year-old drivers.

Exercises

1. $x^5 + 6x^3 + 2x^2 + x + 1$

2. $-5x^6 - 2x^3 + 2x^2 + 3x + 3$

3. $15x^9 + 7x^8 + 5x^3 - x^2 + x$

4. $x^5 - 5x^4 + 6x^3 + 9x - 5$

5. $-5y^8 - y^7 + 9y^6 + 8y^3 - 7y^2$

6. $p^8 - 7p^4 + p^2 + p - 4$

7. $m^6 + m^4$

8. $m^4 - 2m^3 + 1$

9. $13m^3 - 9m + 8$

10. $m^2 - 4m + 1$

11. $-3m^2 + 9mp$

12. $-6m^3p^4 - 2mp - 4m$

13. $12m^4 - 2m + \frac{1}{4}$

14. $4m^3 + m - \frac{1}{2}$

15. 98

16. -34

17. 78

18. 96

19. 9

20. -249

21. -448

22. -6

23. -18

24. -11

25. 19

26. 45

27. -12

28. 51

29. -13

30. 10

31. 5

32. -9

33. 2

34. -1

35. 448.6 or 449 accidents

36. 399 accidents

B

37. A 4-ft by 4-ft sandbox is placed on a square lawn whose side is x ft long. Express the area left over as a polynomial.

38. Express the shaded area in the figure below as a polynomial.

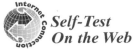

39. *Critical Thinking*   The trinomial $ax^2 + 3x + 7$ is equal to 15 when x is 1, and the trinomial is equal to 33 when x is 2. What is the value of a?

Challenge

Evaluate each expression for the given value.

40. $(-5x^3 + 3x^2 + 6)(7x - 12)$ for $x = 3$

41. $(2x^3 + 3x^2 - 4x + 8)(x^4 - x^2 + 5x)$ for $x = -2$

42. $(4x^5 - 4x^3 + 5x^2 - 4x + 6)(-3x^3 + 6x^2 - x + 8)$ for $x = -1$

43. For a polynomial of degree 2 of the form $ax^2 + bx + c$ where a, b, and c are coefficients, the extreme (highest or lowest) value of the polynomial is the value of x when $2ax = -b$. Find the age with the lowest daily accidents for the polynomial $0.4x^2 - 40x + 1039$, as given for Exercises 35 and 36.

Internet Connection

Self-Test On the Web

Check your progress. Look for a self-test at the Prentice Hall Web site. www.phschool.com

Mixed Review

Simplify.   **44.** $\dfrac{x^2 y^4}{xy}$ **45.** $\left(\dfrac{x^3}{2}\right)^3$ **45.** $\dfrac{4a^9}{a^7}$ **47.** $\dfrac{21c^3}{7a^3}$ *5-2*

Write in standard notation.   **48.** 1.603×10^4 **49.** 7.662×10^{-3} *5-4*

Write an equation and solve.

50. The sum of two consecutive integers is 67. Find the integers. *10-9*

230   Chapter 5   *Exponents and Polynomials*

Exercises

37. $x^2 - 16$
38. $\pi r^2 - 9\pi$
39. $a = 5$
40. -918
41. 24
42. 270
43. $a = 0.4$, $b = -40$
$\qquad 2ax = -b$
$\quad 2(0.4)x = -(-40)$
$\qquad 0.8x = 40$
$\qquad\quad x = 50$
The age with the lowest daily accidents is age 50.

Mixed Review

44. xy^3
45. $\dfrac{x^9}{8}$
46. $4a^2$
47. $\dfrac{3c^3}{a^3}$
48. $16{,}030$
49. 0.007662
50. $n + (n + 1) = 67$; $33, 34$

CA 10.0: Add polynomials; solve multi-step problems using polynomials.

Addition of Polynomials

PART 1 Adding Polynomials

Objective: Add polynomials.

Some situations can be modeled by adding polynomials.

EXAMPLE 1 The areas of these figures can be expressed as polynomials.

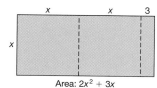

Area: $x^2 - 16$ Area: $2x^2 + 3x$

The total area of the two figures can be found by adding the two polynomials.

$$(x^2 - 16) + (2x^2 + 3x)$$

This sum equals the single polynomial

$$x^2 - 16 + 2x^2 + 3x.$$

By collecting like terms as you have already done in Lessons 1-5, 2-7, and 5-6, the polynomial can be simplified to

$$3x^2 + 3x - 16.$$

Try This

a. Write a polynomial for the area of each figure. Then express the total area of the two figures as a sum of two polynomials and as a simplified polynomial.

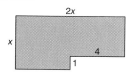

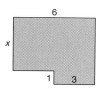

b. Express the perimeter of the triangle as the sum of three polynomials and as a simplified polynomial.

$2x + 1$ $x^2 - x + 4$

$3x^2 - 5$

1. FOCUS

FIRST FIVE MINUTES

Collect like terms and arrange in descending order.

1. $4x^3 + 6x^4 - 2x^4 + 8x$
   $4x^4 + 4x^3 + 8x$
2. $3a - 5a^1 + 5 + 2a^0$
   $3a - 5a + 5 + 2 = -2a + 7$
3. Evaluate $4x^3 + x^2 - 2$
   a. for $x = 0$
   -2
   b. for $x = 1$
   3

2. TEACH the Mathematics

1 **Adding Polynomials**

Point out to students the similarity between collecting like terms and adding polynomials. You may wish to have students do steps mentally if they have demonstrated that they understand the process.

If an expression has two or more variables, we usually arrange them with respect to the variable having the highest degree.

Key Questions

Express the area of each figure as a polynomial.

■ 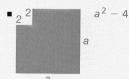 $a^2 - 4$

■ 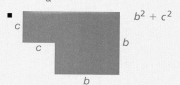 $b^2 + c^2$

■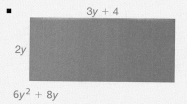

$6y^2 + 8y$

Try This

a. $2x^2 - 4$; $6x + 3$;
   $2x^2 + 6x - 1$
b. $(2x + 1) + (x^2 - x + 4) +$
   $(3x^2 - 5)$; $4x^2 + x$

- Can you add the polynomial $x + y$ to the polynomial $a + b$?
Yes, $x + y + a + b$

Chalkboard Examples

1. Write a polynomial for the area of each figure. Then express the total area of the two figures as a sum of two polynomials and as a simplified polynomial.

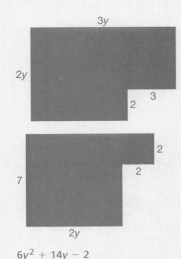

$6y^2 + 14y - 2$

2. $(5x^2 + 3x + 4) + (3x^2 + 5)$
$5x^2 + 3x^2 + 3x + 4 + 5$
$= 8x^2 + 3x + 9$

3. $(7a^2b^3 + ab) + (1 - 2a^2b^3)$
$7a^2b^3 - 2a^2b^3 + ab + 1$
$= 5a^2b^3 + ab + 1$

▼2 **Adding Polynomials in Column Form**

Point out that adding polynomials in column form may be easier for students since the like terms are aligned before they are added.

Chalkboard Example

Add by writing like terms in columns.

1. $(2x^4 - 5x^2 + 4x + 5)$
$+ (5x^4 + 7x^3 - 2x^2 - 2x)$
$2x^4 + 0x^3 - 5x^2 + 4x + 5$
$\underline{5x^4 + 7x^3 - 2x^2 - 2x + 0}$
$7x^4 + 7x^3 - 7x^2 + 2x + 5$

When we add polynomials, we usually arrange the terms in descending order for one of the variables.

EXAMPLES

2 $(3x^3 - 2x - 4) + (4x^3 - 3x^2 + 2)$
$= 3x^3 - 2x - 4 + 4x^3 - 3x^2 + 2$
$= 7x^3 - 3x^2 - 2x - 2$ Collecting like terms

3 $(4m^4n^2 + 3m^2n^3 - 4n) + (2n - 5m^2n^3 + 2m)$
$= 4m^4n^2 - 2m^2n^3 + 2m - 2n$

The answer in Example 3 was arranged in descending order for the variable m. The answer could be arranged in descending order for the variable n:

$$-2m^2n^3 + 4m^4n^2 - 2n + 2m$$

Try This   Add.

c. $(3x^2 + 2x - 2) + (-2x^2 + 5x + 5)$
d. $(31m^4 + m^2 + 2m - 1) + (-7m^4 + 5m^3 - 2m + 2)$
e. $(4a^2b - 5a + 3) + (-2a^2b - 2a - 4)$
f. $(3n^3 - 3m^3n^2 - 5n - 3) + (5n^3 + 2m^3n^2 - 3m - 2n - 2)$

PART 2   **Adding Polynomials in Columns**

Objective: Add polynomials in column form.

We can also add polynomials by writing the polynomials in column form. Align the like terms so they can be easily added.

EXAMPLES   Add by writing like terms in columns.

4 $(9m^5 - 2m^3 + 6m^2 + 3) + (5m^4 - 7m^2 + 6)$

$9m^5 \qquad\quad - 2m^3 + 6m^2 + 3$
$\underline{\qquad\quad 5m^4 \qquad\quad - 7m^2 + 6}$ Aligning like terms
$9m^5 + 5m^4 - 2m^3 - \; m^2 + 9$

5 $(3x^3y + 6x^2y^3 - 4x + 3) + (2x^4y - 4x^3y + 6x - y)$

$\qquad\quad 3x^3y + 6x^2y^3 - 4x \qquad\; + 3$
$\underline{2x^4y - 4x^3y \qquad\qquad\quad + 6x - y}$ Aligning like terms
$2x^4y - x^3y + 6x^2y^3 + 2x - y + 3$

Try This

c. $x^2 + 7x + 3$
d. $24m^4 + 5m^3 + m^2 + 1$
e. $2a^2b - 7a - 1$
f. $8n^3 - m^3n^2 - 7n - 3m - 5$

Try This   Add using columns.

g. $(-2m^3 - 5m^2 - 2m - 4) + (m^4 - 6m^2 + 7m - 10)$
h. $(-3x^4y^3 - 5xy + 2) + (x^4y^3 + x^2 + 2xy + 5)$

5-7 Exercises

Extra Help
On the Web
Look for worked-out examples at the Prentice Hall Web site.
www.phschool.com

A
Express the sum of the areas of the two figures as a simplified polynomial.

1.

2.

Express the perimeter of each triangle as a simplified polynomial.

3.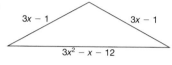

4.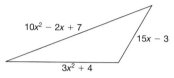

Add.

5. $3x + 2$ and $-4x + 3$

6. $5x^2 + 6x + 1$ and $-7x + 2$

7. $-4x^4 + 6x^2 - 3x - 5$ and $6x^3 + 5x + 9$

8. $5x^3 + 6x^2 - 3x + 1$ and $5x^4 - 6x^3 + 2x - 5$

9. $(7x^3 + 6x^2 + 4x + 1) + (-7x^3 + 6x^2 - 4x + 5)$

10. $(3x^4 - 5x^2 - 6x + 5) + (-4x^3 + 6x^2 + 7x - 1)$

11. $5x^4 - 6x^3 - 7x^2 + x - 1$ and $4x^3 - 6x + 1$

12. $8x^5 - 6x^3 + 6x + 5$ and $-4x^4 + 3x^3 - 7x$

13. $9x^8 - 7x^4 + 2x^2 + 5$ and $8x^7 + 4x^4 - 2x$

14. $4x^5 - 6x^3 - 9x + 1$ and $6x^3 + 9x^2 + 9x$

15. $(-3cd^4 + 6d^2 + 2cd - 1) + (-3d^2 + 2cd + 1)$

Add using columns.

16. $(4m^4 - 3m^3 + 6m^2 + 5m - 4) + (6m^3 - 8m^2 - 3m + 1)$

17. $(5a^4 - 2a^3 + 4a^2 + 5a) + (5a^3 - 5a^2 + 2)$

3. PRACTICE/ASSESS

LESSON QUIZ

1. $4y + 7$ and $-6y - 2$
   $-2y + 5$
2. $-4x^3 + 2x^2 + 5x - 6$ and
   $7x^3 + 5x + 4$
   $3x^3 + 2x^2 + 10x - 2$
3. Add by writing like terms in columns.
   $7x^4 - 3x^2 + 2x - 8$ and
   $2x^4 + 4x^3 + 5x^2 - 6x + 9$
   $9x^4 + 4x^3 + 2x^2 - 4x + 1$

Assignment Guide
To provide flexible scheduling, this lesson can be split into parts.
▼ Core 1–15, 25, 26
   Extension 27, 28, 31–33
▼ Core 16–24
   Extension 29, 30

Use Mixed Review to maintain skills.

Add using columns.

18. $(5t^2 - 2t + 3) + (-3t^4 + 3t^2 + 5t - 3)$

19. $(7y^5 - 6y^4 + 3y^3 - 1) + (6y^4 - 4y^3 + 6y^2 + 5)$

20. $(-x^3y^2 + 6x^2 + 3x + 5) + (x^4 + 2x^3y^2 - 3x^2 + 2)$

21. $(-2h^3 + 3h^2k + 5hk + 3) + (-5h^2k - 2hk + 1)$

22. $(-3x^4y^3 + 6x^3y^3 - 6x^2 + 5xy^5 + 1) + (5x^5 - 3x^3y^3 - 5xy^5)$

23. $(4x^2y - 5xy + 7) + (8x^2y + 7xy^2 + 3xy - 2)$

24. $(4x^3y^4 + 7x^4y^3 - 4x^5 - 6x^4) + (-6x^3y^4 - 3x^4y^3 + 2x^4 - x^3)$

B

25. a. Express the sum of the areas of these rectangles as a polynomial.

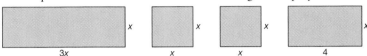

b. Find the sum of the areas when $x = 3$.

c. Find the sum of the areas when $x = 8$.

26. a. Express the sum of the areas of these circles as a polynomial (area $= \pi r^2$).

b. Find the sum of the areas when $r = 5$.

c. Find the sum of the areas when $r = 11.3$.

27. *Multi-Step Problem*   Use the steps below to solve the following problem. Three brothers have ages that are consecutive multiples of five. The sum of their ages two years ago was 69. Find their ages now.

a. Let the youngest brother's age be n. Write an expression for the age of each of the other brothers.

b. Use your answer to part (a) to write an expression for the age of each of the brothers two years ago.

c. Use your answer to part (b) to write an expression for the sum of the brothers' ages two years ago. Simplify the expression.

d. For what value of n will the expression in part (c) equal 69?

e. Use the value of n you found in part (d) to find the age of each of the brothers now.

f. Check: First check that each age you found in part (e) is a multiple of five. Then find the ages of the brothers two years ago. Check that the sum is 69.

Exercises

18. $-3t^4 + 8t^2 + 3t$

19. $7y^5 - y^3 + 6y^2 + 4$

20. $x^4 + x^3y^2 + 3x^2 + 3x + 7$

21. $-2h^3 - 2h^2k + 3hk + 4$

22. $5x^5 - 3x^4y^3 + 3x^3y^3 - 6x^2 + 1$

23. $12x^2y + 7xy^2 - 2xy + 5$

24. $-2x^3y^4 + 4x^4y^3 - 4x^5$
      $- 4x^4 - x^3$

25. a. $3x^2 + x^2 + x^2 + 4x = 5x^2 + 4x$

    b. 57

    c. 352

26. a.
    $\pi r^2 + 9\pi + 4\pi = \pi r^2 + 13\pi$

    b. 38π

    c. 140.69π

27. a. $n + 5, n + 10$

    b. $n - 2, n + 3, n + 8$

    c. $3n + 9$

    d. 20

    e. 20, 25, 30

    f. $\frac{20}{5} = 4, \frac{25}{5} = 5, \frac{30}{5} = 6$;
       18, 23, 28;
       $18 + 23 + 28 = 69$

28. a. Use the lengths of the sides of the parallelogram to explain why the value of n must be greater than 2.

b. Express the perimeter as a simplified polynomial.

c. Why must the perimeter be greater than 16?

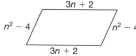

$3n + 2$

$n^2 - 4$ $n^2 - 4$

$3n + 2$

29. *Critical Thinking*   Compare and contrast the column method for adding whole numbers and the column method for adding polynomials.

Challenge

30. The sum of two polynomials is $2x^2 + x + 8$. One polynomial is $x^2 + 3$. What is the other?

31. Addition of real numbers is commutative. That is, $a + b = b + a$ where a and b are real numbers. Show that addition of binomials such as $(ax + b)$ and $(cx + d)$ is commutative.

32. Show that addition of trinomials such as $(ax^2 + bx + c)$ and $(dx^2 + ex + f)$ is commutative.

33. Show that addition of polynomials is commutative. Use
$a_n x^n + a_{n-1} x^{n-1} + \ldots + a_1 x + a_0$ and
$b_n x^n + b_{n-1} x^{n-1} + \ldots + b_1 x + b_0$

Writing Math

The ellipsis points "$\ldots$" indicate that a pattern continues.

Name the properties that guarantee that these statements are true.

34. $a(b + c) = ab + ac$ **35.** $x + (-x) = 0$ **36.** $y \cdot 1 = y$

37. $nm = mn$ **38.** $a + 0 = a$ **39.** $4 + 1 = 1 + 4$ *2-10*

Simplify. **40.** $(2t^3)^5$ **41.** $(3a^5)(6a^2)$ **42.** $x^0 \cdot x^1$ **43.** $(2m^2 n)(6n)$ *5-1, 5-2, 5-3*

Factor.   **44.** $5ac + 12a$ **45.** $xyz + 5y - 9yz$ **46.** $a^2 + a + ab$ *2-7*

HISTORICAL NOTE

In 2000 B.C., the Babylonians used algebraic methods in solving problems. However, they used no mathematical symbols other than primitive numerals. This lack of symbolism in algebra continued until almost 1500 A.D.

The plus, $+$, and minus, $-$, signs first appeared in 1489 A.D. and were regularly used by 1544 A.D. The equal sign, $=$, was first used in 1557 by Robert Recorde in England. The raised dot, $\cdot$, and juxtaposition were first used for multiplication about 1600, and the symbol $\times$ about 1620. The division symbol, $\div$, appeared in 1659.

Exercises

28. a. The length of a side must be greater than 0.
$n^2 - 4 > 0$ when $n > 2$ and when $n < -2$. But n cannot be less than -2 because then $3n + 2$ would be negative.

b. $2n^2 + 6n - 4$

c. When $n = 2$,
$2n^2 + 6n - 4 = 16$. When
$n > 2$, $2n^2 + 6n - 4 > 16$.

29. Answers may vary. Some differences are that coefficients of polynomials cannot be carried and that adding polynomials can involve adding negative coefficients.

30. $x^2 + x + 5$

31. $(ax + b) + (cx + d)$
$= (a + c)x + (b + d)$
$(cx + d) + (ax + b)$
$= (c + a)x + (d + b)$
$= (a + c)x + (b + d)$
Addition of binomials is commutative.

32. See 31 above.

33. See 31 above.

Mixed Review

34. Distributive property of mult. over addition

35. Additive inverse

36. Multiplicative identity

37. Commutative property of multiplication

38. Additive identity

39. Commutative property of addition

40. $32t^{15}$

41. $18a^7$

42. x

43. $12m^2 n^2$

44. $a(5c + 12)$

45. $y(xz + 5 - 9z)$

46. $a(a + 1 + b)$

5-8

TIME-FOCUS METER

1. FOCUS

FIRST FIVE MINUTES

Multiply.

1. $3(4x^2 + 2x + 5)$
   $12x^2 + 6x + 15$
2. $-2(x^2 + 5)$
   $-2x^2 - 10$
3. $-1(5x^3 + 2x^2 + 3)$
   $-5x^3 - 2x^2 - 3$
4. $(-1)(-3x^2 + 4x - 7)$
   $3x^2 - 4x + 7$

2. TEACH the Mathematics

Initially, you may want students to rewrite each polynomial as a sum to identify the coefficients before finding the additive inverse. In Example 1 we could rewrite $4x^5 - 7x - 8$ as $4x^5 + (-7x) + (-8)$.

You may wish to encourage students to subtract mentally if they can without making errors.

Key Questions

■ Is x^{-3} the additive inverse of x^3?
   No
■ Is x^{-3} the additive inverse of $-x^3$?
   No
■ Is x^{-3} the additive inverse of $-x^{-3}$?
   Yes

Chalkboard Examples

1. Find the additive inverse of
   $7x^4 - 3x + 5$.
   $-7x^4 + 3x - 5$
Subtract.
2. $(5x^2 + 3x - 2) - (2x^2 + 1)$
   $5x^2 + 3x - 2 - 2x^2 - 1$
   $= 3x^2 + 3x - 3$
3. $(2a^2b^2 + 3ab^3 - 4b^4)$
   $- (a^2b^2 - 5ab^3 + 3b - 2b^4)$
   $2a^2b^2 + 3ab^3 - 4b^4$
   $- a^2b^2 + 5ab^3 - 3b + 2b^4$
   $= a^2b^2 + 8ab^3 - 2b^4 - 3b$
4. Use columns to subtract.
   $8x^3 + 6x^2 - 3x + 5$ minus
   $5x^3 - 3x^2 + 2x - 4$
   $8x^3 + 6x^2 - 3x + 5$
   $\underline{-5x^3 + 3x^2 - 2x + 4}$
   $3x^3 + 9x^2 - 5x + 9$

What You'll Learn

1 To subtract polynomials

. . . And Why

To perform subtraction by adding the additive inverse

Try This

a. $-12x^4 + 3x^2 - 4x$
b. $13x^6y^4 - 2x^4y + 3x^2 - xy + \frac{5}{13}$

CA 10.0: Subtract polynomials.

5-8 ▷ Subtraction of Polynomials

Objective: Subtract polynomials.

We know that two numbers are additive inverses if their sum is zero. For example, 5 and -5 are additive inverses, since $5 + (-5) = 0$. The same definition holds for polynomials.

Definition

Two polynomials are **additive inverses** of each other if their sum is 0.

Consider the polynomial $8x^2 - 4x + 3$. The additive inverse of $8x^2 - 4x + 3$ is

$-(8x^2 - 4x + 3)$
$= (-1)(8x^2 - 4x + 3)$ Using the property of -1
$= (-1)(8x^2) + (-1)(-4x) + (-1)(3)$ Using the distributive property

$= -8x^2 + 4x - 3$

The additive inverse of a polynomial can be found by replacing each coefficient by its additive inverse.

EXAMPLE 1   Find the additive inverse of $4x^5 - 7x - 8$.

$-4x^5 + 7x + 8$ Changing the sign of each coefficient gives the additive inverse of the polynomial.

Try This   Find the additive inverse of each polynomial.

a. $12x^4 - 3x^2 + 4x$ b. $-13x^6y^4 + 2x^4y - 3x^2 + xy - \frac{5}{13}$

Recall that we can subtract a rational number by adding its additive inverse: $a - b = a + (-b)$. This rule also applies to polynomials.

EXAMPLE 2   Subtract.

$(a^3 - 2a^2 + 4) - (a^4 - 4a^3 - 3a^2)$
$= (a^3 - 2a^2 + 4) + [-(a^4 - 4a^3 - 3a^2)]$ Adding the inverse
$= (a^3 - 2a^2 + 4) + (-a^4 + 4a^3 + 3a^2)$ Using the distributive property

$= -a^4 + 5a^3 + a^2 + 4$ Collecting like terms

236   Chapter 5 *Exponents and Polynomials*

EXAMPLE 3 Subtract.

$(4x^3y + 2x^2y^2 - 3xy + 6) - (x^3y - 2x^2y^2 - 2xy - 3)$
$= (4x^3y + 2x^2y^2 - 3xy + 6) + [-(x^3y - 2x^2y^2 - 2xy - 3)]$
$= (4x^3y + 2x^2y^2 - 3xy + 6) + (-x^3y + 2x^2y^2 + 2xy + 3)$
$= 3x^3y + 4x^2y^2 - xy + 9$

Try This Subtract.

c. $(5x^4 + 4) - (2x^2 - 1)$
d. $(-7m^3 + 2m + 4) - (-2m^3 - 4)$
e. $(-3a^2b^4 + 5ab - 4) - (-4a^3 + 11a^2b^4 - 2a - 6)$

We can also subtract polynomials by arranging like terms in columns.

EXAMPLES Subtract using columns.

4 $(5p^2 - 3p + 6) - (9p^2 - 5p - 3)$

(a) $\begin{array}{l} 5p^2 - 3p + 6 \\ \underline{- (9p^2 - 5p - 3)} \end{array}$ Writing like terms in columns

(b) $\begin{array}{l} 5p^2 - 3p + 6 \\ \underline{+(-9p^2 + 5p + 3)} \end{array}$ Changing subtraction to addition of the inverse

(c) $\begin{array}{l} 5p^2 - 3p + 6 \\ \underline{-9p^2 + 5p + 3} \\ -4p^2 + 2p + 9 \end{array}$ Adding

5 $(3x^3y^2 - 4xy + 1) - (-4x^3y^2 - 3x^2y^2 + 3xy - 5)$

(a) $\begin{array}{l} 3x^3y^2 \qquad\quad - 4xy + 1 \\ \underline{- (-4x^3y^2 - 3x^2y^2 + 3xy - 5)} \end{array}$ Writing like terms in columns

(b) $\begin{array}{l} 3x^3y^2 \qquad\quad - 4xy + 1 \\ \underline{+(4x^3y^2 + 3x^2y^2 - 3xy + 5)} \end{array}$ Changing signs to add

(c) $\begin{array}{l} 3x^3y^2 \qquad\quad - 4xy + 1 \\ \underline{4x^3y^2 + 3x^2y^2 - 3xy + 5} \\ 7x^3y^2 + 3x^2y^2 - 7xy + 6 \end{array}$ Adding

Try This Subtract using columns.

f. $(4x^3 + 2x^2 - 2x - 3) - (2x^3 - 3x^2 + 2)$
g. $(-3ab^2 + 4ab - 7a) - (-2ab^2 - 3a + 4)$

Teach the Mathematics (continued)

5. $2a^4b + 5a^3b^2 - 4a^2b^3$ minus
   $4a^4b + 2a^3b^2 - 4ab$

$\begin{array}{l} 2a^4b + 5a^3b^2 - 4a^2b^3 + 0ab \\ \underline{-4a^4b - 2a^3b^2 + 0a^2b^3 + 4ab} \\ -2a^4b + 3a^3b^2 - 4a^2b^3 + 4ab \end{array}$

Try This

c. $5x^4 - 2x^2 + 5$
d. $-5m^3 + 2m + 8$
e. $4a^3 - 14a^2b^4 + 5ab + 2a + 2$
f. $2x^3 + 5x^2 - 2x - 5$
g. $-ab^2 + 4ab - 4a - 4$

1. Find the additive inverse of the polynomial $5x^4 - 2x^3 + x^2 - 6$.

$-5x^4 + 2x^3 - x^2 + 6$

2. Subtract.

$(7x^3 - 6x^2 + 3x)$
$-(5x^3 - 3x^2 - 5x + 4)$

$7x^3 - 6x^2 + 3x - 5x^3 + 3x^2$
$+ 5x - 4 = 2x^3 - 3x^2 + 8x - 4$

3. Subtract using columns.

$(-4x^4 + 5x^2 + 3x + 5)$
$-(-6x^4 + 2x^3 - 3x^2 + 7)$

$2x^4 - 2x^3 + 8x^2 + 3x - 2$

Assignment Guide

▼ Core 1–37
  Extension 38–44

Use Mixed Review to maintain skills.

Extra Help On the Web

Look for worked-out examples at the Prentice Hall Web site.
www.phschool.com

5-8 Exercises

A

Find the additive inverse of each polynomial.

1. $-5x$

2. $x^2 - 3x$

3. $-x^2 + 10x - 2$

4. $-4x^3 - x^2 - x$

5. $12x^4y - 3x^3 + 3$

6. $4x^3 - 6x^2y^2 - 8xy + 1$

Subtract

7. $(5x^2 + 6) - (3x^2 - 8)$

8. $(7a^3 - 2a^2 + 6) - (7a^2 + 2a - 4)$

9. $(6x^5 - 3x^4 + x + 1) - (8x^5 + 3x^4 - 1)$

10. $\left(\frac{1}{2}x^2 - \frac{3}{2}x + 2\right) - \left(\frac{3}{2}x^2 + \frac{1}{2}x - 2\right)$

11. $(6b^2 + 2b) - (-3b^2 - 7b + 8)$

12. $7x^3 - (-3x^2 - 2x + 1)$

13. $(5m^3 - 3m - 6) - (-2m^3 + 5)$

14. $(-4n^4 + n^3 + 2n^2) - (n^4 - 3n^3 - n^2 + 4)$

15. $(6y^3 - 4y - 7) - (-3y^4 - 2y^3 + y - 4)$

16. $(7t^4 + 4t) - (6t^5 - 3t^4 + 2t^2 + 3t - 1)$

17. $(8v^4u + 6v^2 - 5) - (2v^4u - 3v^2 + 2)$

18. $(-3m^3n^2 + 2m^2 - mn - 4) - (-5m^3n^2 - 4m^2 + 3mn + 2)$

19. $(8mn^5 + n^4 - 3mn^3 + 2n^2) - (-mn^5 - mn^4 - n^2 - 1)$

20. $(3x^4y + 2x^3y - x^2 - 7) - (-2x^6 - 3x^4y + 2x^3y - x^2 - 7)$

Subtract.

21. $\begin{array}{l} x^2 + 5x + 6 \\ \underline{x^2 + 2x} \end{array}$

22. $\begin{array}{l} x^3 \qquad + 1 \\ \underline{x^3 + x^2} \end{array}$

23. $\begin{array}{l} c^4 \qquad - 3c^2 + c + 1 \\ \underline{c^4 - 4c^3} \end{array}$

24. $\begin{array}{l} 3x^2 - 6x + 1 \\ \underline{6x^2 + 8x - 3} \end{array}$

Subtract using columns.

25. $(5x^4 + 6x^3 - 9x^2) - (-6x^4 - 6x^3 + 8x)$

26. $(5x^4 + 6x^2 - 3x + 6) - (6x^3 + 7x^2 - 8x - 9)$

27. $(3m^4 + 6m^2 + 8m - 1) - (4m^5 - 6m^4 - 8m - 7)$

28. $(6x^5 + 3x^2 - 7x + 2) - (10x^5 + 6x^3 - 5x^2 - 2x + 4)$

29. $(x^5y^2 - x^3y^2 + xy - 1) - (x^5y^2 - x^4y^2 - x^3y^2 - x^2y + xy - 1)$

30. $(x^5 + x^4y^2 - x^3 + x^2y - xy + 2) - (x^5 + x^4y^2 + x^3 - x^2y - xy + 2)$

Exercises

1. $5x$

2. $-x^2 + 3x$

3. $x^2 - 10x + 2$

4. $4x^3 + x^2 + x$

5. $-12x^4y + 3x^3 - 3$

6. $-4x^3 + 6x^2y^2 + 8xy - 1$

7. $2x^2 + 14$

8. $7a^3 - 9a^2 - 2a + 10$

9. $-2x^5 - 6x^4 + x + 2$

10. $-x^2 - 2x + 4$

11. $9b^2 + 9b - 8$

12. $7x^3 + 3x^2 + 2x - 1$

13. $7m^3 - 3m - 11$

14. $-5n^4 + 4n^3 + 3n^2 - 4$

15. $3y^4 + 8y^3 - 5y - 3$

16. $-6t^5 + 10t^4 - 2t^2 + t + 1$

17. $6v^4u + 9v^2 - 7$

18. $2m^3n^2 + 6m^2 - 4mn - 6$

19. $9mn^5 + n^4 + mn^4 - 3mn^3 + 3n^2 + 1$

20. $2x^6 + 6x^4y$

21. $3x + 6$

22. $-x^2 + 1$

23. $4c^3 - 3c^2 + c + 1$

24. $-3x^2 - 14x + 4$

25. $11x^4 + 12x^3 - 9x^2 - 8x$

26. $5x^4 - 6x^3 - x^2 + 5x + 15$

27. $-4m^5 + 9m^4 + 6m^2 + 16m + 6$

28. $-4x^5 - 6x^3 + 8x^2 - 5x - 2$

29. $x^4y^2 + x^2y$

30. $-2x^3 + 2x^2y$

B

Simplify.

31. $(y + 4) + (y - 5) - (y + 8)$

32. $(7y^2 - 5y + 6) - (3y^2 + 8y - 12) + (8y^2 - 10y + 3)$

33. $(4a^2 - 3a) + (7a^2 - 9a - 13) - (6a - 9)$

34. $(3x^2 - 4x + 6) - (-2x^2 + 4) + (-5x - 3)$

35. $(-8y^2 - 4) - (3y + 6) - (2y^2 - y)$

36. $(5x^3 - 4x^2 + 6) - (2x^3 + x^2 - x) + (x^3 - x)$

37. $(-xy^4 - 7y^3 + xy^2) + (-2xy^4 + 5y - 2) - (-6y^3 + xy^2)$

38. *Critical Thinking*   The difference of two polynomials is $2x^2 + x + 4$. One polynomial is $3x^2 + x$. What is the other polynomial?

Express the measure of the third side of each triangle as a simplified polynomial. P is the perimeter.

39. $P = 6x + 3$

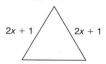
2x + 1   2x + 1

40. $P = 3x^2 - 6$

x² + 2   x² + 2

41. $P = 4x^2 - x - 16$

x − 10   2x² − 14

42. $P = 11x^2 + 10$

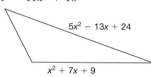
5x² − 13x + 24
x² + 7x + 9

Challenge

43. Does replacing each occurrence of x with its additive inverse in the polynomial $5x^3 - 3x^2 + 2x$ result in the additive inverse of the polynomial? Explain.

44. What is the additive identity for addition of polynomials? Show that subtraction of binomials is not commutative. Is it associative? Justify your answer.

Mixed Review

Write using scientific notation.   **45.** 1594   **46.** 0.772   **47.** 93,610   *5-4*

Identify the terms. Give the coefficient of each term.

48. $5x^3 + 3x^2 - 2x + 1$

49. $5n^4m + 7n^2m^2 - 2m + 3$ *5-5*

Solve.   **50.** $16 - 3a < 5a$ **51.** $21 + 4h = 11h$ *3-5, 4-4*

Exercises

31. $y - 9$

32. $12y^2 - 23y + 21$

33. $11a^2 - 18a - 4$

34. $5x^2 - 9x - 1$

35. $-10y^2 - 2y - 10$

36. $4x^3 - 5x^2 + 6$

37. $-3xy^4 - y^3 + 5y - 2$

38. $x^2 - 4$ or $5x^2 + 2x + 4$

39. $2x + 1$

40. $x^2 - 10$

41. $2x^2 - 2x + 8$

42. $5x^2 + 6x - 23$

43. No, $-3(-x)^2 = -3x^2$

44. a. A zero polynomial, or 0
   b. $(ax + by) - (cx + dy)$
   $= ax + by - cx - dy$
   $= x(a - c) + y(b - d)$
   $(cx + dy) - (ax + by)$
   $= cx + dy - ax - by$
   $= x(c - a) + y(d - b)$
   Since the coefficients a, b, c, and d are rational numbers, and subtraction of rational numbers is not commutative, $(c - a) \neq (a - c)$ and $(b - d) \neq$

$(d - b)$; thus, $(ax + by) - (cx + dy) \neq (cx + dy) - (ax + by)$, and subtraction of binomials is not commutative.
   c. No, subtraction of binomials is not associative. Again the coefficients are rational numbers, and subtraction of rational numbers is not associative.

Mixed Review

45. 1.594×10^3

46. 7.72×10^{-1}

47. 9.361×10^4

48. Terms: $5x^3, 3x^2, -2x, 1$
   Coefficients: 5, 3, −2, 1

49. Terms: $5n^4m, 7n^2m^2, -2m, 3$
   Coefficients: 5, 7, −2, 3

50. $2 < a$

51. 3

5-9

1. FOCUS

FIRST FIVE MINUTES

Multiply.
1. $5(6x - 4)$ $30x - 20$
2. $a(b + c)$ $ab + ac$
3. $-x(y - z)$ $-xy + xz$
4. $(4a^2b)(-3b^3)$ $-12a^2b^4$
5. $p(qrp + p^2)$ $qrp^2 + p^3$

2. TEACH the Mathematics

1 Multiplying a Polynomial by a Monomial

Remind students that negative signs should be distributed along with the monomials.

Key Question

■ Does $-3(3 - x) = -9 - 3x$?
No, $-3(3 - x) = -9 + 3x$.

Chalkboard Examples

Multiply.
1. $3a(6b + 7)$
   $(3a)(6b) + (3a)7$
   $= 18ab + 21a$
2. $2x(3x^2 + x + 4)$
   $(2x)(3x^2) + (2x)x + (2x)4$
   $= 6x^3 + 2x^2 + 8x$

2 Multiplying Two Binomials

Algebra tiles and the FOIL method are both useful tools for multiplying two binomials. Algebra tiles help students understand the multiplication process, and the FOIL method helps them remember how to calculate the product.
Point out that after like terms are collected, terms are usually arranged in descending order.

Key Question

■ Will there always be like terms after multiplying binomials?
No

What You'll Learn

1 To multiply a monomial and a polynomial

2 To multiply two binomials

. . . And Why

To use the FOIL rule to find products of binomials quickly

CA 10.0: Multiply monomials and polynomials.

5-9 ▷ Multiplication of Monomials and Binomials

5-9

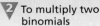

PART 1 Multiplying a Polynomial by a Monomial

Objective: Multiply a monomial and a polynomial.

We can use the rule for multiplying monomials and the distributive property to multiply a polynomial by a monomial.

EXAMPLES Multiply.

1 $2x(5x + 3) = (2x)(5x) + (2x)(3)$ Using the distributive property
$= 10x^2 + 6x$

2 $8p(3q^4 - 2q^3p^2 + 2p) = (8p)(3q^4) + (8p)(-2q^3p^2) + (8p)(2p)$
$= 24q^4p - 16q^3p^3 + 16p^2$

Try This Multiply.

a. $4x(2x + 4)$ **b.** $3a^2(-5a^3 + 2a - 7)$

c. $5s(8t^4 - 4s^2 - 9t - 11)$

PART 2 Multiplying Two Binomials

Objective: Multiply two binomials.

We can use an area model to illustrate multiplication of two binomials.

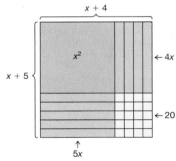

Using the model, the product $(x + 4)(x + 5)$ equals $x^2 + 4x + 5x + 20$, which simplifies to $x^2 + 9x + 20$.

Try This

a. $8x^2 + 16x$
b. $-15a^5 + 6a^3 - 21a^2$
c. $40st^4 - 20s^3 - 45st - 55s$

We can also use the distributive property twice to multiply two binomials. For example, $(x + 5)(x + 4)$.

(1) $(x + 4)(x + 5) = x(x + 5) + 4(x + 5)$ Using the distributive property

(2) $= x \cdot x + x \cdot 5 + 4 \cdot x + 4 \cdot 5$ Using the distributive property again

(3) $= x^2 + 5x + 4x + 20$

(4) $= x^2 + 9x + 20$ Collecting like terms

We can rewrite line (2) above to show a short way to find the product of two binomials.

$$\underset{\text{Last}}{\underbrace{\overset{\text{Outside}}{\overset{\text{First}}{(x + 4)(x + 5)}}}} = \underset{\text{First terms}}{x \cdot x} + \underset{\text{Outside terms}}{5 \cdot x} + \underset{\text{Inside terms}}{4 \cdot x} + \underset{\text{Last terms}}{4 \cdot 5}$$

This is called the **FOIL** method for finding the product of two binomials.

EXAMPLES Multiply.

3 $(x + 6)(x - 6) = x^2 - 6x + 6x - 36$ Using FOIL
$= x^2 - 36$ Collecting like terms

4 $(x + 3)(x - 2) = x^2 - 2x + 3x - 6$
$= x^2 + x - 6$

5 $(x^3 + 5)(x^3 - 5) = x^6 - 5x^3 + 5x^3 - 25$
$= x^6 - 25$

6 $(4x^2 + 5)(3x^2 - 2) = 12x^4 - 8x^2 + 15x^2 - 10$
$= 12x^4 + 7x^2 - 10$

7 $(4m^2 + 5mn)(2mn - 4n) = 8m^3n - 16m^2n + 10m^2n^2 - 20mn^2$

Try This Multiply.

d. $(x + 3)(x + 4)$ **e.** $(x + 3)(x - 5)$

f. $(2x + 1)(x + 4)$ **g.** $(2x^2 - 3)(x - 2)$

h. $(6x^2 + 5)(2x^3 + 1)$ **i.** $(y^3 + 7)(y^3 - 7)$

j. $(2x^5 + x^2)(-x^3 + x)$ **k.** $(3a + b)(-2a - 4b)$

l. $(2xy + 4x)(-2y + y^2)$ **m.** $(3rs + 2r)(r^2 + 2rs^2)$

5-9 *Multiplication of Monomials and Binomials* **241**

Try This

d. $x^2 + 7x + 12$

e. $x^2 - 2x - 15$

f. $2x^2 + 9x + 4$

g. $2x^3 - 4x^2 - 3x + 6$

h. $12x^5 + 10x^3 + 6x^2 + 5$

i. $y^6 - 49$

j. $-2x^8 + 2x^6 - x^5 + x^3$

k. $-6a^2 - 14ab - 4b^2$

l. $2xy^3 - 8xy$

m. $3r^3s + 2r^3 + 6r^2s^3 + 4r^2s^2$

Teach the Mathematics (continued)

Chalkboard Examples

Multiply.

1. $(x + 2)(x + 3)$
$x^2 + 3x + 2x + 6$
$= x^2 + 5x + 6$

2. $(3x + 2)(x + 5)$
$3x^2 + 15x + 2x + 10$
$= 3x^2 + 17x + 10$

3. $(4ab + 3)(2a^2b + 1)$
$(4ab)(2a^2b) + (4ab)1 + 3(2a^2b) + 3 \cdot 1 = 8a^3b^2 + 4ab + 6a^2b + 3$

Use Teaching Transparency T19 to present Chalkboard Example 1.

LESSON ENRICHMENT

Ask students to find the following products using algebra tiles.

1. $(2x - 2)(x + 1)$ $2x^2 - 2$

2. $(x - 4)(x - 2)$ $x^2 - 6x + 8$

3. $(x + 5)(2x)$ $2x^2 + 10x$

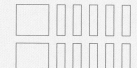

LESSON QUIZ

Multiply and collect like terms.

1. $5x^2(3x + 2)$
   $15x^3 + 10x^2$

2. $(x + 7)(x + 2)$
   $x^2 + 2x + 7x + 14$
   $= x^2 + 9x + 14$

3. $(3x^2 + 4)(5x^3 + 1)$
   $15x^5 + 3x^2 + 20x^3 + 4$
   $= 15x^5 + 20x^3 + 3x^2 + 4$

Assignment Guide

To provide flexible scheduling, this lesson can be split into parts.

▼ Core 1–20
  Extension 59, 60, 65, 67

▼ Core 21–54
  Extension 55–58, 61–64, 66, 68–76

Use Mixed Review to maintain skills.

We can also use columns to multiply. We multiply each term on the top row by each term on the bottom. Then we add.

EXAMPLE 8

Multiply $4x - 3$ and $x - 2$.

$$
\begin{array}{r}
4x - 3 \\
\underline{x - 2} \\
4x^2 - 3x \\
\underline{-8x + 6} \\
4x^2 - 11x + 6
\end{array}
$$

Multiplying the top row by x

Multiplying the top row by -2

Adding

Try This Multiply.

n. $(5x + 3)(x - 4)$

o. $(2y^2 - 3)(3y - 5)$

p. $(3a + b)(2a - b)$

q. $(6m^2 + n)(3m - n^2)$

r. $(4pq - p^2)(pq + p^2)$

s. $\left(\frac{1}{2}r^2s + s\right)\left(\frac{1}{2}r^2s - s\right)$

Extra Help On the Web

Look for worked-out examples at the Prentice Hall Web site.
www.phschool.com

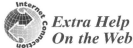

5-9 Exercises

A

Multiply.

1. $3x(-x + 5)$

2. $2y(4y - 6)$

3. $4x^2(3x + 6)$

4. $5a^2(-2a + 1)$

5. $-6m^2(m^2 + x)$

6. $-4x^2(x^2 - x)$

7. $3x^3(x^3 + 5)$

8. $-5m(-3m^5 - 4m^2)$

9. $3y^2(6y^4 + 8y^3)$

10. $4y^4(y^3 - 6y^2)$

11. $2x(3x^2 + 4x - 3)$

12. $-6x(-5x^3 - x^2 + 4)$

13. $-5a^2(-3a^2 - 6a + 7)$

14. $4b^2(-6b^4 + 3b^2 - 4)$

15. $4y^6(-2y^3 - 2y^2 + y - 5)$

16. $-2x^5(x^4 + 2x^3 - x^2 - x + 3)$

17. $-7h^4(k^6 - k^4 - k^3 + k)$

18. $x^3(-y^7 + y^4 - y^3 + y^2 - y)$

19. $2a(-5a^8b + a^2 - 12ab)$

20. $10x(-y^5 - xy^3 + 12x)$

Multiply.

21. $(x + 1)(x^2 + 3)$

22. $(x^2 - 3)(x - 1)$

23. $(x^3 + 2)(x + 1)$

24. $(x^4 + 2)(x + 12)$

25. $(a + 2)(a - 3)$

26. $(x + 2)(x + 2)$

27. $(3x + 2)(3x + 3)$

28. $(4x + 1)(2x + 2)$

Exercises

1. $-3x^2 + 15x$

2. $8y^2 - 12y$

3. $12x^3 + 24x^2$

4. $-10a^3 + 5a^2$

5. $-6m^4 - 6m^2x$

6. $-4x^4 + 4x^3$

7. $3x^6 + 15x^3$

8. $15m^6 + 20m^3$

9. $18y^6 + 24y^5$

10. $4y^7 - 24y^6$

11. $6x^3 + 8x^2 - 6x$

12. $30x^4 + 6x^3 - 24x$

13. $15a^4 + 30a^3 - 35a^2$

14. $-24b^6 + 12b^4 - 16b^2$

15. $-8y^9 - 8y^8 + 4y^7 - 20y^6$

16. $-2x^9 - 4x^8 + 2x^7 + 2x^6 - 6x^5$

17. $-7h^4k^6 + 7h^4k^4 + 7h^4k^3 - 7h^4k$

18. $-x^3y^7 + x^3y^4 - x^3y^3 + x^3y^2 - x^3y$

19. $-10a^9b + 2a^3 - 24a^2b$

20. $-10xy^5 - 10x^2y^3 + 120x^2$

21. $x^3 + x^2 + 3x + 3$

22. $x^3 - x^2 - 3x + 3$

23. $x^4 + x^3 + 2x + 2$

24. $x^5 + 12x^4 + 2x + 24$

25. $a^2 - a - 6$

26. $x^2 + 4x + 4$

27. $9x^2 + 15x + 6$

28. $8x^2 + 10x + 2$

Try This

n. $5x^2 - 17x - 12$

o. $6y^3 - 10y^2 - 9y + 15$

p. $6a^2 - ab - b^2$

q. $18m^3 - 6m^2n^2 + 3mn - n^3$

r. $4p^2q^2 + 3p^3q - p^4$

s. $\frac{1}{4}r^4s^2 - s^2$

Multiply.

29. $(5x - 6)(x + 2)$ **30.** $(x - 8)(x + 8)$

31. $(3x - 1)(3x + 1)$ **32.** $(2x + 3)(2x + 3)$

33. $(4x - 2y)(x - y)$ **34.** $(2x - y)(3x + y)$

35. $\left(x - \frac{1}{4}\right)\left(x + \frac{1}{4}\right)$ **36.** $\left(x + \frac{3}{4}\right)\left(x + \frac{3}{4}\right)$

37. $(x - 0.1)(x + 0.1)$ **38.** $(3x^2 + 1)(x + 1)$

39. $(2x^2 + 6)(x + 1)$ **40.** $(2b^2 + 3)(2b - 1)$

41. $(-2x + 1)(x - 6)$ **42.** $(3x + 4)(2x - 4)$

43. $(x + 7y)(x + 7y)$ **44.** $(2x + 5y)(2x + 5y)$

45. $(3x^5 + 2)(2x^2 + 6)$ **46.** $(1 - 2x)(1 + 3x^2)$

47. $(8x^3 + 1)(x^3 + 8)$ **48.** $(4 - 2x)(5 - 2x^2)$

49. $(4x^2 + 3)(x - 3)$ **50.** $(7x - 2)(2x - 7)$

51. $(4x^4 + x^2)(x^2 + x)$ **52.** $(5x^6 + 3x^3)(2x^6 + 2x^3)$

53. $(ab + 3b^2)(ab - 3b^2)$ **54.** $(m^2n - 5n)(m^2n + 5n)$

B

Multiply.

55. $(a + b)^2$ **56.** $(a - b)^2$ **57.** $(2x + 3)^2$ **58.** $(5y + 6)^2$

Find an expression for the area of the shaded regions.

59.
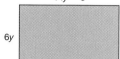
$14y - 5$

$6y$

60.
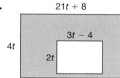
$21t + 8$

$3t - 4$

$4t$

$2t$

Find an expression for the area of the shaded portion of each square.

61.

m

m

7

4

62.
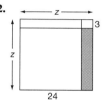
z

3

z

24

63. *Critical Thinking* The product of two binomials is $2x^2 + 5x + 2$.
One of the binomials is $(x + 2)$. What is the other binomial?

Exercises

29. $5x^2 + 4x - 12$

30. $x^2 - 64$

31. $9x^2 - 1$

32. $4x^2 + 12x + 9$

33. $4x^2 - 6xy + 2y^2$

34. $6x^2 - xy - y^2$

35. $x^2 - \frac{1}{16}$

36. $x^2 + \frac{3}{2}x + \frac{9}{16}$

37. $x^2 - 0.01$

38. $3x^3 + 3x^2 + x + 1$

39. $2x^3 + 2x^2 + 6x + 6$

40. $4b^3 - 2b^2 + 6b - 3$

41. $-2x^2 + 13x - 6$

42. $6x^2 - 4x - 16$

43. $x^2 + 14xy + 49y^2$

44. $4x^2 + 20xy + 25y^2$

45. $6x^7 + 18x^5 + 4x^2 + 12$

46. $1 - 2x + 3x^2 - 6x^3$

47. $8x^6 + 65x^3 + 8$

48. $20 - 10x - 8x^2 + 4x^3$

49. $4x^3 - 12x^2 + 3x - 9$

50. $14x^2 - 53x + 14$

51. $4x^6 + 4x^5 + x^4 + x^3$

52. $10x^{12} + 16x^9 + 6x^6$

53. $a^2b^2 - 9b^4$

54. $m^4n^2 - 25n^2$

55. $a^2 + 2ab + b^2$

56. $a^2 - 2ab + b^2$

57. $4x^2 + 12x + 9$

58. $25y^2 + 60y + 36$

59. $84y^2 - 30y$

60. $78t^2 + 40t$

61. $m^2 - 28$

62. $z^2 - 24(z - 3) - (24 \cdot 3)$
    $- 3(z - 24) = z^2 - 27z + 72$

63. $2x + 1$

Error Analysis   Study each of the products below. Which are correct and which are incorrect? For those that are incorrect, give the correct answer and state what error was made.

64. $(x^2 + 3y^3)(2x^2 - y) = 2x^2 - x^2y + 6x^2y^3 - 3y^3$

65. $(4m^3)(2m^2 - 2m + 1) = 8m^5 - 8m^4 + 4m^3$

66. $(ab + 2b^2)(ab - 2b^2) = a^2b^2 + 4b$

67. $-2x^2(x^3 + 3x^2 - 3x + 2) = -2x^6 - 6x^4 + 6x^2 - 4x^2$

68. *Critical Thinking*   A student claimed that the product of two binomials always results in a polynomial with at least three terms. Provide a counterexample to show that the student's claim is incorrect.

Challenge

69. A box with a square bottom is to be made from a 12-inch square piece of cardboard. Squares with side x are cut out of the corners, and the sides are folded up. Express the volume and the surface area of the outside of the box as polynomials.

Compute.

70. a. $(x + 3)(x + 6) + (x + 3)(x + 6)$

b. $(x + 4)(x + 5) - (x + 4)(x + 5)$

71. a. $(x - 2)(x - 7) + (x - 2)(x - 7)$

b. $(x - 6)(x - 2) - (x - 6)(x - 2)$

72. a. $(x + 5)(x - 3) + (x + 5)(x - 3)$

b. $(x + 9)(x - 4) - (x + 9)(x - 4)$

73. a. $(x + 7)(x - 8) + (x - 7)(x + 8)$

b. $(x + 2)(x - 5) - (x - 2)(x + 5)$

74. If a and b are positive, how many terms are there in $(x - a)(x - b) + (x - a)(x - b)$?

75. If a and b are positive, how many terms are there in $(x + a)(x - b) + (x - a)(x + b)$?

76. If a and b are positive, how many terms are there in $(x + a)(x - b) - (x + a)(x - b)$?

Mixed Review

Write as an algebraic expression.   **77.** half of the sum of a number and 3
78. 9 more than the product of a number and 6 **79.** 3 times the difference of 7 and a number   **80.** the sum of two consecutive integers   *1-6*

Solve.   **81.** $15r = 3(r + 28)$ **82.** $25 = 4(m - 3) - 3$

83. $13k = 19k + 12$ **84.** $12x = 16(x - 2) + 48$ *3-5*

Exercises

64. There are two errors. $x^2(2x^2) = 2x^4$ and $3y^3(-y) = -3y^4$. The correct answer is $2x^4 - x^2y + 6x^2y^3 - 3y^4$.

65. The answer is correct.

66. The last term is incorrect. The correct answer is $a^2b^2 - 4b^4$.

67. The first term should be $-2x^5$. The third term should be $6x^3$. The correct answer is $-2x^5 - 6x^4 + 6x^3 - 4x^2$.

68. $(x - 2)(x + 2) = x^2 - 4$

69. Formulas are in Appendix.

$V = lwh$

$V = (12 - 2x)(12 - 2x)x$

$= (4x^2 - 48x + 144)x$

$= 4x^3 - 48x^2 + 144x$

$S = $ area of sides + area of base

$= 4x(12 - 2x) + (12 - 2x)^2$

$= -4x^2 + 144$

70. a. $2x^2 + 18x + 36$

b. 0

71. a. $2x^2 - 18x + 28$

b. 0

72. a. $2x^2 + 4x - 30$

b. 0

73. a. $2x^2 - 112$

b. $-6x$

74. 3

75. 2

76. 1

Mixed Review

77. $\frac{n + 3}{2}$

78. $6n + 9$

79. $3(7 - n)$

80. $n + (n + 1)$

81. 7

82. 10

83. -2

84. -4

CA 10.0: Multiply polynomials; solve multi-step problems using polynomials.

Multiplying Binomials: Special Products

 **5-10**

 5-10 TIME-FOCUS METER

Objective: Multiply the sum and the difference of two expressions.

You have learned the FOIL method for multiplying two binomials. Here are some products found using the FOIL method.

$$(x + 2)(x - 2) = x^2 - 2x + 2x - 4$$
$$= x^2 - 4$$
$$(3x - 5)(3x + 5) = 9x^2 + 15x - 15x - 25$$
$$= 9x^2 - 25$$
$$(3 + x)(3 - x) = 9 - 3x + 3x - x^2$$
$$= 9 - x^2$$

In these examples, the first terms of the binomials are the same and the last terms differ only in sign. These examples suggest the following rule for multiplying the sum and the difference of the same terms.

Product of $(A + B)$ and $(A - B)$

The product of the sum and the difference of two terms is the square of the first term minus the square of the second.
$$(A + B)(A - B) = A^2 - B^2$$

EXAMPLES Multiply.

1 $(x + 4)(x - 4) = x^2 - 4^2$ Squaring the first expression and subtracting the square of the second

$$= x^2 - 16$$ Simplifying

2 $(2w + 5)(2w - 5) = (2w)^2 - 5^2$
$$= 4w^2 - 25$$

3 $(-4x - 10y)(-4x + 10y) = (-4x)^2 - (10y)^2$
$$= 16x^2 - 100y^2$$

Try This Multiply.

a. $(x + 2)(x - 2)$ **b.** $(x^2 + 7)(x^2 - 7)$

c. $(3t + 5)(3t - 5)$ **d.** $(2x^3 + y)(2x^3 - y)$

Try This
a. $x^2 - 4$
b. $x^4 - 49$
c. $9t^2 - 25$
d. $4x^6 - y^2$

What You'll Learn

1 To multiply the sum and difference of two expressions

2 To square a binomial

... And Why

To use rules to find special products quickly

---

1. FOCUS

FIRST FIVE MINUTES

1. Simplify.
$4x^2 - 2x + 4 + 3x^2 + 4x - 1$
$7x^2 + 2x + 3$

Multiply.

2. $(x + 7)(x - 2)$
$x^2 - 2x + 7x - 14$
$= x^2 + 5x - 14$

3. $(3x + 9)(7x - 1)$
$21x^2 - 3x + 63x - 9$
$= 21x^2 + 60x - 9$

4. $(x - 1)(x + 1)$
$x^2 + x - x - 1$
$= x^2 - 1$

---

2. TEACH the Mathematics

1 Multiplying a Sum and a Difference

Students may find it helpful to state the rule "the square of the first, minus the square of the second" as they do the multiplication.

Key Question

■ When multiplying the sum and difference of two expressions, why does the product always have at most two terms?
The other terms are additive inverses of each other, and therefore total zero.

Chalkboard Examples
Multiply.
1. $(r + 2)(r - 2)$
$r^2 - 4$
2. $(2x + 3)(2x - 3)$
$4x^2 - 9$
3. $(ab + c)(ab - c)$
$a^2b^2 - c^2$
4. $(-3x + 4y)(-3x - 4y)$
$9x^2 - 16y^2$

Teach the Mathematics (continued)

 Squaring Binomials

Demonstrate that squaring a binomial with the FOIL method always leads to the combining of the outside and inside terms.

You may also wish to illustrate the squaring of a binomial with the following diagram.

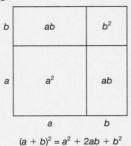

$(a + b)^2 = a^2 + 2ab + b^2$

Avoiding Common Errors

One of the most common errors made in a beginning algebra class is to give the square of a binomial such as $(x + 5)^2$ as $x^2 + 25$.

You can require that students who consistently make this error write $(x + 5)^2$ as $(x + 5)(x + 5)$ and use FOIL. You may want to show by substitution that $(x + 5)^2 \neq x^2 + 25$. Let $x = 2$.

$$(2 + 5)^2 \ ? \ 2^2 + 25$$
$$7^2 \quad ? \quad 4 + 25$$
$$49 \quad \neq \quad 29$$

Chalkboard Examples

Multiply.

1. $(x + 5)^2$
   $x^2 + 2 \cdot x \cdot 5 + 25$
   $= x^2 + 10x + 25$

2. $(y - 3)^2$
   $y^2 - 2 \cdot y \cdot 3 + 9$
   $= y^2 - 6y + 9$

3. $(2a - 3b)^2$
   $(2a)^2 - 2 \cdot (2a)(3b) + (3b)^2$
   $= 4a^2 - 12ab + 9b^2$

Objective: Square a binomial.

Multiplying a binomial by itself is called *squaring the binomial*. Look for a pattern.

$$(x + 2)^2 = (x + 2)(x + 2)$$
$$= x^2 + 2x + 2x + 4$$
$$= x^2 + 4x + 4$$
$$(x - 2)^2 = (x - 2)(x - 2)$$
$$= x^2 - 2x - 2x + 4$$
$$= x^2 - 4x + 4$$
$$(3x + 5)^2 = (3x + 5)(3x + 5)$$
$$= 9x^2 + 15x + 15x + 25$$
$$= 9x^2 + 30x + 25$$
$$(3x - 5y)^2 = (3x - 5y)(3x - 5y)$$
$$= 9x^2 - 15xy - 15xy + 25y^2$$
$$= 9x^2 - 30xy + 25y^2$$

There is a quick way to square a binomial.

Squaring Binomials

The square of a binomial is the square of the first term, plus or minus twice the product of the two terms, plus the square of the last term.

$$(A + B)^2 = A^2 + 2AB + B^2$$
$$(A - B)^2 = A^2 - 2AB + B^2$$

EXAMPLES   Multiply.

4 $(x + 3)^2 = x^2 + 2 \cdot x \cdot 3 + 3^2$
$$= x^2 + 6x + 9$$

5 $(t - 5)^2 = t^2 - 2 \cdot t \cdot 5 + 5^2$
$$= t^2 - 10t + 25$$

6 $(2x + 7)^2 = (2x)^2 + 2 \cdot 2x \cdot 7 + 7^2$
$$= 4x^2 + 28x + 49$$

7 $(3x - 5y)^2 = (3x)^2 - 2 \cdot 3x \cdot 5y + (5y)^2$
$$= 9x^2 - 30xy + 25y^2$$

Try This   Multiply.

e. $(x + 2)(x + 2)$ **f.** $(y - 9)(y - 9)$ **g.** $(4x - 5)^2$

h. $(a - 4)^2$ **i.** $(5x^2 + 4)(5x^2 + 4)$ **j.** $(4x^2 - 3x)^2$

Try This

e. $x^2 + 4x + 4$
f. $y^2 - 18y + 81$
g. $16x^2 - 40x + 25$
h. $a^2 - 8a + 16$
i. $25x^4 + 40x^2 + 16$
j. $16x^4 - 24x^3 + 9x^2$

A

Multiply.

1. $(x + 4)(x - 4)$

2. $(a + 1)(a - 1)$

3. $(d - 6)(d + 6)$

4. $(y - 5)(y + 5)$

5. $(6 - m)(6 + m)$

6. $(8 + m)(8 - m)$

7. $(2x + 1)(2x - 1)$

8. $(3y - 1)(3y + 1)$

9. $(4a - 7)(4a + 7)$

10. $(5b - 2)(5b + 2)$

11. $(4x^2 - 3)(4x^2 + 3)$

12. $(2x^2 + 3)(2x^2 - 3)$

13. $(3x^4 + 2)(3x^4 - 2)$

14. $(6t^5 - 5)(6t^5 + 5)$

15. $(x^6 - x^2)(x^6 + x^2)$

16. $(3a - 4b)(3a + 4b)$

17. $(7c - 2d)(7c + 2d)$

18. $(-3m + 2n)(-3m - 2n)$

19. $(-6t + s)(-6t - s)$

20. $(x^2 + y^2)(x^2 - y^2)$

Multiply.

21. $(x + 2)^2$

22. $(a + 3)^2$

23. $(t - 3)^2$

24. $(r - 2)^2$

25. $(2x - 1)^2$

26. $(3c - 1)^2$

27. $(4a - 3b)^2$

28. $(7a - 2b)^2$

29. $(4s + 5t)^2$

30. $\left(x - \frac{1}{2}\right)^2$

31. $\left(x - \frac{1}{4}\right)^2$

32. $\left(a + \frac{2}{3}\right)^2$

33. $(2x + 7)(2x + 7)$

34. $(4x + 3)(4x + 3)$

35. $(3x - 2y)(3x + 2y)$

36. $(7x - 5y)(7x + 5y)$

37. $(5x^2 - 1)(5x^2 - 1)$

38. $(12 - 3x^2)(12 + 3x^2)$

39. $\left(2x - \frac{1}{5}\right)\left(2x - \frac{1}{5}\right)$

40. $\left(3x + \frac{3}{4}\right)\left(3x - \frac{3}{4}\right)$

41. $(2x^3 - 0.3)(2x^3 + 0.3)$

42. $(t^2 - 0.2)(t^2 + 0.2)$

B

43. a. Find the area of the 4 small rectangles.

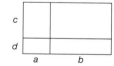 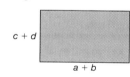

b. What is the sum of the areas?

c. Find the area of the blue rectangle.

Compare your result with your answer to part b.

Internet Connection

***Extra Help
On the Web***

Look for worked-out
examples at the Prentice
Hall Web site.

www.phschool.com

3. PRACTICE/ASSESS

LESSON QUIZ

Multiply.

1. $(x + 9)(x - 9)$

   $x^2 - 81$

2. $(2x - y)(2x + y)$

   $4x^2 - y^2$

3. $(x + 7)^2$

   $x^2 + 14x + 49$

4. $(x - 8)^2$

   $x^2 - 16x + 64$

Assignment Guide

To provide flexible scheduling, this
lesson can be split into parts.

▼ Core 1–20
   Extension 43, 44

▼ Core 21–42
   Extension 45–52

Use Mixed Review to maintain skills.

Exercises

1. $x^2 - 16$

2. $a^2 - 1$

3. $d^2 - 36$

4. $y^2 - 25$

5. $36 - m^2$

6. $64 - m^2$

7. $4x^2 - 1$

8. $9y^2 - 1$

9. $16a^2 - 49$

10. $25b^2 - 4$

11. $16x^4 - 9$

12. $4x^4 - 9$

13. $9x^8 - 4$

14. $36t^{10} - 25$

15. $x^{12} - x^4$

16. $9a^2 - 16b^2$

17. $49c^2 - 4d^2$

18. $9m^2 - 4n^2$

19. $36t^2 - s^2$

20. $x^4 - y^4$

21. $x^2 + 4x + 4$

22. $a^2 + 6a + 9$

23. $t^2 - 6t + 9$

24. $r^2 - 4r + 4$

25. $4x^2 - 4x + 1$

26. $9c^2 - 6c + 1$

27. $16a^2 - 24ab + 9b^2$

28. $49a^2 - 28ab + 4b^2$

29. $16s^2 + 40st + 25t^2$

30. $x^2 - x + \frac{1}{4}$

31. $x^2 - \frac{1}{2}x + \frac{1}{16}$

32. $a^2 + \frac{4}{3}a + \frac{4}{9}$

33. $4x^2 + 28x + 49$

34. $16x^2 + 24x + 9$

35. $9x^2 - 4y^2$

36. $49x^2 - 25y^2$

37. $25x^4 - 10x^2 + 1$

38. $144 - 9x^4$

39. $4x^2 - \frac{4}{5}x + \frac{1}{25}$

40. $9x^2 - \frac{9}{16}$

41. $4x^6 - 0.09$

42. $t^4 - 0.04$

43. a. ac, ad, bc, bd

    b. $ac + ad + bc + bd$

    c. $ac + ad + bc + bd$, equal

Multiply.

35. $(6a^3 - 1)(6a^3 + 1)$ **36.** $(2b^2 - 7)(3b^2 + 9)$

37. $(2 - 3x)(2 + 3x)$ **38.** $(4 + 5x)(4 - 5x)$

39. $(6x^4 + 4)^2$ **40.** $(8 - 6x^4)^2$

41. $-6x^2(x^3 + 8x - 9)$ **42.** $-5x^2(x^3 - 2x + 4)$

43. $(6q^3 - 1)(2q^2 + 1)$ **44.** $(7p^2 + 4)(5p^2 - 8)$

45. $\left(\frac{3}{4}x + 1\right)\left(\frac{3}{4}x + 2\right)$ **46.** $\left(\frac{1}{5}x^2 + 9\right)\left(\frac{3}{5}x^2 - 7\right)$

47. $(x^2 + 2x + 3)(4x + 5)$ **48.** $(x^2 + 2x)(3x^2 + 4x + 5)$

49. $(x^3 - 4x^2)(3x^2 - 2x + 5)$ **50.** $(x^3 - 4x^2 + 5)(3x^2 - 2x)$

B

51. Find $(x + y)^3$.   **52.** Find $(x + y)^4$.

53. *Critical Thinking*   Study the pattern of your answers for Exercises 51 and 52. Without multiplying, find $(x + y)^5$.

Challenge

Multiply. Look for patterns.

54. **a.** $(x^2 + x + 1)(x - 1)$ **b.** $(x^2 + x + 1)(x + 1)$

    c. $(x^2 - x + 1)(x - 1)$ **d.** $(x^2 - x + 1)(x + 1)$

    e. $(-x^2 + x - 1)(x - 1)$ **f.** $(-x^2 + x - 1)(x + 1)$

    g. $(x^3 + x^2 + x + 1)(x - 1)$ **h.** $(x^3 + x^2 + x + 1)(x + 1)$

    i. $(x^3 - x^2 + x - 1)(x - 1)$ **j.** $(x^3 - x^2 + x - 1)(x + 1)$

    k. $(-x^3 + x^2 - x + 1)(x - 1)$ **l.** $(-x^3 + x^2 - x + 1)(x + 1)$

55. What polynomial times $(x - 1)$ equals $x^5 - 1$?

56. What polynomial times $(x + 1)$ equals $x^5 + 1$?

57. What polynomial times $(x - 1)$ equals $x^6 - 1$?

58. Find $(x^2 + xy + y^2)^2$.

59. Find a trinomial $ax^2 + bx + c$ and a binomial $dx + e$ so that when they are multiplied, the coefficient of the x term is 1.

Mixed Review

Multiply.   **60.** $(x - 3)^2$ **61.** $(x + 3)^3$ **62.** $(x - 3)(x + 3)$ *5-10*

Give the additive inverse.   **63.** $7a$ **64.** $-21n$ **65.** $3y^2 - 9y + 1$ *2-3*

Write in standard notation.   **66.** 1.1×10^{-5} **67.** 2.1×10^7 *5-9*

Identify the degree of each term and the degree of the polynomial.

68. $3n^2 - 4n + 11$ **69.** $3x^3y^4 + 9x^2y - 24$ **70.** $9a + 6$ *5-5*

71. On a scale drawing of a certain building, 1 in. represents 2.5 ft. The length of one wall in the drawing is 3.6 in. What is the actual length of that wall?   *3-9*

Exercises

35. $36a^6 - 1$

36. $6b^4 - 3b^2 - 63$

37. $-9x^2 + 4$

38. $-25x^2 + 16$

39. $36x^8 + 48x^4 + 16$

40. $36x^8 - 96x^4 + 64$

41. $-6x^5 - 48x^3 + 54x^2$

42. $-5x^5 + 10x^3 - 20x^2$

43. $12q^5 + 6q^3 - 2q^2 - 1$

44. $35p^4 - 36p^2 - 32$

45. $\frac{9}{16}x^2 + \frac{9}{4}x + 2$

46. $\frac{3}{25}x^4 + 4x^2 - 63$

47. $4x^3 + 13x^2 + 22x + 15$

48. $3x^4 + 10x^3 + 13x^2 + 10x$

49. $3x^5 - 14x^4 + 13x^3 - 20x^2$

50. $3x^5 - 14x^4 + 8x^3 +$
    $15x^2 - 10x$

51. $x^3 + 3x^2y + 3xy^2 + y^3$

52. $x^4 + 4x^3y + 6x^2y^2 +$
    $4xy^3 + y^4$

53. $x^5 + 5x^4y + 10x^3y^2 + 10x^2y^3$
    $+ 5xy^4 + y^5$

54. a. $x^3 - 1$

    b. $x^3 + 2x^2 + 2x + 1$

    c. $x^3 - 2x^2 + 2x - 1$

    d. $x^3 + 1$

    e. $-x^3 + 2x^2 - 2x + 1$

    f. $-x^3 - 1$

    g. $x^4 - 1$

    h. $x^4 + 2x^3 + 2x^2 + 2x + 1$

    i. $x^4 - 2x^3 + 2x^2 - 2x + 1$

    j. $x^4 - 1$

    k. $-x^4 + 2x^3 - 2x^2 + 2x - 1$

    l. $-x^4 + 1$

55. $x^4 + x^3 + x^2 + x + 1$

56. $x^4 - x^3 + x^2 - x + 1$

57. $x^5 + x^4 + x^3 + x^2 + x + 1$

58. $x^4 + 2x^3y + 3x^2y^2 +$
    $2xy^3 + y^4$

59. Answers may vary.
    Ex. $(x^2 - x + 2)(x + 1)$

Mixed Review

60. $x^2 - 6x + 9$

61. $x^3 + 9x^2 + 27x + 27$

62. $x^2 - 9$

63. $-7a$

64. $21n$

65. $-3y^2 + 9y - 1$

66. 0.000011

67. $21,000,000$

68. $2, 1, 0; 2$

69. $7, 3, 0; 7$

70. $1, 0; 1$

71. 9 ft